Handbook of Mathematical Psychology

Volume I, Chapters 1-8

Handbook of

Volume I, Chapters 1-8

WITH CONTRIBUTIONS BY

Patrick Suppes	R. Duncan Luce
Joseph L. Zinnes	William J. McGill
Robert R. Bush	Allen Newell
Eugene Galanter	Herbert A. Simon

New York • *London* • *Sydney*

Mathematical Psychology

EDITED BY

R. Duncan Luce, *University of Pennsylvania*

Robert R. Bush, *University of Pennsylvania*

Eugene Galanter, *University of Washington*

John Wiley and Sons, Inc.

150.72
L96h
v. 1

Library of Congress Catalog Card Number: 63-9428
Printed in the United States of America

Preface

The term mathematical psychology did not come into common use until recently, although the field itself is almost the fraternal twin of experimental psychology: G. T. Fechner was both an experimental and a mathematical psychologist. From 1870 until about 1930 the limited mathematical work in psychology was mainly the incidental product of experimentalists who had had some training in engineering or physics. In the 1930's and 40's two changes occurred with the flowering of the psychometric school under the leadership of L. L. Thurstone. The work became much more extensive and elaborate; however, a temporary cleavage between mathematical and experimental psychology ensued because the mathematical research focussed on the scaling and multidimensional representation of responses to questionaire items and attended less to the traditional problems of experimental psychology.

The more normal interplay of mathematical theories and experimental data was reestablished during World War II when experimentalists were thrust into close working relations with engineers, physicists, and mathematicians. The effects of this contact continued some time after the war. A number of psychologists became actively interested and involved in the Cybernetic movement and the closely allied development of information theory, and others explored somewhat more peripheral areas including game and decision theory. A much more detailed exposition of the historical trends of mathematical applications is given by Miller.[1]

The stage was well set for the rapid growth of mathematical psychology during the 1950's. As an indication of the rate of growth, we estimate that something less than a quarter of these three *Handbook* volumes could have been written in 1950. Since that time a number of psychologists have discovered and studied some branches of modern mathematics that seem better suited for formulating their problems than the much more familiar, and then much more accessible, classical analysis which had served physics so well. Their study was facilitated both by interested mathematicians and mathematical statisticians and by organizations such as the Social Science Research Council, the Ford Foundation, the Office of

[1] G. A. Miller. *Mathematics and psychology* (Perspectives in Psychology Series). New York: Wiley, in press, 1963.

v

Naval Research, the National Science Foundation, and the National Institutes of Health, as well as several universities that sponsored a series of summer training and research seminars and a number of more permanent research projects.

During the last five years this teaching responsibility has begun to be absorbed into the normal university framework, thus creating a demand for various text materials. This demand is especially severe when the responsibility falls upon a professor not primarily a specialist in mathematical psychology or on a relatively inexperienced young faculty member. Although a number of research monographs and a few specialized texts have appeared, no comprehensive graduate or undergraduate text is yet available. We wanted such a text and for a brief period we considered writing one. It soon became apparent, however, that there was too little preliminary organization of the somewhat scattered research literature to make the task feasible within a reasonable time. So we settled for the more catalytic role of inducing others (as well as ourselves) to present systematically their subfields in a way that would be useful to two groups: other mathematical psychologists, both in their roles as students and as teachers, and experimental psychologists with some mathematical background. And so the *Handbook of Mathematical Psychology* was born.

We originally conceived the *Handbook* as a single volume with an associated volume of *Readings in Mathematical Psychology* that would include many of the more commonly used journal articles. As the project developed, it became apparent that most chapters were running appreciably longer than we had anticipated, that they could not be significantly abridged without severe loss, and that several topics we had not originally included should be added. We estimated approximately 2400 pages of manuscript, which could only be comfortably handled in three volumes. The number of important journal articles also far exceeded our initial estimates, and again convenience dictated that we divide the *Readings* into two volumes.

The organization of these volumes would have been somewhat different than it is had all the material been available at one time; however, the project grew gradually and the authors did not work at the same pace. The first volume of the *Handbook* includes measurement and psychophysics and also two largely methodological chapters. The second volume presents the main body of mathematical learning theory and the aspects of social behavior that have received mathematical treatment: language and social interaction. Volume three contains miscellaneous chapters on sensory mechanisms, learning, preference, and mathematics. The first volume of *Readings* includes papers on measurement, psychophysics, and learning. The second volume includes everything else.

As this outline indicates, most of the *Handbook* chapters are primarily concerned with traditional psychological topics treated from a mathematical point of view. Some, however, are primarily methodological: For example, Chapter 7 describes the uses of computers in psychology. As Newell and Simon point out, it is an historical accident that we include such a chapter in a book on mathematical psychology. And Chapter 8 discusses special statistical issues of interest to model builders which are not treated extensively in statistical texts.

Despite the length of this *Handbook*, some topics of mathematical psychology are not covered. All but one omission was planned because good summaries already exist. For example, information theory is not treated (it is used in several chapters) because summaries of it and its uses in psychology can be found in Attneave[2] or Luce;[3] there has not yet been enough new work since Licklider's[4] comprehensive presentation of linear and quasi-linear analyses of tracking behavior to warrant a new chapter at this time; psychometric scaling is systematically handled in Torgerson's[5] relatively recent book; and factor analysis has been thoroughly exposited in several books, for example, Harman[6] and Thurstone.[7] The only unintentional omission is what, in our planning jargon, we loosely called "psychometrics," meaning whatever topic a prospective author of the psychometric tradition judged to be most central. The most likely possibility was test theory, but we wanted the author to define the chapter as he saw fit. Even with this flexibility and despite the fact that we approached five people, the chapter failed to materialize. We encountered much less difficulty with the other chapters: fifteen of the twenty were written by the first person or persons approached and the remaining five by the second.

What assumptions have the authors made in writing their chapters? That is always difficult to answer; however, we can list the assumptions that we asked them to make. First, we said that the reader should be presumed to know foundational mathematics at the level of a course based

---

[2] F. Attneave. *Applications of information theory to psychology.* New York: Holt-Dryden, 1959.

[3] R. D. Luce. The theory of selective information and some of its behavioral applications. In R. D. Luce (Ed.), *Developments in mathematical psychology.* Glencoe, Ill.: The Free Press, 1960. Pp. 1–119.

[4] J. C. R. Licklider. Quasi-linear operator models in the study of manual tracking. In R. D. Luce (Ed.), *Developments in mathematical psychology.* Glencoe, Ill.: The Free Press, 1960. Pp. 168–279.

[5] W. S. Torgerson. *Theory and methods of scaling.* New York: Wiley, 1958.

[6] H. H. Harman. *Modern factor analysis.* Chicago: University of Chicago Press, 1960.

[7] L. L. Thurstone. *Multiple factor analysis.* Chicago: University of Chicago Press, 1947.

on Kemeny, Snell, & Thompson,[8] Kershner & Wilcox,[9] or May[10]; calculus at the level of Randolph & Kac[11] or May[10]; probability at the level of Feller[12]; and statistics at the level of Mood,[13] Hoel,[14] or Brunk.[15] In those cases in which an author felt obliged to use other mathematical techniques (e.g., matrix theory) we asked him to footnote the relevant sections, indicating what additional knowledge is needed and where it can be found.

Second, we said that the reader should be assumed to have or to have easy access to a series of books in mathematical psychology (the list is reproduced below) and that the author should feel free to reference proofs or sections in such books if he wished.

Third, we asked that authors give both an introduction to the subject matter and a balanced treatment of the main results without, however, feeling compelled to be exhaustive. The aim was to introduce the field to those who knew little about it and at the same time to provide a guided tour of the research literature of sufficient depth to be of value to an expert.

We did not ask for original research contributions; however, in several cases new results are included which are not available elsewhere. And in some cases the organization of ideas is so novel that it constitutes an original contribution.

To what use can these chapters be put? Their most obvious role is in the education of mathematical psychologists, either by their own reading or in courses on mathematical psychology. In such courses one or more chapters can serve as an annotated outline and guide for more detailed reading in the research literature. There are, however, a number of other courses for which some chapters should prove useful. First, some Departments of Mathematics are now offering courses on the mathematics employed in the behavioral sciences; these chapters provide a variety of

[8] J. G. Kemeny, J. L. Snell, & G. L. Thompson. *Introduction to finite mathematics.* Englewood Cliffs, N.J.: Prentice-Hall, 1957.

[9] R. B. Kershner, & L. R. Wilcox. *The anatomy of mathematics.* New York: Ronald, 1950, Chs. 1–6.

[10] K. O. May. *Elements of modern mathematics.* Reading, Mass.: Addison-Wesley, 1959.

[11] J. F. Randolph & M. Kac. *Analytic geometry and calculus.* New York: Macmillan, 1949.

[12] W. Feller. *An introduction to probability theory and its applications,* Vol. I (2nd ed.), New York: Wiley, 1957.

[13] A. McF. Mood. *Introduction to the theory of statistics.* New York: McGraw-Hill, 1950.

[14] P. G. Hoel. *Introduction to mathematical statistics* (3rd ed.), New York: Wiley, 1962.

[15] H. D. Brunk. *An introduction to mathematical statistics.* Boston: Ginn, 1960.

psychological illustrations. Second, within Departments of Psychology certain substantive experimental courses can draw on some chapters. Examples: (1) Chapters 9 and 10 of Volume II are relevant to courses on learning; (2) selected parts of Chapters 3, 4, and 5 along with the chapters on sensory mechanisms in Volume III can be used to supplement the more traditional treatments of sensory processes; and (3) various chapters raise issues of experimental methodology that go beyond the topics usually discussed in courses on experimental method and design.

In closing we wish to express our appreciation to various people and organizations for their assistance in our editorial tasks. Mrs. Judith White carried much of the administrative load, organizing the editors sufficiently so that the project moved smoothly from stage to stage. In addition, she did an enormous amount of typing, assisted in part by Miss Ada Katz. Mrs. Kay Estes ably took charge of the whole problem of indexing, for which we are extremely grateful. Although editing of this sort is mostly done in spare moments, the cumulative amount of work over three years is really quite staggering and credit is due the agencies that have directly and indirectly supported it, in our case the Universities of Pennsylvania and Washington, the National Science Foundation, and the Office of Naval Research.

Philadelphia, Pennsylvania   R. Duncan Luce
January 1963   Robert R. Bush
                                                 Eugene Galanter

Basic References in Mathematical Psychology

The authors of the Handbook chapters were asked to assume that their readers have or have easy access to the following books, which in our opinion form a basic library in mathematical psychology. A few of the most recent books were not, of course, included in the original list, which was sent out in 1960.

Arrow, K. J. *Social choice and individual values.* New York: Wiley, 1951.

Arrow, K. J., Karlin, S., & Suppes, P. *Mathematical methods in the social sciences, 1959.* Stanford: Stanford University Press, 1960.

Attneave, F. *Applications of information theory to psychology.* New York: Holt-Dryden, 1959.

Bush, R. R., & Estes, W. K. (Eds.) *Studies in mathematical learning theory.* Stanford: Stanford University Press, 1959.

Bush, R. R., & Mosteller, F. *Stochastic models for learning.* New York: Wiley, 1955.

Campbell, N. R. *Foundations of science.* New York: Dover, 1957.

Cherry, E. C. *On human communication.* New York: Wiley, 1957.

Chomsky, N. *Syntactic structures.* 's-Gravenhage: Mouton, 1957.

Churchman, C. W., & Ratoosh, P. (Eds.) *Measurement: definitions and theories.* New York: Wiley, 1959.

Criswell, Joan, Solomon, H., & Suppes, P. (Eds.) *Mathematical methods in small group processes.* Stanford: Stanford University Press, 1962.

Davidson, D., Suppes, P., & Siegel, S. *Decision making.* Stanford: Stanford University Press, 1957.

Garner, W. R. *Uncertainty and structure as psychological concepts.* New York: Wiley, 1962.

Guilford, J. P. *Psychometric methods.* New York: McGraw-Hill, 1954.

Gulliksen, H., & Messick, S. (Eds.), *Psychological scaling.* New York: Wiley, 1960.

Harman, H. H. *Modern factor analysis.* Chicago: University of Chicago Press, 1960.

Lazarsfeld, P. F. *Mathematical thinking in the social sciences.* Glencoe, Ill.: The Free Press, 1954.

Lindzey, G. (Ed.) *The handbook of social psychology.* Reading, Mass.: Addison-Wesley, 1954.

Luce, R. D. *Individual choice behavior.* New York: Wiley, 1959.

Luce, R. D. (Ed.) *Developments in mathematical psychology.* Glencoe, Ill.: The Free Press, 1960.

Luce, R. D., & Raiffa, H. *Games and decisions.* New York: Wiley, 1957.

Miller, G. A. *Language and communication.* New York: McGraw-Hill, 1951.

Miller, G. A., Galanter, E., & Pribram, K. *Plans and the structure of behavior.* New York: Holt, 1960.

National Research Council. *Human factors in underseas warfare.* Washington, 1949.

Osgood, C. E. *Method and theory in experimental psychology.* New York: Oxford University Press, 1953.

Quastler, H. (Ed.) *Information theory in psychology.* Glencoe, Ill.: The Free Press, 1955.

Restle, F. *Psychology of judgment and choice.* New York: Wiley, 1961.

Rosenblith, W. A. (Ed.) *Sensory communication.* New York: Wiley, 1961.

Savage, L. J. *The foundations of statistics.* New York: Wiley, 1954.

Siegel, S., & Fouraker, L. E. *Bargaining and group decision making.* New York: McGraw-Hill, 1960.

Simon, H. A. *Models of man.* New York: Wiley, 1957.

Solomon, H. *Mathematical thinking in the measurement of behavior.* Glencoe, Ill.: The Free Press, 1960.

Stevens, S. S. (Ed.) *Handbook of experimental psychology.* New York: Wiley, 1951.

Stouffer, S. A. (Ed.) *Measurement and prediction,* Vol. IV. Princeton: Princeton University Press, 1950.

Suppes, P., & Atkinson, R. C. *Markov learning models for multiperson interactions.* Stanford: Stanford University Press, 1960.

Thrall, R. M., Coombs, C. H., & Davis, R. L. *Decision processes.* New York: Wiley, 1954.

Thurstone, L. L. *Multiple factor analysis.* Chicago: University of Chicago Press, 1947.

Thurstone, L. L. *The measurement of values.* Chicago: University of Chicago Press, 1959.

Torgerson, W. S. *Theory and methods of scaling.* New York: Wiley, 1958.

Woodworth, R., & Schlosberg, H. *Experimental psychology.* New York: Holt, 1954.

Contents

I

Basic Measurement Theory

Patrick Suppes
Stanford University

Joseph L. Zinnes
Indiana University

1. The research on which this chapter is based has been supported by the Group Psychology Branch of the Office of Naval Research under Contract NR 171-034 with Stanford University. Reproduction in whole or part is permitted for any purpose of the United States Government.
2. We are indebted to John Tukey for a number of helpful comments on an earlier draft.

Contents

Basic Measurement Theory

Although measurement is one of the gods modern psychologists pay homage to with great regularity, the subject of measurement remains as elusive as ever. A systematic treatment of the theory is not readily found in the psychological literature. For the most part, a student of the subject is confronted with an array of bewildering and conflicting catechisms, catechisms that tell him whether such and such a ritual is permissible or, at least, whether it can be condoned. To cite just one peculiar, yet uniformly accepted, example, as elementary science students we are constantly warned that it "does not make sense" (a phrase often used when no other argument is apparent) to add numbers representing distinct properties, say, height and weight. Yet as more advanced physics students we are taught, with some effort no doubt, to multiply numbers representing such things as velocity and time or to divide distance numbers by time numbers. Why does multiplication make "more sense" than addition?

Rather than chart the etiology and course of these rituals, our purpose in this chapter is to build a consistent conceptual framework within which it is possible to discuss many (hopefully most) of the theoretical questions of measurement. At the same time, we hope to suppress as much as possible the temptation to enunciate additional dogmas or to put our stamp of approval on existing ones. Our overriding faith, if we may call it that, is that once the various theoretical issues have been formulated in the terms set forth here simple and specific answers with a clear logical basis can be given. To be sure, in some cases the answers to questions phrased within this framework are not so simple and may require extensive mathematical work. It may, for example, be a difficult mathematical problem to show that a given scale is (or is not) an interval scale, but this is not to suggest that the existence of an interval scale is a matter for philosophical speculation or that it depends on the whims and fancies or even the position of the experimenter. On the contrary, the answers to questions of measurement have the same unambiguous status as the answers to mathematical questions posed in other fields of science.

1. GENERAL THEORY OF FUNDAMENTAL MEASUREMENT

One systematic approach to the subject of measurement begins by the formulation of two fundamental problems. Briefly stated, the first problem is *justification of the assignment of numbers to objects or phenomena.* The second problem concerns *the specification of the degree to which this assignment is unique.* Each problem is taken up separately. [The general viewpoint to be developed in this section was first articulated in Scott & Suppes (1958).]

1.1 First Fundamental Problem: The Representation Theorem

The early history of mathematics shows how difficult it was to divorce arithmetic from particular empirical structures. The ancient Egyptians could not think of 2 + 3, but only of 2 bushels of wheat plus 3 bushels of wheat. Intellectually, it is a great step forward to realize that the assertion that 2 bushels of wheat plus 3 bushels of wheat equal 5 bushels of wheat involves the same mathematical considerations as the statement that 2 quarts of milk plus 3 quarts of milk equal 5 quarts of milk.

From a logical standpoint there is just one arithmetic of numbers, not an arithmetic for bushels of wheat and a separate arithmetic for quarts of milk. The first problem for a theory of measurement is to show how various features of this arithmetic of numbers may be applied in a variety of empirical situations. This is done by showing that certain aspects of the arithmetic of numbers have the same structure as the empirical situation investigated. The purpose of the definition of *isomorphism* to be given later is to make the rough-and-ready intuitive idea of "same structure" precise. The great significance of finding such an isomorphism of structures is that we may then use many of our familiar computational methods of arithmetic to infer facts about the isomorphic empirical structure.

More completely, we may state the first fundamental problem of an exact analysis of any procedure of measurement as follows:

Characterize the formal properties of the empirical operations and relations used in the procedure and show that they are isomorphic to appropriately chosen numerical operations and relations.

Since this problem is equivalent to proving what is called a numerical representation theorem, the first fundamental problem is hereafter referred to as the *representation problem* for a theory or procedure of measurement.

We may use Tarski's notion (1954) of a *relational system* to make the representational problem still more precise. A relational system is a finite sequence of the form $\mathfrak{A} = \langle A, R_1, \ldots, R_n \rangle$, where A is a nonempty set of elements called the *domain* of the relational system $\mathfrak{A}$, and $R_1, \ldots, R_n$ are relations on A.[3]

Two simple examples of relational systems are the following. Let A_1 be the set of human beings now living and let R_1 be the binary relation on A_1 such that, for all a and b in A_1, aR_1b if and only if a was born before b. $\mathfrak{A}_1 = \langle A_1, R_1 \rangle$ is then a relational system in the sense just defined. Let A_2 be a set of sounds and let D_2 be the quaternary relation representing judgment by a subject of relative magnitude of differences of pitch among the elements of A_2, i.e., for any a, b, c, and d in A_2, $abDcd$ if and only if the subject judges the difference in pitch between a and b to be equal to or less than the difference between c and d. The ordered couple $\mathfrak{A}_2 = \langle A_2, D_2 \rangle$ is then also a relational system.

The most important formal difference between $\mathfrak{A}_1$ and $\mathfrak{A}_2$ is that R_1 is a binary relation of ordering and D_2 is a quaternary relation for ordering of differences. It is useful to formalize this difference by defining the *type* of relational system. If $s = \langle m_1, \ldots, m_n \rangle$ is an n-termed sequence of positive integers, then a relational system $\mathfrak{A} = \langle A, R_1, \ldots, R_n \rangle$ is of type s if for each $i = 1, \ldots, n$ the relation R_i is an m_i-ary relation. Thus $\mathfrak{A}_1$ is of type $\langle 2 \rangle$ and $\mathfrak{A}_2$ is of type $\langle 4 \rangle$. Note that the sequence s reduces to a single term for these two examples because each has exactly one relation. A relational system $\mathfrak{A}_3 = \langle A_3, P_3, I_3 \rangle$ where P_3 and I_3 are binary relations on A_3 is of type $\langle 2, 2 \rangle$. The point of stating the type of relational system is to make clear the most general set-theoretical features of the system. We say that two relational systems are *similar* if they are of the same type.

We now consider the important concept of isomorphism of two similar relational systems. Before stating a general definition it will be helpful to examine the definition for systems of type $\langle 2 \rangle$, that is, systems like $\mathfrak{A}_1$. Let $\mathfrak{A} = \langle A, R \rangle$ and $\mathfrak{B} = \langle B, S \rangle$ be two systems of type $\langle 2 \rangle$. Then $\mathfrak{A}$ and $\mathfrak{B}$ are *isomorphic* if there is a one-one function f from A onto B such that for every a and b in A

$$aRb \quad \text{if and only if} \quad f(a) \, Sf(b).$$

[3] It is no restriction on generality to consider only relations, for from a formal standpoint operations are simply certain special relations. For example, a ternary relation T is a binary operation if whenever $T(x, y, z)$ and $T(x, y, z')$ then $z = z'$, and we may define the binary operation symbol "$\circ$" by the equation

$$x \circ y = z \quad \text{if and only if} \quad T(x, y, z).$$

Moreover, there are reasons special to theories of measurement to be mentioned in Sec. 3.5 for minimizing the role of operations.

As already stated, the intuitive idea is that $\mathfrak{A}$ and $\mathfrak{B}$ are isomorphic just when they have the same structure.

For instance, let

$$A = \{1, 3, 5, 7\},$$
$$A' = \{1, 4, 20, -5\},$$
$$R = \leqslant,$$
$$R' = \geqslant.$$

Then $\mathfrak{A} = \langle A, R \rangle$ and $\mathfrak{A}' = \langle A', R' \rangle$ are isomorphic. To see this, let

$$f(1) = 20,$$
$$f(3) = 4,$$
$$f(5) = 1,$$
$$f(7) = -5.$$

On the other hand, let

$$R'' = <.$$

Then $\mathfrak{A} = \langle A, R \rangle$ and $\mathfrak{A}'' = \langle A', R'' \rangle$ are not isomorphic, for suppose they were. Then there would exist a function f such that $f(1)\, R''\, f(1)$, that is,

$$f(1) < f(1), \tag{1}$$

because $1\,R\,1$, that is, $1 \leqslant 1$, but Eq. 1 is absurd.

To illustrate another point, let

$$A = \{1, 2\},$$
$$A' = \{8, 9, 10\},$$
$$R = <,$$
$$R' = >.$$

Then $\mathfrak{A} = \langle A, R \rangle$ and $\mathfrak{A}' = \langle A', R' \rangle$ are not isomorphic just because A and A' do not have the same number of elements and thus there can be no one-one function from A to A'.

From this discussion it should be clear how the general definition of isomorphism runs. Let $\mathfrak{A} = \langle A, R_1, \ldots, R_n \rangle$ and $\mathfrak{B} = \langle B, S_1, \ldots, S_n \rangle$ be similar relational systems. Then $\mathfrak{B}$ is an *isomorphic* image of $\mathfrak{A}$ if there is a one-one function f from A onto B such that, for each $i = 1, \ldots, n$ and for each sequence $\langle a_1, \ldots, a_{m_i} \rangle$ of elements of A, $R_i(a_1, \ldots, a_{m_i})$ if and only if $S_i(f(a_1), \ldots, f(a_{m_i}))$. Instead of saying that $\mathfrak{B}$ is an isomorphic image of $\mathfrak{A}$, we also often simply say that $\mathfrak{A}$ and $\mathfrak{B}$ are *isomorphic*.

On occasion it is too strict to require that the function f be one-one, for it may be natural in some cases to assign the same number to two distinct objects; for instance, two objects may have the same weight or length.

In such cases we weaken the definition by dropping the requirement that f be one-one and then speak of $\mathfrak{B}$ as the *homomorphic* image of $\mathfrak{A}$.

The formal definitions given thus far are not special to the theory of measurement. A more direct connection is made by first distinguishing between a *numerical relational system* and an *empirical relational system*. A numerical relational system is a relational system $\langle A, R_1, \ldots, R_n \rangle$ whose domain A is a set of real numbers. Although this definition places no restrictions on the relations R_i in the numerical system, these relations in practice are limited to certain common relations obtaining between numbers. It is possible, for example, to define a numerical relational system $\langle A, R_1 \rangle$ in which

$$A = \{1, 3, 5, 7\}$$
$$R_1 = \{\langle 1, 3 \rangle, \langle 5, 7 \rangle, \langle 7, 7 \rangle\},$$

but such a numerical system will not prove useful. The relational systems described in the preceding discussion of isomorphism are examples of more common (and useful) numerical systems. It should be obvious, but nevertheless it bears emphasizing, that a numerical relational system is not necessarily isomorphic to what is ordinarily called the real number system. For example, let Re be the set of all real numbers and let $<$ be the ordinary numerical relation of *less than*; then the numerical relational system $\langle \text{Re}, < \rangle$ is certainly not isomorphic to the usual system of real numbers employing the operations of addition and multiplication.

An empirical relational system is a relational system whose domain is a set of identifiable entities, such as weights, persons, attitude statements, or sounds. If, for example, the domain A of the relational system $\langle A, R_2 \rangle$ consisted of weights, then the relation R_2 would likely be the relation *is less heavy than*, that is, for a and b in A, aR_2b indicates that weight a is less heavy than b.

The first fundamental problem of measurement may be cast as the problem of showing that *any empirical relational system that purports to measure (by a simple number) a given property of the elements in the domain of the system is isomorphic (or possibly homomorphic) to an appropriately chosen numerical relational system.*

There are two aspects to this statement of the representation problem that perhaps need further amplification. Since, as we have emphasized, the numerical relational system does not completely characterize the real number system, the homomorphism that is required by the representation problem is *not* a homomorphism between the empirical relational system and the real number system. This does *not* mean, as is often suggested, that manipulations of the numbers in the domain of a given numerical system—to infer facts about the elements in the domain of the corresponding empirical system—must involve only those relations in the given numerical system. Relations neither contained in a given numerical system nor having a direct correspondence in the related empirical system may nevertheless be used. There are, of course, certain limitations imposed upon the manipulations of the numbers of a numerical system, but these limitations relate to certain criteria of meaningfulness of individual sentences rather than to those relations contained in a numerical system. These matters are discussed in detail in Sec. 5.

The second aspect of the representation problem needing amplification concerns the phrase "appropriately chosen numerical relational system" which appears in the last statement of the representation problem. The representation problem is not adequately solved if the isomorphism is established between a given empirical system and a numerical system employing unnatural or "pathological" relations. In fact, if the empirical system is finite or denumerable (i.e., has a finite or denumerable domain), some numerical system can always be found that is isomorphic to it. It is of no great consequence therefore merely to exhibit some numerical system that is isomorphic to an empirical system. It is of value, however, to exhibit a numerical system that is not only isomorphic to an empirical system but employs certain simple and familiar relations as well. A complete or precise categorization of the intuitively desirable relations is unfortunately somewhat elusive, so for this reason the statement of the representation problem refers merely to an "appropriately chosen" numerical system.

1.2 Second Fundamental Problem: The Uniqueness Theorem

Solution of the representation problem for a theory of measurement does not completely lay bare the structure of the theory, for it is a banal fact of methodology that there is often a formal difference between the kind of assignment of numbers arising from different procedures of measurement. As an illustration, consider the following five statements:

1. The number of people now in this room is 7.
2. Stendhal weighed 150 on September 2, 1839.
3. The ratio of Stendhal's weight to Jane Austen's on July 3, 1814, was 1.42.
4. The ratio of the maximum temperature today to the maximum temperature yesterday is 1.10.
5. The ratio of the difference between today's and yesterday's maximum temperature to the difference between today's and tomorrow's maximum temperature will be 0.95.

The empirical meaning of statements 1, 3, and 5 is clear, provided we make the natural assumptions, namely, for (3) that the same scale of weight, whether avoirdupois or metric, was being used, and for (5) that the same temperature scale is being used, whether Fahrenheit or centigrade. In contrast, (2) and (4) have no clear empirical meaning unless the *particular* scale used for the measurement is specified. On the basis of these five statements we may formally distinguish three kinds of measurement. Counting is an example of an *absolute* scale. The number of members of a given collection of objects is determined uniquely. There is no arbitrary choice of unit or zero available. In contrast, the usual measurement of mass or weight is an example of a *ratio* scale. A chemist, measuring a sample of a certain ferric salt on an equal arm balance with a standard series of metric weights, might make the statement:

6. This sample of ferric salt weighs 1.679 grams. But this statement may be replaced by the statement:
7. The ratio of the mass of this sample of ferric salt to the gram weight of my standard series is 1.679, and the manufacturer of my series has certified that the ratio of my gram weight to the standard kilogram mass of platinum iridium alloy at the International Bureau of Weights and Measures, near Paris, is 0.0010000.

In general, any empirical procedure for measuring mass does not determine the unit of mass. The choice of a unit is an empirically arbitrary decision made by an individual or group of individuals. Of course, once a unit of measurement has been chosen, such as the gram or pound, the numerical mass of every other object in the universe is uniquely determined. Another way of stating this is to say that the measurement of mass is unique up to multiplication by a positive constant. (The technical use of "up to" will become clear later). The measurement of distance is a second example of measurement of this sort. The ratio of the distance between Palo Alto and San Francisco to the distance between Washington and New York is the same whether the measurement is made in miles or yards.

The usual measurement of temperature is an example of the third formally distinct kind of measurement mentioned earlier. An empirical procedure for measuring temperature by use of a thermometer determines neither a unit nor an origin. (We are excluding from consideration here the measurement of absolute temperature whose zero point is not arbitrary.) In this sort of measurement the ratio of any two intervals is independent of the unit and zero point of measurement. For obvious reasons measurements of this kind are called *interval* scales. Examples other than measurement of temperature are provided by the usual measurements of temporal dates, linear position, or cardinal utility.

In terms of the notion of absolute, ratio, and interval scales, we may formulate the second fundamental problem for any exact analysis of a procedure of measurement: *determine the scale type of the measurements resulting from the procedure.* We have termed this problem the *uniqueness* problem for a theory of measurement. The reason for this terminology is that from a mathematical standpoint the determination of the scale type of measurements arising from a given system of empirical relations is the determination of the way in which any two numerical systems are related when they use the same numerical relations and are homomorphic to the given empirical system. In the case of mass, for example, the four following statements are equivalent.

8. The measurement of mass is on a ratio scale.
9. The measurement of mass is unique up to multiplication by a positive number (the number corresponding to an arbitrary choice of unit).
10. The measurement of mass is unique up to a similarity transformation (such a transformation is just multiplication by a positive number).
11. Given any empirical system for measuring mass, then any two numerical systems that use the same numerical relations and are homomorphic to the given empirical system are related by a similarity transformation.

The validity of statement 11 is demonstrated in Sec. 3.5, where an axiom system for measuring mass is presented.

1.3 Formal Definition and Classification of Scales of Measurement

It is unusual to find in the literature of measurement an exact definition of scales. Within the formal framework developed in this chapter it is possible to give an exact characterization that seems to correspond rather closely to many of the intuitive ideas of a scale.

Two preliminary definitions are needed. First, we say that a numerical relational system is *full* if its domain is the set of all real numbers. Second, a *subsystem* of a relational system $\mathfrak{A}$ is a relational system obtained from $\mathfrak{A}$ by taking a domain that is a subset of the domain of $\mathfrak{A}$ and restricting all relations of $\mathfrak{A}$ to this subset. For example, let

$$\text{Re} = \text{the set of all real numbers,}$$
$$< \ = \text{less than,}$$
$$N = \text{the set of nonnegative integers,}$$
$$<_N \ = \text{less than restricted to } N.$$

Then $\langle N, <_N \rangle$ is a subsystem of $\langle \mathrm{Re}, < \rangle$, which is itself a full numerical relational system. As a second example, let

$$A = \{1, 2, 3\},$$
$$R = \{\langle 1, 1 \rangle, \langle 2, 2 \rangle, \langle 1, 2 \rangle, \langle 3, 3 \rangle\},$$
$$B = \{1, 2\},$$
$$S_1 = \{\langle 1, 1 \rangle, \langle 2, 2 \rangle, \langle 1, 2 \rangle\},$$
$$S_2 = \{\langle 1, 1 \rangle, \langle 2, 2 \rangle\}.$$

Then $\mathfrak{B}_1 = \langle B, S_1 \rangle$ is a subsystem of $\mathfrak{A} = \langle A, R \rangle$, but $\mathfrak{B}_2 = \langle B, S_2 \rangle$ is not such a subsystem, for S_2 is not the relation R restricted to the set B.

We may now define scales. Let $\mathfrak{A}$ be an empirical relational system, let $\mathfrak{N}$ be a full numerical relational system, and let f be a function that maps $\mathfrak{A}$ homomorphically onto a subsystem of $\mathfrak{N}$. (If no two distinct objects in the domain of $\mathfrak{A}$ are assigned the same number, f is an isomorphic mapping.) We say then that the ordered triple $\langle \mathfrak{A}, \mathfrak{N}, f \rangle$ is a *scale*.

As should be apparent from the discussion in Sec. 1.2, the type of scale is determined by the relative uniqueness of the numerical assignment f. We say, for instance, that a ratio scale is unique up to a similarity transformation. (A function ϕ from the set of real numbers to the set of real numbers is a similarity transformation if there exists a positive real number α such that, for every real number x, $\phi(x) = \alpha x$.) How may we make this uniqueness statement precise in terms of our definition of scales? The answer is reasonably simple. Let $\langle \mathfrak{A}, \mathfrak{N}, f \rangle$ be a scale and g be any function having the property that $\langle \mathfrak{A}, \mathfrak{N}, g \rangle$ is also a scale. Then $\langle \mathfrak{A}, \mathfrak{N}, f \rangle$ is a *ratio* scale if there exists a similarity transformation ϕ such that

$$g = \phi \circ f,$$

where $\circ$ denotes the composition of functions [i.e., $(\phi \circ f)(a) = \phi(f(a))$]. Note that in general f and g map $\mathfrak{A}$ into different subsystems, although both are subsystems of the same full numerical relational system. This is necessary in order not to have different numerical interpretations of the basic empirical relations. That such different interpretations are possible even for the measurement of mass is illustrated in Sec. 3.5.

The definition of other types of scales is analogous to the one just given for ratio scales, and we may briefly state them by giving the restriction on the transformation ϕ. For a given scale, the transformation ϕ is frequently called an *admissible transformation*.

For *absolute* scales, ϕ must be the identity transformation, that is, $\phi(x) = x$, and we say that an absolute scale is unique up to the identity transformation.

For *interval* scales, ϕ must be a (positive) linear transformation, that is, there is a positive real number α and a number β (positive, zero, or negative) such that, for every real number x, $\phi(x) = \alpha x + \beta$. If in the measurement of temperature we wish to convert x in degrees Fahrenheit to centigrade we use the linear transformation defined by $\alpha = \frac{5}{9}$ and $\beta = -\frac{160}{9}$; that is,

$$y = \frac{5}{9}(x - 32) = \frac{5}{9}x - \frac{160}{9}.$$

Obviously every similarity transformation is a linear transformation with $\beta = 0$.

Another scale which is less well known but nevertheless useful is a *difference scale*.[4] For this scale the function ϕ is a translation transformation, that is, there is a real number β such that, for every real number x, $\phi(x) = x + \beta$. The assignment of numbers on a difference scale is unique up to an additive constant. (One example of a difference scale is discussed in Sec. 4.2.)

Still another type of scale is one which is *arbitrary except for order*. Moh's hardness scale, according to which minerals are ranked in regard to hardness as determined by a scratch test, and the Beaufort wind scale, whereby the strength of a wind is classified as calm, light air, light breeze, etc., are examples. We define them as follows. For *ordinal* scales ϕ must be a monotone transformation. Rather than define monotone transformations directly, it is convenient first to define monotone increasing and monotone decreasing transformations. A function ϕ is a *monotone increasing transformation* if and only if for all numbers x and y in the domain of ϕ, if $x < y$, then $\phi(x) < \phi(y)$. Obviously every linear transformation is a monotone increasing transformation on the set of all real numbers. The squaring function, that is, the function ϕ such that

$$\phi(x) = x^2, \tag{2}$$

is not a linear transformation but is monotone increasing on the set of nonnegative real numbers. Notice that it does not have this property on the set of all real numbers for $-5 < 4$ but

$$\phi(-5) = 25 > 16 = \phi(4).$$

It is important to realize that a monotone increasing transformation need not be definable by some simple equation like Eq. 2. For example, consider the set

$$A = \{1, 3, 5, 7\}$$

---

[4] As far as we know this terminology was first suggested by Donald Davidson.

and let ϕ be the function defined on A such that

$$\phi(1) = -5,$$
$$\phi(3) = 5,$$
$$\phi(5) = 289,$$
$$\phi(7) = 993.$$

Clearly ϕ is monotone increasing on A but does not satisfy any simple equation.

A function ϕ is a *monotone decreasing transformation* if and only if for all numbers x and y in the domain of ϕ, if $x < y$, then $\phi(x) > \phi(y)$. Two examples of monotone decreasing transformations on the set of all real numbers are

$$\phi(x) = -x$$

and

$$\phi(x) = -x^3 + 2.$$

As another instance, consider the set A again, and let ϕ be defined on A such that

$$\phi(1) = 6,$$
$$\phi(3) = 4,$$
$$\phi(5) = 2,$$
$$\phi(7) = -10.$$

Obviously ϕ is monotone decreasing on A.

It will be noted that monotone transformations are simply transformations that are either monotone increasing or monotone decreasing. Although we have characterized ordinal scales in terms of monotone transformations, in practice it is often convenient to consider only monotone increasing or monotone decreasing transformations, but this restriction is mainly motivated by hallowed customs and practices rather than by considerations of empirical fact.

Numbers are also sometimes used for *classification*. For example, in some states the first number on an automobile license indicates the county in which the owner lives. The assignment of numbers in accordance with such a scale may be arbitrary except for the assignment of the same number to people in the same county and distinct numbers to people in distinct counties.

The weakest scale is one for which numbers are used simply to name an object or person. The assignment is completely arbitrary. Draft numbers and the numbers of football players are examples of this sort of measurement. Such scales are usually called *nominal* scales.

For classificatory and nominal scales, ϕ is required to be only a one-one transformation.

In addition to these classical scale types, four of which were originally proposed by Stevens (1946), another type may be mentioned: *hyperordinal scales*. These scales are similar to the ordered metric scales proposed by Coombs (1952) and are characterized by transformations (called *hypermonotone*) which preserve first differences. More formally, a function ϕ is a *hypermonotone (increasing) transformation* if and only if ϕ is a monotone transformation, and for every x, y, u, and v in the domain of ϕ, if

$$x - y < u - v,$$

then

$$\phi(x) - \phi(y) < \phi(u) - \phi(v).$$

Naturally every linear transformation is a hypermonotone increasing transformation, but the converse is not true. Consider, for example,

$$A = \{1, 2, 4, 8\}$$

and the function ϕ such that

$$\phi(1) = 1,$$
$$\phi(2) = 2,$$
$$\phi(4) = 5,$$
$$\phi(8) = 15.$$

Clearly ϕ is hypermonotone increasing but not linear on A. Various methods of measuring sensation intensities or utility yield hyperordinal scales.

There is, strictly speaking, a nondenumerable infinity of types of scales which are characterized by various groups of numerical transformations, but most of them are not of any real empirical significance. Also, it is possible to extend the notion of measurement to relational systems like lattices and partial orderings which cannot be represented numerically in any natural way. [Such an extension is urged in Coombs, Raiffa, & Thrall (1954).]

By way of summary and to point out the major differences with current usage, the following aspects of the uniqueness question should be noted. Numerical assignments and scales are two different entities: the first is a function that maps an empirical system homomorphically onto a numerical system; the second is a triple, one of whose terms is a numerical assignment. If only the numerical assignment is known, its scale type or degree of uniqueness cannot be determined. To determine its uniqueness, we need to know the scale, which means that we need to know both an empirical relational system and a full numerical relational system. From a knowledge of the scale, we can, at least theoretically, infer precisely what the uniqueness properties of the numerical assignment are. In general, it should be noted that if the full numerical system is changed, then the numerical assignment will have quite different uniqueness properties, despite the fact that the empirical relational system may be unchanged. Therefore, when we speak of the uniqueness properties of a numerical assignment or equivalently of the admissible numerical assignments, it must always be relative to an explicit or implicit scale.

Some writers of measurement theory appear to define scales in terms of the existence of certain empirical operations. Thus interval scales are described in terms of the existence of an empirical operation which permits the subject (observer or experimenter) to compare intervals and to indicate in some way whether or not they are equal. In the present formulation of scale type, no mention is made of the kinds of "direct" observations or empirical relations that exist (in the empirical relational system). Scale type is defined entirely in terms of the class of numerical assignments which map a given empirical system homomorphically onto a subsystem of the same full numerical system. If in a given instance these numerical assignments are related by a linear transformation, then we have an interval scale. Precisely what empirical operations are involved in the empirical system is of no consequence. It may contain operations that permit the subject to compare intervals "directly," or the operations may be considerably more subtle.

One merit in this approach is that it takes away some of the implications generally associated with the question of scale type. For example, instead of asking how we know certain intervals are "really" equal, we ask if all the admissible numerical assignments are related by a linear transformation.

1.4 Extensive and Intensive Properties

Following Campbell (1920), most measurement theorists distinguish between quantities (or extensive properties) and qualities (or intensive properties) and between fundamental and derived measurement. Campbell defines these terms essentially as follows. Quantities are properties for each of which there exists an empirical operation similar to the arithmetical operation of addition. Qualities are characterized by an absence of this additive operation. Measurement is fundamental if it involves no previous measurement (Campbell, 1928, p. 14). If it does, it is derived. It should be added that measurement, for Campbell, implies obtaining at least an interval (or possibly a ratio) scale.

The relationship that Campbell attributes to these two pairs of terms leads to another (implicit) definition of fundamental measurement. Only quantities, he maintains, are amenable to fundamental measurement. Frequently, therefore, Campbell implicitly defines fundamental measurement in terms of the existence of an additive operation. Thus, in his discussion of temperature measurements, he concludes that such measurements cannot be fundamental since "there is no physical process of addition for temperature" (Campbell, 1920, p. 396). [Eight years later Campbell says, in regard to temperature, " . . . the temperature which is actually employed in physics is, in principle, as arbitrary and empirical as the hardness employed in mineralogy" (1928, p. 119).]

More recent writers (e.g., Cohen & Nagel, 1934; Guilford, 1954) have tended to follow the essential position developed by Campbell (either that fundamental measurement *is* the measurement of extensive properties or, more precisely, that it can be performed only on extensive properties).

It is of historical interest to note that a complete and rigorous set of axioms for extensive properties was given as early as 1901 by Hölder. His axioms specify, among other things, precisely the properties the addition operation is to have (see Sec. 3.5). The search for fundamental scales in psychology has frequently been identified with the search for an additive operation. [Some notable exceptions are Hempel (1952), Stevens (1951), and Torgerson (1958).] Since it is generally recognized that additive operations are so far almost nonexistent in psychology, it has been suggested that fundamental scales of mental tests will occur only when we have direct observation of underlying physiological phenomena (Comrey, 1951).

Since we attach no special virtue to the existence or nonexistence of an additive operation, we shall not attempt to give a more formal definition of the extensive-intensive distinction. In the next section, however, we give a definition of derived measurement. Our definition of fundamental measurement should be evident from the preceding sections. We may state it explicitly as follows. A function that maps an empirical relational system $\mathfrak{A}$ homomorphically onto a numerical relational system is said to be a *fundamental numerical assignment* for the empirical system $\mathfrak{A}$. In other words, if $\langle \mathfrak{A}, \mathfrak{N}, f \rangle$ is a scale, then the function f is a fundamental numerical assignment for the empirical system $\mathfrak{A}$. And, finally, *fundamental measurement* of set A with respect to the empirical system $\mathfrak{A}$ involves the establishment of a fundamental numerical assignment for $\mathfrak{A}$; in other words, it involves the establishment of a representation theorem for $\mathfrak{A}$. Note that to establish a fundamental numerical assignment for $\mathfrak{A}$ it is obviously necessary and sufficient to find just one numerical system homomorphic to $\mathfrak{A}$.

The fact that fundamental measurement procedures exist that are not based on an addition operation but that lead to ratio (interval or ordinal) scales is amply demonstrated in Sec. 3. Furthermore, in Sec. 5 it will be evident (we hope) that the specification of the meaningful functional relationships between scales requires only a knowledge of the relevant scale types (the admissible transformations) but does not require a knowledge of the relations that are involved in the corresponding empirical or numerical relational systems.

2. GENERAL THEORY OF DERIVED MEASUREMENT

The preceding section has been concerned with the general theory of fundamental measurement. Fundamental measurement of a set A is always with respect to an empirical system $\mathfrak{A}$. (A scale $\langle \mathfrak{A}, \mathfrak{R}, f \rangle$ we shall henceforth call a *fundamental* scale.)

In contrast, derived measurement does not depend on an empirical relational system directly but on other numerical assignments. The classic example of a derived measurement is that of density defined as the ratio of mass to volume.

The central issue for a theory of derived measurement is the status of the two basic problems of fundamental measurement, the representation and uniqueness problems.

2.1 The Representation Problem

We began the discussion of the representation problem for fundamental measurement by introducing the notion of an empirical relational system. In derived measurement the role of that concept is played by the concept of what we shall call a *derived measurement system* $\mathfrak{B} = \langle B, f_1, \ldots, f_n \rangle$ where B is a nonempty set of objects and $f_1, \ldots, f_n$ are numerical-valued functions defined on B or on Cartesian products of B with itself. Thus in the case of density, $\mathfrak{B}$ would be the triple $\langle B, m, V \rangle$, where m is the mass function and V is the volume function. In the case of pair comparison methods of scaling, the derived measurement system is a couple $\mathfrak{B} = \langle B, p \rangle$ such that p is defined on $B \times B$ and for all a, b in B, $0 < p_{ab} < 1$, $p_{ab} + p_{ba} = 1$, and $p_{aa} = \frac{1}{2}$. The usual interpretation of p_{ab} is that it is the relative frequency with which a is preferred to or is, in some sense, greater than b. A number of derived measures defined in terms of $\langle B, p \rangle$ have been considered in the literature; these measures are variously interpreted, sometimes as measures of utility, often as measures of response strength. We consider them in some detail later (Sec. 4).

Our approach to the representation problem is to define, in terms of derived measurement systems, *derived scales.* Let $\mathfrak{B} = \langle B, f_1, \ldots, f_n \rangle$ be a derived measurement system, let g be a numerical-valued function on B (or Cartesian products of B with itself), and let R be a relation between $f_1, \ldots, f_n$ and g. We say that the triple $\langle \mathfrak{B}, R, g \rangle$ is a *derived scale, R* is the *representing relation* for the scale, and g is the *derived numerical assignment.* In most cases R is defined by an equation.

To make the ideas clearer, let us consider two examples, beginning with density. As we have already said, $\mathfrak{B} = \langle B, m, V \rangle$ is the derived measurement of density and the representing relation R is defined by

$$R(m, V, d) \tag{3}$$

if and only if for every a in B

$$d(a) = \frac{m(a)}{V(a)}.$$

The triple $\langle \mathfrak{B}, R, d \rangle$ is then the derived scale of density. The particularly simple form of the representing relation R for density is deceptive. The definition of Eq. 3 is an equation explicitly defining d in terms of m and V. Matters are not always this simple, as our second example will show.

Let $\mathfrak{B} = \langle B, p \rangle$ be a derived system for pair comparisons. We may define Bradley-Terry-Luce derived scales in the following manner. Let v be the derived numerical assignment of response strength and let R_1 be the representing relation such that $R_1(p, v)$ if and only if for every a and b in B

$$\frac{v(a)}{v(a) + v(b)} = p_{ab}. \tag{4}$$

Then $\langle \mathfrak{B}, R_1, v \rangle$ is a Bradley-Terry-Luce derived scale of response strength. First, the important point for the moment is that Eq. 4 does not explicitly define the function v in terms of p. As is evident from Eq. 4, we could determine v only up to a similarity transformation. Second, it is equally clear that unless some restrictions are placed on the relative frequencies p_{ab}, the function p may not stand in the relation R_1 to any v, that is, the set of equations defined by Eq. 4 may not have a solution in terms of the unknown quantities $v(a)$, $v(b)$, etc.

From this last example it should be clear how we may formulate the representation problem for derived measurements. Given a derived system $\mathfrak{B}$ and the definition of a representing relation R, the representation problem is solved by showing that there exists a derived numerical assignment g such that $\langle \mathfrak{B}, R, g \rangle$ is a derived scale. In the case of density, the proof of the existence of g is trivial. For Bradley-Terry-Luce scales such a function does not in general exist. In Sec. 4.1 we state necessary and sufficient conditions for the existence of g.

We have already pointed out that more than one representation theorem may be proved for empirical relational systems of a given kind. Similarly, different representations leading to different derived scales for a given derived system may be obtained by selecting a different representing relation R. Later (Sec. 4) we examine the possibilities for pair comparison data in some detail.

2.2 The Uniqueness Problem

In the earlier discussion of fundamental scales we defined scale type in a relatively simple way. For instance, if $\langle \mathfrak{A}, \mathfrak{N}, f \rangle$ is a fundamental scale such that, for any other scale $\langle \mathfrak{A}, \mathfrak{N}, f' \rangle$, f and f' are related by a similarity transformation, then $\langle \mathfrak{A}, \mathfrak{N}, f \rangle$ is a ratio scale.

A natural analogue of this definition may be formulated for derived scales. Ratio scales are defined as follows. Let $\langle \mathfrak{B}, R, g \rangle$ be a derived scale. Then it is a *ratio scale in the narrow sense* if for any other scale $\langle \mathfrak{B}, R, g' \rangle$, g and g' are related by similarity transformation. We have specified "in the narrow sense" for the following reason. According to this definition, density is an absolute scale because for a fixed $\mathfrak{B} = \langle B, m, V \rangle$ the function d is uniquely determined. This is not true for the response strength function v for pair comparison data, as we shall see later.

The definition of the other standard scale types is an immediate generalization of that given for ratio scales. A more important problem is to distinguish other senses of uniqueness. Density may again furnish a paradigm. It is commonly said that density is a derived ratio scale, and it is not difficult to define a second sense of ratio scale that catches this idea. The basis for the idea is, of course, that if we change measurements of mass from $m(a)$ to $\alpha m(a)$ and measurements of volume from $V(a)$ to $\beta V(a)$ then we change measurements of density from $d(a)$ to $\alpha m(a)/\beta V(a)$, and the ratio α/β defines a derived similarity transformation on the density function d.

The formal definition that corresponds to this example runs as follows: let $\langle \mathfrak{B}, R, g \rangle$ be a derived scale, let $\mathfrak{B}'$ result from $\mathfrak{B}$ by applying admissible transformations to the numerical assignments of $\mathfrak{B}$. Then $\langle \mathfrak{B}, R, g \rangle$ is a *ratio scale in the wide sense* if for any scale $\langle \mathfrak{B}', R, g' \rangle$, g and g' are related by a similarity transformation. Obviously density is a ratio scale in the wide sense.

The reason for the separation between narrow and wide scale types is to distinguish between independent and dependent admissible transformations of derived numerical assignments. The narrow admissible transformations, those defined by the narrow scale types, can be performed without at the same time transforming one of the fundamental assignments in the derived system. For the wide admissible transformations this is not necessarily the case. These transformations of the derived numerical assignments may need to be accompanied by related transformations to certain fundamental numerical assignments. This property of wide scale types will be seen to be important in Sec. 5.

2.3 Pointer Measurement

In addition to fundamental and derived measurements, a third type, called *pointer measurement*, may be noted. By pointer measurement we mean a numerical assignment (either fundamental or derived) based on the direct readings of some validated instrument. An instrument is validated if it has been shown to yield numerical values that correspond to those of some fundamental or derived numerical assignment. Consider the measurement of mass. The fundamental measurement of mass is a long and tedious operation (see Sec. 3.5). However, once this has been accomplished, there is no need to go through this procedure to determine the mass (or weight proportional to it) of some particular object such as a steak. As every housewife knows, the weight of a steak is determined by placing it on a measuring instrument (a "scale") and then noting the deflection of the pointer. The housewife assumes, however, that the stamp of approval on the scale (by, say, the department of weights and measures) means that someone has taken the trouble to verify that the deflections of the pointer under certain "standard" conditions do indeed correspond to the values of a given fundamental or derived numerical assignment. In other words, the housewife assumes that the instrument has been validated.

To construct an instrument that will provide direct or at least quick measurement of some fundamental or derived scale, it is generally necessary to utilize some established empirical law or theory involving the fundamental or derived scale in question. In the case of mass an instrument is frequently constructed that is based on Hooke's law (the extension of a spring is proportional to the force acting on the spring) and on the law of gravity (the force exerted by an object is proportional to its mass). Once a spring has been selected that satisfies Hooke's law within the accuracy desired (under "standard" conditions of temperature, humidity, etc.), the next step is to calibrate the spring, that is, to determine what amount of mass would be required to produce each possible extension of the spring or, equivalently, each possible deflection of the pointer attached to the spring. Generally, the calibration is performed by selecting two known weights, say 32 and 212 kg, and then spacing off 180 equal divisions between the two deflections corresponding to the two weights. If higher accuracy is required and if it is possible, further division of the "scale" is carried out.

Although the construction and use of a pointer instrument is obviously an important practical problem, it is not our purpose to treat it in detail here. There are two aspects of pointer measurements of theoretical interest, and these pertain to the two fundamental problems of measurement theory: the problem of justifying the numerical assignment, in this case the readings of the instrument, and that of specifying the uniqueness of the numerical assignment. The answer to the first problem for pointer measurement has already been given; the readings are justified by comparing them to the appropriate fundamental or derived numerical assignment. All too often in the behavioral sciences a direct reading instrument is available (and used) despite the fact that its readings are not justified; the readings do not correspond to any *known* fundamental or derived numerical assignment. On the surface it would appear that such pseudopointer instruments would be useless and their readings meaningless. Their prevalence in psychology (e.g., mental tests, questionnaires, indices), however, suggests that this conclusion may be too strong. The difficulty with rejecting out of hand pseudopointer instruments is that they may be converted (all too easily) into a fundamental measurement procedure yielding an absolute scale. This can be done by merely asserting first that the instrument is not intended to be a pointer instrument; it is not intended to give readings corresponding to some *known* numerical assignment. Second, the readings are based entirely on the counting operation, the readings merely referring to the number of divisions that are to the left (or right) of the pointer after each deflection. Since the counting operation can always yield a fundamental absolute scale, there can be no logical quarrel with anyone who uses this procedure to convert what would appear to be a pseudopointer instrument into a fundamental measuring instrument. One can, however, ask the question: what is accomplished by the use of such an instrument? Generally speaking, the answer seems to be that the instrument may be able to predict some future event of practical importance. A mental test score, for example, based on the number of correct answers may be able to predict success in college or in a job. The justification in the use of such instruments would then lie solely in the degree to which they are able to predict significant events, not as with most "normal" fundamental measures, in the homomorphism between an empirical system and a numerical system.

The answer to the second problem, the uniqueness problem, for pointer measurement has been the source of some confusion. The uniqueness of the readings is determined by the uniqueness of the corresponding fundamental or derived numerical assignment, not, as might appear, by the method of calibrating the pointer instrument. The fact that the pointer instrument for measuring mass gives a ratio scale is not because of the equal spacing of the divisions on the dial; it would be quite possible to use a nonlinear spring and have the divisions of the dial unequally spaced without altering the scale type. On the other hand, neither is it because of the fact that two points (e.g., 32 kg and 212 kg) are generally fixed or determined by the calibration procedure. Suppose, for example, the fundamental measurement of mass yielded only an ordinal scale and the extension of the spring were monotonically related to mass. Then, although precisely the same calibration procedure could be carried out, that is, two points could be fixed and the dial divided into equally spaced divisions, the resulting readings of the instrument would nevertheless be only on an ordinal scale. Thus the scale type of a pointer instrument derives directly from the scale type of the corresponding fundamental or derived numerical assignment. As a corollary to this, it follows that merely inspecting the divisions on the dial of a pointer instrument, or even observing the calibration procedures of the instrument, does not enable one to infer the scale type of the measurements obtained from the instrument.

3. EXAMPLES OF FUNDAMENTAL MEASUREMENT

In this section some concrete examples of different empirical systems are given, and in each case solutions to the representation and uniqueness problems are exhibited. The empirical systems themselves are not necessarily of interest. Many are too restrictive in one way or another to have direct application to significant psychological situations. These systems, however, permit bringing into focus some of the essential aspects of measurement.

The proofs establishing representation and uniqueness theorems are generally long and involved. For most empirical systems, therefore, we shall have to content ourselves with simply stating the results. This means that for each empirical system described a full numerical system is stated, and then, more particularly, at least one subsystem which is a homomorphic image of the empirical system is given. The uniqueness problem is answered by giving the relationship between any two subsystems (of the full system) that are homomorphic images of the empirical system. Two proofs are given in Sec. 3.1 and 3.2. The first proof (Sec. 3.1) is relatively simple and it will serve to introduce some of the necessary terms and ideas that are generally encountered. The second proof (Sec. 3.2) is considerably more difficult so that it will give some notion of the complexity of the representation problem.

There is, as was indicated previously (Sec. 1.1), some degree of arbitrariness in the selection of a full numerical system for a given empirical system. In each case other full numerical systems could have been chosen and a different representation theorem established. Thus it should be emphasized that, although the representation problem is solved for each empirical system by exhibiting *one* homomorphic numerical system having certain reasonably natural and simple properties, the existence of other, perhaps equally desirable, numerical systems is not ruled out.

3.1 Quasi-Series

Nominal and classificatory scales are somewhat trivial examples of measurements so that we shall consider first an empirical system leading to an ordinal scale. The empirical system to be described is one that might, for example, be applicable to a lifted weight experiment in which subjects are given the weights in pairs and are instructed to indicate whether one weight of each pair seems heavier or whether they seem equally heavy.

Some useful definitions are as follows. A relational system $\mathfrak{A} = \langle A, R \rangle$ consisting of a set A and a single binary relation R is called a *binary system*. A binary system $\langle A, I \rangle$ is called a *classificatory* system if and only if I is an *equivalence relation* on A, that is, if and only if I has the following properties:

1. Reflexive: if $a \in A$, then aIa;
2. Symmetric: if $a, b \in A$ and aIb, then bIa;
3. Transitive: if $a, b, c \in A$ and if aIb, bIc, then aIc,

where $a \in A$ means that a is a member of the set A. A common example of an equivalence relation is the identity relation $=$. In psychological contexts it is convenient to think of the indifference relation or the "seems alike" relation as an equivalence relation, although there are many cases in which the transitivity property fails to hold.

We can now define a quasi-series (Hempel, 1952).

Definition 1. *The relational system* $\mathfrak{A} = \langle A, I, P \rangle$ *is a* quasi-series *if and only if*

1. $\langle A, I \rangle$ *is a classificatory system*;
2. P *is a binary, transitive relation.*
3. *If* $a, b \in A$, *then exactly one of the following holds*: aPb, bPa, aIb.

If, for example, A were a set of persons, I the relation *the same height as*, and P the relation *shorter in height than*, then the relational system $\langle A, I, P \rangle$ would be a quasi-series. An important feature of a quasi-series is that the subject may be permitted to express his indifference when two stimuli seem alike.

Let us assume that the quasi-series $\langle A, I, P \rangle$ is an empirical relational system, A being a certain set of stimuli and I and P being observable or empirical binary relations. Solving the representation problem for this empirical system will mean finding a (simple) homomorphic, rather than isomorphic, numerical system. If two elements a and b in A are related by I, that is, if aIb, we can reasonably expect that it will be necessary to assign the same number to both a and b. Hence the numerical assignment cannot be one-one.

One way of establishing a representation theorem for a quasi-series and at the same time dealing with the easier notion of isomorphism is to group or partition the elements of A in certain subsets. If the subsets have been selected judiciously enough, then it may be possible to establish an isomorphism between these subsets and a numerical system. All the elements within a given subset could then be assigned the same number; the numerical assignment defined on the subsets would be one-one, that is, each subset would correspond to a distinct number. To accomplish this end, we introduce the notion of I-equivalence classes.

If a is in A, then the *I-equivalence class of which a is a member* is the set of all elements b in A such that aIb. This equivalence class is denoted by $[a]$. In symbols

$$[a] = \{b \mid b \in A \ \& \ aIb\}.$$

The set of all I-equivalence classes obtainable from A is denoted by A/I. As an example, let A be the set of persons born in the United States. If I is the relation of equivalence such that aIb if and only if a and b are born in the same state, then [Abraham Lincoln] is the set of all persons born in Kentucky and [Robert Taft] the set of all persons born in Ohio. In this example there are approximately 400 million elements in A and 50 elements (corresponding to the 50 states) in the set A/I.

One of the properties of equivalence classes that is important is their property of partitioning the set A into disjoint subsets or classes. Each element of A then belongs to one and only one equivalence class. We state this property as a theorem.

Theorem 1.   *If $[a]$, $[b] \in A/I$ then either $[a] = [b]$ or $[a] \cap [b] = \emptyset$.*

PROOF.   Assume that $[a] \cap [b] \neq \emptyset$. Let c be an element in both $[a]$ and $[b]$ and let a' be an arbitrary element of $[a]$. We have then aIc, bIc, and aIa' from the definition of equivalence classes. From the symmetry and transitivity of I, we infer bIa', whence $[a] \subseteq [b]$. By an exactly similar argument $[b] \subseteq [a]$, whence $[a] = [b]$, and the theorem is proved.

Thus if each element in A/I is assigned a unique number—and this is our aim—every element of A will be associated with exactly one number. The net effect then of obtaining a numerical system isomorphic to an empirical system having A/I as its domain is to obtain the desired homomorphic numerical system for the system $\langle A, I, P \rangle$.

There is another useful property of equivalence classes which should also be apparent. If a, $b \in A$ and if aIb, then the equivalence class of a equals the equivalence class of b, and conversely. This property is also stated as a theorem.

Theorem 2. *If $[a]$, $[b] \in A/I$, then $[a] = [b]$ if and only if aIb.*

PROOF. First, assume aIb. Let a' be an arbitrary element in $[a]$. Then aIa' by the definition of $[a]$, and bIa from the symmetry of I, hence bIa'. Consequently by definition of $[b]$, $a' \in [b]$. Since a' is an arbitrary element of $[a]$, we have then established that $[a] \subseteq [b]$. By a similar argument, it is easy to show that $[b]$ is a subset of $[a]$. Since $[a] \subseteq [b]$ and $[b] \subseteq [a]$, we conclude that $[a] = [b]$.

Next, assume $[a] = [b]$. Since $b \in [b]$, using our assumption we infer at once that $b \in [a]$, hence aIb. Q.E.D.

We next want to define a relation on the elements of A/I. So far only the relations I and P have been defined on the elements of A and obviously to establish the desired isomorphism we shall have to have a relation defined on A/I. This relationship should of course correspond in some way to the relation P. Accordingly, we define the binary relation P^* as follows.

Definition 2. *$[a]P^*[b]$ if and only if aPb.*

This definition needs some preliminary justification because it could lead to contradictions. We must rule out the possibility that for some element $a' \in [a]$, and for some element $b' \in [b]$, both $b'Pa'$ and aPb hold. The following two theorems are therefore required before we can safely proceed to use Def. 2. The first theorem asserts that if aPb, then every element in $[a]$ may be substituted for a.

Theorem 3. *If aPb and $a'Ia$, then $a'Pb$.*

PROOF. Assume $a'Ia$ and aPb. From Assumption 3 of a quasi-series exactly one of the following must hold: $a'Ib$, bPa', and $a'Pb$. However, we cannot have $a'Ib$, since by the transitivity and symmetry property of I, $a'Ib$ and $a'Ia$ imply aIb, which contradicts our initial assumption. Furthermore, we cannot have bPa', since, by the transitivity property of P, aPb, and bPa' imply aPa', which also contradicts our initial assumption. Hence we must have $a'Pb$. Q.E.D.

Theorem 4. *If aPb and $b'Ib$, then aPb'.*

The proof is similar to the proof of Theorem 3.

Both theorems taken together imply that if aPb, then, for any element $a' \in [a]$ and for any element $b' \in [b]$, $a'Pb'$.

From Theorems 3 and 4 it follows that the relation P^* will not lead to inconsistencies; hence we define the relational system $\mathfrak{A}/I = \langle A/I, P^* \rangle$, which is obtained from the quasi-series $\mathfrak{A} = \langle A, I, P \rangle$. The representation problem can then be solved by establishing an isomorphism between $\langle A/I, P^* \rangle$ and an appropriate numerical relational system. The numerical relational system to be used for this purpose is called a *numerical series*. (It is not a series of numerical terms.) Consider first the definition of a *series*. A binary system $\langle A, R \rangle$ is a *series* if R has the following properties:

1. R is asymmetric in A, that is, if aRb then not bRa;
2. R is transitive in A;
3. R is connected in A, that is, if $a \neq b$, then either aRb or bRa.

By a *numerical series* we mean a binary numerical relational system $\langle N, R \rangle$ in which N is a set of real numbers and R is either the arithmetical relation *less than* or the arithmetical relation *greater than* restricted to the set N. Clearly R satisfies the properties of asymmetry, transitivity, and connectedness so that a numerical series is a series. As would be expected, we also have the following theorem.

Theorem 5. *If $\langle A, I, P \rangle$ is a quasi-series then $\langle A/I, P^* \rangle$ is a series, that is, P^* is asymmetric, transitive and connected in A/I.*

Theorem 5 follows directly from the definition of P^* in Def. 2 and from the properties of P and I given in the definition of the quasi-series $\langle A, I, P \rangle$.

The representation theorem for a finite or denumerable quasi-series can now be stated. Some additional restrictions are needed for the non-denumerable case.

Theorem 6 *(Representation Theorem).* *Let the relational system $\mathfrak{A} = \langle A, I, P \rangle$ be a quasi-series where A/I is a finite or denumerable set. Then there exists a numerical series isomorphic to $\langle A/I, P^* \rangle$.*

PROOF. We give the proof for the denumerable case. The proof for A/I finite is much simpler and is essentially a special case.

Because A/I is a denumerable set, its elements may be enumerated as $a_1, a_2, \ldots, a_n, \ldots$ (It is important to note that this is in general *not* the ordering of A/I under P^* but is rather an ordering we know exists under the hypothesis that A/I is denumerable.) We now define by induction the appropriate isomorphism function f—the induction being on the enumeration $a_1, a_2, \ldots, a_n, \ldots$ We first set

$$f(a_1) = 0,$$

and then consider a_n. There are three cases, the first two of which are very simple.

Case 1. $a_i P^* a_n$, for $i = 1, 2, \ldots, n - 1$. Then set

$$f(a_n) = n.$$

Case 2. $a_n P^* a_i$, for $i = 1, 2, \ldots, n - 1$. Here set

$$f(a_n) = -n.$$

Case 3. There are integers i and j less than n such that $a_i P^* a_n P^* a_j$. Define

$$a_n^* = \max \{a_i \mid a_i P^* a_n \ \& \ i < n\}$$
$$b_n^* = \min \{a_j \mid a_n P^* a_j \ \& \ j < n\}.$$

The maximum and minimum are with respect to the ordering P^*, for example, a_n^* is such that $a_n^* P^* a_n$ and for every $i < n$ if $a_i \neq a_n^*$ then $a_i P^* a_n^*$. The existence of a unique greatest lower bound a_n^* just before a_n under P^* and somewhere before a_n in the enumeration $a_1, a_2, \ldots,$ $a_n, \ldots,$ and the similar existence of the unique least upper bound b_n^* depends on all the axioms for a series as well as the fact that the number of elements of A/I before a_n in the enumeration $a_1, a_2, \ldots, a_n, \ldots$ is finite. If P^* is not connected, there could be two elements a_n^* and a_n^{**} satisfying the condition that they both preceded a_n in the ordering P^* and nothing else was between each of them and a_n under the ordering P^*. Similar difficulties could ensue if either transitivity or asymmetry were dropped as conditions on P^*. On the other hand, the finiteness of the number of elements a_i, for $i < n$, is necessary to establish that at least one maximal a_n^* and one minimal b_n^* exist.

At this point we need to use the fact that the rational numbers are also denumerable and thus may be enumerated as $r_1, r_2, \ldots, r_n, \ldots$. We define $f(a_n)$ as a rational number for each a_n, and more particularly, for Case 3, we define $f(a_n)$ as the first r_i between $f(a_n^*)$ and $f(b_n^*)$ in our enumeration of the rational numbers; if $f(a_n^*) < f(b_n^*)$ and $f(a_n^*) \geqslant f(b_n^*)$, we set $f(a_n) = 0$. (The existence of r_i for $f(a_n^*) < f(b_n^*)$ follows immediately from the fact that between any two rational numbers there exists another rational number.)

We want to show that this second possibility—$f(a_n^*) \geqslant f(b_n^*)$—leads to absurdity and thereby establish at the same time that

$$a_i P^* a_j \quad \text{if and only if} \quad f(a_i) < f(a_j). \tag{5}$$

Let a_n be the first element in our enumeration for which, for $i, j < n$, Eq. 5 does not hold. Thus Eq. 5 holds for $i, j < n - 1$, and the failure must be due to $i = n - 1$ or $j = n - 1$. Now a_{n-1} must follow under one of the three cases. Clearly, if it falls under Case 1 or 2, Eq. 5 is satisfied. Consider now Case 3. Because a_{n-1}^* and b_{n-1}^* precede a_{n-1} in the enumeration and because by definition of a_{n-1}^* and b_{n-1}^*, together with the transitivity of P^*, we must have $a_{n-1}^* P^* b_{n-1}^*$, it follows from Eq. 5 that $f(a_{n-1}^*) < f(b_{n-1}^*)$. But then by definition of $f(a_{n-1})$, we have

$$f(a_{n-1}^*) < f(a_{n-1}) < f(b_{n-1}^*),$$

and also $a_{n-1}^* P^* a_{n-1} P^* b_{n-1}^*$ and, contrary to our supposition, Eq. 5 holds for a_{n-1}. Thus Eq. 5 holds for every n, and our theorem is established. (Note that the one-one character of f follows at once from Eq. 5.) Q.E.D.

To complete the solution of the representation problem for quasi-series, two definitions are needed to characterize necessary and sufficient conditions for an infinite quasi-series which is not finite or denumerable to be numerically representable. The classical example to show that additional restrictions are needed is the lexicographic ordering of the set of all ordered pairs of real numbers. The ordering P is defined as follows for any real numbers x, y, u, and v.

$$\langle x, y \rangle P \langle u, v \rangle \quad \text{if and only if} \quad x < u \quad \text{or} \quad (x = u \quad \text{and} \quad y < v).$$

The proof that the set of pairs of real numbers under the ordering P cannot be represented as a numerical series we leave as an exercise.

One definition is needed. Let the binary system $\mathfrak{A} = \langle A, R \rangle$ be a series and let B be a subset of A. Then B is *order-dense in* $\mathfrak{A}$ if and only if for every a and b in A and not in B there is a c in B such that aRc and cRb. Speaking loosely in terms of sets rather than relational systems, the set of rational numbers is a subset that is order-dense in the real numbers with respect to the natural ordering less than. Observe that the notions just defined could have been defined for arbitrary relational systems $\mathfrak{A} = \langle A, R \rangle$, which are not necessarily series, but then certain relational systems which are not dense in any intuitive sense would turn out to be dense under the definition. A simple example is the system $\langle N, \leqslant \rangle$ where N is the set of positive integers.

Theorem 7 (Representation Theorem). *Let the structure* $\mathfrak{A} = \langle A, I, P \rangle$ *be a quasi-series in which* A/I *is an infinite set. Then a necessary and sufficient condition for the existence of a numerical series isomorphic to* $\langle A/I, P^* \rangle$ *is the existence of a denumerable subset* B *of* A/I *which is order dense in* $\langle A/I, P^* \rangle$.

The proof of this theorem is omitted. A proof may be found in Birkhoff (1948, p. 32). It may be remarked that the proof of necessity requires the axiom of choice. Economists and others interested in applications of theorems like Theorem 7 to utility theory or demand analysis often deal with questions of continuity concerning the isomorphism function. Various sufficient topological conditions are given in Debreu (1954). He does not treat necessary conditions, which would require an extremely difficult topological classification of quasi-series.

Theorems 6 and 7 together give necessary and sufficient conditions for any quasi-series to be representable by a numerical series. We now turn to the simple solution of the uniqueness problem for quasi-series.

Theorem 8 (Uniqueness Theorem). *Let $\mathfrak{A} = \langle A, I, P \rangle$ be a quasi-series. Then any two numerical series isomorphic to $\mathfrak{A}/I$ are related by a monotone transformation.*

PROOF. Let $\langle N_1, R_1 \rangle$ and $\langle N_2, R_2 \rangle$ be two numerical series isomorphic to $\mathfrak{A}/I$. (R_1 and R_2 may each be either the relation $<$ or the relation $>$.) We want to find a function ϕ such that the domain of ϕ is N_1 and the range is N_2, that is,

$$D(\phi) = N_1$$
$$R(\phi) = N_2$$

and for every x, y in N_1, if xR_1y then $\phi(x)R_2\,\phi(y)$, that is, we want a monotonic function which maps N_1 onto N_2.

Let f_1 and f_2 be two functions satisfying the hypothesis, that is, f_1 maps $\langle A/I, P^* \rangle$ isomorphically onto the numerical series $\langle N_1, R_1 \rangle$ and f_2 maps $\langle A/I, P^* \rangle$ isomorphically onto the numerical series $\langle N_2, R_2 \rangle$. Consider the domains and ranges of f_1 and f_2 and their inverses:

$$D(f_1) = D(f_2) = R(f_1^{-1}) = R(f_2^{-1}) = A/I$$
$$R(f_1) = D(f_1^{-1}) = N_1$$
$$R(f_2) = D(f_2^{-1}) = N_2.$$

Consider then the function $f_2 \circ f_1^{-1}$. Has it the desired properties?

$$D(f_2 \circ f_1^{-1}) = N_1$$
$$R(f_2 \circ f_1^{-1}) = N_2.$$

Suppose $x, y \in N_1$ and xR_1y. Then $f_1^{-1}(x)P^*f_1^{-1}(y)$; hence from the definition of f_2, $f_2(f_1^{-1}(x))R_2f_2(f_1^{-1}(y))$, that is, $(f_2 \circ f_1^{-1})(x)R_2\,(f_2 \circ f_1^{-1})(y)$, which completes the proof.

We have shown that given any two isomorphic numerical series they are related by a monotone transformation. That in general the numerical series are not related by any stronger transformation can be easily proved by a counterexample.

3.2 Semiorders

In Luce (1956) the concept of a semiorder is introduced as a natural and realistic generalization of quasi-series. The intuitive idea is that in many situations judgments of indifference concerning some attribute of stimuli, like the pitch or loudness of tones or the utility of economic goods, is not transitive. Thus a subject may judge tone *a* to be just as loud as tone *b* and tone *b* to be just as loud as tone *c* but find to his surprise that he judges tone *a* definitely louder than tone *c*.

In his original paper Luce uses a system consisting of two binary relations, that is, the kind of system used above for quasi-series. In Scott & Suppes (1958) Luce's axioms are simplified and only a binary system is used. The latter analysis is considered here.

Definition 3. *A* semiorder *is a binary system* $\mathfrak{A} = \langle A, P \rangle$ *in which the following three axioms are satisfied for all a, b, c, d in A*:

1. *Not aPa;*
2. *If aPb and cPd then either aPd or cPb;*
3. *If aPb and bPc then either aPd or dPc.*

In the case of loudness, *P* is interpreted as *definitely louder than*. To make the last two axioms more intuitive, we may illustrate (3) by a simple geometrical picture. We place *a, b*, and *c* on the line such that they are separated by at least one *jnd*. The axiom asserts that for any element *d* it is then the case that either *aPd* or *dPc*. The four different kinds of positions *d* can have are shown as d_1, d_2, d_3, and d_4 in the drawing below. It is evident that for d_1 and d_2 we have d_1Pc and d_2Pc; and for d_3 and d_4 the other alternative holds, namely, aPd_3 and aPd_4.

The indifference relation *I* can be defined in terms of *P* as follows.

Definition 4. *aIb if and only if not aPb and not bPa.*

In contrast to a quasi-series, the indifference relation *I* in a semiorder is not an equivalence relation. It lacks the transitivity property. However, we may define a relation *E* in terms of *I* which is an equivalence relation.

Definition 5. *aEb if and only if, for every c in A, aIc if and only if bIc.*

The fact that *E* is an equivalence relation, that it is reflexive, symmetric, and transitive can easily be verified. As in the case of a quasi-series we introduce a relation *P*** corresponding to *P* defined on the *E*-equivalence classes of *A*, that is, on the elements of *A/E*.

Definition 6. *[a]P**[b] if and only if aPb.*

To justify Def. 6, theorems corresponding to Theorems 3 and 4 are needed. They are easily proved.

Theorem 9. *If aPc and aEb, then bPc.*

Theorem 10. *If cPa and aEb, then cPb.*

Unlike the relation *P** in Def. 2, the relation *P*** does not have the connectedness property. In fact, we may define the relation I^* as follows.

Definition 7. $[a]I^*[b]$ *if and only if aIb.*

It may be seen that $[a]I^*[b]$ does *not* imply that $[a] = [b]$ so that P^{**} is, in fact, not connected. This means that the relational system $\langle A/E, P^{**}\rangle$ is not a series and, moreover, P^{**} does not order the elements of A/E as was the case for the relation P^* and the set A/I of a quasi-series. A relation R which does order the elements of A/E can be defined in terms of P^{**} as follows.

Definition 8. $[a]R[b]$ *if and only if for all* $[c]$ *in* A/E, *if* $[c]P^{**}[a]$ *then* $[c]P^{**}[b]$, *and if* $[b]P^{**}[c]$ *then* $[a]P^{**}[c]$.

The relation R, it can be verified, is a *simple order*, that is, it is reflexive, antisymmetric ($[a]R[b]$ and $[b]R[a]$ implies $[a] = [b]$), transitive, and connected in A/E. The connection between P^{**} and R is clearer if one notices that $[a]P^{**}[b]$ implies $[a]R[b]$ but not conversely. The simple ordering property of R will be useful in the proof establishing the representation theorem. The representation problem consists of establishing an isomorphism between the relational system $\mathfrak{A}/E = \langle A/E, P^{**}\rangle$ and an appropriate numerical relational system.

In Luce (1956) no representation theorem in our sense is proved for semiorders because a just noticeable difference function is introduced, which varies with the individual elements of A, that is, the jnd function is defined on A, and no fixed numerical interpretation of P and I is given which holds for all elements of A. Actually, it would be intuitively more desirable if Luce's results were the strongest possible for semiorders. Unfortunately, a stronger result than his can be proved, namely a numerical interpretation of P can be found, which has as a consequence that the jnd function is constant for all elements of A.

We turn now to the formal solution of the representation problem for semiorders. The proof is that given in Scott & Suppes (1958).

The numerical relational system to be selected for the representation theorem is called a *numerical semiorder*. A binary system $\langle N, \gg_\delta\rangle$ is a *numerical semiorder* if and only if N is a set of real numbers, and the relation $\gg_\delta$ is the binary relation having the property that for all x and y in N, $x \gg_\delta y$ if and only if $x > y + \delta$. The number δ is the numerical measure of the jnd. It is easily checked that the relation $\gg_\delta$ satisfies the axioms for a semiorder and thus any numerical semiorder is a semiorder. Furthermore, it is an immediate consequence of $\gg_\delta$ that δ is positive.[5]

The representation theorem for finite sets is as follows.

---

[5] It is a technical point worth noting that it would not be correct to define a numerical semiorder as a triple $\langle N, \gg, \delta\rangle$ for there is nothing in $\langle A/E, P^{**}\rangle$ of which δ is the isomorphic image. Taking the course we do makes δ part of the definition of $\gg$.

Theorem 11 (Representation Theorem). *Let the binary system $\mathfrak{A} = \langle A, P \rangle$ be a semiorder and let A/E be a finite set. Then $\langle A/E, P^{**} \rangle$ is isomorphic to some numerical semiorder.*

PROOF.   Under the relation R, A/E is simply ordered. Let $A/E = \{a_0, a_1, \ldots, a_n\}$ where $a_i R\, a_{i-1}$ and $a_i \neq a_{i-1}$. To simplify the notation of the proof, we set $\delta = 1$ and write $\geqslant$ instead of $\geqslant_1$. (The proof shows in fact that we may always take $\delta = 1$ if we so desire.)   Define the function f as follows:
$$f(a_i) = x_i, \qquad i = 0, 1, \ldots n,$$
where x_i is determined uniquely by the following two conditions:

1. If $a_i I^* a_0$, then $x_i = \dfrac{i}{i+1}$.
2. If $a_i I^* a_j$ and $a_i P^{**} a_{j-1}$ where $j > 0$, then
$$x_i = \frac{i}{i+1}\, x_j + \frac{1}{i+1}\, x_{j-1} + 1.$$

Condition 1 holds when a_i and a_0 are separated by less than a jnd, but x_i is defined so that $x_{i-1} < x_i$. Similar remarks apply to condition 2. Note that in (2) the hypothesis implies that $j \leqslant i$. Note further that every element a_i comes either under (1) or (2). If for no j, $a_i P^{**} a_{j-1}$, then $a_i I^* a_0$ and (1) applies. Also if $a_i I^{**} a_j$ and $a_i I^{**} a_{j-1}$, we find an earlier a_j in the ordering such that $a_i P^{**} a_{j-1}$.

To show that the numerical semiorder $\langle \{x_i\}, \geqslant \rangle$ is an isomorphic image of $\langle A/E, P^{**} \rangle$, we must show that f is one-one and $a_i P^{**} a_j$ if and only if $x_i \geqslant x_j$.

The one-one property of f can be shown by proving that $x_i > x_{i-1}$. This we do by induction on i. To simplify the presentation, we give an explicit breakdown of cases.

Case 1. $a_i I^* a_0$. Then also $a_{i-1} I^* a_0$, and
$$x_i = \frac{i}{i+1} > x_{i-1} = \frac{i-1}{i}.$$

Case 2. $a_i I^* a_j$ and $a_i P^{**} a_{j-1}$ for some j.
    2a. $a_{i-1} I^* a_0$. Then $x_{i-1} < 1$ and, since $x_{j-1} > x_0 = 0$, from (2), $x_i > 1$.
    2b. $a_{i-1} P^{**} a_0$. Let a_k be the first element such that $a_{i-1} I^* a_k$ and $a_{i-1} P^{**} a_{k-1}$. By definition
$$x_{i-1} = \frac{i-1}{i}\, x_k + \frac{1}{i}\, x_{k-1} + 1.$$

We then have two subcases of subcase 2b to consider.

2b1. $j = i$. Then by virtue of (2)

$$x_i = \frac{i}{i+1} x_i + \frac{1}{i+1} x_{i-1} + 1,$$

whence simplifying

$$x_i = x_{i-1} + i + 1,$$

and thus

$$x_i > x_{i-1}.$$

2b2. $j < i$. It is easily shown that by selection of k, $k \leqslant j$. We know that for this case $a_i R a_{i-1}$, $a_{i-1} R a_j$, and $a_i I^* a_j$, whence $a_{i-1} I^* a_j$ because a_{i-1} is "between" a_i and a_j (with possibly $a_j = a_{i-1}$). If $k > j$, then, from definition of R, $a_{i-1} P^{**} a_{j-1}$, which contradicts the assumption that k is the first element (in the ordering generated by R) such that $a_{i-1} I^* a_k$ and $a_{i-1} P^{**} a_{k-1}$, and so we conclude $k \leqslant j$.

If $k = j$, we have at once from (2)

$$x_{i-1} = x_k - \frac{1}{i}(x_k - x_{k-1}) + 1$$

$$x_i = x_k - \frac{1}{i+1}(x_k - x_{k-1}) + 1,$$

and, since $1/(i+1) < 1/i$, we infer that $x_i > x_{i-1}$.

If $k < j$, the argument is slightly more complex. By our inductive hypothesis $x_k < x_j$ and $x_{k-1} < x_{j-1}$, whence $x_k \leqslant x_{j-1}$. Now from (2)

$$x_{i-1} < x_k + 1$$

$$x_i > x_{j-1} + 1,$$

whence $x_i > x_{j-1} + 1 \geqslant x_k + 1 > x_{i-1}$, and the proof that $x_{i-1} < x_i$ is complete for all cases.

The next step is to prove that, if $a_i P^{**} a_k$, then $x_i > x_k + 1$. Let a_j be the first element such that $a_i I^* a_j$ and $a_i P^{**} a_{j-1}$. We have $j - 1 \geqslant k$, and, in view of the preceding argument, $x_{j-1} \geqslant x_k$. But $x_{j-1} + 1 < x_i$, whence $x_i > x_k + 1$.

Conversely, we must show that if $x_i > x_k + 1$ then $a_i P^{**} a_k$. The hypothesis, of course, implies $i > k$. Assume by way of contradiction that not $a_i P^{**} a_k$. It follows that $a_i I^* a_k$. Let a_j be the first element such that $a_i I^* a_j$; then $k \geqslant j$ and $x_k \geqslant x_j$. If $j = 0$, then $a_i I^* a_0$ and $a_k I^* a_0$ because $a_i R a_k$. But then $0 \leqslant x_i < 1$ and $0 \leqslant x_k < 1$, which contradicts the inequality $x_i > x_k + 1$. We conclude that $j > 0$. Now $x_i < x_j + 1$, but $x_k \geqslant x_j$, and thus $x_i < x_k + 1$, which again is a contradiction. Q.E.D.

The proof just given is not necessarily valid for the denumerable case, and which is the strongest representation theorem that may be proved when A/E is an infinite set is an open problem.

The uniqueness problem for semiorders is complicated and appears to have no simple solution.

3.3 Infinite Difference Systems

A relational system $\langle A, D \rangle$ is called a *quaternary system* if D is a quaternary relation. In this section and the one following quaternary systems leading to interval scales are considered.

The notion behind the quaternary relation D is that $abDcd$ holds when the subjective (algebraic) difference between a and b is equal to or less than that between c and d. In the case of utility or value, the set A would be a set of alternatives consisting of events, objects, experiences, etc. The interpretation $abDcd$ is that the difference in preference between a and b is not greater than the difference in preference between c and d. Such an interpretation could be made, for example, if a subject having in his possession objects a and c decides that he will not pay more money to replace a by b than he will to replace c by d, or if he does not prefer the pair a and d to the pair b and c. Similar interpretations of utility differences can be made using gambles or probability mixtures as alternatives. [A detailed analysis of a probabilistic interpretation of quaternary systems is to be found in Davidson, Suppes, & Siegel (1957).] If the set A consisted of color chips, the interpretation of $abDcd$ could be that stimuli a and b are at least as similar to each other as are stimuli c and d.

The empirical relational system to be considered here is a quaternary system that is an *infinite difference system* (abbreviated as i.d. system). To define an i.d. system it is convenient to introduce certain relations defined in terms of the quaternary relation D.

Definition 9.   *aPb if and only if not $abDaa$.*

For the case of utility measurement, the relation P is interpreted as a strict preference relation, a relation that is transitive and asymmetric in A.

Definition 10.   *aIb if and only if $abDba$ and $baDab$.*

The relation I is the familiar relation of indifference. Note, of course, that the expected properties (like transitivity) of the binary relations P and I cannot be proved merely on the basis of these definitions. For that purpose the axioms to be given in the definition of the i.d. system are needed.

Definition 11.   *$abMcd$ if and only if $abDcd$, $cdDab$ and $b\,I\,c$.*

If we think of a, b, c, and d as points on a line, then $abMcd$ implies that the interval (a, b) equals the interval (c, d) and the points b and c coincide. Higher powers of the relation M are defined recursively.

Definition 12. *abM^1cd if and only if $abMcd$; $abM^{n+1}cd$ if and only if there exists e and f in A such that abM^nef and $efMcd$.*

Again letting a, b, c, and d be points on a line, the relation abM^ncd implies that the intervals (a, b) and (c, d) are of the same length and that there are $(n - 1)$ intervals of this length between b and c. More particularly consider the following diagrams:

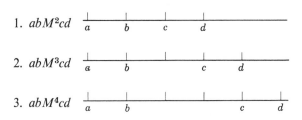

The interval (a, d) under (1) is three times the length of the interval (a, b); under (2) it is four times, etc. Thus from M and its powers we may infer specific length relations. Later, when we discuss the Archimedean axiom, we shall see that the relation M enables us to establish commensurability of all differences with each other.

We are now in position to define an infinite difference system.

Definition 13. *A quaternary system $\mathfrak{A} = \langle A, D \rangle$ is an* infinite difference system *if and only if the following seven axioms are satisfied for every a, b, c, d, e, and f in A:*

1. *If $abDcd$ and $cdDef$, then $abDef$;*
2. *$abDcd$ or $cdDab$,*
3. *If $abDcd$, then $acDbd$,*
4. *If $abDcd$, then $dcDba$,*
5. *There is a c in A such that $acDcb$ and $cbDac$,*
6. *If aPb and not $abDcd$, then there is an e in A such that aPe, ePb, and $cdDae$,*
7. *If aPb and $abDcd$, then there are e, f in A and an n such that ceM^nfd and $ceDab$.*[6]

These axioms are essentially those given in Suppes & Winet (1955). The first four axioms establish some of the elementary properties of the relation

---

[6] We are indebted to Michael Levine for showing that the following axiom is a consequence of Axioms 1 to 3 and thus may be eliminated: if bIa or bPa and $bcDef$, then $acDef$.

D. Axiom 1 indicates that *D* is transitive and Axiom 2 that it is strongly connected in *A*.

The last three are existence axioms and are basic to the proof of the representation and uniqueness theorems. Axiom 5 may be interpreted to mean that between any two elements in *A* there exists a third element in *A* which is a midpoint. A direct consequence of this axiom is that the set *A* is infinite (in all nontrivial cases). Axiom 6 postulates a kind of continuity condition; and 7 is the Archimedean axiom. The general Archimedean principle may be formulated as follows. Let L_1 be a distance no matter how large, and let L_2 be a distance no matter how small. Then there is a positive integer *n* such that an *n*th part of L_1 is smaller than L_2. On the other hand, there is a positive integer *m* such that if we lay off L_2 *m* times on a line the resulting distance or length will be greater than L_1. In other words, any two quantities in an Archimedean system are comparable in measurement. Every system of measurement that leads to an interval or ratio scale must satisfy the Archimedean principle in some form in order for a numerical representation theorem to be proved. Axiom 7 is one appropriate formulation for the system at hand.

The numerical relational system that we shall use to establish the representation theorem for an i.d. system is called a *numerical infinite difference system* or, more simply, a *numerical i.d. system*. This numerical relational system is defined as follows. Let *N* be a nonempty set of real numbers closed under the formation of midpoints, that is, if *x* and *y* are in *N*, then $(x + y)/2$ is in *N*. Let Δ be the quaternary relation restricted to *N* such that for any real numbers *x*, *y*, *z*, *w* in *N*

$$xy \, \Delta \, zw \quad \text{if and only if} \quad x - y \leqslant z - w.$$

Then the quaternary system $\mathfrak{N} = \langle N, \Delta \rangle$ is a *numerical i.d. system*.

As usual we may state the representation theorem either in terms of a homomorphism or in terms of an isomorphism between empirical and numerical relational systems. To utilize this alternative, we need merely introduce the relational system $\mathfrak{A}/I = \langle A/I, D^* \rangle$ where the set A/I consists of the *I*-equivalence classes of *A* and the relation D^* is defined as follows.

Definition 14. $[a][b]D^*[c][d]$ *if and only if ab Dcd.*

Thus, using the isomorphism concept, the representation theorem for an i.d. system may now be stated.

Theorem 12 (Representation Theorem). *If a quaternary system* $\mathfrak{A} = \langle A, D \rangle$ *is an i.d. system, then* $\mathfrak{A}/I = \langle A/I, D^* \rangle$ *is isomorphic to a numerical i.d. system.*

The proof is omitted. [See Suppes & Winet (1955), which also includes a proof of the next theorem.] For the uniqueness problem we have the following theorem.

Theorem 13 (Uniqueness Theorem). *If a quaternary system $\mathfrak{A} = \langle A, D \rangle$ is an i.d. system, then any two numerical i.d. systems isomorphic to $\mathfrak{A}/I = \langle A/I, D^* \rangle$ are related by a linear transformation.*

The proof of Theorem 13 is also omitted. However, we shall give the much simpler proof of a related theorem. The point of this related theorem is that as long as we restrict ourselves to the primitive and defined notions of quaternary systems it is not possible to do better than obtain measurement unique up to a linear transformation. Thus Theorem 13 cannot be improved by adding additional axioms to those given in the definition of the i.d. system. Since the proof does not depend on any of the axioms of an i.d. system, we may state it for arbitrary quaternary systems. Generalizing the numerical i.d. system slightly, a quaternary system $\mathfrak{N} = \langle N, \Delta \rangle$ is a *numerical difference system* if N is a set of real numbers and Δ is the numerical quaternary relation defined previously. We may then formulate our result.

Theorem 14. *Let a quaternary system $\mathfrak{A} = \langle A, D \rangle$ be isomorphic to a numerical difference system $\mathfrak{N} = \langle N, \Delta \rangle$, and let $\mathfrak{N}' = \langle N', \Delta' \rangle$ be a numerical difference system related to $\mathfrak{N}$ by a linear transformation. Then $\mathfrak{A}$ is isomorphic to $\mathfrak{N}'$.*

PROOF. The proof of the theorem is very simple; it hinges upon the purely set-theoretical, axiom-free character of the definition of isomorphism. Since the relation of being isomorphic is transitive, to show that $\mathfrak{A}$ and $\mathfrak{N}'$ are isomorphic it suffices to show that $\mathfrak{N}$ and $\mathfrak{N}'$ are isomorphic.

Let f be the linear transformation from N to N'. It is clear that f is the appropriate isomorphism function, for it is one-one, and, if for every x in N,

$$f(x) = \alpha x + \beta, \qquad \alpha > 0,$$

we have the following equivalences for any $x, y, u,$ and v in N:

$$xy \, \Delta \, uv$$

if and only if

$$x - y \leqslant u - v$$

if and only if

$$(\alpha x + \beta) - (\alpha y + \beta) \leqslant (\alpha u + \beta) - (\alpha v + \beta)$$

if and only if

$$f(x) - f(y) \leqslant f(u) - f(v)$$

if and only if

$$f(x) f(y) \, \Delta' \, f(u) f(v). \qquad \text{Q.E.D.}$$

One interpretation of infinite difference systems is of sufficiently general importance to be emphasized. This interpretation is closely related to classical scaling methods for pair comparisons, about which more is said in Sec. 4.1. Subjects are asked to choose between alternatives or stimuli, and they are asked to make this choice a number of times. There are many situations—from judging the hue of colors to preference among economic bundles—in which subjects vacillate in their choices. The probability p_{ab} that a will be chosen over b may be estimated from the relative frequency with which a is so chosen. From inequalities of the form $p_{ab} \leqslant p_{cd}$ we then obtain an interpretation of the quaternary relation $abDcd$. Thus the representation and uniqueness theorems proved here have direct application to pair comparison methods.

An important problem for infinite difference systems is the idealization involved in the transitivity of the indifference relation I, which is a consequence of the first four axioms. The question naturally arises: can infinite difference systems be generalized in the way that semiorders generalize series or simple ordering? Surprisingly enough, mathematical work on this problem goes back to an early paper of Norbert Wiener (1921). Unfortunately, Wiener's paper is extremely difficult to read: it is written in the notation of the latter two volumes of Whitehead and Russell's *Principia Mathematica*;[7] no clear axioms are formulated, and no proofs are given. On the other hand, the focus of the paper is the important problem of explicitly considering nontransitivities that arise from subliminal phenomena. A discussion of similar problems in economic contexts is to be found in the interesting series of papers of W. E. Armstrong (1939), (1948) and (1951). An exact axiomatic reconstruction of Wiener's ideas is to be found in the dissertation of Muriel Wood Gerlach (1957); her axioms are too complicated to state here. Moreover, they suffer from not making distinguishability of stimuli a probabilistic concept, although a probabilistic interpretation similar to that just given for the quaternary relation D is also possible for her primitive concepts.

3.4 Finite Equal Difference Systems

Since the infinite difference systems of the preceding section are not easily realized in many empirical situations, it is desirable to have at hand a finite empirical relational system that yields the same measurement results. To this end we now develop briefly the theory of finite equal

---

[7] It is of some historical interest to note that a rather elaborate theory of measurement is given in Vol. 3 of *Principia Mathematica*, but as far as we know it has had little impact on the theory of measurement—actually with good reason, for the developments there are more closely connected with classical mathematical topics like Eudoxus' theory of proportion and the construction of the real numbers than with any formal questions which arise in an empirical context.

difference systems, abbreviated as f.d. systems, (Davidson & Suppes, 1956; Suppes, 1957, Chapter 12). The intuitive idea is that we select a finite set of stimuli so that when we order the stimuli according to some characteristic, such as hue, pitch, or utility, two stimuli adjacent in the ordering will have the same difference in intensity as any two other such adjacent stimuli. It is to be emphasized that no sort of underlying physical scale need be assumed to apply this theory. It is not a psychophysical theory of measurement.

One new elementary definition is needed.

Definition 15. *aJb if and only if aPb and for all c in A if aPc, then either bIc or bPc.*

The indifference relation *I* and the strict preference relation *P* appearing in Def. 15 are defined in Defs. 9 and 10. The interpretation of *J* is that *aJb* holds when *a* is an immediate predecessor of *b* with respect to the relation *P*. In the following definition of an f.d. system the final axiom referring to the relation *J* replaces the three existence axioms that were used to characterize an infinite difference system. Note that the first four axioms below are just the same as those for i.d. systems.

Definition 16. *A* finite equal difference system *is a quaternary system* $\mathfrak{A} = \langle A, D \rangle$ *in which A is a finite set, and for every a, b, c, d, e, and f in A the following five axioms are satisfied.*

1. *If abDcd and cdDef, then abDef;*
2. *abDcd or cdDab;*
3. *If abDcd, then acDbd;*
4. *If abDcd, then dcDba;*
5. *If aJb and cJd, then abDcd and cdDab.*

In Axiom 5 the equal spacing assumption is imposed.

For the corresponding numerical relational system we have a *numerical f.d. system* which we define as follows. Let *N* be a finite, nonempty set of numbers such that differences between numbers adjacent under the natural ordering < are equal, and let Δ be the numerical quaternary relation already defined restricted to *N*. Then the quaternary system $\mathfrak{N} = \langle N, \Delta \rangle$ is a *numerical f.d. system.*

We may now state representation and uniqueness theorems for finite equal difference systems.

Theorem 15 (Representation Theorem). *If a quaternary system* $\mathfrak{A} = \langle A, D \rangle$ *is an f.d. system, then* $\mathfrak{A}/I = \langle A/I, D^* \rangle$ *is isomorphic to a numerical f.d. system.*

Theorem 16 (Uniqueness Theorem). *If a quaternary system* $\mathfrak{A} = \langle A, D \rangle$ *is an f.d. system, then any two numerical f.d. systems isomorphic to* $\mathfrak{A}/I$ *are related by a linear transformation.*

One might be tempted to conjecture that the first four axioms of Def. 16 would characterize all finite difference systems for which a numerical representation could be found (the representations of a given system would not necessarily be related by a linear transformation). The resulting theory would then represent one formalization of Coombs' ordered metric scale. However, Scott and Suppes (1958) have proved that the theory of all representable finite difference systems is not characterized by these four axioms and, worse still, cannot be characterized by any simple finite list of axioms.

The f.d. systems are not as artificial or as impractical as they may seem. One theory for approximating these systems is to be found in Davidson, Suppes, & Siegel (1957, Chapter 2). However, these systems can have more general usefulness if they are used to establish a "standard set" of stimuli. In the case of tones, for example, a set of tones may be selected in a successive manner so that the set satisfies Axiom 5. If this standard set of tones also satisfies the remaining four axioms, then we know from Theorem 15 that the tones may be assigned numbers that are on an interval scale. Arbitrary tones that are not in the standard set but that satisfy the first four axioms may then be located within intervals bounded by adjacent tones in the standard set. This means that by decreasing the spacing between the standard tones any arbitrary tone may be measured within any desired degree of accuracy. This is in fact what a chemist does in using a standard set of weights and an equal arm balance to determine the weight of an unknown object. His accuracy of measurement is limited by the size of the smallest interval between the standard weights or, if he also uses a rider, by the gradations on the rider.

Other relational systems closely related to f.d. systems may appropriately be mentioned at this point. Among the simplest and most appealing are the *bisection* systems $\mathfrak{A} = \langle A, B \rangle$, where B is a ternary relation on the set A with the interpretation that $B(a, b, c)$ if and only if b is the midpoint of the interval between a and c. The method of bisection, which consists in finding the midpoint b, has a long history in psychophysics. The formal criticism of many experiments in which it has been used is that the variety of checks necessary to guarantee isomorphism with an appropriate numerical system is not usually performed. For example, if $B(a, b, c)$ implies that aPb and bPc, where P is the usual ordering relation, then from the fact that $B(a, b, c)$, $B(b, c, d)$, and $B(c, d, e)$ we should be able to infer $B(a, c, e)$. But the explicit test of this inference is too seldom made. Without it there is no real guarantee that a subjective scale for a stimulus dimension has been constructed by the method of bisection.

Because of the large number of axiomatic analyses already given in this section, we shall not give axioms for bisection systems. The axioms in any case are rather similar to those of Def. 16, and the formal connection between the difference relation D and the ternary bisection relation B should be obvious:

$$B(a, b, c) \quad \text{if and only if} \quad ab\,Dbc \text{ and } bc\,Dab.$$

As an alternative to giving general axioms for bisection systems, it may be of some interest to look at the problem of characterizing these systems in a somewhat different manner, namely, by simply listing for a given number n of stimuli the relations that must hold. In perusing this list it should be kept in mind that we assume that bisection systems have the same property of equal spacing possessed by f.d. systems. As examples, let us consider the cases of $n = 5$ and $n = 6$.

For $n = 5$; let $A = \{a, b, c, d, e\}$ with the ordering $aPbPcPdPe$. We then have exactly four instances of the bisection relation, namely, $B(a, b, c)$, $B(b, c, d)$, $B(c, d, e)$, and $B(a, c, e)$.

For $n = 6$, we may add the element f to A with the ordering $aPbPcPdPePf$. To the four instances of the bisection relation for $n = 5$, we now add two more, namely, $B(d, e, f)$ and $B(b, d, f)$. We may proceed in this manner for any n to characterize completely the bisection system with n stimuli, none of which is equivalent with respect to the property being studied. Establishing the representation and uniqueness theorems is then a trivial task. The disadvantages of this approach to characterizing those relational systems for which numerical representation theorems exist are twofold. In the first place, in contrast to the statement of general axioms, the listing of instances does not give us general insight into the structure of the systems. Second, for systems of measurement that have a more complicated or less sharply defined structure than bisection systems, the listing of instances can become tedious and awkward—semiorders provide a good example.

3.5 Extensive Systems

We consider next a relational system leading to a ratio scale. Since this relational system contains an operation ∘ that corresponds to an addition operation, we may justifiably call this system an *extensive system* (see Sec. 1.4). The axioms that we shall use to define an extensive system (Suppes, 1951) are similar to those first developed by Hölder (1901). Hölder's axioms, however, are more restrictive than necessary in that they require the homomorphic numerical relational systems to be nondenumerable (and nonfinite). The present set of axioms applies both to denumerable and nondenumerable but infinite relational systems.

Definition 17. *An* extensive system $\langle A, R, \circ \rangle$ *is a relational system consisting of the binary relation R, the binary operation* $\circ$ *from* $A \times A$ *to A, and satisfying the following six axioms for a, b, c in A.*

1. *If aRb and bRc, then aRc;*
2. $(a \circ b) \circ cRa \circ (b \circ c);$
3. *If aRb, then* $a \circ cRc \circ b;$
4. *If not aRb, then there is a c in A such that* $aRb \circ c$ *and* $b \circ cRa;$
5. *Not* $a \circ bRa;$
6. *If aRb, then there is a number n such that bRna where the notation na is defined recursively as follows:* $1a = a$ *and* $na = (n-1) a \circ a.$

It can be shown that the relation R is a weak ordering (it is transitive and strongly connected) of the elements of A. If A is a set of weights, then the interpretation of aRb is that a is either less heavy than b or equal in heaviness to b. The interpretation of $a \circ b$ for weights is simply the weight obtained by combining the two weights a and b, for example, by placing both on the same side of an equal arm balance. Axiom 2 establishes the associativity property of the operation $\circ$. Axiom 5 implies that mass, for example, is always positive. This axiom together with the order properties of R and the definition of $\circ$ as an operation from $A \times A$ to A imply that the set A is infinite. Axiom 6 is another form of the Archimedean principle mentioned earlier.

Again we introduce the indifference relation I so that A may be partitioned into equivalence classes.

Definition 18. *aIb if and only if aRb and bRa.*

Corresponding to R and $\circ$, we define R^* and $\circ^*$ which are defined for the elements of A/I.

Definition 19. $[a]R^*[b]$ *if and only if aRb.*

Definition 20. $[a]\circ^*[b] = [a \circ b].$

For the representation theorem we seek now a numerical relational system isomorphic to $\langle A/I, R^*, \circ^* \rangle$. The numerical system we shall use for this purpose is defined as follows. Let $\langle N, \leqslant, + \rangle$ be a numerical relational system in which N is a nonempty set of positive real numbers closed under addition and subtraction of smaller numbers from larger numbers, that is, if $x, y \in N$ and $x > y$, then $(x + y) \in N$ and $(x - y) \in N$. Let $\leqslant$ be the usual numerical binary relation and $+$ the usual numerical binary operation of addition, both relations restricted to the set N. Then $\langle N, \leqslant, + \rangle$ is a *numerical extensive system.* An example of a numerical extensive system is the system consisting of the set of positive integers (together with $\leqslant$ and $+$).

The representation and uniqueness theorems can now be expressed as follows.

Theorem 17 (Representation Theorem). *If a relational system* $\mathfrak{A} = \langle A, R, \circ \rangle$ *is an extensive system, then* $\mathfrak{A}/I = \langle A/I, R^*, \circ^* \rangle$ *is isomorphic to a numerical extensive system.*

The proof of this theorem, which we omit (see Suppes, 1951), consists in defining the numerical assignment f as follows:

$$f([a]) = \text{the greatest lower bound of } S([a], [e]),$$

where $S([a], [e])$, a set of rational numbers, is given by

$$S([a], [e]) = \left\{ \frac{m}{n} \;\middle|\; n[a]R^*m[e], \, n, m \text{ positive integers} \right\},$$

and e is an arbitrarily chosen element from A and where $n[a]$ is defined recursively: $1[a] = [a]$ and $n[a] = (n-1)[a] \circ^* [a]$. Since $f([e]) = 1$, the choice of $[e]$ corresponds to the choice of a unit. The remainder of the proof consists in showing that f has the required properties, namely, that

1. $[a]R^*[b]$ if and only if $f([a]) \leqslant f([b])$;
2. $f([a] \circ^* [b]) = f([a]) + f([b])$;
3. If $[a] \neq [b]$, then $f([a]) \neq f([b])$, that is, f is one-one.

Theorem 18 (Uniqueness Theorem). *If a relational system* $\mathfrak{A} = \langle A, R, \circ \rangle$ *is an extensive system, then any two numerical extensive systems isomorphic to* $\mathfrak{A}/I = \langle A/I, R^*, \circ^* \rangle$ *are related by a similarity transformation.*

PROOF. Let g be any numerical assignment establishing an isomorphism between the system $\langle A/I, R^*, \circ^* \rangle$ and some numerical extensive system. It will suffice to show that g is related by a similarity transformation to the function f defined above. Let $g([e]) = \alpha$. We show by a *reductio ad absurdum* that for every a in A

$$g([a]) = \alpha f([a]). \tag{6}$$

Suppose now that for some a in A

$$g([a]) < \alpha f([a]). \tag{7}$$

From Eq. 7 it follows that a rational number m/n exists such that

$$\frac{g([a])}{\alpha} < \frac{m}{n} < f([a]), \tag{8}$$

which from the definition of f implies that

$$m[e]R^*n[a]. \tag{9}$$

However, by our initial assumption g is also a numerical assignment which establishes the desired isomorphism. Hence from Eq. 9 we have

$$mg([e]) \leqslant ng([a]),\tag{10}$$

which, because $g([e]) = \alpha$, can be written as

$$\frac{m}{n} \leqslant \frac{g([a])}{\alpha}.\tag{11}$$

But Eq. 11 contradicts Eq. 8. Similarly, by assuming an a exists in A such that $\alpha f([a]) < g([a])$, we may also arrive at a contradiction. Hence Eq. 6 is established. Q.E.D.

Although Theorem 18 asserts that extensive systems lead to ratio scales, this should not be construed as implying, as some have suggested (see Sec. 1.4), that *only* extensive systems will yield these scales. As a brief example of a nonextensive system (a system not containing the operation ◦) leading to a ratio scale, let us construct a system along the lines of an i.d. or f.d. system $\langle A, D \rangle$, but with the following modifications. Let B be a set of elements drawn from $A \times A$, that is, if $e = (a, b)$ is in B, then a and b are in A. Let S be the binary relation on B corresponding to the relation D, that is, if $e = (a, b)$ and $f = (c, d)$ are in B, then eSf if and only if $abDcd$. By using a set of axioms corresponding to those of an i.d. or f.d. system we may conclude that the relational system $\langle B, S \rangle$ will yield a ratio scale. This follows from the fact that infinite difference and finite difference systems lead to interval scales and that the intervals of such a scale lie on a ratio scale.

There are two remarks we want to make about extensive systems to conclude this brief analysis of them. The first concerns the necessity of interpreting the operation ◦ as numerical addition. That this is not necessary is shown by the fact that it is a simple matter to construct another representation theorem in which the operation ◦ corresponds to the multiplication operation · . One simple way of establishing the existence of a numerical system $\mathfrak{N}^* = \langle N^*, \leqslant, \cdot \rangle$ homomorphic to the extensive system $\mathfrak{A} = \langle A, R, \leqslant \rangle$ is to apply an exponential transformation to $\mathfrak{N} = \langle N, \leqslant, + \rangle$; that is, let

$$N^* = \{y \mid y = e^x \text{ for some } x \text{ in } N\}.$$

Obviously $\mathfrak{N}$ is isomorphic to $\mathfrak{N}^*$, and since $\mathfrak{A}$ is homomorphic to $\mathfrak{N}$ it is therefore homomorphic to $\mathfrak{N}^*$ as well. From a mathematical standpoint the representation theorem based on $\mathfrak{N}^*$ is as valid and useful as the one based on $\mathfrak{N}$, so there is no basis for interpreting the operation ◦ as intrinsically an addition operation rather than, say, a multiplication operation.

The representation theorem you choose does, of course, affect the uniqueness properties of the numerical assignment. The numerical assignment $f(a)$, which maps $\mathfrak{A}$ onto $\mathfrak{N}$, we know from Theorem 18 is determined up to a similarity transformation. But since $y = \exp(x)$, if x is transformed to kx, then y will transform to y^k. Thus the numerical assignment $f'(a)$, which maps $\mathfrak{A}$ onto $\mathfrak{N}^*$, is determined up to a power transformation, not a similarity transformation.

The second remark concerns the fact that for any extensive system $\mathfrak{A} = \langle A, R, \circ \rangle$ the set A must be infinite. It is the most patent fact of empirical measurement that to determine the weight or length of a physical object it is sufficient to consider only a finite number of objects. The difficulty with Def. 17 is a too slavish imitation of the number system. The essential point is that the empirical ternary relation of combination that is meant to correspond to the arithmetical operation of addition should not actually have all the formal properties of numerical addition. In particular, in order to avoid the infinity of A, it is simplest to drop the closure requirement on the operation $\circ$ in Def. 18 and replace it by a ternary relation that is technically not a binary operation on A. With this change we can then construct a theory of finite extensive systems which is similar to the theory of finite difference systems. Finite extensive systems thus constructed correspond closely in structure to standard series of weights and measures commonly used in physical and chemical laboratories. We do not pursue in this chapter the axiomatic analysis of finite extensive systems because they are more pertinent to physics than to psychology. The important methodological point is that from the standpoint of fundamental measurement there is no difference between difference systems and extensive systems, finite or infinite. One system is just as good a methodological example of fundamental measurement as the other.

3.6 Single and Multidimensional Coombs Systems

Up to this point the requirements of fundamental measurement have been formulated in terms of a homomorphism between empirical and numerical relational systems. There are several ways in which this definition of fundamental measurement can be extended.

One extension can be obtained by broadening the notion of an empirical relational system to encompass more than one domain, that is, more than one set of physical entities to be measured. In many empirical situations subjects and stimuli have different, noninterchangeable roles, so that it is often convenient to group them separately. For example, if

a is a subject, α and β pictures, and T the relation $T(a, \alpha, \beta)$ if and only if a likes α at least as much as β, then we can be certain that $T(\alpha, a, \beta)$ does not obtain. In fact, if A_1 is a set of subjects, A_2 a set of stimuli, and T is defined as above, then we can expect $T(a, \alpha, \beta)$ to imply that $a \in A_1$ and $\alpha, \beta \in A_2$. Thus, if it were desirable to measure both subjects and stimuli simultaneously, it would be natural to define the empirical system $\mathfrak{A}^* = \langle A_1, A_2, T \rangle$ consisting of the two domains A_1 and A_2 and the ternary relation T. Although it is clear how one could then proceed to obtain separate numerical assignments for A_1 and A_2, another approach can be taken, which, although somewhat less natural, is more appropriate to the general framework we have constructed.

Let $A = A_1 \cup A_2$, that is, let A be the union of the sets A_1 and A_2. Using the fact that a subset of A is a one-place relation, the system $\mathfrak{A} = \langle A, A_1, A_2, T \rangle$ is nothing more than a relational system. Hence the usual notions of homomorphism, etc., are directly relevant. Let us carry this example a bit further to illustrate how Coombs' unfolding technique (1950) may be formalized in terms of fundamental measurement.

Let A, A_1, and A_2 be sets such that $A = A_1 \cup A_2$ and T a ternary relation such that $T(a, \alpha, \beta)$ implies $a \in A_1$ and $\alpha, \beta \in A_2$. Then the relational system $\langle A, A_1, A_2, T \rangle$ is a *preferential system*. By a *numerical preferential system* we mean a numerical relational system $\mathfrak{N} = \langle N, N_1, N_2, S \rangle$ in which N, N_1, and N_2 are sets of real numbers, $N = N_1 \cup N_2$, and S is a ternary numerical relation such that for all $x \in N_1$ and $\zeta, \omega \in N_2$

$$S(x, \zeta, \omega) \quad \text{if and only if} \quad |x - \zeta| \leqslant |x - \omega|.$$

To map a preferential system $\langle A, A_1, A_2, T \rangle$ homomorphically onto a numerical preferential system $\langle N, N_1, N_2, S \rangle$, we desire a function f such that for all $a \in A_1$ and $\alpha, \beta \in A_2$

$$T(a, \alpha, \beta) \quad \text{if and only if} \quad |f(a) - f(\alpha)| \leqslant |f(a) - f(\beta)|.$$

If such a function exists for the preferential system $\langle A, A_1, A_2, T \rangle$, then the system can be called a *Coombs system*. (What we here call a Coombs system corresponds to Quadrant Ia data in Coombs, 1960.) Obviously, if a preferential system is a Coombs system, then a representation theorem involving a numerical preferential system can be readily established. Although, apparently, there are no simple necessary and sufficient conditions to indicate when a given preferential system is a Coombs system, some necessary conditions can easily be stated. For example: for all a in A_1, and α, β, γ in A_2

1. if $T(a, \alpha, \beta)$ and $T(a, \beta, \gamma)$ then $T(a, \alpha, \gamma)$;
2. $T(a, \alpha, \beta)$ or $T(a, \beta, \alpha)$.

Define for each subject a, a binary relation Q_a as follows on A_2:

$$\alpha Q_a \beta \quad \text{if and only if} \quad T(a, \alpha, \beta).$$

It follows at once from (1) and (2) that

3. if $\alpha Q_a \beta$ and $\beta Q_a \gamma$, then $\alpha Q_a \gamma$;
4. $\alpha Q_a \beta$ or $\beta Q_a \alpha$.

From (3) and (4) we may derive for each subject a a simple ordering of the stimuli or, in Coombs' terminology, obtain a set of I-scales. Although assumptions (1) and (2) do not guarantee the existence of a Coombs system, in actual practice, when the number of stimuli is not too large, it is a relatively simple matter to determine from inspection of the I-scales whether a given preferential system is a Coombs system. The uniqueness question or scale type of a Coombs system also has no simple general solution, but again for any particular instance certain statements can be made about the order relation between some of the numerical intervals.

A second modification of fundamental measurement can be made to include multidimensional scaling methods. The extension to multi-dimensional methods is actually quite simple and direct.

Let us define an r-dimensional numerical vector relational system $\langle N_r, S_1, \ldots, S_N \rangle$ as follows: N_r is a set of r-dimensional vectors $\mathbf{x} = (x_1, x_2, \ldots, x_r)$, where each x_i is a real number and $S_1, \ldots, S_N$ are relations on the vectors in N_r. Then the definition of an r-*dimensional homomorphism* (or isomorphism) between an empirical relational system $\langle A, R_1, \ldots, R_N \rangle$ and an r-dimensional numerical relational system $\langle N_r, S_1, \ldots, S_N \rangle$ is an obvious extension of the one-dimensional case. The difference is merely this: the range of the numerical assignment f is now a set of vectors or r-tuples rather than a set of real numbers. An r-*dimensional representation theorem* can be defined in terms of the estab-lishment of an r-dimensional homomorphism.

As an illustration of a multidimensional measurement theory, let us consider further the theory of preferential systems. To obtain an r-dimensional representation theorem for a given preferential system $\langle A, A_1, A_2, T \rangle$, we wish to show that the preferential system is an r-*dimensional Coombs system*. This means that the preferential system is homomorphic to an r-*dimensional numerical preferential system* $\langle N_r, N_1, N_2, S \rangle$ in which N_r, N_1, N_2 are sets of r-dimensional vectors, $N_1 \cup N_2 = N_r$, and S is a numerical relation on N_r such that for all $\mathbf{x} \in N_1$ and $\boldsymbol{\xi}, \boldsymbol{\omega} \in N_2$

$$S(\mathbf{x}, \boldsymbol{\xi}, \boldsymbol{\omega}) \quad \text{if and only if} \quad |\mathbf{x} - \boldsymbol{\xi}| \leqslant |\mathbf{x} - \boldsymbol{\xi}| ,$$

the notation $|\mathbf{x}|$ denoting the magnitude of vector $\mathbf{x}$. By using the notation

$\mathbf{x} \cdot \mathbf{x}$ or $\mathbf{x}^2$ to indicate the scalar product of vector $\mathbf{x}$ with itself, the relation S may also be defined as

$$S(\mathbf{x}, \boldsymbol{\xi}, \boldsymbol{\omega}) \quad \text{if and only if} \quad (\mathbf{x} - \boldsymbol{\xi})^2 \leqslant (\mathbf{x} - \boldsymbol{\omega})^2.$$

Letting $\mathbf{x} = (x_1, x_2, \ldots, x_r)$, $\boldsymbol{\xi} = (\xi_1, \xi_2, \ldots, \xi_r)$, and $\boldsymbol{\omega} = (\omega_1, \omega_2, \ldots, \omega_r)$, the relation S can also be expressed in terms of the components of the vectors:

$$S(\mathbf{x}, \boldsymbol{\xi}, \boldsymbol{\omega}) \quad \text{if and only if} \quad (x_1 - \xi_1)^2 + (x_2 - \xi_2)^2 + \ldots (x_r - \xi_r)^2$$
$$\leqslant (x_1 - \omega_1)^2 + (x_2 - \omega_2)^2 + \ldots + (x_r - \omega_r)^2.$$

The restrictions to be imposed on a preferential system to guarantee the existence of an r-dimensional Coombs system (hence an r-dimensional representation theorem) are not easy to state. Some general statements can be made if the preferential system satisfies the two assumptions described above. If, for example, the number of stimuli in A_1 is n, then an $(n - 1)$ dimensional representation theorem will always exist. Generally, however, it is desirable to prove an r-dimensional representation theorem in which r, the dimensionality of the space, is minimal. Conditions that establish a lower bound on the value of r for which an r-dimensional representation theorem can be proved are given by Bennett and Hays (1960).

4. EXAMPLES OF DERIVED MEASUREMENT

To explore in some depth the formal issues that arise in derived measurement, we mainly concentrate in this section on pair comparison methods.

4.1 Bradley-Terry-Luce Systems for Pair Comparisons

We have already sketched the formal properties of these systems in Sec. 2, but we shall recapitulate briefly here. The theory is based on Bradley & Terry (1952); Bradley (1954a, 1954b, 1955); Luce (1959).

Let B be a nonempty, finite set of objects or stimuli and p a numerical assignment on $B \times B$ such that for all a, b, in B, $0 < p_{ab} < 1$, $p_{ab} + p_{ba} = 1$, and $p_{aa} = \frac{1}{2}$. Then a derived measurement system $\mathfrak{B} = \langle B, p \rangle$ is called a pair comparison system. Generally p_{ab} is the relative frequency with which a is preferred to, or is greater, in some sense, than b. Note that a pair comparison system is not a relational system because the values of the function p do not form a subset of B; hence at the outset it should be clear that we are not involved in the present discussion with fundamental measurement.

We recall that a derived scale is a triple $\langle \mathfrak{B}, R, g \rangle$ where $\mathfrak{B}$ is a derived measurement system, R is a representing relation and g is a numerical assignment defined on B. In order for numerical assignments to satisfy the usual representing relations for the Bradley-Terry-Luce (or B.T.L.) theory, it is necessary to impose a restriction on pair comparison systems.

Definition 21. *A pair comparison system* $\mathfrak{B} = \langle B, p \rangle$ *is a* B.T.L. *system if and only if the multiplication condition holds, that is, if and only if for all a, b, c in B,*

$$\left(\frac{p_{ab}}{p_{ba}}\right)\left(\frac{p_{bc}}{p_{cb}}\right) = \frac{p_{ac}}{p_{ca}} .$$

The standard representing relation for B.T.L. systems is the following, which we label R_1, and, following notation in the literature, let v_1 be the derived numerical assignment.

Definition 22. $R_1(p, v_1)$ *if and only if for all a, b in B*

$$\frac{v_{1a}}{v_{1a} + v_{1b}} = p_{ab}.$$

(Here and subsequently we often write v_a instead of $v(a)$ for the value of the numerical assignment v.)

We may easily prove the following representation theorem.

Theorem 19 (Representation Theorem 1). *If a pair comparison system* $\mathfrak{B} = \langle B, p \rangle$ *is a B.T.L. system, then there exists a numerical assignment* v_1 *such that* $\langle \mathfrak{B}, R_1, v_1 \rangle$ *is a derived scale.*

PROOF. We define a function v on B as follows (for convenience of notation we omit the subscript on v). Let a be any element of B and let v_a be any positive real number. For every b in B we then define

$$v_b = \frac{p_{ba}}{p_{ab}} v_a.$$

We then have for any b and c in B

$$\frac{v_b}{v_b + v_c} = \frac{(p_{ba}/p_{ab})v_a}{(p_{ba}/p_{ab})v_a + (p_{ca}/p_{ac})v_a} .$$

Now by virtue of the multiplication rule of Def. 22,

$$\frac{p_{ca}}{p_{ac}} = \left(\frac{p_{cb}}{p_{bc}}\right)\left(\frac{p_{ba}}{p_{ab}}\right) .$$

Substituting this result in the above and canceling v_a, we obtain

$$\frac{v_b}{v_b + v_c} = \frac{p_{ba}/p_{ab}}{p_{ba}/p_{ab} + (p_{cb}/p_{bc})(p_{ba}/p_{ab})}$$

$$= \frac{1}{1 + (p_{cb}/p_{bc})}$$

$$= \frac{p_{bc}}{p_{bc} + (1 - p_{bc})}$$

$$= p_{bc},$$

the desired result.

It can also be readily established that the existence of a derived scale $\langle \mathfrak{B}, R_1, v \rangle$ is a sufficient condition for the pair comparison system $\mathfrak{B} = \langle B, p \rangle$ to be a B.T.L. system.

When the numerical assignments in the derived measurement system $\mathfrak{B}$ are all on an absolute scale, it is evident that the narrow and wide senses of scale type defined in Sec. 2 coincide. This is the situation for pair comparison systems because the relative frequency function p_{ab} is on an absolute scale. We may easily prove that any two derived assignments v_1 and v_1' for a B.T.L. system are related by a positive or negative similarity transformation. Let us call a scale for which an admissible similarity transformation may be either positive or negative a *generalized ratio scale*.

Theorem 20 (Uniqueness Theorem I). *If $\mathfrak{B} = \langle B, p \rangle$ is a B.T.L. system, then a derived scale $\langle \mathfrak{B}, R_1, v_1 \rangle$ is a generalized ratio scale in both the narrow and wide senses.*

PROOF. Let $\langle \mathfrak{B}, R_1, v \rangle$ and $\langle \mathfrak{B}, R_1, v' \rangle$ be two derived scales. We show that v and v' related by a positive or negative similarity transformation. First we observe that for all a in B, $v_a \neq 0$ and $v_a' \neq 0$, for otherwise we would not have $p_{aa} = \frac{1}{2}$. Let a be any element of B. Then there must be a k such that either $k > 0$ or $k < 0$ and

$$v_a' = kv_a.$$

Suppose now that there is a b in A such that

$$v_b' \neq kv_b.$$

Let

$$v_b' = (k + \epsilon)v_b,$$

with $\epsilon \neq 0$. On the basis of Def. 22,

$$\frac{v_a}{v_a + v_b} = p_{ab} = \frac{v_a'}{v_a' + v_b'}, \tag{12}$$

but

$$\frac{v_a{}'}{v_a{}' + v_b{}'} = \frac{kv_a}{kv_a + kv_b + \epsilon v_b}. \qquad (13)$$

Combining Eqs. 12 and 13, cross multiplying, and then simplifying, we have at once that

$$\epsilon v_a v_b = 0,$$

which is absurd on the basis of our supposition. This establishes that in fact $\langle \mathfrak{B}, R_1, v \rangle$ is a generalized ratio scale.

We may require that v be positive by modifying Def. 22.

Definition 23. $R_2(p, v_2)$ *if and only if for all a, b in B*

$$\frac{v_{2a}}{v_{2a} + v_{2b}} = p_{ab}, \qquad v_{2a} > 0.$$

The existence of a function v_2 follows immediately from the proof of Theorem 19.

Theorem 21 (Representation Theorem II). *If* $\mathfrak{B} = \langle B, p \rangle$ *is a B.T.L. system, then there exists a numerical assignment* v_2 *such that* $\langle \mathfrak{B}, R_2, v_2 \rangle$ *is a derived scale.*

By the same argument used to establish Theorem 20 we also have the following:

Theorem 22 (Uniqueness Theorem II). *If* $\mathfrak{B} = \langle B, p \rangle$ *is a B.T.L. system, then a derived scale* $\langle \mathfrak{B}, R_2, v_2 \rangle$ *is a ratio scale in both the narrow and wide senses.*

As far as we can see the choice between representing relations R_1 and R_2 is essentially arbitrary, although it is perhaps intuitively more satisfactory to have $v_a > 0$.

However, R_1 and R_2 do not exhaust the possibilities, as we now wish to show.

Definition 24. $R_3^{(k)}(p, v_3)$ *if and only if for all a, b in B*

$$\frac{v_{3a}{}^k}{v_{3a}{}^k + v_{3b}{}^k} = p_{ab}, \qquad v_{3a} > 0, \quad k > 0.$$

In this case, v_a is raised to a power k and k is a parameter of the relation $R_3^{(k)}$. We have as before:

Theorem 23 (Representation Theorem III). *If* $\mathfrak{B} = \langle B, p \rangle$ *is a B.T.L. system, then there exists a function* v_3 *such that* $\langle \mathfrak{B}, R_3^{(k)}, v_3 \rangle$ *is a derived scale.*

PROOF. Use the function v_1 defined in the proof of Theorem 19 and take the kth root of v_{1a} for each a in B to obtain the numerical assignment needed for the present theorem.

For fixed k, that is, for the parameter k of R_3, it is easily seen that we have a ratio scale.

Theorem 24 (Uniqueness Theorem III). *If $\mathfrak{B} = \langle B, p \rangle$ is a B.T.L. system, then a derived scale $\langle \mathfrak{B}, R_3^{(k)}, v_3 \rangle$ is a ratio scale in both the narrow and wide senses.*

On the other hand, by letting k change from one derived assignment to another we obtain a *log interval scale*, that is, there exist $\alpha, \beta > 0$ such that for all x,

$$\phi(x) = \alpha x^\beta,$$

where ϕ is an admissible transformation of the scale. The definition of R_4 is as follows:

Definition 25. *$R_4(p, v_4)$ if and only if there is a $k > 0$ such that for all a and b in A*

$$\frac{v_{4a}^{\,k}}{v_{4a}^{\,k} + v_{4b}^{\,k}} = p_{ab}, \qquad v_{4a} > 0.$$

Since the description of alternative representation theorems parallel Theorem 19 and since their proofs also follow directly from this theorem, we shall henceforth omit further explicit descriptions of these representation theorems. For the uniqueness theorem corresponding to $R_4(p, v_4)$ we have the following:

Theorem 25 (Uniqueness Theorem IV). *If $\mathfrak{B} = \langle B, p \rangle$ is a B.T.L. system, then a derived scale $\langle \mathfrak{B}, R_4, v_4 \rangle$ is a log interval scale in both the narrow and wide senses.*

PROOF. We first observe that if $\langle \mathfrak{B}, R_4, v \rangle$ is a derived scale for $\mathfrak{B}_1$ (again omitting the subscript for convenience) and we define for a in B

$$v_a' = \alpha v_a^\beta,$$

with $\alpha, \beta > 0$, then $\langle \mathfrak{B}, R_4, v' \rangle$ is also a derived scale for $\mathfrak{B}$. For

$$v_a = \left(\frac{v_a'}{\alpha} \right)^{1/\beta},$$

and thus from

$$\frac{v_a^{\,k}}{v_a^{\,k} + v_b^{\,k}} = p_{ab},$$

we infer

$$\frac{(v_a'/\alpha)^{k/\beta}}{(v_a/\alpha)^{k/\beta} + (v_b'/\alpha)^{k/\beta}} = p_{ab},$$

but from the right-hand side of the last equation we may cancel $(1/\alpha)^{k/\beta}$ and, letting $k' = k/\beta$, we have

$$\frac{v_a'^{\,k'}}{v_a'^{\,k'} + v_b'^{\,k'}} = p_{ab}.$$

On the other hand, let $\langle \mathfrak{B}, R_4, v \rangle$ and $\langle \mathfrak{B}, R_4, v' \rangle$ be two derived scales for $\mathfrak{B}$. We show that they are related by a power transformation $\phi(x) = \alpha x^\beta$. Let k' and k be the powers associated with v' and v by (4). As above, we then let $\beta = k/k'$. Let a be any element of B. There must be an $\alpha > 0$ such that

$$v_a' = \alpha v_a^\beta.$$

Suppose now, contrary to the theorem, that there is a b in B such that

$$v_b' \neq \alpha v_b^\beta.$$

Let

$$v_b' = \alpha v_b^\beta + \epsilon.$$

Then on the basis of (4)

$$\frac{v_a'^{k'}}{v_a'^{k'} + v_b'^{k'}} = \frac{v_a^k}{v_a^k + v_b^k} = p_{ab}.$$

Substituting and cross multiplying, we have

$$\alpha v_a^{\beta k' + k} + \alpha v_a^{\beta k'} v_b^k = \alpha v_a^{\beta k' + k} + v_a^k (\alpha v_b^\beta + \epsilon)^{k'}.$$

Remembering that $\beta = k/k'$, we see that this equation can hold only if $\epsilon = 0$ contrary to our supposition, which establishes the theorem.

Still another representing relation for B.T.L. systems is $R_5(p, v_5)$ defined as follows:

Definition 26. $R_5(p, v_5)$ if and only if there is a $k > 0$ such that for all a and b in A

$$\frac{v_{5a} + k}{v_{5a} + v_{5b} + 2k} = p_{ab}.$$

The representation theorem for B.T.L. systems based on $R_5(p, v_5)$ is an immediate consequence of Theorem 19. For the uniqueness theorem we have the following:

Theorem 26 (Uniqueness Theorem V). If $\mathfrak{B} = \langle B, p \rangle$ is a B.T.L. system then $\langle \mathfrak{B}, R_5, v_5 \rangle$ is an interval scale in both the narrow and wide senses.

The proof of Theorem 26 depends upon the observation that if the function v_{5a} satisfies Def. 26 then the function $v_{5a}' = \alpha v_a + \beta$, $\alpha, \beta > 0$ will also satisfy Def. 26; that is,

$$\frac{v_{5a}' + k'}{v_{5a}' + v_{5b}' + 2k'} = p_{ab},$$

where $k' = k\alpha - \beta$.

Finally, we note that by appropriate choice of the representing relation we may also obtain a difference scale for B.T.L. systems.

Definition 27. $R_6(p, v_6)$ *if and only if for all a, b in B*

$$\frac{1}{1 + e^{v_{6b} - v_{6a}}} = p_{ab}.$$

To prove the representation theorem based on $R_6(p, v_6)$, it is simplest to transform the function v_1 given in Def. 1 by a log transformation. The following uniqueness theorem is also easily proved:

Theorem 27 (Uniqueness Theorem VI).   *If* $\mathfrak{B} = \langle B, p \rangle$ *is a B.T.L. system, then* $\langle \mathfrak{B}, R_6, v_6 \rangle$ *is a difference scale in both the narrow and wide senses.*

In the discussion in Sec. 3 of that most classical of all cases of measurement, extensive systems, we saw that radically different representation theorems could be proved with resulting variations in scale type. Precisely the same thing obtains in derived measurement, as we have shown in the present section by exhibiting six different representing relations for B.T.L. systems. The choice among them, it seems to us, can be based objectively only on considerations of computational convenience. It is not possible to claim that a B.T.L. system has as its only correct numerical assignment one that lies on a ratio, log interval, or difference scale. Any one of the three, and others as well, are acceptable.

It may be observed, however, that, although there is no strict mathematical argument for choosing a representation, say R_2, that yields a ratio scale rather than one, say R_4, that yields a log interval scale, it does not seem scientifically sensible to introduce an additional parameter such as k that is not needed and has no obvious psychological interpretation. If a representation like R_4 is used, it is hard to see why a representation introducing additional parameters may not also be considered. For example:

Definition 28. $R_7(p, v)$ *if and only if there are positive numbers* k_1, k_2, *and* k_3 *such that for all a, b in B*

$$\frac{k_1 v_a^{k_2} + k_3}{k_1 v_a^{k_2} + k_3 + k_1 v_b^{k_2} + k_3} = p_{ab}.$$

But once this line of development is begun it has no end. When a mathematically unnecessary parameter is introduced, there should be very strong psychological arguments to justify it.

4.2 Thurstone Systems for Pair Comparisons

In contrast to a B.T.L. system, a Thurstone system imposes somewhat different restrictions on a pair comparison system. We shall consider here just two of the five versions or cases described by Thurstone (1927).

Although these cases can be described by using less restrictive assumptions than those originally proposed by Thurstone (see Torgerson, 1958), for the purpose of simplicity we shall follow Thurstone's treatment.

Although it would be desirable to define a Thurstone system entirely in terms of p_{ab}, p_{bc}, p_{ac}, etc., as we did in Def. 21 for a B.T.L. system, there is unfortunately no simple analogue of the multiplication theorem for Thurstone systems; that is, there is no *simple* equation that places the appropriate restriction on a pair comparison system. This means that we are forced to define a Thurstone system in terms of the existence of one of the representing relations. Consequently, the representation theorem based on this relation is a trivial consequence of the definition.

Let $N(x)$ be the unit normal cumulative, that is, the cumulative distribution function with mean zero and unit variance. We then have the following definitions of Case III- and Case V-Thurstone systems.

Definition 29. *A pair comparison system* $\mathfrak{B} = \langle B, p \rangle$ *is a* Case III-Thurstone system *if and only if there are functions* μ_a *and* $\sigma_a{}^2$ *such that for all a, b in B*

$$p_{ab} = N\left(\frac{\mu_a - \mu_b}{\sqrt{\sigma_a{}^2 + \sigma_b{}^2}}\right).$$

If, moreover, for all a and b in B, $\sigma_a{}^2 = \sigma_b{}^2$, $\mathfrak{B}$ *is a* Case V-Thurstone system.

The additional restriction for Case V is equality of the variances for the normal distributions corresponding to elements of B. The first representing relation we shall consider for Case V-Thurstone systems is the obvious one:

1. $S_1(p, \mu)$ if and only if there is a $\sigma > 0$ such that for all a and b in B

$$p_{ab} = N\left(\frac{\mu_a - \mu_b}{\sqrt{2}\sigma}\right).$$

The proof of the representation theorem for Case V-Thurstone systems based on $S_1(p, \mu)$ is as we indicated an obvious consequence of Def. 29. We shall nevertheless state the theorem to show the analogue of Theorem 19 for B.T.L. systems.

Theorem 28 (Representation Theorem I). *If a pair comparison system* $\mathfrak{B} = \langle B, p \rangle$ *is a Case V-Thurstone system, then there exists a function* μ *such that* $\langle \mathfrak{B}, s_1, \mu \rangle$ *is a derived scale.*

The uniqueness theorem corresponding to this representation theorem is as follows.

Theorem 29 (Uniqueness Theorem I). *If* $\mathfrak{B} = \langle B, p \rangle$ *is a Case V-Thurstone system, then* $\langle \mathfrak{B}, s_1, \mu \rangle$ *is an interval scale in both the narrow and wide senses.*

We shall omit detailed proofs of the uniqueness theorems in this section except to point out that the admissible transformations described by the uniqueness theorems do lead to numerical assignments which also satisfy the appropriate representing relation. Here it may be observed that if μ satisfies $S_1(p, \mu)$ then $\mu' = \delta\mu + \beta$, $\delta > 0$ will satisfy $S_1(p, \mu')$ when $\sigma' = \delta\sigma$, since

$$\frac{\mu_a - \mu_b}{\sqrt{2}\sigma} = \frac{\mu_a' - \mu_b'}{\sqrt{2}\sigma'}.$$

In other words, if $\langle \mathfrak{B}, S_1, \mu \rangle$ is a derived scale for $\mathfrak{B}$, then so is $\langle \mathfrak{B}, S_1, \mu' \rangle$. Other representation theorems can be proved for Case V-Thurstone systems in which σ plays somewhat different roles. We consider two such possibilities.

   2. $S_2^{(\sigma)}(p, \mu)$ if and only if for all a, b in B

$$p_{ab} = N\left(\frac{\mu_a - \mu_b}{\sqrt{2}\sigma}\right).$$

Here σ is a parameter of the relation $S_2^{(\sigma)}(p, \mu)$. The representation theorem for $S_2^{(\sigma)}(p, \mu)$ corresponds, *mutatis mutandis*, to Theorem 28. For a fixed σ we obviously have a difference scale rather than an interval scale; that is, if $\mu' = \mu + \beta$, then if $\langle \mathfrak{B}, S_2^{(\sigma)}, \mu \rangle$ is a derived scale so is $\langle \mathfrak{B}, S_2^{(\sigma)}, \mu' \rangle$.

Theorem 30 (Uniqueness Theorem II). *If $\mathfrak{B}$ is a Case V-Thurstone system, then $\langle \mathfrak{B}, S_2^{(\sigma)}, \mu \rangle$ is a difference scale in both the narrow and wide senses.*

   Another treatment of the σ parameter is to suppress it entirely by defining the numerical assignment $\mu_a' = \mu_a/\sqrt{2}\sigma$. In terms of representing relations we have the following:

   3. $S_3(p, \mu)$ if and only if for all a, b in B

$$p_{ab} = N(\mu_a - \mu_b).$$

Clearly $\langle \mathfrak{B}, S_3, \mu \rangle$ is a difference scale also, so that we shall omit explicit description of both the representation and uniqueness theorems based on S_3.

   To demonstrate the possibility of obtaining ratio scales for Case V-Thurstone systems, we introduce the following representing relation:

   4. $S_4(p, \mu)$ if and only if for all a, b in B

$$p_{ab} = N\left(\log\frac{\mu_a}{\mu_b}\right).$$

The proof of the representation theorem based on S_4 follows from Theorem 28, for if we let

$$\mu_a = \exp \frac{\mu_a{'}}{\sqrt{2}\sigma}$$

then, if μ' satisfies $S_1(p, \mu')$, μ will satisfy $S_4(p, \mu)$. For the uniqueness theorem we have the following:

Theorem 31 (Uniqueness Theorem IV). *If $\mathfrak{B}$ is a Case V-Thurstone system, then $\langle \mathfrak{B}, S_4, \mu \rangle$ is a generalized ratio scale in both the narrow and wide senses.*

We observe that the similarity transformation is certainly an admissible transformation, for, if $\mu' = \delta\mu$,

$$\log \frac{\mu_a}{\mu_b} = \log \frac{\mu_a{'}}{\mu_b{'}} .$$

To obtain a log interval scale for Case V-Thurstone systems, we define the following:

5. $S_a(p, \mu)$ if and only if there exists a k such that for all a, b in B

$$p_{ab} = N \left(k \log \frac{\mu_a}{\mu_b} \right) .$$

The corresponding representation theorem can easily be proved from the previous (unstated) representation theorem by defining the function μ as the kth root of the function μ' which satisfies $S_4(p, \mu')$. It may be verified that if the function μ exists which satisfies $S_5(p, \mu)$ then the function $\mu' = \delta\mu^\beta$ satisfies $S_5(p, \mu')$ when $k' = k/\beta$, because

$$k \log \frac{\mu_a}{\mu_b} = k' \log \frac{\mu_a{'}}{\mu_b{'}} .$$

Again we merely state the uniqueness theorem without proof.

Theorem 32 (Uniqueness Theorem V). *If $\mathfrak{B}$ is a Case V-Thurstone system, then $\langle \mathfrak{B}, S_5, \mu \rangle$ is a generalized log interval scale in both the narrow and wide senses.*

For Case III-Thurstone systems, we mention just one representation relation:

6. $S_6(p, \mu)$ if and only if for every a and b in A there exist positive numbers σ_a^2 and σ_b^2 such that

$$p_{ab} = N \left(\frac{\mu_a - \mu_b}{\sqrt{\sigma_a^2 + \sigma_b^2}} \right) .$$

As in previous examples, we omit the obvious representation theorem. The uniqueness theorem, on the other hand, does not appear to be simple, and as far as we know the exact solution is not known. The following simple counterexample shows that the result must be something weaker than an interval scale. Let

$$\mu_a = 1 \qquad \sigma_a{}^2 = 1$$
$$\mu_b = 2 \qquad \sigma_b{}^2 = 2$$
$$\mu_c = 5 \qquad \sigma_c{}^2 = 3.$$

We now transform to a new function μ' without changing p_{ab}:

$$\mu_a{}' = 1 \qquad \sigma_a{}'^2 = \tfrac{13}{72}$$
$$\mu_b{}' = 2 \qquad \sigma_b{}'^2 = \tfrac{203}{72}$$
$$\mu_c{}' = 6 \qquad \sigma_c{}'^2 = \tfrac{437}{72}.$$

It is at once evident that no linear transformation can relate μ and μ' for

$$\frac{\mu_b - \mu_a}{\mu_c - \mu_a} \neq \frac{\mu_b{}' - \mu_a{}'}{\mu_c{}' - \mu_a{}'}.$$

The fact that both B.T.L. and Thurstone systems yield either ratio or difference scales in a natural way raises the question whether a given pair comparison system can be both a B.T.L. and Thurstone system. In the trivial case that $p_{ab} = \tfrac{1}{2}$ for all a and b in A this is indeed true, but it is easy to construct pair comparison systems that are B.T.L. but not Case V-Thurstone systems, or Case V-Thurstone but not B.T.L. systems. Interesting open problems are (1) the complete characterization of the pair comparison systems which are both B.T.L. and Case V-Thurstone systems and (2) detailed analysis of the relation between B.T.L. and Case III-Thurstone systems [for some further discussion see (Luce, 1959, pp. 54–58)].

4.3 Monotone Systems for Pair Comparisons

Some important similarities between B.T.L. and Thurstone systems can be brought out by considering further at this point the infinite difference systems of Sec. 3.3. It was indicated in Sec. 3.3 that the quaternary relation D could be interpreted as follows:

$$abDcd \quad \text{if and only if} \quad p_{ab} \leqslant p_{cd}. \tag{14}$$

If the quaternary system $\mathfrak{A} = \langle A, D \rangle$ with D interpreted as in Eq. 14 satisfies the assumptions of an infinite difference system, then from

Theorem 12 we know that a numerical assignment f_1 will exist such that for a, b, c, d in B,

$$p_{ab} \leqslant p_{cd} \quad \text{if and only if} \quad f_1(a) - f_1(b) \leqslant f_1(c) - f_1(d). \qquad (15)$$

And from Theorem 13 it follows that the numerical assignment f is unique up to a linear transformation. Following Adams and Messick (1957), we use Eq. 15 to define *monotone systems*.

Definition 30. *Let* $\mathfrak{B} = \langle B, p \rangle$ *be a pair comparison system. Then* $\mathfrak{B}$ *is a monotone system if and only if there is a numerical assignment* f_1 *defined on A such that for a, b, c, and d in A*

$$p_{ab} \leqslant p_{cd} \quad \textit{if and only if} \quad f_1(a) - f_1(b) \leqslant f_1(c) - f_1(d).$$

The representation theorem corresponding to this definition is obvious and need not be stated.

It is at once obvious that any B.T.L. or Case V-Thurstone system is a monotone system; the converse is, of course, not true. Also any pair comparison system that is an infinite difference or finite difference system under the interpretation given by Eq. 14 is also a monotone system. The first four axioms are the same for both i.d. and f.d. systems and are satisfied by any monotone system; the theory of measurement would be a much simpler subject if conversely any system that satisfied these four axioms were also a monotone system. That this converse is not true is shown in Scott & Suppes (1958).

In the context of the discussion of pair comparisons it is worth noting that, under the interpretation given by Eq. 14, Axiom 3 for f.d. and i.d. systems expresses what Davidson and Marschak (1959) call the *quadruple condition*. Axioms 2 and 5 have as a consequence the principle of *strong stochastic transitivity*, that is, if $p_{ab} \geqslant \frac{1}{2}$ and $p_{bc} \geqslant \frac{1}{2}$ then $p_{ac} \geqslant p_{ab}$ and $p_{ac} \geqslant p_{bc}$. It follows from the remarks in the preceding paragraph that any B.T.L. system or Case V-Thurstone system satisfies the quadruple condition and the principle of strong stochastic transitivity.

Finally, we remark that other representation theorems may be proved for monotone systems. We may for example define a representing relation $R(p, f_2)$ involving ratios rather than differences as follows:

$R(p, f_2)$ if and only if for all a, b, c, and d in B $p_{ab} \leqslant p_{cd}$ if and only if

$$\frac{f_2(a)}{f_2(b)} \leqslant \frac{f_2(c)}{f_2(d)}.$$

By letting

$$f_2(a) = e^{f_1(a)},$$

the representation theorem for monotone systems based on $R(p, f_2)$ follows directly from Def. 30.

The general conclusion is that for all monotone systems, as well as those that are B.T.L. or Thurstone systems, there is no intrinsic reason for choosing derived numerical assignments expressing the observable relations of pair comparison probabilities in terms of numerical differences rather than numerical ratios.

4.4 Multidimensional Thurstone Systems

To illustrate a *multidimensional derived assignment*, we shall consider a multidimensional extension of a Case V-Thurstone system.

Let A be a nonempty set of stimuli and q a real valued function from $A \times A \times A \times A$ to the open interval $(0, 1)$ satisfying the following properties for a, b, c, d in A: $q_{ab,cd} = 1 - q_{cd,ab}$, $q_{ab,cd} = q_{ab,dc} = q_{ba,cd}$, and $q_{ab,ab} = \frac{1}{2}$. Then $\mathfrak{A} = \langle A, q \rangle$ is a *quadruple system*. The usual interpretation of $q_{ab,cd}$ is that it is the relative frequency with which stimuli (a, b) are judged more similar to each other than the stimuli (c, d). To achieve an r-dimensional derived assignment for $\mathfrak{A}$, we wish to define an r-dimensional vector $\mathbf{x}_a$ in terms of the function q for each element a in A.

The multidimensional extension of a Thurstone system in Torgerson (1958) involves assuming that the distance d_{ab} between the r-dimensional vectors $\mathbf{x}_a$ and $\mathbf{x}_b$ is normally distributed and that

$$q_{ab,cd} = P(d_{ab} < d_{cd}). \tag{16}$$

The difficulty with this approach is that since d_{ab} is the magnitude of the distance between x_a and x_b it cannot be normally distributed because it cannot take on negative values. A more consistent and direct extension of a Thurstone system would be to assume that for each vector $\mathbf{x}_a$ associated with stimulus a in A, the *projection* of the vector $\mathbf{x}_a$ on the ith axis, x_{ia}, is normally and independently distributed with mean μ_{ia} and variance σ_{ia}^2. The distribution of $x_{ia} - x_{ib}$, the projection of the vector $(\mathbf{x}_a - \mathbf{x}_b)$ on the ith axis, is then also normally distributed with a mean $\mu_{ia} - \mu_{ib}$ and variance $\sigma_{ia}^2 + \sigma_{ib}^2$. Making the Case V assumptions, we may set $\sigma_{ia}^2 + \sigma_{ib}^2$ equal to a constant, and for simplicity we set it equal to one. A weaker multidimensional interpretation of the Case V assumptions is to let $\sigma_{ia}^2 + \sigma_{ib}^2 = \sigma_i^2$ for all a, b in A. With some minor modifications, the following equation will incorporate this weaker assumption as well.

If y_{ab} is the random variable corresponding to the distance between $\mathbf{x}_a$ and $\mathbf{x}_b$, then, as Hefner (1958) has pointed out, since

$$y_{ab}^2 = \sum_{i=1}^{r} (x_{ia} - x_{ib})^2, \tag{17}$$

y_{ab}^2 is distributed as a noncentral χ^2 with r degrees of freedom and with noncentrality parameter D_{ab}^2 equal to

$$D_{ab}^2 = \sum_{i=1}^{r} (\mu_{ia} - \mu_{ib})^2. \tag{18}$$

For the case $a = b$, two interpretations are possible. We can assume that y_{aa} is identically equal to zero or that it represents the distance between two vectors $\mathbf{x}_a$ and $\mathbf{x}_a'$ independently sampled from the same distribution. Which interpretation is better would depend on how the experiment was conducted, whether, for example, $q_{aa,bc}$, ($b \neq c$) is necessarily equal to one or whether it may be less than one. To minimize the mathematical discussion, we shall assume that $y_{aa} = |\mathbf{x}_a - \mathbf{x}_a'|$ so that y_{aa}^2 is then distributed as a central χ^2.

We shall also assume that

$$q_{ab,cd} = P(y_{ab}^2 \leqslant y_{cd}^2) \tag{19}$$

or, equivalently, that

$$q_{ab,cd} = P\left(\frac{y_{ab}^2}{y_{cd}^2} \leqslant 1\right). \tag{20}$$

Hence, letting $w_{ab,cd} = y_{ab}^2/y_{cd}^2$ and letting the probability density of $w_{ab,cd}$ be $f(w)$,

$$q_{ab,cd} = \int_0^1 f_{ab,cd}(w)\, dw. \tag{21}$$

To specify the nature of the density $f(w)$, we need to be clear about whether y_{ab}^2 and y_{cd}^2 are independently distributed for all a, b, c, d in A. Again, one special case arises when $a = c$ or $b = d$. The interpretation for this case would generally depend on whether $q_{ab,ac}$ is derived from trials in which only three stimuli are presented or from trials in which four stimuli (two of which are equivalent) are presented. We shall make the latter assumption here so that it will be reasonable to assume that y_{ab}^2 and y_{ac}^2 are independently distributed for all a, b, c in A and therefore that in general y_{ab}^2 and y_{cd}^2 are independent random variables.

Since w is then the ratio of two independent noncentral χ^2 variates, $f(w)$ is a noncentral F density with r degrees of freedom and with noncentrality parameters D_{ab}^2 and D_{cd}^2. With this in mind, we can define an r-dimensional Thurstone system as follows.

Definition 31. *If* $\mathfrak{A} = \langle A, q \rangle$ *is a quadruple system, then it is an r-dimensional Thurstone system if there exists real valued functions* $\mu_i(a)$ *for each* $a \in A$, $i = 1, \ldots, r$, *and noncentral F densities* $f_{ab,cd}(w)$ *with r degrees of freedom and noncentrality parameters* D_{ab}^2, D_{cd}^2 *such that for a, b, c, d in A*

$$q_{ab,cd} = \int_0^1 f_{ab,cd}(w)\, dw, \tag{22}$$

and such that

$$D_{ab}^2 = \sum_{i=1}^{r} (\mu_i(a) - \mu_i(b))^2. \tag{23}$$

The second condition, Eq. 23, in Def. 31 can be expressed more elegantly by utilizing the Young-Householder theorem (Young & Householder, 1938). Define an $(n - 1) \times (n - 1)$ matrix B_e whose elements b_{ab} are

$$b_{ab} = \tfrac{1}{2}(D_{ea}^2 + D_{eb}^2 - D_{ab}^2), \tag{24}$$

where e is some arbitrarily chosen element in A. Then condition 23 will hold if and only if the matrix B is positive semidefinite.

Rather than state an r-dimensional representation theorem we define a derived numerical (or vector) assignment for an r-dimensional Thurstone system as the function g such that for a in A

$$g(a) = (\mu_{1a}, \ldots, \mu_{ra}). \tag{25}$$

4.5 Successive Interval Systems

In the method of successive intervals a subject is presented with a set B of stimuli and asked to sort them into k categories with respect to some attribute. The categories are simply ordered from the lowest (category 1) to the highest (category k). Generally, either a single subject is required to sort the stimuli a large number of times or else many subjects do the sorting, not more than a few times, possibly once, each. The proportion of times $f_{a,i}$ that a given stimulus a is placed in category i is determined from subjects' responses.

The intuitive idea of the theory associated with the method is that each category represents a certain interval on a one-dimensional continuum and that each stimulus may be represented by a probability distribution on this continuum. The relative frequency with which subjects place stimulus a in category i should then be equal to the probability integral of the distribution of the stimulus a over the interval representing the category i. In the standard treatments the probability distributions of stimuli are assumed to be normal distributions and the scale value of the stimulus is defined as the mean of the distribution. It is important to emphasize that in the formal analysis we give here it is not necessary to assume, and we do not assume, equality of the variances of the various normal distributions. It is also pertinent to point out that the use of normal distributions is not required. As Adams and Messick (1958) show, a much wider class of distributions may be considered without disturbing the structure of the theory in any essential way. For convenience we shall, however, restrict ourselves to the normality assumption.

To formalize these intuitive ideas, we shall use the following notation. Let B be a nonempty set and for a in B let f_a be a probability distribution on the set $\{1, \ldots, k\}$ of integers, that is, $f_{a,i} \geqslant 0$ for $i = 1, \ldots, k$ and $\sum_{i=1}^{k} f_{a,i} = 1$. A system $\mathfrak{B} = \langle B, k, f \rangle$ is called a *successive interval system*. Using the notation that $N(x)$ is the unit normal cumulative, we define an Adams-Messick system as follows:

Definition 32. *A successive interval system* $\mathfrak{B} = \langle B, k, f \rangle$ *is an* Adams-Messick (or A.M.) system *if and only if for all a, b in B and* $i = 1, \ldots, k$ *there exist real numbers* $z_{a,i}$, $z_{b,i}$, α_{ab}, *and* β_{ab} *such that*

$$\sum_{j=1}^{i} f_{a,j} = N(z_{a,i}) \tag{26}$$

and

$$z_{a,i} = \alpha_{ab} z_{bi} + \beta_{ab}. \tag{27}$$

As with the various pair comparison systems already described, several simple representation theorems can be established for A.M. systems. Corresponding to each representation theorem there is a distinct uniqueness theorem. Rather than emphasize again the nonuniqueness aspect of the representation theorem, we shall limit the present discussion to describing just one of the simple (and customary) representing relations.

Let $N_a(x, \mu_a, \sigma_a^2)$ be the normal cumulative distribution having a mean μ_a and variance σ_a^2. Then we define the relation $R(k, f, \mu)$ as follows:

$R(k, f, \mu)$ if and only if there are normal cumulatives $N_a(x, \mu_a, \sigma_a^2)$, and there are real numbers $t_0, t_1, \ldots, t_k$ with $t_0 = -\infty$, $t_k = \infty$, and $t_{i-1} \leqslant t_i$ such that

$$f_{a,i} = N_a(t_i, \mu_a, \sigma_a^2) - N_a(t_{i-1}, \mu_a, \sigma_a^2).$$

The intended interpretation of the numbers t_i should be obvious. The number t_{i-1} is the lower endpoint of category i, and t_i is its upper endpoint.

The following two theorems are established by Adams and Messick (1958).

Theorem 33 (Representation Theorem). *If the successive interval system* $\mathfrak{B} = \langle B, k, f \rangle$ *is an A.M. system, then there exists a function* μ *such that* $\langle \mathfrak{B}, R, \mu \rangle$ *is a derived scale.*

In other words, the function μ defined by $R(k, f, \mu)$ is indeed a derived numerical assignment for an A.M. system. Adams and Messick also show the converse of Theorem 33, namely, that if $\langle \mathfrak{B}, R, \mu \rangle$ is a derived scale, the successive interval system $\mathfrak{B}$ is an A.M. system.

For the uniqueness theorem we have the following:

Theorem 34 (Uniqueness Theorem). *If the successive interval system* $\mathfrak{B} = \langle B, k, f \rangle$ *is an A.M. system, then the derived scale* $\langle \mathfrak{B}, R, \mu \rangle$ *is an interval scale in both the narrow and wide senses.*

Adams and Messick also note that if the values of μ_a and σ_a are fixed for one stimulus or, alternatively, if one of the normal cumulatives associated with the stimuli is fixed, then the derived numerical assignment μ is uniquely determined.

For completeness we should point out that the numbers $t_0, t_1, \ldots, t_k$ can also be thought of as the values of a derived numerical assignment for the category boundaries; that is, separate representation and uniqueness theorems can be established for the boundaries as well as for the stimuli, but since the theorems for the boundaries are similar to those just described for the stimuli we shall not pursue these details further.

5. THE PROBLEM OF MEANINGFULNESS

Closely related to the two fundamental issues of measurement—the representation and uniqueness problems—is a third problem which we shall term the meaningfulness problem. Although this problem is not central to a theory of measurement, it is often involved with various aspects of how measurements may be used, and as such it has engendered considerable controversy. It therefore merits some discussion here, although necessarily our treatment will be curtailed.

5.1 Definition

To begin with, it will be well to illustrate the basic source of the meaningfulness problem with two of the statements, (4) and (5), given previously in Sec. 1.2. For convenience they are repeated here.

4. The ratio of the maximum temperature today (t_n) to the maximum temperature yesterday (t_{n-1}) is 1.10.
5. The ratio of the difference between today's and yesterday's maximum temperature $(t_n$ and $t_{n-1})$ to the difference between today's and tomorrow's maximum temperature $(t_n$ and $t_{n+1})$ will be 0.95.

In Sec. 1.2 statement 4 was dismissed for having no clear empirical meaning and (5), on the other hand, was said to be acceptable. Here we wish to be completely explicit regarding the basis of this difference. Note first that both statements are similar in at least one important respect: neither statement specifies which numerical assignment from the set of admissible numerical assignments is to be used to determine the validity or truth of the statement. Are the temperature measurements to be made on the centigrade, Fahrenheit, or possibly the Kelvin scale? This question is not answered by either statement.

The distinguishing feature of (4) is that this ambiguity in the statement is critical. As an example, suppose by using the Fahrenheit scale we found that $t_n = 110$ and $t_{n-1} = 100$. We would then conclude that (4) was a true statement, the ratio of t_n to t_{n-1} being 1.10. Note, however, that if the temperature measurements had been made on the centigrade scale we would have come to the opposite conclusion, since then we would have found that $t_n = 43.3$ and $t_{n-1} = 37.8$ and a ratio equal to 1.15 rather than 1.10. In the case of (4) the selection of a particular numerical assignment influences the conclusions we come to concerning the truth of the statement.

In contrast, consider statement 5. The choice of a specific numerical assignment is not critical. To illustrate this point assume that when we measure temperature on a Fahrenheit scale we find the following readings: $t_{n-1} = 60$, $t_n = 79.0$, and $t_{n+1} = 99.0$. Then the ratio described in (5) is equal to

$$\frac{60 - 79}{79 - 99} = \frac{-19}{-20} = 0.95$$

which would indicate that (5) was valid. Now, if, instead, the temperature measurements had been made on the centigrade scale, we would have found that $t_{n-1} = 15.56$, $t_n = 26.11$, and $t_{n+1} = 37.20$. But, since the ratio of these numbers is

$$\frac{15.56 - 26.11}{26.11 - 37.20} = \frac{-10.55}{-11.09} = 0.95,$$

we would also have come to the conclusion that (5) was true. In fact, it is easy to verify that if we restrict ourselves to numerical assignments which are linearly related to each other then we will always arrive at the same conclusion concerning the validity of (5). If the statement is true for one numerical assignment, then it will be true for all. And, furthermore, if it is untrue for one numerical assignment, then it will be untrue for all. For this reason we can say that the selection of a specific numerical assignment to test the statement is not critical.

The absence of units in (4) and (5) is deliberate because the determination of units and an appreciation of their empirical significance comes *after*, not before, the investigation of questions of meaningfulness. The character of (4) well illustrates this point. If the Fahrenheit scale is specified in (4), the result is an empirical statement that is unambiguously true or false, but it is an empirical statement of a very special kind. It tells us something about the weather relative to a completely arbitrary choice of units. If the choice of the Fahrenheit scale were not arbitrary, there would be a meteorological experiment that would distinguish between Fahrenheit and centigrade scales and thereby narrow the class of admissible transformations. The recognized absurdity of such an experiment is direct evidence for the arbitrariness of the scale choice.

From the discussion of (4) and (5) it should be evident what sort of definition of meaningfulness we adopt.

Definition 33. *A numerical statement is* meaningful *if and only if its truth (or falsity) is constant under admissible scale transformations of any of its numerical assignments, that is, any of its numerical functions expressing the results of measurement.*

Admittedly this definition should be buttressed by an exact definition of "numerical statement," but this would take us further into technical matters of logic than is desirable in the present context. A detailed discussion of these matters, including construction of a formalized language, is to be found in Suppes (1959)[8]. The kind of numerical statements we have in mind will be made clear by the examples to follow. The import of the definition of meaningfulness will be clarified by the discussion of these examples.

It will also be convenient in what follows to introduce the notion of *equivalent statements.* Two statements are equivalent if and only if they have the same truth value. In these terms we can say that a numerical statement is meaningful in the sense of Def. 33 if admissible transformations of any of its numerical assignments always lead to equivalent numerical statements.

5.2 Examples

To point out some of the properties and implications of Def. 33, we discuss a number of specific examples. In each case a particular numerical statement is given as well as the transformation properties of all the numerical assignments referred to in the statement. For each example we ask the question: is it meaningful? To show that it is meaningful, admissible transformations are performed on all the numerical assignments

[8] It can also be well argued that Def. 33 gives a necessary but not sufficient condition of meaningfulness. For example, a possible added condition on the meaningfulness of statements in classical mechanics is that they be invariant under a transformation to a new coordinate system moving with uniform velocity with respect to the old coordinate system [cf. McKinsey & Suppes (1955)]. However, this is not a critical matter for what follows in this section.

and the transformed numerical statement is shown to be equivalent to the initial one. In most cases, when the two statements are in fact equivalent, the transformed statement can generally be reduced to the original statement by using various elementary rules of mathematics or logic. To show that a statement is meaningless, we must show that the transformed statement is not equivalent or cannot be reduced to the original. When this is not obvious, the simplest way of proceeding is to construct a counterexample, an example in which the truth value of the statement is not preserved after a particular admissible transformation is performed.

In the following examples we conform, for simplicity, to common usage and denote numerical assignments by x, y, and z instead of by $f(a)$ or $g(a)$. Thus instead of writing

$$\text{for all } a \in A, f(a) = \phi(g(a)),$$

we simply write

$$y = \phi(x).$$

When it is necessary to distinguish between the values of a given numerical assignment for two distinct objects a and b, subscript notation is used. Thus, for example, x_a and x_b might be the masses of two weights a and b. The parameters of the admissible transformations are j, k, l, m, $\ldots$ and the numerical assignments that result from these transformations of x, y, and z are x', y', and z', respectively.

Example I.

$$x_a + x_b > x_c. \tag{28}$$

First assume that the numerical assignment x is unique up to a similarity transformation. Then if x is transformed to kx, Eq. 28 becomes

$$kx_a + kx_b > kx_c, \tag{29}$$

and Eq. 29 is obviously equivalent to Eq. 28. Hence Eq. 28, under the assumption that x lies on a ratio scale, is meaningful.

Assume instead that x is specified up to a linear transformation. Then when x transforms to $kx + l$, Eq. 28 transforms to

$$(kx_a + l) + (kx_b + l) > (kx_c + l), \tag{30}$$

which does not reduce to Eq. 28. For a specific counterexample, let $x_a = 1$, $x_b = 2$, $x_c = 2$, $k = 1$, and $l = -1$. Equation 28 then becomes

$$1 + 2 > 2. \tag{31}$$

But substituting the transformed values of x_a and x_b into Eq. 28 gives

$$(1 - 1) + (2 - 1) > (2 - 1)$$

or

$$0 + 1 > 1, \tag{32}$$

which obviously does not have the same truth value as Eq. 31. Hence Eq. 28 is meaningless when x lies on an interval scale. Thus we can say, for example, that if mass is on a ratio scale it is meaningful to say that the sum of the masses of two objects exceeds the mass of a third object. On the other hand, if temperature is on an interval scale, then it is not meaningful to say that the sum of the maximum temperatures on two days exceeds the maximum temperature on a third day.

These last remarks should not be interpreted to mean that addition can always be performed with ratio scales and never with interval scales. Consider the statement

$$x_a + x_b > (x_c)^2. \tag{33}$$

This statement is meaningless for a ratio scale, since

$$(kx_a) + (kx_b) > (kx_c)^2 \tag{34}$$

is clearly not equivalent to Eq. 33.

An example of a meaningful numerical statement which involves both addition and multiplication of a numerical assignment having only interval scale properties is the following.

Example 2. Let S_1 and S_2 be two sets having n_1 and n_2 members, respectively. Then

$$\frac{1}{n_1} \sum_{a \in S_1} x_a > \frac{1}{n_2} \sum_{b \in S_2} x_b. \tag{35}$$

One interpretation of Eq. 35 is that the mean maximum temperature of the days in January exceeds the mean maximum temperature of the days in February. We wish to show that when x is unique up to a linear transformation

$$\frac{1}{n_1} \sum_{a \in S_1} x_a' > \frac{1}{n_2} \sum_{b \in S_2} x_b' \tag{36}$$

is equivalent to Eq. 35 where x' is another admissible numerical assignment. Substituting $x' = kx + l$ into Eq. 35 gives

$$\frac{1}{n_1} \sum_{a \in S_1} (kx_a + l) > \frac{1}{n_2} \sum_{b \in S_2} (kx_b + l)$$

or

$$\frac{1}{n_1} [k(\sum_{a \in S_1} x_a) + n_1 l] > \frac{1}{n_2} [k(\sum_{b \in S_2} x_b) + n_2 l] \tag{37}$$

and Eq. 37 can be reduced to Eq. 35. Hence Eq. 35 is meaningful under these conditions. In general, it may be observed that the question whether a particular mathematical operation can be used with a particular scale cannot be answered with a simple yes or no. The admissibility of any mathematical operation depends not only on the scale type of the relevant numerical assignments but on the entire numerical statement of which the operation is a part.

Example 3.

$$x_a x_b > x_c. \tag{38}$$

If x is unique up to a similarity transformation, then Eq. 38 is meaningless, since

$$(kx_a)(kx_b) > (kx_c) \tag{39}$$

does not reduce to Eq. 38 for all values of k. Since Eq. 38 is meaningless for a ratio scale, it follows a fortiori that it is meaningless for an interval scale as well. It does not follow that Eq. 38 is meaningless for all scales. As an example, let x be unique up to a power transformation (see Sec. 3.5 for an illustration). Then as x is transformed to x^k, Eq. 39 becomes

$$x_a{}^k x_b{}^k > x_c{}^k,$$

and since this is equivalent to Eq. 39 statement 39 is meaningful.

In the following examples we consider numerical statements involving at least two independent numerical assignments, x and y.

Example 4.

$$y = \alpha x. \tag{40}$$

If the numerical assignments x and y are not completely unique, then it is clear that Eq. 40 will in general be meaningless, since most nonidentity transformations applied to x and y will transform Eq. 40 to a nonequivalent statement. One approach frequently used to make Eq. 40 meaningful under more general conditions permits the constant α to depend upon the parameters $k, l, m, n, \ldots$ of the admissible transformations (but not on x or y). This approach is used here, so that in the remaining discussion statement 40 will be understood to mean the following: there exists a real number α such that for all $a \in A$, $y_a = \alpha x_a$. If x is transformed to x' and y to y', then Eq. 40 interpreted in this way will be meaningful if there exists an α', not necessarily equal to α, such that $y_a' = \alpha' x_a'$ for all $a \in A$.

Assume that x and y are specified up to a similarity transformation. Letting x go to kx, y to my, and α to α' (at present unspecified), Eq. 40 transforms to

$$my = \alpha' k x. \tag{41}$$

If we let $\alpha' = (m/k)\alpha$, then Eq. 41 will be equivalent to Eq. 40 for all (nonzero) values of m and k and therefore Eq. 40 will be meaningful.

Assume instead that x and y are both specified up to linear transformations. Let x transform to $(kx + l)$, y to $(my + n)$, and α to α'. We then have

$$(my + n) = \alpha'(kx + l). \tag{42}$$

Inspection of Eq. 42 suggests that no transformation of α to α' that depends solely on the parameters k, l, m, or n will reduce Eq. 42 to Eq. 40. This conclusion can be established more firmly by constructing a counterexample. Consider the following in which $A = \{a, b\}$. Let $x_a = 1$, $y_a = 2$, $y_b = 2$, and $y_b = 4$. Then, if $\alpha = 2$, Eq. 40 will be true for all a in A. Now let x go to $(kx + l)$, y to $(my + n)$, where $k = l = m = n = 1$, and α to α'. Equation 40 then becomes for a in A

$$3 = \alpha'2, \tag{43}$$

indicating that if the truth value of Eq. 40 is to be preserved we must have $\alpha' = \frac{3}{2}$. However, for $b \in A$ we have

$$5 = \alpha'3, \tag{44}$$

which can be true only if $\alpha' = \frac{5}{3}$ and, in particular, is false if $\alpha' = \frac{3}{2}$. Both Eqs. 43 and 44 cannot be true and the truth value of Eq. 40 is not preserved in this example. Hence, under these conditions, Eq. 40 is meaningless.

Example 5.

$$x + y = \alpha. \tag{45}$$

In this example we assume first that x and y are unique up to a similarity transformation. One interpretation of Eq. 45 would then be that the sum of the weight and height of each person in A is equal to a constant. As usual we let x transform to kx, y to my, and α to α'. Then Eq. 45 becomes

$$kx + my = \alpha', \tag{46}$$

but, since it is evident that no value of α' will reduce this equation to one equivalent to Eq. 45, we may conclude that Eq. 45 is meaningless under these assumptions.

Although this result confirms the common-sense notion that it does not make sense to add weight and length, there are conditions under which Eq. 45 is certainly meaningful. One example is the assumption that x and y lie on difference scales; that is, they are unique up to an additive constant. This can be verified by letting x transform to $x + l$, y to $y + n$, and α to $(\alpha + l + n)$, for then Eq. 45 transforms to

$$(x + l) + (y + n) = \alpha + l + n, \tag{47}$$

which is certainly equivalent to Eq. 45.

To illustrate the effects of a derived numerical assignment, as well as another set of assumptions for which Eq. 45 is meaningful, consider the following. Assume that y is a derived numerical assignment and that it depends in part on x. Assume that when x is transformed to kx, y is transferred to $(ky + 2k)$. Therefore, if α transforms to α' Eq. 45 becomes

$$kx + (ky + 2k) = \alpha', \tag{48}$$

and, clearly, if $\alpha' = k(\alpha + 2)$, this equation will be equivalent to Eq. 45. Equation 45 is therefore meaningful under these conditions. Thus, whether it is meaningful to add weight and length depends not so much on the physical properties of bodies but on the uniqueness properties of the numerical assignments associated with weight and length.

Another common dictum frequently encountered is that one can take the logarithm only of a numerical assignment that lies on an absolute scale or, as it is customarily said, of a dimensionless number. With this in mind, we consider the following example.

Example 6.

$$y = \alpha \log x. \tag{49}$$

Assume first that x and y have ratio scale properties. Then as x transforms to kx, y to my, and α to α', Eq. 49 transforms to

$$my = \alpha' \log kx$$

or to

$$my = \alpha' \log x + \alpha' \log k, \tag{50}$$

and Eq. 50 cannot be made equivalent to Eq. 49 by any value of α'. Therefore, under these assumptions, we again have the common-sense result, viz., that Eq. 49 is meaningless.

However, assume next that x is unique up to a power transformation and that y is unique up to a similarity transformation. Then when x transforms to x^k, y to my, and α to $(m/k)\alpha$ Eq. 49 transforms to

$$my = \left(\frac{m}{k}\right) \alpha \log (x^k). \tag{51}$$

Since Eq. 51 is clearly equivalent to Eq. 49, the latter is meaningful under these conditions, common sense notwithstanding.

Another example involving the logarithm of a nonunique numerical assignment is the following.

Example 7.

$$y = \log x + \alpha. \tag{52}$$

From the previous example it should be evident that Eq. 52 will not be meaningful when x and y have ratio scale properties. But if y is on a difference scale and x is on a ratio scale, then Eq. 52 will be meaningful. This can be verified by letting x transform to kx, y to $y + n$, and α to $\alpha + n - \log k$, since then Eq. 52 transforms to

$$(y + n) = \log kx + (\alpha + n - \log k) \qquad (53)$$

and Eq. 53 is equivalent to Eq. 52. The interesting feature of Eq. 52 is that the required transformation of α is not a simple or elementary function of the parameters k and n. Although most, if not all, of the "dimensional constants" encountered in practice have simple transformation properties (usually a power function of the parameters), there is no a priori reason why these constants cannot be allowed to have quite arbitrary transformations. Of course, if the transformation properties of the constants are limited, the conditions under which numerical statements will be meaningful will ordinarily be changed.

5.3 Extensions and Comments

It will be noted that the definition of meaningfulness in Def. 33 contains no reference to the physical operations that may or may not have been employed in the measurement procedure. There are at least two other points of view on this issue that the reader should be aware of.

One point of view (e.g., Weitzenhoffer, 1951) asserts that meaningful statements may employ only mathematical operations that correspond to known physical operations. In terms of empirical and relational systems, this point of view may be described as requiring that for each empirical system the admissible mathematical operations be limited to those contained in the selected homomorphic numerical system (or alternatively in *some* homomorphic numerical system).

The second point of view (e.g., Guilford, 1954) appears to be less severe. It asserts that all rules of arithmetic are admissible when physical addition exists (and, presumably, satisfies some set of axioms such as those in Sec. 3.5). Without physical addition the application of arithmetic is limited (to some undefined set of rules or operations). In terms of relational systems, this point of view appears to imply that all statements "satisfying" the rules of arithmetic are meaningful when the selected homomorphic numerical system contains the arithmetical operation of addition (or, perhaps, when at least one homomorphic numerical system exists which contains the addition operation). When this is not the case, fewer statements are meaningful.

In contrast to these two positions, Def. 33 implies that the meaningfulness of numerical statements is determined solely by the uniqueness properties of their numerical assignments, not by the nature of the operations in the empirical or numerical systems.

One of our basic assumptions throughout this section has been that a knowledge of the representation and uniqueness theorems is a prerequisite to answering the meaningfulness question. It can be argued, though, that these assumptions are too strong, since in some cases the uniqueness properties of the numerical assignments are not precisely known. For example, although we have a representation theorem for semiorders (Sec. 3.2), we have no uniqueness theorem. In these cases we often have an approximation of a standard ordinal, interval, or ratio scale. Without stating general definitions, the intuitive idea may be illustrated by consideration of an example.

Suppose we have an empirical quaternary system $\mathfrak{A} = \langle A, D \rangle$ for which there exists a numerical assignment f such that $abDcd$ if and only if

$$f(a) - f(b) \leqslant f(c) - f(d). \tag{54}$$

We also suppose that the set A is finite. In addition, let $\mathfrak{N}$ be the full numerical relational system defined by Eq. 54. Let $\langle \mathfrak{A}, \mathfrak{N}, f \rangle$ be a scale and $\langle \mathfrak{A}, \mathfrak{N}, g \rangle$ be any scale such that, for two elements a and b in A, $f(a) \neq f(b)$, $f(a) = g(a)$, and $f(b) = g(b)$; that is, f and g assign the same number to at least two elements of A that are not equivalent. We then say that $\langle \mathfrak{A}, \mathfrak{N}, f \rangle$ is an ϵ-approximation of an interval scale if

$$\max_{a,g} |f(a) - g(a)| \leqslant \epsilon,$$

where the maximum is taken over all elements of A and numerical assignments g satisfying the condition just stated. It is clearly not necessary that there be an ϵ such that the scale $\langle \mathfrak{A}, \mathfrak{N}, f \rangle$ be an ϵ-approximation of an interval scale. Consider, for instance, the three element set $A = \{a, b, c\}$, with $f(a) = 1$, $f(b) = 1.5$, and $f(c) = 3$. Then, if $g(a) = 1$ and $g(b) = 1.5$, we may assign any number for the value $g(c)$ provided $g(c) > 2$, and thus there is no finite $\max |f(a) - g(a)|$. On the other hand, if A has 20 or more elements, say, and no intervals are too large or too small in relation to the rest, $\langle \mathfrak{A}, \mathfrak{N}, f \rangle$ will be an ϵ-approximation of an interval scale for ϵ reasonably small in relation to the scale of f.

The relation between ϵ-approximations of standard scales and issues of meaningfulness is apparent. A statement or hypothesis that is meaningful for interval or ratio scales has a simple and direct analogue that is meaningful for ϵ-approximations of these scales. For example, consider the standard proportionality hypothesis for two ratio scales, that is, there exists a positive α such that for every a in A

$$f(a) = \alpha \, h(a). \tag{55}$$

This equation is meaningful, as we have seen (Sec. 5.2, Example 4), when f and h are determined up to a similarity transformation. If f and h, or more exactly $\langle \mathfrak{A}, \mathfrak{R}, f \rangle$ and $\langle \mathfrak{A}', \mathfrak{R}', h \rangle$, are ϵ- and δ-approximations of ratio scales, respectively, then Eq. 55 is no longer meaningful but the appropriate analogue of Eq. 55, namely

$$|f(a) - \alpha \, h(a)| \leqslant \epsilon + \alpha \delta$$

is meaningful.

Problems of meaningfulness and the issue of the applicability of certain statistics to data that are not known to constitute an interval or ratio scale have been closely tied in the psychological literature. Unfortunately, we have insufficient space to analyze this literature. We believe that the solution lies not in developing alternative definitions of meaningfulness but rather in clarifying the exact status of the measurements made. One way is to make explicit the empirical relational system underlying the empirical procedures of measurement. A second is along the lines we have just suggested in sketching the theory of ϵ-approximations. A third possibility for clarification is to give a more explict statement of the theory or hypotheses to which the measurements are relevant.

References

Adams, E. W., & Messick, S. *An axiomatization of Thurstone's successive intervals and paired comparison scaling models.* Tech. Rept. No. 12, Contr. Nonr 225(17), Applied Math. and Stat. Lab., Stanford Univer., 1957.

Adams, E. W., & Messick, S. An axiomatic formulation and generalization of successive intervals scaling. *Psychometrika*, 1958, **23**, 355–368.

Armstrong, W. E. The determinateness of the utility function. *Econ. J.*, 1939, **49**, 453–467.

Armstrong, W. E. Uncertainty and the utility function. *Econ. J.*, 1948, **58**, 1–10.

Armstrong, W. E. Utility and the theory of welfare. *Oxford Economic Papers*, 1951, **3**, 259–271.

Bennett, J. F., & Hays, W. L. Multidimensional unfolding: determining the dimensionality of ranked preference data. *Psychometrika*, 1960, **25**, 27–43.

Birkhoff, G. *Lattice theory.* (Rev. ed.) American Math. Society, colloq. series, 1948, **25**.

Bradley, R. A. Incomplete block rank analysis: on the appropriateness of the model for a method of paired comparisons. *Biometrics*, 1954, **10**, 375–390. (a)

Bradley, R. A. Rank analysis of incomplete block designs. II. Additional tables for the method of paired comparisons. *Biometrika*, 1954, **41**, 502–537. (b)

Bradley, R. A. Rank analysis of incomplete block designs. III. Some large-sample results on estimation and power for a method of paired comparisons. *Biometrika*, 1955, **42**, 450–470.

Bradley R. A., & Terry, M. E. Rank analysis of incomplete block designs. I. The method of paired comparisons. *Biometrika*, 1952, **39**, 324–345.

Campbell, N. R. *Physics: the elements.* London: Cambridge Univer. Press, 1920. (Reprinted as *Foundations of Science.* New York: Dover, 1957. Pagination references pertain to this edition.)

Campbell, N. R. *An account of the principles of measurements and calculations.* London: Longmans, Green, 1928.

Cohen, M. R., & Nagel, E. *An introduction to logic and scientific method.* New York: Harcourt, Brace, 1934.

Comrey, A. L. Mental testing and the logic of measurement. *Educational and Psychological Measurement*, 1951, **11**, 323–34.

Coombs, C. H. Psychological scaling without a unit of measurement. *Psychol. Rev.*, 1950, **57**, 145–158.

Coombs, C. H. A theory of psychological scaling. *Engr. Res. Instit. Bull.* No. 34. Ann. Arbor: Univer. of Mich. Press, 1952.

Coombs, C. H. A theory of data. *Psychol. Rev.*, 1960, **67**, 143–159.

Coombs, C. H., Raiffa, H., & Thrall, R. M. Some views on mathematical models and measurement theory. *Psychol. Rev.*, 1954, **61**, 132–144.

Davidson, D., & Marschak, J. Experimental tests of a stochastic decision theory. In C. W. Churchman and P. Ratoosh (Eds.), *Measurement: definition and theories.* New York: Wiley, 1959. Pp. 233–269.

Davidson, D., & Suppes, P. A finitistic axiomatization of subjective probability and utility. *Econometrica*, 1956, **24**, 264–275.

Davidson, D., Suppes, P., & Siegel, S. *Decision-making: an experimental approach.* Stanford: Stanford Univer. Press, 1957.

Debreu, G. Representation of a preference ordering by a numerical function. In R. M. Thrall, C. H. Coombs and R. L. Davis (Eds.), *Decision processes.* New York: Wiley, 1954. Pp. 159–165.

Gerlach, Muriel W. *Interval measurement of subjective magnitudes with subliminal differences.* Tech. Rept. No. 7, Contr. Nonr 225(17), Applied Math. and Stat. Lab., Stanford Univer., 1957.

Guilford, J. P. *Psychometric methods.* (2nd ed.) New York: McGraw-Hill, 1954.

Hefner, R. *Extensions of the law of comparative judgment to discriminable and multidimensional stimuli.* Unpublished doctoral dissertation, Univer. of Mich., 1958.

Hempel, C. G. Fundamentals of Concept formation in empirical science. *International Encyclopedia of Unified Science, II*, No. 7. Chicago: Univer. of Chicago Press, 1952.

Hölder, O. Die Axiome der Quantität und die Lehre von mass. *Ber. Säch., Gesellsch. Wiss., Math-Phy. Klasse*, 1901, **53**, 1–64.

Luce, R. D. Semi-orders and a theory of utility discrimination. *Econometrica*, 1956, **24**, 178–191.

Luce, R. D. *Individual choice behavior.* New York: Wiley, 1959.

McKinsey, J. C. C., & Suppes, P. On the notion of invariance in classical mechanics. *British Journal for Philosophy of Science*, 1955, **5**, 290–302.

Scott, D., & Suppes, P. Foundational aspects of theories of measurement. *J. Symbolic Logic*, 1958, **23**, 113–128.

Stevens, S. S. On the theory of scales of measurement. *Science*, 1946, **103**, 677–680.

Stevens, S. S. Mathematics, measurement and psychophysics. In S. S. Stevens (Ed.), *Handbook of experimental psychology.* New York: Wiley, 1951, Pp. 1–49.

Suppes, P. A set of independent axioms for extensive quantities. *Portugaliae Mathematica*, 1951, **10**, 163–172.

Suppes, P. *Introduction to logic*. Princeton, N.J.: Von Nostrand, 1957.

Suppes, P. Measurement, empirical meaningfulness and three-valued logic. In C. W. Churchman and P. Ratoosh (Eds.), *Measurement: definition and theories*. New York: Wiley, 1959. Pp. 129–143.

Suppes, P., & Winet, Muriel. An axiomatization of utility based on the notion of utility differences. *Mgmt. Sci.*, 1955, **1**, 259–270.

Tarski, A. Contributions to the theory of models, I, II. *Indagationes Mathematicae*, 1954, **16**, 572–588.

Thurstone, L. L. A law of comparative judgment. *Psychol. Rev.*, 1927, **34**, 273–286.

Torgerson, W. S. *Theory and methods of scaling*. New York: Wiley, 1958.

Weitzenhoffer, A. M. Mathematical structures and psychological measurement. *Psychometrika*, 1951, **16**, 387–406.

Wiener, N. A new theory of measurement: a study in the logic of mathematics. *Proc. London Math. Soc.*, 1921, **19**, 181–205.

Young, G., & Householder, A. S. Discussion of a set of points in terms of their mutual distances. *Psychometrika*, 1938, **3**, 19–22.

2

Characterization and Classification of Choice Experiments[1,2]

Robert R. Bush
University of Pennsylvania

Eugene Galanter
University of Washington

R. Duncan Luce
University of Pennsylvania

1. This work was supported in part by grants NSF G-8864, G-14839, and G-17637 from the National Science Foundation to the University of Pennsylvania and by the Office of Naval Research, Contract NONR-551(37). Reproduction in whole or part is permitted for any purpose of the United States Government.
2. We wish to thank Ward Edwards, Francis W. Irwin, Elizabeth F. Shipley, and Richard L. Solomon for their extremely helpful comments and criticisms of drafts of this material and our students whose puzzlement over various paragraphs or sections revealed some fuzziness in our thinking, which, hopefully, is less apparent now.

Contents

Characterization and Classification of Choice Experiments

A large part of the naturalistic analysis and an even larger part of the successful experimental and mathematical analysis of human and animal behavior involves the notion of choice. Whenever an organism, either in its natural environment or in the laboratory, is confronted with a set of two or more mutually exclusive courses of action—responses—and it selects or performs one of them, we say that a choice has occurred. If the word "choice" suggests a conscious decision by the organism, that is unfortunate. To be sure, some choices may reasonably be called "conscious"; for example, in a psychophysical discrimination experiment a person says "louder" after having "consciously" decided that the second tone is louder than the first. But decisions are not usually called "conscious" when a rat "chooses" to turn right or left in a T-maze, and we want to call that a choice. The term is strictly behavioristic. What an experimenter elects to observe determines, in part, whether or not choices are made. The scientific significance of these observations, however, probably rests on the wisdom of the experimenter's choices.

By a choice experiment, then, we mean one in which there is a set of two or more empirically defined alternative responses from which the subject chooses just one whenever he is given an opportunity to do so. We call these opportunities "trials." The set of response alternatives is usually finite, often having only two or three elements, but occasionally infinite sets are employed.

In all theories about experimental choice behavior a measure function is imposed over the response set; most commonly it is a probability measure, but other measures have been used as well (e.g., Luce, 1959; Audley, 1960). But neither the kinds of measures occurring in a theory nor the types of behavioral observations actually made (response frequency or response time, for example) have anything to do with classifying an experiment as a choice design.

In psychophysics and learning the vast majority of experiments performed are choice ones, as we are using the term. Signal detection, discrimination, T-maze learning, and binary prediction studies are obvious examples. Nevertheless, there are some notable exceptions. Simple reaction time experiments are not of the choice variety because only a single experimentally defined response is made on every trial. For the same reason, animal-runway and many operant conditioning experiments are not choice designs. Some analyses of reaction time and runway studies (McGill, Chapter 6; Estes, 1950; Bush & Mosteller, 1955, Chapter 14) postulate unobservable responses in order that existing choice models can be used to analyze the phenomena, but this does not alter our classification of the experiments; the experimentally identified response set contains only one element, and so they are not choice experiments.

At the other extreme the obvious identification of responses in some experiments leads to extremely large response sets. For example, in magnitude estimation studies the response set is well defined but non-denumerable, for the subject is restricted only to choosing nonnegative real numbers. It seems clear that only much smaller, finite, but unknown subsets are actually available to most subjects. Similarly, in verbal conditioning experiments in which the subject is asked to emit any word that comes to mind and the experimenter reinforces a certain class of words, such as plural nouns, the set of possible responses is finite and well defined but large. Again, however, the set of all words is much larger than the real but unknown response set which at most is the subject's vocabulary.

It is very difficult to see how to exclude either of these studies formally from the class of choice experiments, yet few theoreticians feel that there is much hope in trying to analyze them exactly as we do choice experiments with small response sets except possibly when some appreciable redefinition of the responses can be made. For example, in verbal conditioning we might define as one response the class of plural nouns and as the other all remaining words, in which case we then view the experiment as an example of two-response learning. Admittedly, these two-response classes are most heterogeneous, but that is in no way unique to this experiment. We have little assurance—indeed, there is evidence to the contrary—that responses such as left turns in a T-maze are homogeneous. The conclusion, then, is that any experiment that can be viewed as a choice experiment can always be so viewed in several different ways. For many experiments, however, the identification of the response set seems so obvious and unambiguous that there is little to be decided. For example, no one has suggested any radical reduction in the responses for a magnitude estimation experiment, and theorists have been obliged to work with continuous response theories rather than with the simpler discrete theories postulated for most other psychophysical experiments.

Another troublesome class of experiments contains those for which the response set is well defined and small, but a trial is terminated either when one of these responses occurs or when a fixed time has elapsed following the stimulus presentation. Thus no prescribed response need occur on a trial.

Examples are (1) avoidance training in which an animal avoids or escapes a shock by a particular response or, failing escape in a certain time, the shock is automatically terminated; (2) free-recall verbal learning in which a subject either recalls a word or not in a specified time; and (3) classical Pavlovian conditioning in which the (conditioned) response may or may not occur, following the presentation of the conditioned stimulus, within the observation period of a trial.

If the prescribed responses are taken to form the response set, then these are not choice experiments because a response need not always occur during a trial. If, however, the response set is augmented by including what may be called the "null" response, namely, any behavior not previously prescribed as a response, then formally it is a choice experiment. Some theorists are uneasy about treating the null response as a response because they do not feel that a choice is made in the same sense in the two cases. But this is little more than a feeling, and the ultimate decision about the appropriate identifications of responses probably can be made only when we know whether these experiments demand inherently different theories from those used to account for behavior in what are clearly choice experiments.

In branches of psychology other than psychophysics, learning, and preference studies the choice experiment paradigm has been little used. Although mathematics is employed extensively in psychometrics, for example, the concern there has not been primarily with behavior as such, but rather behavioral data are used to establish "cultural" scales of social variables. Similarly, modern psychological studies of language are less concerned with the behavior of the speaker and listener than with the formal structure of language itself (see Chapters 11, 12, and 13). Some social psychological experiments, such as those of small group behavior, are designed with an implicit or explicit choice paradigm in mind, but many others are not (see Chapter 14).

Nonetheless, a sizable fraction of all the work done in mathematical psychology is currently concerned with choice experiments, and a considerable unity and systematization has evolved over the years. For this reason, a chapter devoted to a fairly careful characterization and classification of choice experiments seemed useful to us. What we have to say is directly relevant to the expositions found in Chapters 3, 4, 5, 8, 9, 10; it is largely irrelevant to most of the other chapters in this work.

1. THE ABSTRACT STRUCTURE OF A CHOICE EXPERIMENT

1.1 The Classical Stimulus-Response Paradigm

For several decades stimulus-response psychology has been based mostly on a single skeletal design which identifies three significant events that occur in experimental trials. In brief, it is

$$\text{stimulus} \rightarrow \text{response} \rightarrow \text{outcome}.$$

A stimulus—be it called that, an environmental situation, signal, collection of cues, or some other similar term—is presented by the experimenter. Next, the subject whose behavior is under study makes a response or performs an act which may be motor, verbal, or physiological (e.g., GSR). This is followed by experimenter-determined events, whatever they may be, which we call outcomes. Outcomes are sometimes termed rewards and punishments, environmental events, or payoffs; the first two terms are, however, also used as theoretical notions in some theories. Outcomes may be the presentation of tangible objects or substances, or they may be signals that convey information. Sometimes they are omitted from the design, as in much of classical psychophysics, in many modern studies on the scaling of stimuli, and in classical conditioning.

The paradigm is general, and so its identifications are bound to be ambiguous, but little violence is done to the basic ideas if we say stimuli are particular aspects of the environment during the period of the trial that precedes the response and outcomes are particular aspects during the period of the trial that follows the response. Stimulus-response behavior theories are concerned with how the subject sets up a "connection" between his responses and the stimuli, but we need not deal with this problem here. Our present goal is to characterize the experiment, not to describe or explain the subject's behavior. Of course, later chapters in this work are primarily concerned with behavior theory as such.

The S-R-O framework has had a controlling influence on essentially all mathematical learning models developed in the last decade. Estes (1950) in one of the founding papers made the parts of the paradigm quite explicit. Bush and Mosteller (1951a, 1951b, 1955) and Bush, Mosteller, and Thompson (1954) made them more or less explicit, depending upon the problem discussed. The psychophysical literature, both experimental and mathematical, seems to have taken the paradigm for granted, except for the traditional lack of concern about outcomes. Galanter and Miller (1960) pointed out and objected to this strong S-R influence on mathematical psychology. Rather than describe or discuss their objections here, we shall attempt instead to formalize and clarify the S-R-O paradigm and to present a somewhat new classification of experiments. This necessarily leads to some new nomenclature.

Because we want a scheme that applies to several different substantive areas, each of which has its own conventional notations for the same notions, we are forced to create a compromise notation that is not entirely consistent with any of the existing ones. In fact, we have departed more than is strictly necessary in order to satisfy certain conventions that seem useful: insofar as possible we denote sets by italic capital Latin letters and their elements by the corresponding letters in lower case; we use as the names of sets the first letter of the word that describes the elements; and we denote functions by the lower-case Greek letters corresponding to the symbol for the set of elements constituting the range of the function. If this or any other consistent notation were accepted and used in the several fields, certain advantages of communication would accrue.

1.2 Stimulus Presentations

The flow diagram of Fig. 1, which is explained fully in the following pages, gives much of our scheme for a choice experiment. A more detailed summary appears in Table 1, p. 96.

In all of the experiments we shall consider, the events that occur are partitioned into a sequence of *trials*. The sequence of trials may therefore

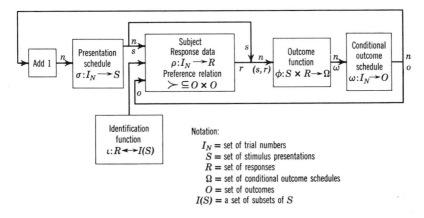

Fig. 1. Flow diagram of a choice experiment.

be identified with the sequence $I_N = \langle 1, 2, \ldots, n, \ldots, N \rangle$ of the first N integers, where N is the total number of trials in the experimental run. Although in some experiments N is a random variable, sometimes dependent upon the subject's behavior, it is often fixed in advance.

We enter the flow diagram at the left box which issues the trial number n. Given this, the experimenter enters a table or schedule, represented by the next box, which he has prepared in advance of the experiment, to find out which of several possible stimulus presentations is actually to be presented to the subject. This schedule may or may not depend upon the previous behavior of the subject.

Let S denote the set of possible *stimulus presentations*, its typical element being denoted s, or sometimes s_i, possibly with a prime or superscript. For example, in a simple discrimination study one of the presentations might be a 100-ms, 60-db, 1000-cps tone followed in 20 ms by a 100-ms, 62-db, 1000-cps tone; in such a design the set S consists of all the ordered pairs of tones that are presented to the subject during the experimental run. Later, in Sec. 2.1, we discuss more fully the structure of S. In a simple learning experiment the set S typically has only a single element; the same stimulus presentation occurs on every trial. (The reader should not confuse the elements of our set S with the "stimulus elements" of the stimulus-sampling models described in Chapter 10.) In so-called "discrimination learning" experiments S usually has two elements, each of which is presented on half the trials.

The *presentation schedule*, then, is simply a function

$$\sigma : I_N \to S.$$

In many experiments σ is decided upon by some random device with the property that

$$P(s) = \text{Pr } [\sigma(n) = s]$$

is a function of $s \in S$ but not of the trial number n. We call these *simple random presentation schedules* and refer to $P(s)$ as the *presentation probability* of s. Of course,

$$\sum_{s \in S} P(s) = 1.$$

Although many experiments use simple random schedules, some do not. For example, the schedules used in studying the perception of periodic sequences as well as those having probabilities conditional upon the response are not simple random.

1.3 Responses

Following each presentation, the subject is required to choose one response alternative from a given set R of two or more possible *responses*. Typically, we use r or r_j for elements of R. By his choice, the subject assigns a response alternative, say $\rho(n) \in R$, to the trial number n. This is to say, his responses generate a function ρ, where

$$\rho : I_N \to R.$$

This function we call the *response data* of the experiment. For example, in a discrimination experiment the subject may be asked to state whether the second of two tones forming the presentation is louder or softer than the first, in which case $R = \{\text{louder, softer}\}$, and ρ is nothing more than the abstract representation of the data sheet with its assignment of "louder" or "softer" to each of the trial numbers.

In many contemporary models a probability mechanism is assumed to underlie the generation of the response data. Moreover, in spite of some evidence to the contrary, most analyses of psychophysical data and most psychophysical models assume that the responses are independent in the sense that they depend directly upon only the immediately preceding stimulus presentation. Thus the postulated probabilities are

$$p_n(r \mid s) = \Pr\left[\rho(n){=}r \mid \sigma(n){=}s\right],$$

where

$$\sum_{r \in R} p_n(r \mid s) = 1, \qquad (s \in S,\ n \in I_N).$$

1.4 Outcome Structure

For a time, let us ignore the preference relation located in the box in Fig. 1 marked "subject" and the identification function feeding in from below and turn to the two boxes to the right. These are intended to represent the mechanism for feeding back information and payoffs, if any, to the subject. In many psychophysical experiments today, and in almost all before 1950, this structure simply is absent, but for reasons that will become apparent later many psychophysicists now feel that it should be an integral part of the design of many experiments, as it is in most learning experiments.

The set O, which we call the set of possible experimental *outcomes* (in learning theory certain outcomes are called reinforcers), consists of the direct, immediate, experimenter-controlled consequences to the subject which depend in part upon his behavior. We let o or o_k denote typical elements of O. If there is only feedback about the correctness of the responses, then $O = \{correct, incorrect\}$; if there are payoffs as well, such as 5¢ for a correct response and -5¢ for an incorrect one, then $O = \{5$¢ and correct, -5¢ and incorrect$\}$. This last set is usually just written $\{5$¢, -5¢$\}$, on the assumption that the sign of the payoff indicates which response is correct. This is not, however, a necessary correlation (see Sec. 3.3).

Although in psychophysics it has been usual for the outcomes, when they are used at all, to be determined uniquely by the presentation-response pair, in learning and preference studies matters have not been so simple. The more general scheme could and some day may very well be used in psychophysics also. Instead of selecting an outcome directly, the presentation s and the response r select a function, denoted as ω or ω_l, from a set Ω of such functions. In turn, this function assigns an outcome to the trial number, that is, if $\omega \in \Omega$, then

$$\omega : I_N \to O.$$

Such a function we call a *conditional outcome* (or reward) *schedule*. Usually ω is determined by some sort of random device; if so and if

$$\pi(o \mid \omega) = \text{Pr } [\omega(n) = o]$$

is independent of n, then we say that it is a *simple random conditional schedule*. Of course,

$$\sum_{o \in O} \pi(o \mid \omega) = 1.$$

The function ϕ that selects the conditional schedule to be used,

$$\phi : S \times R \to \Omega,$$

we call the *outcome function*.

In the mathematical learning literature an outcome function is said to be noncontingent if and only if it is independent of the response, that is,

$$\phi(s, r) = \phi(s, r')$$

for all $s \in S$ and all $r, r' \in R$. Otherwise, it is called contingent.

The sequence of events, then, is that a presentation s on trial n elicits a response r, and, given these, the outcome function ϕ selects a conditional outcome schedule $\omega = \phi(r, s)$, which in turn prescribes the outcome $o = \omega(n)$ to be administered to the subject.

As we have said, in contemporary psychophysics the conditional outcome schedules, if they are used at all, are random (independent of n) with the very special property that $\pi(o \mid \omega) = 0$ or 1. In these cases we can by-pass Ω entirely and think of ϕ as a function from $S \times R$ into O by defining

$$\phi(s, r) = o \quad \text{if and only if} \quad \phi(s, r) = \omega \quad \text{and} \quad \pi(o \mid \omega) = 1.$$

When we do this, we say Ω does not exist and refer to ϕ as a *payoff function*.

In simple learning experiments in which there is only one stimulus presentation, it is usual to suppress explicit reference to the outcome function ϕ and simply to subscript the conditional outcome schedules by the corresponding response symbol under ϕ. When this is done, it is usual to speak of the schedule rather than the outcome function as contingent or noncontingent, even though strictly this does not make sense.

In certain studies having simple random conditional outcome schedules it is necessary to refer to or to describe the random mechanisms that generate the schedules. For example, we may ask a subject to choose which of two schedules is to be used when all he knows is the nature of the devices that generate the schedules. We let $\boldsymbol{\omega}$ denote the device, or a description of it, as the case may be, that generates ω and $\boldsymbol{\Omega}$ the set of devices or descriptions of them, corresponding to the set Ω of schedules. It is, of course, perfectly possible for the same device to generate two different schedules, that is, for $\boldsymbol{\omega} = \boldsymbol{\omega}'$ even though $\omega \neq \omega'$.

It is generally assumed that subjects have preferences among the elements of O. Usually, these are assumed to be representable by an asymmetric (therefore, irreflexive), transitive binary (preference) relation $\succ$. In principle, a separate experiment must be performed to discover $\succ$ (see Irwin, 1958). The form of this experiment is (1) $S \subseteq O \times O$, (2) $R = \{1, 2\}$, (3) Ω does not exist, and (4) if $s = \langle o^1, o^2 \rangle \in S$, then $\phi(s, r) = o^r$. The assumption that $\succ$ is a relation is equivalent to the assumption that $p_n(r \mid s)$ has the value 0 or 1, independent of n. Should this prove false, then a more complicated preference structure over O must be postulated. In practice such experiments are rarely carried out because the results are presumed to be known: a subject is thought to prefer being correct to incorrect, a larger to a smaller sum of money, no shock to a shock, etc. It is clear, however, that if we come to perform experiments with conflicting components to the outcomes—for example, 5¢ and a shock if correct versus $-3¢$ if incorrect—then these preference subexperiments cannot be by-passed.

Following the selection and administration of the outcome to the subject or, when there is no outcome structure, following his response, the system returns the trial number n to the box labeled "Add 1" which then generates the next trial number, $n + 1$, unless $n = N$, in which case the experimental run is terminated.

In the course of developing this description of the class of choice experiments, we have omitted several topics. We turn to these now.

2. CLASSIFICATION OF THE ENVIRONMENT

2.1 Stimuli

The presentation set S is often constructed from a simpler set $\mathscr{S}$, which we may call the *stimulus set*. For example, in a psychophysical discrimination experiment, S may consist of pairs of tones, in which case it is reasonable to say that $\mathscr{S}$ is the set of these tones and that

$$S \subseteq \mathscr{S} \times \mathscr{S} = \{\langle \mathit{s}^1, \mathit{s}^2 \rangle \mid \mathit{s}^1, \mathit{s}^2 \in \mathscr{S}\}.$$

Normally we use s and s_i to denote typical elements of $\mathscr{S}$, but when a Cartesian product is involved we use superscripts to indicate the several components. Thus $\langle \mathit{s}^1, \mathit{s}^2, \ldots, \mathit{s}^k \rangle$ and $\langle \mathit{s}_i{}^1, \mathit{s}_i{}^2, \ldots, \mathit{s}_i{}^k \rangle$ are both typical elements of $\mathscr{S} \times \mathscr{S} \times \ldots \times \mathscr{S}$ (k times), which is abbreviated $\mathscr{S}^k$.

In most psychophysical studies it is not very difficult to decide which physical events should be identified as the elements of S and $\mathscr{S}$, even though in principle they are not always uniquely defined. Often, $\mathscr{S}$ is a fairly homogeneous set in the sense that its elements are identical except on one or at most a very few simple physical dimensions, such as amplitude, intensity, frequency, or mass. The most important condition that the stimuli must satisfy is reproducibility: we must be able to generate an occurrence of a particular stimulus at will within an error tolerance that is small compared with the subject's ability to discriminate. For some purposes, but not all, it is also important to characterize the stimuli in terms of well-known physical measures, so that, among other things, other laboratories can reproduce them.

In the psychophysical experiments considered in Chapters 3, 4, and 5, it is always possible to define $\mathscr{S}$ in a natural way so that $S \subseteq \mathscr{S}^k$, and the order of the Cartesian product corresponds either to the time order of presentation or, if the stimuli comprising a presentation occur simultaneously, to their spatial location. For example, in the psychophysical discrimination experiment we have mentioned previously $S \subseteq \mathscr{S}^2$, so $s = \langle \mathit{s}^1, \mathit{s}^2 \rangle$ is a typical presentation in which s^1 is the first tone presented and s^2 is the second. If an experiment involves visual displays of sets of three objects arranged in some fixed pattern and $\mathscr{S}$ is the set of all objects used, then $S \subseteq \mathscr{S}^3$, where each $\mathscr{S}$ is associated with one of the locations.

In so-called "discrimination learning" experiments one often feels that he can identify the set $\mathscr{S}$ as well as S. Indeed, the now conventional distinction between "successive" and "simultaneous" discrimination is based upon just such identifications (Spence, 1960). Suppose we have two "stimuli," a black card and a white card. If the black card is presented on some trials and the white on the rest, then it is called "successive discrimination." It is natural to say $S = \mathscr{S} = \{$black card, white card$\}$. If both cards are present on each trial but on some the black is to the left of white and on others to the right, then it is called "simultaneous discrimination." If $\mathscr{S}$ continues to be defined as above, then $S \subseteq \mathscr{S}^2$. If, however, $\mathscr{S}$ is defined as a black-white and a white-black card, as might seem natural if the presentations were two cards, one of which was black on the left and white on the right and the other just the reverse, then $S = \mathscr{S}$. Thus, the distinction between successive and simultaneous procedures rests upon the experimenter's identification of $\mathscr{S}$. It is easy to invent pairs of stimulus presentations which are difficult to decompose into separate stimuli. For example, one element of S might consist of a rectangular grid of black lines, and the other, a number of concentric circles. In such a case, it is anyone's guess what the stimuli (elements of $\mathscr{S}$) are, but all would agree that there are two distinct and readily identified stimulus presentations. We conclude, then, that when it is possible and useful to identify the elements of $\mathscr{S}$, the set S can be generated as ordered k-tuples from it. If not, we simply identify the elements of S directly. Our position on this point is essentially atheoretical; our goal here is to characterize and classify experimental procedures, not to discuss substantive questions such as the influence on behavior of the geometric and physical properties of the elements of S.

2.2 Background and Residual Environment

The remainder of the subject's environment we divide into two classes of events, the background and the residual environment. *The background* consists of experimenter-controlled constant stimulation that often is relevant in some direct way to the choice being made. The background is usually measured in physical terms by the experimenter and reported in the description of the experiment, and it may very well be altered as an experimental parameter in different experimental runs. For example, in many signal detection experiments a background of white noise is present throughout the run and, at regular intervals, stimuli, such as short bursts of a tone, are introduced into the background. In the quantal experiments a fixed energy level of a tone is present at all times, except periodically, when the level is raised slightly for a fraction of a second. These energy increments are considered the stimuli, and the always present energy, the background. Like the definition of $\mathscr{S}$, the defining characteristics of the background are subject to debate, and probably there is no way of fully defining it in the abstract, but again in practice there is usually little difficulty in gaining agreement about what constitutes the background.

All remaining stimulation not included in the presentation or background we refer to as the *residual environment*. Little attempt is made to characterize this except in the most general terms: "The subject sat at a desk in a small, sound-attenuating room" or "The subject's eye was kept 30 cm from the target, and the room was totally dark." Attempts are usually made to control the residual environment, but very little of it is measured. As it is sometimes impossible to control relevant extraneous stimulation adequately, a well-controlled background may be used to mask it.

3. INSTRUCTIONS, PRETRAINING, AND THE IDENTIFICATION FUNCTION

3.1 Instructions and Pretraining

We have not yet discussed one feature of every human experiment, namely, the instructions. These have at least the following two roles. First, they inform the subject about the nature of the stimulus presentations and background (usually by example); about the response set R and how responses are to be made; and about the outcome set O, the generation of the conditional outcome schedules $\omega \in \Omega$, and the outcome function ϕ. Second, they attempt to convey to him the judgment it is desired he make or, what is the same thing, what significance his responses will have to the experimenter.

Verbal or written instructions pose, shall we say, technical difficulties in animal experiments, and so various kinds of pretraining procedures are substituted. Prior to an experimental run of "reward training," the animal is generally partially deprived of food, water, or whatever is to be used as a reward, and in pretraining he finds out what sorts of behavior can possibly lead to reward. In escape and avoidance training studies a known "noxious" stimulus is used to motivate responding. These procedures have much the same purpose as telling a human subject that "your task is to do ... in order to be correct." Where the human subject can be told what elements compose the stimulus, response, and outcome sets, the animal must find them out through experience. This learning is sometimes effected during preliminary trials before the choice experiment begins, as, for example, by forced trials in a pretraining phase of a T-maze experiment. This preliminary process, interesting as it is, has not been much studied.

3.2 Identification Functions

Returning to human experiments, three examples of instructions are the following:

Two tones will be presented, one right after the other. One will always be louder than the other, and you are to report whether the second is louder or softer than the first. If you think that the second is louder, push the button marked "louder;" if you think that the second is softer, push the "softer" button.

At regular intervals this light will come on for one second. During that time a tone may or may not be introduced into the noise. If you think the tone is there, push the Yes button; if not, push the No button.

Three different tones will be presented successively. You are to decide whether the first is more similar to the second or the third. If you think it is more similar to the second, push the button labeled "2;" if it is more similar to the third, push the button labeled "3."

Although these instructions are extremely parallel, the third is really quite different from the first two because in those the subject knows that the experimenter has an unambiguous physical criterion to decide whether or not a response is correct. The experimenter knows which tone is more intense or whether a tone is present, but he has no nonarbitrary criterion to decide which of two tones is more similar to a third (when all three are different).

Let us consider for the moment situations in which the experimenter has an unambiguous criterion to decide for each stimulus presentation the response or subset of responses that is "correct." In other words, we assume a relation of "correctness" on $R \times S$. If $\langle r_j, s_i \rangle$ is an element of this subset, we say that response r_j is correct for presentation s_i and, by making that response, the subject has correctly identified the stimulus presentation. For this reason we call the "correct" subset of $R \times S$ an *identification relation*. It is possible to design experiments such that one or more responses are not correct for any presentation or such that for one or more presentations no response is correct. Because these designs are not common, we shall not consider them further, that is, we shall deal only with identification relations in which every response maps into (is correct for) at least one presentation and every presentation is assigned to at least one response.

In terms of the identification relation, we can define an *identification function* ι by letting $\iota(r)$ denote the subset of presentations for which r is a correct response. The range of the function ι, which is a subset of the power set of S (i.e., of the set of subsets of S), is denoted by

$$I(S) = \{\iota(r) \mid r \in R\}.$$

If each stimulus has a unique correct response, then $I(S)$ is simply a partition of S.

Part of the role of the instructions and pretraining in many human experiments is to convey the identification function ι to the subject. To the degree that this has been successful, we feel entitled to interpret a response of r to a stimulus presentation as meaning that the subject believes the presentation to have been an element of $\iota(r)$, whether or not it was in fact.

When the experimenter has no objective criterion of correctness but uses such terms as "similar," "equally spaced categories," "half-way between," and the like, in instructing human subjects, it is tacitly assumed that these words induce in the subject something analogous to an identification function. The purpose of such experiments usually is to discover this induced criterion, which we assume is at least partially revealed by his behavior during the course of the experiment. Of course it is possible, and may sometimes be useful, to impose an arbitrary identification function and to look for effects it may have on behavior.

In animal studies in which one response is always rewarded for a particular stimulus presentation and the others are not, it is natural enough to say that the rewarded response is "correct." This does not mean that the identification and outcome functions are identical, because a variety of different outcomes can be consistent with a single identification function, but they seem to amount to nearly the same thing. When the responses of animals are partially reinforced (with fixed probabilities), it is not so clear that it is useful to think of an identification function as existing at all because it is not evident what the correct responses are. The response having the largest probability of reward is a possible candidate, but this definition leads to difficulties when the maximum reward probability is not the same for all presentations. For example, suppose the probability of reward is 1 for s_1 and 0.7 for s_2. It seems reasonable to view s_1's 100 per cent rewarded response as somehow "more correct" than s_2's 70 per cent rewarded one.

In spite of the fact that identification functions may be of less importance for animal experiments than for human ones (see the next section for further comments on this point), they are nonetheless sometimes useful in classifying animal experiments. For example, in what has conventionally been called "discrimination learning," one normally presents stimuli that are so clearly different from one another that there can be little doubt about the animal's ability to discriminate them perfectly in the usual psychophysical sense. Yet learning occurs. If the animal is not learning to discriminate the stimuli, what is it learning? It seems evident that it is discovering the experimentally prescribed identification function, for, in spite of pretraining, the animal can obtain "information" about that function only through experience in the choice experiment itself. This point leads us to discard the term "discrimination learning" as seriously misleading; instead, we propose "identification learning." True discrimination experiments in the psychophysical sense are rarely performed with animal subjects; nevertheless, the word discrimination should be reserved for them and not be used in other ways.

3.3 Compatibility of Payoffs with the Identification Function

Although the notion of an identification function has not, to our knowledge, been formally discussed in the literature, there seems to have been some tendency to act as if correctness is synonymous with the outcome structure. This is clearly not so. In classical psychophysics an identification function was often defined, but there was no experimental outcome structure. But even when both are defined they need not be compatible with one another; however, it has been generally felt that they should be coordinated in some way.

This is done through the binary preference relation which the subject is assumed to have over the elements of O. With $\succ$ known and Ω nonexistent, we say that a payoff function ϕ and an identification function ι are *compatible* if

1. $s, s' \in \iota(r)$ and $r \in R$ imply $\phi(s, r') = \phi(s', r')$ for all $r' \in R$;
2. $\iota(r) = \iota(r')$, $r, r' \in R$ imply $\phi(s, r) = \phi(s, r')$ for all $s \in S$;
3. $s \in \iota(r)$ and $s \notin \iota(r')$, $r, r' \in R$ imply $\phi(s, r) \succ \phi(s, r')$.

In words, the first condition states that if two presentations have the same correct response then they have the same outcome pattern over all responses. The second, that if two responses designate the same set of stimuli then they have the same outcome pattern for all stimuli. And the last, that the outcome of a correct response to a presentation is preferred to the outcomes resulting from incorrect ones.

When the payoff and identification functions are compatible, it is often possible to describe the payoff function as a square matrix. The columns are identified with sets of equivalent responses, the rows with the subsets $\iota(r)$ of stimulus presentations, and the entries with the outcomes. By condition iii, the most preferred entry of each row is in the main diagonal, assuming the usual coordination of columns with rows.

It is not at all clear, as we noted earlier, what it means for an outcome structure that is not a payoff function (i.e., partial reinforcement) to be compatible with an identification function. Indeed, in animal experiments an identification function cannot exist without there being a compatible payoff function because we have no choice but to use the payoffs to "teach" the animal the identification function. Of course, having done the teaching, we can place the animal in a new experiment with a different outcome function, but we would probably interpret the results by saying that the animal extinguished on the old identification and learned a new one. In general, the distinction between identification and outcome functions is less clear in animal studies than it is in human ones. People can be told what is correct and at the same time be rewarded for being wrong, but this is not easily arranged with animals.

This remark, however, suggests a way to think about identification functions which may reduce the apparent differences between animal and human experiments. If we treat the identification function in human experiments as a very special kind of outcome structure, namely a payoff function in which the outcomes are necessarily the concepts of being correct and incorrect, then we can say that in these human experiments there are two distinct outcome structures. When they are compatible, as is usually the case, they can be treated as one, but the fact that they can be put into conflict if we choose shows that they are distinct. Viewed this way, the analogous animal experiment must also have two independent outcome structures, and these may or may not be compatible. One might use food outcomes for the one and shock for the other. When the first, say, is a payoff function and the second is not, then the first can be treated as inducing an identification function and the second as the outcome structure. Although experiments of this kind are rare in the animal literature, they have been performed to demonstrate the acquisition of "moral" behavior in animals (R. L. Solomon, in preparation). In these experiments punishment is used to induce an identification function that is incompatible with the natural preference ordering for two different foodstuffs that serve as the outcomes of choice. Thus a formal parallel with the human experiment exists, but it cannot be considered more than formal until it is shown to have the same sort of special properties that human identification functions seem to have. Little has yet been done to develop mathematical theories for behavior in the presence of conflicting outcomes, but such research seems potentially interesting and important (see introduction to Chapter 5).

4. DEFINITION AND CLASSIFICATION OF CHOICE EXPERIMENTS

4.1 Definition of Choice Experiments

Much of what we have said so far is summarized for convenient reference in Table 1. We make the following assumptions. The response data function ρ and, in principle, the preference relation $\succ$ are generated by the subject and observed by the experimenter. The presentation schedule σ is generated in some manner by the experimenter, and it is not usually revealed to the subject. Psychologists generally feel that if σ is revealed to the subject then his responses may be biased by that knowledge and, at least at this stage of development, that this is undesirable. There are exceptions, such as psychophysical quantal experiments in which σ is known to the subject, and that aspect of their design has been one major criticism of them. The presentation set S and the set $\mathscr{S}$, if it is defined, are chosen by the experimenter; sometimes they are completely described to human subjects (e.g., in recognition experiments) and at other times they are only partially described (e.g., in discrimination experiments in which the subjects are only informed that pairs of tones will be presented, but not the specific pairs). The outcome function ϕ, the set Ω of conditional outcome schedules, and the set of outcomes O are selected by the experimenter, and they are more or less completely described or revealed in pretraining to the subject. Often the specific conditional outcome schedules are not revealed, but the means of generating them may be.

Any experiment in which these assumptions are met and in which the response set R is well defined and contains two or more elements is called a *choice experiment*. Psychophysical experiments are almost always choice experiments, but open-ended designs are not because at least the experimenter has no real idea what R is.

4.2 Identification Experiments

The class of choice experiments can be divided into those for which an identification function exists and those for which it does not. If that function exists, the choice experiment is called an *identification experiment*.

Table 1 A Summary of the Concepts Involved in a Choice Experiment

Name	Mathematical Status	Symbol	Relation to Other Symbols	Remarks
Trials	Sequence	I_N	$I_N = \langle 1, 2, \ldots, n, \ldots N \rangle$.	Total number of trials, N, may be a random variable.
Stimulus set	Set	$\mathscr{S}$	$\mathscr{a}, \mathscr{a}_i, \mathscr{a}^h \in \mathscr{S}$.	Consists of the "elementary" stimuli defined by the experimenter.
Stimulus presentation set	Set	S	$S \subseteq \mathscr{S}^k$, $s, s_i \in S$; image of σ; part of domain of ϕ.	Consists of the stimuli that are presented on a trial to the subject, which when $\mathscr{S} \neq S$ are ordered k-tuples of elementary stimuli.
Range of ι	Set of sets	$I(S)$	A set of subsets of S in $1:1$ correspondence with R under ι.	
Response set	Set	R	$r, r_j \in R$; in $1:1$ correspondence with $I(S)$ under ι; part of domain of ϕ.	Consists of two or more responses prescribed by the experimenter.
Set of conditional outcome schedules	Set	Ω	Ω is the set of the functions ω; image of ϕ.	The set of random devices generating the ω's in Ω is denoted $\mathbf{\Omega}$.
Outcome set	Set	O	$o, o_k \in O$; range of ω.	Consists of the immediate information feedback and outcomes prescribed by the experimenter.
Preference relation	Relation	$\succ$	$\succ \subseteq O \times O$; $\succ$ is assumed to be asymmetric and transitive.	Although $\succ$ is often presumed known, it is a property of the subject and is therefore discovered experimentally.
Presentation schedule	Function	σ	$\sigma : I_N \to S$ (onto)	It is said to be simple random if $\Pr[\sigma(n) = s]$ is independent of n.

Table 1   (continued)

Name	Mathematical Status	Symbol	Relation to Other Symbols	Remarks
Response data	Function	ρ	$\rho : I_N \to R$ (into)	In many theories $p_n(r \mid s) = \Pr [\rho(n) = r \mid \sigma(n) = s]$ is assumed to exist, and the basic problem is to account for these probabilities.
Outcome function	Function	ϕ	$\phi : S \times R \to \Omega$ (onto)	It is called a payoff function if $\Pr [\omega(n) = o] = 0$ or 1 independent of n. Such functions are usually compatible with $\succ$ and ι.
Conditional outcome schedule	Function	ω	$\omega : I_N \to O$	It is simple random if $\pi(o \mid \omega) = \Pr [\omega(n) = o]$ is independent of n. The random device generating ω is denoted $\boldsymbol{\omega}$.
Identification function	Function	ι	$\iota : R \leftrightarrow I(S)\,(1:1)$	Prescribed by the experimenter if it exists at all.

It seems useful to us to partition such experiments still further in terms of the type of identification that exists; one possible and reasonable partition is described in the following four paragraphs.

O N E : O N E.   Suppose the identification function is a one-to-one correspondence between the sets R and S; that is, each response is correct for one and only one presentation and each presentation has precisely one correct response. In this case it is called a *complete identification experiment* because the subject completely and uniquely identifies each presentation (correctly or incorrectly) when he makes a response. Clearly, the number of elements in R must equal the number of elements in S. One example is a simple detection experiment in which there is a noise background and either nothing or a particular tone is presented on each trial and the subject responds either "yes" or "no." In another detection design a tone is presented in the noise in precisely one of k time intervals, and the subject picks the interval. Still another example is the classical paired-associates learning design, provided that the experimentally defined associate symbols are considered to be the response set R.

ONE:MANY. An experiment in which some response is correct for two or more presentations, but only one response is correct for each, is called *partial identification*. Each element of R may map into several elements of S, but each element of S maps into only one element of R. Put another way, $I(S)$ is a partition of S that is not identical to S. Clearly, S must have more elements than R because $I(S)$ is in one-to-one correspondence with R. An example is a psychophysical discrimination experiment in which numerous pairs of tones are presented on different trials, and the subject responds either "louder" or "softer" to each. The identification is partial because the subject does not uniquely identify each pair of tones; he only assigns the pair (correctly or not) to one of two classes. Similarly, the usual concept formation experiments involve partial identification because the several instances of the concept require the same response.

MANY:ONE. The logical counterpart of the preceding class of designs is that in which two or more responses are correct for at least one presentation but in which each response is correct for only one presentation. We call this *optional identification* because there is at least one presentation for which the subject has an option of which response to make. The identification relation defines a partition of R that is in one-to-one correspondence with S, hence R must contain more elements than S. Although it is not difficult to invent such a design, we know of no classical ones that fit this description. In most standard experiments in psychophysics and learning the various correct responses for a particular stimulus presentation are not distinguished and so they are collapsed into a single response element. For example, the responses "yes," "yep," and "uh huh" are treated as equivalent in a detection experiment. The only purpose that we can see in performing an optional identification experiment would be to study the effects of some variable, for example, the amount of work required, that differentiates the optional correct responses. Although an extensive literature exists on the work involved in responses (Solomon, 1948), none of the studies used choice designs.

MANY:MANY. When at least one response is correct for more than one presentation and at least one presentation has more than one correct response, we call the experiment *ambiguous identification*. As an example, we could have r_1 correct for s_1 and s_2, r_2 correct for s_2 and s_3, etc. There is no restriction on the relative numbers of elements in R and S. Again, we know of no standard experiment that falls into this category. Presumably, it is so complex that it is not of any real research interest at the moment; however, the prevalence of such complexity in everyday language suggests that these experiments may ultimately be important. Many different vehicles (stimulus presentations) are partially identified by the optional terms (responses) "automobiles," "autos," and "cars."

The simplest identification experiment of all is the two-response, two-presentation case in which r_1 is correct when and only when s_1 is presented and r_2 is correct when and only when s_2 is presented. This experiment is a special problem. In our scheme it is classed as the simplest example of a complete identification experiment. It is equally easy, however, to think of it as, and to revamp the definition so that it is classed as, the simplest example of a two-response partial identification design. Our choice, therefore, may be misleading from either an empirical or theoretical viewpoint or both. For example, the limiting case of the standard psychophysical discrimination design involves two stimuli presented in the two possible orders. Whether the data are best described by a model for partial identification discrimination in which there are two or more pairs of stimuli but only two responses or by a model for complete identification in which the stimulus presentation and response sets are in one-to-one correspondence is an open question. Perhaps the answer depends upon the instructions used, whether the subject is asked to say which tone is louder or merely asked to identify each presentation by one of two neutral labels, or perhaps they are equivalent, in which case it does not matter how we class it. It is a question of fact, and the information apparently is not available.

4.3 Asymptotic and Nonasymptotic Behavior

Our second mode of classifying experiments is of a different sort, for it rests upon assumptions about the nature of the behavior. It is thus a behavioral division rather than a methodological one. It is simply the question of whether the behavior is, or is assumed to be, statistically unchanging.

In psychophysics we frequently assume that the response probability $p_n(r \mid s)$ is independent of n, in which case we say that the behavior is *strictly asymptotic*. In an attempt to satisfy this assumption, pretraining is usually carried out to get the subject beyond the learning phase, and, to check it, simple statistical tests are often made. This strong assumption is surely wrong, however, if the behavior is thought to be the end product of a learning process in which the individual response probabilities continue to fluctuate even after stochastic equilibrium has been reached. Current learning models specify a branching process, so one must deal with a distribution of $p_n(r \mid s)$ on a particular trial. If that distribution is independent of n, we say that the behavior is *stochastically asymptotic*. We will sometimes speak simply of *asymptotic* behavior when we do not wish to say whether it is strict or stochastic.

In most models one can estimate the mean of the asymptotic distribution either by averaging over identical subjects on a single trial or by averaging over many trials for a single subject. Most work in psychophysics—both experimental and theoretical—is devoted to asymptotic choice behavior. Possibly more attention should be paid to the preasymptotic behavior of subjects in psychophysical experiments and to the asymptotic fluctuations predicted by learning models. On the other hand, learning experiments of the choice variety usually focus on the transient preasymptotic behavior and seldom provide adequate information about asymptotic behavior, the main exceptions being some over-learning experiments with partial reinforcement. Although most operant conditioning studies do not use choice designs, it is worth noting that the interest is mostly in asymptotic behavior and the changes in asymptotes as various experimental factors are manipulated.

4.4 Summary of Classifications

Using the existence or nonexistence of an outcome structure as a third important mode of classification, Tables 2 and 3 summarize the distinctions we have made. Where standard examples are known, they are listed in the appropriate cell.

Most of the examples mentioned in the tables are familiar learning and psychophysical experiments, and they fall naturally within our scheme. It is less apparent how the experiments that have been performed to study preferences among outcomes are to be characterized. These are the ones that have come to be known as gambling experiments and that are associated with theoretical studies of the notion of utility. They can be partially described by (1) $\mathscr{S} = \Omega$, where it will be recalled Ω is the set of random devices which generate the conditional outcome schedules, (2) $S \subseteq \Omega^k$ (usually $k = 2$), (3) $R = \{1, 2, \ldots, k\}$, (4) ι does not exist, and (5) if $s = \langle \omega^1, \omega^2, \ldots, \omega^k \rangle \in S$, then $\phi(s, r) = \omega^r$. It is easy to see that this is simply a generalization of the previously described experiment used to determine the preference relation $\succ$ over O. Such experiments are of considerable interest, and formally they are intriguing because of the intimate connection between the stimulus presentation set and the outcome structure which does not exist in other experiments.

A notable feature of Tables 2 and 3 is the pattern of omissions. First, there seem to be no standard psychological experiments we could classify as optional or ambiguous identification. It is not clear to us whether this represents a serious gap in experimentation or whether such experiments are considered to be of little interest. It is evident that most complete identification experiments could be viewed as optional ones with responses within a class being treated alike by the experimenter. It is well known that animals often develop idiosyncratic, stereotyped, or "superstitious" behavior in situations in which several response patterns are equally "functional," but this has seldom been studied systematically.

Table 2   Identification Experiments

	Complete Identification (one:one) $N(R) = N(S)$	Partial Identification (one:many) $N(R) < N(S)$	Optional Identification (many:one) $N(R) > N(S)$	Ambiguous Identification (many:many)
Nonasymptotic	Simple animal "discrimination learning" Classical paired-associates learning	Concept formation		
Asymptotic	Simple detection Simple recognition k-alternative forced-choice detection	Psychophysical discrimination Detection of unknown stimulus Method of single stimuli		

Second, within the nonempty cells of Tables 2 and 3 there is a remarkable complementary relation between the asymptotic and nonasymptotic rows. It appears that standard designs in learning are nonexistent in psychophysics and vice versa. This seems unfortunate because independently

Table 3   Nonidentification Choice Experiments

	$N(S) = 1$	$N(S) > 1$ Outcome Structure Exists	$N(S) > 1$ No Outcome Structure Exists
Nonasymptotic	Simple learning		
Asymptotic	Overlearning	Gambling experiments	Similarity experiments Category judgments Attitude scaling Magnitude estimation

developed theories may well be inconsistent. A single theory should predict both learning and asymptotic behavior, and both sets of predictions should be tested experimentally. Few such tests have been carried out.

References

Audley, R. J. A stochastic model for individual choice behavior. *Psychol. Rev.*, 1960, **67**, 1–15.

Bush, R. R. & Mosteller, F. A mathematical model for simple learning. *Psychol. Rev.*, 1951, **58**, 313–323(a).

Bush, R. R. & Mosteller, F. A model for stimulus generalization and discrimination. *Psychol. Rev.*, 1951, **58**, 413–423(b).

Bush, R. R. & Mosteller, F. *Stochastic models for learning.* New York: Wiley, 1955.

Bush, R. R., Mosteller, F. & Thompson, G. L. A formal structure for multiple choice situations. In R. M. Thrall, C. H. Coombs, and R. L. Davis (Eds.), *Decision processes.* New York: Wiley, 1954. Pp. 99–126.

Estes, W. K. Toward a statistical theory of learning. *Psychol. Rev.*, 1950, **57**, 94–107.

Galanter, E. & Miller, G. A. Some comments on stochastic models and psychological theories. In K. J. Arrow, S. Karlin, and P. Suppes (Eds.), *Mathematical methods in the social sciences*, 1959. Stanford: Stanford Univer. Press, 1960. Pp. 277–297.

Irwin, F. W. An analysis of the concepts of *discrimination* and *preference. Amer. J. Psychol.*, 1958, **71**, 152–165.

Luce, R. D. *Individual choice behavior: a theoretical analysis.* New York: Wiley, 1959.

Solomon, R. L. The influence of work on behavior. *Psychol. Bul.*, 1948, **45**, 1–40.

Spence, K. W. *Behavior theory and learning.* Englewood Cliffs, N.J.: Prentice-Hall, 1960.

3

Detection and Recognition[1,2]

R. Duncan Luce
University of Pennsylvania

1. This work was supported in part by grants NSF G-8864 and NSF G-17637 from the National Science Foundation to the University of Pennsylvania.
2. I wish to thank Robert R. Bush, Eugene Galanter, D. M. Green, Francis W. Irwin, M. V. Mathews, B. S. Rosner, Elizabeth F. Shipley, S. S. Stevens, and W. P. Tanner, Jr., for their careful reading and criticism of various drafts of this material. Numerous conversations with Dr. Galanter during the last four years have led to the view of psychophysics that is reflected in this as well as in Chapters 4 and 5.

Contents

Detection and Recognition

Modern psychophysics is concerned with asymptotic choice behavior when subjects respond to four general types of questions about simple physical stimuli:

1. Is a stimulus there? (The absolute threshold and, more generally, detection problems.)
2. Which of several possibilities is it? (The recognition problem.)
3. Is this stimulus different from that? (The discrimination problem.)
4. How different is this one from that? (The scaling problem.)

These, then, are the problems confronting the mathematical psychologist who attempts to create formal theories to summarize the empirical findings of psychophysics and to guide further research. A report of these mathematical studies for the first two questions is given in this chapter; for question 3, in the next; and for question 4, in Chapter 5.

In addition to this intuitive classification of the chapters, there is a more formal one based on the concepts defined in Chapter 2. Except for Sec. 9, the models in this chapter are for complete identification experiments, those in the next are for partial identification designs, and those in the scaling chapter are for choice experiments in which no identification function is defined.

It will be recalled from Chapter 2 that in complete identification experiments the experimenter establishes, and explains to the subject, a one-to-one correspondence ι between the response set R and the stimulus presentation set S. Because of this correspondence, each response designates a unique presentation both to the experimenter and to the subject.

Among the possible complete identification experiments, two substantively different groups of studies have been performed. Those called *detection experiments* have the set of stimuli $\mathscr{S} = \{\mathscr{A}, \emptyset\}$, where $\emptyset$ denotes the null and $\mathscr{A}$ a nonnull stimulus, a presentation set $S \subseteq \mathscr{S}^k$, and there may or may not be a background. In the simplest of these detection experiments the subject decides on each trial whether $\mathscr{A}$ or $\emptyset$ is added to the background; in more complicated ones he decides in which of several time intervals or spatial locations $\mathscr{A}$ has been added to the background.

In terms of the stimulation used, three types of detection experiments may be distinguished:

1. Absolute threshold studies—the classic procedure—in which no

background is introduced by the experimenter and Δ is so near the lower limit of perception that the subject is not perfectly certain when it is present.

2. Quantal studies in which there is a simple background, such as a pure tone, and Δ is simply an increment (or decrement) in one dimension of the background; for example, in energy or frequency.

3. Signal detection studies in which there is a complex background and Δ differs from it on more than one dimension; in an extreme but frequent case, the background is white noise and Δ, a pure tone.

In *recognition experiments*, our other main category, the stimulus set includes at least two stimuli different from the null one and, with few exceptions, $S = \mathscr{S}$. In most recognition studies $\mathscr{S}$ does not include the null stimulus, but, as I shall argue in Sec. 7.1, this is a dubious practice when the stimuli are not perfectly detectable.

The data from complete identification experiments are often first summarized into what are called *confusion matrices*. The rows of such a matrix are identified with the stimulus presentations and the columns with the responses, ordered so that the ordinary correspondence between rows and columns is the same as that defined by the identification function ι. The entries are either the absolute frequencies f_{sr} or the relative frequencies

$$\hat{p}(r \mid s) = \frac{f_{sr}}{\sum_{r' \in R} f_{sr'}}$$

of response r to presentation s.

The relative frequency $\hat{p}(r \mid s)$ is generally interpreted as an estimate of a corresponding conditional response probability $p(r \mid s)$ which in most models is assumed to be a constant independent of the trial. In addition, the responses on different trials are usually assumed to be statistically independent. The first assumption is easily dropped by reinterpreting $\hat{p}(r \mid s)$ as an estimate of the expectation of $p_n(r \mid s)$ at asymptote; however, most of the models actually assume that the probabilities themselves, not just their expectations, are constant. The assumption of response independence is a good deal more troublesome, for there is considerable evidence (e.g., Neisser, 1955; Senders, 1953; Senders & Sowards, 1952; Speeth & Mathews, 1961) indicating that it is incorrect. We persist in making it, in spite of the evidence, because of the difficulty in constructing models that are tractable and have response dependencies. Although no one has formulated and proved any results to this effect, one suspects that there may be judicious ways to add dependencies to response-independent models so that certain of the asymptotic properties are unchanged. Such results are needed to justify many of our current practices of data analysis.

At one time the data from recognition experiments were either presented in uncondensed form as confusion matrices or they were summarized by one or another of the standard contingency-table statistics. Until quite recently, nothing like a coherent theory had evolved, and the empirical generalizations were few. Three may be mentioned. Let the presentations be labeled $s_1, s_2, \ldots, s_k$ and the responses, 1, 2, $\ldots$, k in such a way that $\iota(r) = s_r$. First, the largest entry in row s_r is generally the main diagonal one, $\hat{p}(r \mid s_r)$. Second, although the matrix is not strictly symmetric in the sense that $\hat{p}(r \mid s_{r'}) = \hat{p}(r' \mid s_r)$, there is a definite tendency in that direction. Third, when the presentations are physically ordered—for example, by intensity, size, frequency—so that $s_1 < s_2 < \ldots < s_k$, then the value of $\hat{p}(r \mid s_r)$ dips down rapidly from $\hat{p}(1 \mid s_1)$, reaches a plateau in the midrange, and then rises again rapidly to $\hat{p}(k \mid s_k)$. In other words, plots of $\hat{p}(r \mid s_r)$ versus r are usually U-shaped. Their exact nature depends upon the number and spacing of the presentations as well as upon the experimental conditions. Examples of size, color, and position confusion matrices can be found in Shepard (1958b).

In the early 1950's a number of psychologists began to analyze recognition confusion matrices in terms of Shannon's information measure, and several comparatively simple generalizations resulted. These we discuss in Sec. 7 on recognition experiments. What is still lacking is an adequate, detailed response theory to explain these somewhat gross results.

The study of detection has proceeded largely independently of the work on recognition, with, however, some fusion developing in the last several years. Detection research began early in the history of experimental psychology with determinations of absolute and difference thresholds. Theoretical contributions were scattered until the early 1950's when a program of theoretical and experimental research emerged at the University of Michigan. Somewhat later several related programs developed elsewhere in the United States.

Our study begins with the several analyses of detection experiments which are currently of interest, and in Secs. 7 and 8 some of the same ideas are applied to recognition experiments.

1. REPRESENTATIONS OF THE RESPONSE PROBABILITIES

Attempts to account for the behavioral relations among various types of identification experiments, both complete and partial, have so far resulted in three distinct response theories. In this section each is described in moderately general terms with little reference to specific experiments;

in the remainder of the chapter and in much of the next two they are applied to specific designs. The reader may well wonder why three different theories for the same behavior should be presented, when, after all, at most one can be correct. One reason is that there is no assurance that the same response theory is appropriate for all modalities or for different tasks within one modality, but more important, it has been impossible so far to choose among them on empirical grounds even for a single type of experiment within one modality. Their predictions tend to be similar, and where there are differences the experimental results have been either inconclusive or contradictory. This situation is hopefully transitory; in fact, considerable clarification can be expected in the next few years.

1.1 Signal Detectability Theory

The notions underlying signal detectability theory originally took root in psychology during the period bounded by Fechner and Thurstone. Later they reappeared in a slightly different guise explaining not just discrimination but also detection and recognition. W. P. Tanner, Jr., and his colleagues at the University of Michigan reinterpreted and modified analyses of optimal physical detection of electrical signals in noise (Peterson, Birdsall, & Fox, 1954; van Meter & Middleton, 1954) into a psychophysical theory. Some of the same ideas were also developed by Smith and Wilson (1953). In addition to the theory, a series of interrelated experiments have been performed (Birdsall, 1955, 1959; Clarke, Birdsall, & Tanner, 1959; Creelman, 1959, 1960; Egan, Schulman, & Greenberg, 1959; Green, 1958, 1960; Green, Birdsall, & Tanner, 1957; Speeth & Mathews, 1961; Swets, 1959, 1961b; Swets & Birdsall, 1956; Swets, Shipley, McKey, & Green, 1959; Swets, Tanner, & Birdsall, 1955, 1961; Tanner, 1955, 1956, 1960, 1961; Tanner & Birdsall, 1958; Tanner, Birdsall, & Clarke, 1960; Tanner & Norman, 1954; Tanner & Swets, 1954a,b; Tanner, Swets, & Green, 1956; Veniar, 1958a,b,c). These researches go under the name of *signal detection*, or, as Tanner prefers, *signal detectability theory*. Survey papers by Green (1960), Licklider (1959), and Swets (1961a) give summaries of the central ideas and experimental findings.

The main notion is that the pertinent information available to the subject as a result of the stimulation can be summarized by a number; however, repeated presentations of the same stimulus produce not the same number but a distribution of them. The subject is assumed to behave as if he knew these distributions. He evaluates the particular number arising on a trial in terms of the distributions from which it could have arisen, much as a statistician evaluates an observation to decide between a null and an alternative hypothesis (Wald, 1950). Indeed, the two models are formally the same.

The theory does not say where these distributions come from, although their usually assumed normality easily suggests a pseudoneurology in which many small independent neuronal errors accumulate to form the resultant error; nor does it tell how the subject comes to know the distributions, but a learning process during pretraining seems a likely candidate; nor does it suggest how the subject carries out the various needed transformations and calculations. Unexplained, "internal" numerical representations such as these are characteristic of almost all psychophysical theories and they simply indicate, I suspect, the relatively primitive state of the theory. Nonetheless, we are no more obliged to account for them in, say, physiological terms than were the authors of the first macroscopic physical theories required to explain planetary motions in terms of elementary particle properties.

Tanner and his colleagues arrived at the representation in this way. The effect of a presentation s is supposed to be a random vector $\mathbf{s}$ which assumes values in a k-dimensional Euclidean space E_k; that is, the effect of stimulation is assumed to be adequately described by a k-tuple of numbers. Not only does this seem moderately plausible, but for frequency bounded temporal signals the important sampling, or $2WT$, theorem (Shannon & Weaver, 1949) shows that in the limit as $T \to \infty$ such a representation of their physical properties is indeed possible.

If $\mathbf{x} \in E_k$, the probability density that stimulus s produces the effect $\mathbf{x}$, $p^{(k)}(\mathbf{x} \mid s)$ is assumed to exist. Suppose, for the moment, that one of two presentations, s or s', occurs on each trial and that on a particular trial an observation $\mathbf{x}$ occurs. The subject must use it and his assumed knowledge of the distributions $p^{(k)}(\cdot \mid s)$ and $p^{(k)}(\cdot \mid s')$ to decide which of the two presentations fathered it. In such matters there is an inherent uncertainty. It is plausible that he might decide by considering the relative likelihood of the two presentations generating $\mathbf{x}$. Specifically, let us suppose that he calculates the likelihood ratio

$$l(\mathbf{x}) = \frac{p^{(k)}(\mathbf{x} \mid s)}{p^{(k)}(\mathbf{x} \mid s')}. \tag{1}$$

If this number is large, it is only sensible to say that s was presented; if small, s'. This suggests that the subject should establish a *cut-point* (or *criterion*) c and use the *decision rule*:

$$\text{respond that } \begin{Bmatrix} s \\ s' \end{Bmatrix} \text{ was presented if } \log l(\mathbf{x}) \begin{Bmatrix} > \\ < \end{Bmatrix} c, \tag{2}$$

where the logarithmic transformation has been introduced for convenience later.

Assuming such a rule, we wish to calculate the response probabilities. To do so, we need expressions for the distributions of log l corresponding to the two presentations. Define the set

$$L(z) = \{x \mid \log l(x) = z\},$$

then if

$$p(z \mid s) = \int_{L(z)} p^{(k)}(x \mid s) \, dx$$

$$p(z \mid s') = \int_{L(z)} p^{(k)}(x \mid s') \, dx$$

(3)

exist, they are the desired distributions. These are usually assumed to be normal distributions; one of the main reasons for this assumption is given in Sec. 6.1.

With the decision rule given in Eq. 2, the expressions for the response probabilities are easily seen to be

$$p(r \mid s) = \int_c^\infty p(z \mid s) \, dz$$

$$p(r \mid s') = \int_c^\infty p(z \mid s') \, dz,$$

(4)

where r is the response such that $\iota(r) = s$.

Several comments and cautions. First, why, aside from plausibility, have we assumed that the decision axis is (the logarithm of) the likelihood ratio axis? The main reason, as we shall see in Sec. 5.1, is this. Had we begun with an uninterpreted decision axis, as Thurstone did in his analysis of discrimination problems, and were we to assume that the decision procedure is optimal in the sense of maximizing the expected payoff, then the decision axis must be the likelihood ratio axis or a monotonic function of it. The logarithm is, of course, a monotonic function.

Second, is a cut-point decision rule reasonable? It seems to be if the two distributions are like those of Fig. 1. Moreover, when they are distributions of likelihood ratios, it can be shown that cut-points lead to optimal behavior for various definitions of optimality. Were it possible, however, for the distributions to be multimodal, as, for example, in Fig. 2, then a cut-point rule would clearly be inappropriate. It is not difficult to show that distributions such as those in Fig. 2 cannot occur for a decision axis which is a monotonic function of likelihood ratio, For a given

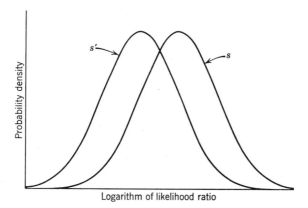

Fig. 1. Typical normal distributions of the logarithm of the likelihood ratio for two different stimulus presentations.

likelihood ratio l, we know by Eq. 1 that for any $\mathbf{x} \in L(\log l)$, then $p^{(k)}(\mathbf{x} \mid s) = lp^{(k)}(\mathbf{x} \mid s')$. Thus, by Eq. 2,

$$p(z \mid s) = \int_{L(z)} p^{(k)}(\mathbf{x} \mid s)\, d\mathbf{x}$$

$$= \int_{L(z)} lp^{(k)}(\mathbf{x} \mid s')\, d\mathbf{x}$$

$$= lp(z \mid s').$$

Thus the two distributions must be closely related to one another; specifically, the ratio of the two values at $z = \log l$ must be just l. Therefore, because the ratio l is a monotonic function of $z = \log l$, distributions such as those shown in Fig. 2 are impossible.

Third, what happens when there are three or more presentations? This is a fairly subtle matter. In many of the experiments to which the

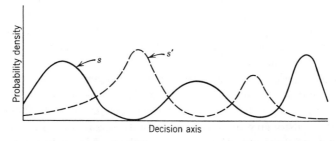

Fig. 2. Multimodal distributions for which a cut-point decision rule is not appropriate but which cannot occur if the decision axis is a monotonic function of likelihood ratio.

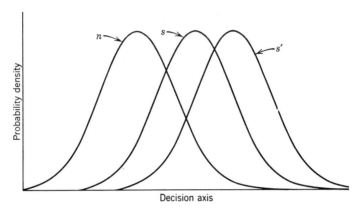

Fig. 3. Three normal distributions on a single decision axis, which cannot occur if the decision axis is a monotonic function of likelihood ratio.

theory has been applied one of the presentations, n, is a noise background that contains no stimulus and the others, s, s', . . . , consist of stimuli embedded in the noise. The several distributions of effects over the Euclidean k-space are assumed to be statistically independent of each other. If we suppose that the stimuli s and s' differ only on one dimension, say energy, it seems plausible to think of the three distributions as existing over a common decision axis, as in Fig. 3. Unfortunately, such a simple representation in terms of a likelihood ratio axis does not follow from the argument just given for two stimuli. The trouble is that when we compare n and s the likelihood ratio noise distribution, $p(z \mid n)$, depends not only upon $p^k(\cdot \mid n)$, which by assumption is independent of the other presentations, but also upon the set $L(z)$. Because $L(z)$ is defined in terms of the likelihood ratio, it depends upon $p^k(\cdot \mid s)$ as well as upon $p^k(\cdot \mid n)$. That is to say, in terms of likelihood ratio each stimulus has its own separate noise distribution. Or we may see it another way. In the two-stimulus case we have just shown that $p(\log l \mid s)/p(\log l \mid s') = l$, so where two distributions intersect, that is, where $p(\log l \mid s) = p(\log l \mid s')$, the likelihood ratio must be 1. But there are three such intersections in Fig. 3, all of which would have to correspond to the same likelihood ratio of 1, which is clearly impossible.

This means that complete identification experiments with more than two presentations cannot usually be reduced to a one-dimensional representation because each pair of presentations has its own likelihood ratio axis. It is customary in signal detectability theory to assume that the logarithms of these several axes can be embedded in an Euclidean space of appropriate dimension. Two serious problems result: when should the separate axes be assumed to be orthogonal and to what class of partitions should the decision rule be restricted? No class of rules seems nearly so compelling for a space as does the cut-point rule for a line.

1.2 Choice Theory

Choice theory has been discussed, in one variant or another, by Bradley (1954a,b, 1955), Bradley and Terry (1952), Clarke (1957), Luce, (1959), Restle (1961),[3] Shepard (1958a,b), and Shipley (1960, 1961) for either complete or partial identification experiments or both. No very systematic statement of the intuitions underlying these models has yet been given. Although I shall attempt some clarification, I am still far from a completely satisfactory axiomatic statement of all that is involved. First, the basic representation will be stated, and then I shall consider briefly some of the justifications that have been given for it.

Two ratio scales (i.e., scales unique up to multiplication by positive constants)

$$\eta: S \times S \to \text{positive real numbers}$$
$$b: R \to \text{positive real numbers}$$

are assumed to exist such that when ι is the identification function the response probabilities are of the form

$$p_\iota(r \mid s) = \frac{\eta[s, \iota(r)]\, b(r)}{\sum\limits_{r' \in R} \eta[s, \iota(r')]\, b(r')}. \tag{5}$$

The scale η is interpreted as a measure of the similarity between the presented stimulus s and the one, $\iota(r)$, for which r is the correct response. The scale b, which is associated only with responses, is interpreted as a measure of response bias.

At present, Eq. 5 is useful only if we make certain additional assumptions. Those we make, which are in large part suggested by Shipley's (1961) work, all arise from preconceived notions about the intuitive meaning of the η scale and from considerations of mathematical simplicity; they are neither obviously necessary nor clearly dictated by data, even though their consequences have received some empirical support.

The first three assumptions can be interpreted as formalizing our interpretation of η as a measure of the similarity between stimuli or, equally well, as postulating that the logarithm of η behaves like a measure of "psychological distance."

---

[3] Although I had an opportunity to read Restle's interesting book in manuscript form, it was not available to me when this chapter was being drafted and so no attempt has been made to incorporate his ideas directly.

Assumption 1.   *For all s, $s' \in S$, $\eta(s, s') = \eta(s', s)$.*
Assumption 2.   *For all $s \in S$, $\eta(s, s) = 1$.*
Assumption 3.   *For all s, s', $s'' \in S$, $\eta(s, s'') \geqslant \eta(s, s')\eta(s', s'')$.*

The heart of Assumption 2 is that the number $\eta(s, s)$ is independent of s; setting it equal to 1 merely fixes the unit of the η scale.

It is easy to see that

$$d(s, s') = -\log \eta(s, s') \tag{6}$$

satisfies the usual distance axioms, namely:

1. $d(s, s') = d(s', s)$.
2. $d(s, s') \geqslant 0$ and $d(s, s) = 0$.
3. $d(s, s'') \leqslant d(s, s') + d(s', s'')$.

These three assumptions are used in all applications of the choice theory later. In addition, a fourth assumption, which is suggested by the interpretation of d as a distance measure, will sometimes be made. It plays exactly the same role in the choice theory as the orthogonal embeddings of the logarithm-of-likelihood-ratio axes into Euclidean spaces which are used in signal detectability theory.

Assumption 4.   *If $S = S_1 \times S_2 \times \ldots \times S_k$ and if η is defined over S and over each of the S_i, then for $s = \langle s^1, s^2, \ldots, s^k \rangle$ and $t = \langle t^1, t^2, \ldots, t^k \rangle \in s$,*

$$d(s, t)^2 = \sum_{i=1}^{k} d(s^i, t^i)^2,$$

where d is defined by Eq. 6.

This states that if the stimuli can be viewed as having k distinct components—the S_i—then the several distance measures are interrelated as one would expect them to be, provided that the S_i were to correspond to the orthogonal dimensions of an Euclidean k-space and the distance, to the natural metric in that space. It is, of course, possible to write a weaker assumption in which the coordinates are not orthogonal, but this adds many more parameters to the model, namely the angles between the coordinates. Because we do not need this weaker version, it will not be described in detail.

The origins of this particular representation lie in two papers, a book, Shipley's thesis, and some unpublished work. Shepard (1957) suggested what amounts to Eq. 5 and Assumptions 1 to 3 to relate either stimuli to stimuli or responses to responses, and later Shepard (1958a) suggested the formula

$$\left[\frac{p_i(r \mid s')}{p_i(r' \mid s')} \frac{p_i(r' \mid s)}{p_i(r \mid s)} \right]^{\frac{1}{2}},$$

where $\iota(r) = s$ and $\iota(r') = s'$, as a "measure of stimulus generalization" between s and s'. By Eq. 5 and Assumptions 1 and 2, this equals

$$\left\{ \frac{\eta[s', \iota(r)]b(r)}{\eta[s', \iota(r')]b(r')} \frac{\eta[s, \iota(r')]b(r')}{\eta[s, \iota(r)]b(r)} \right\}^{\frac{1}{2}} = \left\{ \frac{\eta(s', s)}{\eta(s', s')} \frac{\eta(s, s')}{\eta(s, s)} \right\}^{\frac{1}{2}} = \eta(s, s'),$$

which is what was just termed a measure of stimulus similarity. Probably the same intuitions are involved, although the terminology differs.

Clarke (1957) proposed a model much like Eq. 5. Suppose that (S, R, ι) and (S', R', ι') are two complete identification experiments for which $s \in S' \subset S$, $r \in R' \subset R$, and ι' is the restriction of ι to R'; then he assumed what he called the *constant ratio rule*, namely,

$$p_{\iota'}(r \mid s) = \frac{p_\iota(r \mid s)}{\sum_{r' \in R'} p_\iota(r' \mid s)}.$$

In terms of Eq. 5, this assumption is equivalent to asserting that stimulus similarity $\eta(s, s')$ is independent of the particular S employed, with which I would agree, and that the response bias $b(r)$ is independent of the particular R employed, which I doubt. Both hypotheses must, of course, be subjected to experimental scrutiny, but in my view the model stands or falls on the first being correct; the second is not in the least crucial, given that b is interpreted as a response bias, and so it is not assumed here.

In *Individual Choice Behavior* (1959) I wrote down choice models for several specific detection and recognition experiments, but Eq. 5 was not stated in its full generality. These particular models, sometimes slightly modified to be consistent with Eq. 5, reappear below as applications of Eq. 5.

Recently, Bush, Luce, and Rose (1963) have shown that Eq. 5 arises as the asymptotic mean response probability of a simple experimenter-controlled (i.e., response-independent) linear learning model for complete identification experiments. (For a detailed discussion of stochastic learning models, see Chapter 9 of Vol. II). Specifically, they suppose that when stimulus s' is presented and r' is the correct response, that is, $\iota(r') = s'$, on trial i, then on trial $i + 1$

$$p_{i+1}(r \mid s) = p_i(r \mid s) + \eta(s, s')\theta(r')[\delta_{rr'} - p_i(r \mid s)],$$

where $\delta_{rr'}$ is the Kronecker delta (equal to 1 when $r = r'$ and 0 otherwise). They interpret $\theta(r')$ as a basic learning rate parameter associated with the response that the subject should have made and $\eta(s, s')$ as a similarity parameter representing the generalization from presentation s to presentation s'. It is clearly possible to define the learning rates so that $\eta(s, s) = 1$

for all $s \in S$. We see that whenever s' is presented the conditional probability of response r' occurring to any presentation is linearly increased, whereas the probabilities of all other responses are linearly decreased. The amount of the increase depends both upon the learning rate parameter and upon the generalization between s and s'.

Summing over the equation, it is easy to see that

$$\sum_{r \in R} p_{i+1}(r \mid s) = \sum_{r \in R} p_i(r \mid s) = 1,$$

so the model is consistent.

Let $P(s)$ denote the presentation probability of s, then

$$E[p_{i+1}(r \mid s) \mid p_i(r \mid s)] = p_i(r \mid s) \sum_{s' \in S} P(s') + P[\iota(r)]\eta[s, \iota(r)]\theta(r)$$

$$- p_i(r \mid s) \sum_{r' \in R} P[\iota(r')]\eta[s, \iota(r')]\theta(r').$$

If we calculate expectations over $p_i(r \mid s)$, then take the limit as $i \to \infty$, and finally solve, we obtain

$$\lim_{i \to \infty} E[p_i(r \mid s)] = \frac{\eta[s, \iota(r)]b(r)}{\sum_{r' \in R} \eta[s, \iota(r')]b(r')},$$

where $b(r) = P[\iota(r)]\theta(r)$.

Thus the learning model not only leads to Eq. 5 as the asymptotic expected response probabilities, but it says that each response bias parameter is the product of the corresponding presentation probability and the learning rate parameter. The stimulus parameters are again interpreted as measures of similarity. In addition to accounting for Eq. 5, the learning model is of interest because it generates some sequential complexity in the trial-by-trial response patterns. As yet, however, little work has been done on the details of this stochastic model.

1.3 Threshold (or Neural Quantum) Theory

In the traditional psychological literature a chapter called "detection" is not found; however, what amount to detection experiments and some related theory are included, along with other designs, under the titles of "absolute" and "difference thresholds." The notion of a threshold, which is at least as old as Greek philosophy, is that some energy configurations, or differences, simply are not noted because of limitations imposed by the sensory and neural mechanisms. A characterization of this feature of the receptor system—when it exists—forms a partial description of the dynamics of that system, and a theory of its role in generating responses constitutes a partial description of the response mechanism of the organism.

Absolute and difference threshold experiments differ in this way. When the subject is asked to detect whether or not a stimulus has been presented, we are usually concerned with the value of the absolute threshold. But when he is asked to detect the difference between two temporal or spatial regions of stimulation, we are concerned with the difference threshold. Because the first can be viewed as detecting a difference between two regions of stimulation, one of which is null, no attempt is made in the formal theory to distinguish between the two problems.

The value of the absolute threshold is generally defined to be that level of stimulation that is detected 50 (or some other arbitrarily chosen) per cent of the time when the observing conditions are relatively ideal. The actual techniques used are various; some are rapid and probably yield biased or variable estimates, others are more painstaking. But, however the determinations may be made, two things are important to us. First, although the resulting numbers are called threshold values, there is nothing to prevent the procedures from yielding the numbers even if there are no thresholds. Both the detectability and choice theories, which postulate no thresholds, lead one to expect that "threshold" values can be determined. Second, the behavior of the subject is not really the object of study; rather, attention is paid to the limiting characteristics of his sensory system. When the behavior has been examined, it has usually been for "methodological" reasons—to improve the reliability or speed of the techniques. Examples of such research can be found in Blackwell's (1953) monograph on the determination of visual thresholds. Thus, although the threshold literature is large, it still remains for other psychologists to derive behavioral predictions from a threshold model, to use these to discover whether thresholds really exist, and to determine how such a psychophysical theory interacts with other factors affecting behavior.

In making threshold determinations, valued outcomes, or even information feedback, have rarely been used. Often the subject is instructed to minimize his "false-alarm" rate, and during pretraining he may be informed about his errors on catch trials. Some experimenters wait until the false alarm rate is sufficiently low—as they say, until the subject has established a "good criterion"—before proceeding to the main part of the experiment. Others simply estimate the false-alarm rate from the pretraining trials, and still others include catch trials during the experiment proper from which they estimate the rate. Sometimes these rates are simply reported; at other times they are used to "correct for guessing." I shall discuss the model for this correction presently (Sec. 2.3).

The existing threshold model was developed in two stages. The first, which in essence is a discrete analogue of the Thurstone-Tanner statistical model for stimulus effects, was initially stated along with supporting evidence by Békésy (1930); later Stevens, Morgan, and Volkmann (1941) refined the statement and added appreciably to the evidence. The second stage, which is concerned with the biases introduced by the subject, began with the model for correcting for guessing, was reformulated by Tanner and Swets (1954a), and was then extended by Luce (1963). For a general discussion of many of the issues involved and for some alternatives to the model we will discuss, see Swets (1961b).

The Békésy-Stevens model assumes that the effects of stimulation are discrete, not continuous as in the other two models. There is supposed to be a finite (or countable) sequence of "neural" quanta, which we may identify by the integers 1, 2, 3, ... A neural quantum is not identified with any particular neural configuration, although presumably it has some physiological correlate. At a given moment, stimulation is assumed to "excite" the first j of these quanta, but because of irregular fluctuations this number does not necessarily remain fixed over time, even when the stimulation is constant. The main feature of this quantal structure is that two stimuli, no matter how different they may be physically, cannot be different to the subject if they excite the same number of neural quanta. If this model is correct, the only changes that he can possibly notice are those producing a change in the number of excited quanta.

Let us suppose that just prior to the presentation of s on trial i, j quanta are excited by the residual environment plus the background, if any. When s is presented, suppose j' quanta are excited. The change, then, is $j' - j$, and so we can think of the effect of presenting s on trial i as $\theta(s, i) = j' - j$, that is, the presentations generate a function

$$\theta: S \times I_N \to I,$$

where I denotes the set consisting of zero and the positive and negative integers. Because the background is assumed to have a fluctuating effect, $\theta(0, i)$ is not necessarily 0, as one might first think.

The subject can detect a presentation only if $\theta(s, i)$ is not zero, but there are situations in which it is reasonable for a subject to require a change of more than one quantum before responding that a stimulus was presented. With that in mind, we have the following class of "internal" *detection rules:*

A presentation s on trial i is detected as $\begin{Bmatrix} \text{the same as} \\ \text{different from} \end{Bmatrix}$ *the background*

if $\begin{Bmatrix} -k \leqslant \theta(s, i) \leqslant k' \\ \theta(s, i) < -k \text{ or } > k' \end{Bmatrix}$, *where k and k' are nonnegative integers.* (7)

Although the evidence makes one suspicious, it is generally assumed that Pr $[\theta(s, i) < -k$ or $> k']$ is independent of i but not of k and k'. We denote this probability by $q(s, k, k')$, or simply by $q(s)$ when k and k' are assumed fixed, and we speak of it as the *true detection probability*. This is not necessarily the same as the corresponding response probability which one estimates from experimental data—there may be response biases.

The second component of the model is the effect of the outcome structure. The obvious parallel to signal detectability theory is to suppose that biases are introduced by the selection of the cut-points k and k'. This model should be explored, but it has not been. Rather, it has been assumed that k and k' are fixed in a given situation and that the subject biases his responses in the light of the payoff structure simply by falsely converting some detection observations into negative responses or some no-detection observations into positive ones.

As in the other two models, there are two types of parameters. The true detection probabilities $q(s)$ are considered to be stimulus-determined, and the proportions of falsified responses are bias parameters which depend upon, among other things, the outcomes. The main body of the Békésy-Stevens work is concerned with the dependence of the stimulus parameters upon the stimulus (see Secs. 6.2 and 6.3), whereas other authors have focused more upon the response model and the dependence of the biasing parameters upon the outcome structure (see Secs. 5.2 and 6.3).

We turn now to two of the simplest detection experiments and show in turn how each of these three theories tries to account for the behavior.

2. SIMPLE DETECTION

Of the possible detection experiments, the simplest is the *Yes-No* design. At regular time intervals, which define the trials and which are marked off by, say, lights, a stimulus may or may not be added to a continuous background. Following each such interval, the subject responds, usually by pressing one of two buttons, to the effect that "Yes, a stimulus was present" or "No, none was there." Each presentation, stimulus plus background and background alone, is repeated some hundreds of times according to a random schedule, and the conditional choice probabilities are estimated by the relative frequencies of choices.

This is easily seen to be a complete identification experiment in which $\mathcal{S} = \{\measuredangle, \emptyset\}$, where $\emptyset$ is the null stimulus, $S = \mathcal{S}$, and $R = \{Y, N\}$, where Y means Yes and N, No. The identification function is, of course, $\iota(Y) = \measuredangle$ and $\iota(N) = \emptyset$. It is convenient to think of the background as noise and to change notation to the extent that s denotes "$\measuredangle$ plus noise" and n denotes "$\emptyset$ plus noise," that is, noise alone. So we treat $\{s, n\}$ as the presentation set. In summary, the confusion matrix is

Presentation Probability	Stimulus Presentation	Response
		Y $\qquad$ N
P	s	$\begin{bmatrix} p(Y \mid s) & p(N \mid s) \\ p(Y \mid n) & p(N \mid n) \end{bmatrix}$,
$1 - P$	n	

where $p(Y \mid x) + p(N \mid x) = 1$, $x = s$ or n.

Next in complexity is the *two-alternative forced-choice design* in which two time intervals (or space locations) are marked off, and the subject is told that the stimulus is in one of the two intervals, but not both. The subject responds by indicating whether he believes the stimulus was in the first or the second interval. Otherwise, the experimental conditions are the same as in the Yes-No design. So, $\mathscr{S} = \{\varlambda, \emptyset\}$, $S = \{\langle \varlambda, \emptyset \rangle, \langle \emptyset, \varlambda \rangle\}$, $R = \{1, 2\}$, and $\iota(1) = \langle \varlambda, \emptyset \rangle$ and $\iota(2) = \langle \emptyset, \varlambda \rangle$. Again, we write the presentations as $\langle s, n \rangle$ and $\langle n, s \rangle$ to emphasize the addition of the noise background. The confusion matrix is

Presentation Probability	Stimulus Presentation	Response
		$1 \qquad\qquad 2$
P	$\langle s, n \rangle$	$\begin{bmatrix} p(1 \mid \langle s, n \rangle) & p(2 \mid \langle s, n \rangle) \\ p(1 \mid \langle n, s \rangle) & p(2 \mid \langle n, s \rangle) \end{bmatrix}$,
$1 - P$	$\langle n, s \rangle$	

where $p(1 \mid x) + p(2 \mid x) = 1$, $x = \langle s, n \rangle$ or $\langle n, s \rangle$.

2.1 Signal Detectability Analysis

Because we have already discussed the signal detectability model for a general two-element presentation set, the model for the Yes-No experiment follows from Eq. 4 simply by making the appropriate notational changes:

$$p(Y \mid s) = \int_c^\infty p(z \mid s) \, dz$$

$$p(Y \mid n) = \int_c^\infty p(z \mid n) \, dz. \qquad (8)$$

Nothing has really been specified, however, until the forms of the density functions $p(z \mid s)$ and $p(z \mid n)$ are known. Throughout signal detectability theory they are assumed to be normal in z, the logarithm of the likelihood ratio. There is no loss of generality if we set the mean of the noise distribution at zero, for the location of the zero of the decision axis is arbitrary. Of course, the specific magnitude and sign of c depends upon that choice. Let the mean of the stimulus distribution be d. For the while, let us assume that the variances of the two distributions are equal, the common value being σ^2, even though later certain data force us to abandon this in favor of an assumption that $\sigma_s > \sigma_n$. Under these assumptions, Eq. 8 becomes

$$p(Y \mid s) = \frac{1}{\sqrt{2\pi}\sigma} \int_c^\infty \exp\left[-\frac{(z-d)^2}{2\sigma^2} \right] dz$$
$$p(Y \mid n) = \frac{1}{\sqrt{2\pi}\sigma} \int_c^\infty \exp\left[-\frac{z^2}{2\sigma^2} \right] dz. \tag{9}$$

In effect, the stimulus simply displaces the noise distribution to the right by the amount d. Because the unit of the decision axis is arbitrary, we can choose it to be σ, in which case the displacement is $d' = d/\sigma$. This normalized distance is a basic parameter of the signal detectability model. It is interpreted as a measure of the subject's sensitivity to the stimulus and it is thought to be independent of other experimental conditions such as the payoffs. The cut-point c is thought to be a bias that depends upon factors such as the presentation probability and the payoffs.

There is no question at this point that the model accounts for the observed response probabilities because there are two parameters, d' and c, and only two independent probabilities. (Of course, it may not account for sequential properties of the data). So we turn to the two-alternative forced-choice design to see whether the same stimulus parameter can be used to predict the data that are obtained there.

We make exactly the same assumptions as in the Yes-No experiment about the effect of a presentation of either s or n: the distributions are both normal, they have the same standard deviation, and the difference of the means is d. In the forced-choice design the subject makes two observations, X_1 and X_2 in the logarithm of likelihood ratio, corresponding to the two intervals. It is plausible that he uses the following decision rule:

$$\textit{For some value } c', \textit{ respond } \begin{Bmatrix} 1 \\ 2 \end{Bmatrix} \textit{if } X_1 - X_2 \begin{Bmatrix} \geq \\ < \end{Bmatrix} c'. \tag{10}$$

For stimulus presentation $\langle s, n \rangle$, $X_1 - X_2 = S - N$, and for $\langle n, s \rangle$, $X_1 - X_2 = N - S$.

The question is: how are these two differences distributed? When the background and stimulus plus background differ simply in one dimension, such as energy or frequency in the quantal experiments (see Secs. 6.2 and

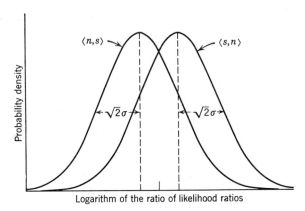

Logarithm of the ratio of likelihood ratios

Fig. 4. Normal distributions of $\mathbf{X}_1 - \mathbf{X}_2$ for the two-alternative forced-choice design assuming $\mathbf{S}$ and $\mathbf{N}$ are normally distributed with standard deviation σ and separated by an amount d.

6.3), or when each interval includes a stimulus and they differ only in one dimension, as in the traditional discrimination experiments (see Sec. 3.1 of Chapter 4), then it is usually assumed that the effects of successive presentations are correlated. No very firm argument has been given why this should be, but the feeling seems to be something to the effect that the random errors introduced by the subject are due to comparatively slow changes in his reactions to the dimension being varied. When, however, the background is random noise and the stimulus is a tone, it is believed that it is more plausible to suppose that successive presentations have effects that are independent of one another. Under that assumption, it is easy to determine the two distributions we need by invoking the well-known fact that the distribution of the difference of two independent, normally distributed random variables is normal with mean equal to the difference of the means and variance equal to the sum of the variances. Thus the distribution of effects from $\langle s, n \rangle$ is normal with mean d and standard deviation $\sqrt{2}\sigma$, and that from $\langle n, s \rangle$, normal with mean $-d$ and standard deviation also $\sqrt{2}\sigma$. The situation is shown graphically in Fig. 4. From this and the assumed decision rule, Eq. 10, we obtain

$$p(1 \mid \langle s, n \rangle) = \frac{1}{2\sqrt{\pi}\sigma} \int_{c'}^{\infty} \exp\left[-\frac{(z - d)^2}{4\sigma^2} \right] dz$$

$$p(1 \mid \langle n, s \rangle) = \frac{1}{2\sqrt{\pi}\sigma} \int_{c'}^{\infty} \exp\left[-\frac{(z + d)^2}{4\sigma^2} \right] dz. \tag{11}$$

Observe that $c' = 0$ corresponds to no bias in the sense that $p(1 \mid \langle s, n \rangle) = p(2 \mid \langle n, s \rangle)$. The data from two-alternative experiments suggest that there is little or no bias when the presentation probability is $\frac{1}{2}$ and the payoff matrix is symmetric, so we will assume that $c' = 0$ for such studies. The common response probability, the probability of a correct response, is denoted $p_2(C)$ —2 for the number of alternatives and C for "correct." Given an estimate of $p_2(C)$ from data, we can calculate the corresponding normal deviate $2d/\sqrt{2}\sigma = \sqrt{2}d'$, where d' is the sensitivity parameter used in the analysis of the corresponding Yes-No experiments. Thus d' can be independently estimated from both Yes-No and two-alternative forced-choice experiments. Later, in Sec. 2.4, we compare Yes-No and forced-choice estimates for two sets of data.

2.2 Choice Analysis

If we assume that the choice model, Eq. 5 and Assumptions 1 to 3, hold, and if we denote $\eta(s, n)$ by η, $b(N)/b(Y)$ by b, and recall that $\eta(s, s) = 1$, then the scale values for the Yes-No experiment are

$$
\begin{array}{cc}
 & \text{Response} \\
 & \begin{array}{cc} Y & N \end{array}
\end{array}
$$

$$
\begin{array}{cc}
\text{Stimulus} & s \\
\text{Presentation} & n
\end{array}
\begin{bmatrix}
1 & \eta b \\
\eta & b
\end{bmatrix}.
$$

The corresponding confusion matrix is

$$
\begin{array}{cc}
Y & N
\end{array}
$$

$$
\begin{array}{c}
s \\
\\
n
\end{array}
\begin{bmatrix}
\dfrac{1}{1 + \eta b} & \dfrac{\eta b}{1 + \eta b} \\[2ex]
\dfrac{\eta}{\eta + b} & \dfrac{b}{\eta + b}
\end{bmatrix}. \tag{12}
$$

In what follows, we usually write down only the tables of scale values and not the corresponding probability tables, which are obtained by dividing each scale value by the sum of the scale values in its row.

As with signal detectability theory, this model describes the response frequencies perfectly: there are two parameters to account for two independent probabilities. The equations for the parameters are

$$
\eta = \left[\frac{p(N \mid s)}{p(Y \mid s)} \frac{p(Y \mid n)}{p(N \mid n)} \right]^{\frac{1}{2}}
$$

$$
b = \left[\frac{p(N \mid s)}{p(Y \mid s)} \frac{p(N \mid n)}{p(Y \mid n)} \right]^{\frac{1}{2}}. \tag{13}
$$

Our interest in η and b is not as simple transformations of the Yes-No data but in the possibility that they can be used to predict other data. This possibility stems from our interpretation of the two scales: under otherwise fixed experimental conditions and for a given subject, η is supposed to depend only upon the stimuli and b, upon the payoffs, presentation probabilities, and instructions. It is believed that η is a measure of the subject's detection sensitivity, just as d' is in the first model, and that b is a bias which, like c, reflects the relative attractiveness to him of the two responses.

The matrix of scale values for the two-alternative, forced-choice design is

$$
\begin{array}{cc}
& \begin{array}{cc} 1 & \qquad\qquad 2 \end{array} \\
\begin{array}{c} \langle s, n \rangle \\ \langle n, s \rangle \end{array} &
\begin{bmatrix} \eta(\langle s, n \rangle, \langle s, n \rangle)b(1) & \eta(\langle s, n \rangle, \langle n, s \rangle)b(2) \\ \eta(\langle n, s \rangle, \langle s, n \rangle)b(1) & \eta(\langle n, s \rangle, \langle n, s \rangle)b(2) \end{bmatrix}.
\end{array}
$$

By Assumption 2, we know that

$$\eta(\langle s, n \rangle, \langle s, n \rangle) = \eta(\langle n, s \rangle, \langle n, s \rangle) = 1,$$

and because $S \subset \mathcal{S} \times \mathcal{S}$, it is reasonable to invoke Assumption 4 under the same conditions as we did the independence assumption in the signal detectability model (e.g., a noise background) yielding

$$
\begin{aligned}
[-\log \eta(\langle n, s \rangle, \langle s, n \rangle)]^2 &= [-\log \eta(n, s)]^2 + [-\log \eta(s, n)]^2 \\
&= 2[-\log \eta(s, n)]^2 \\
&= [-\sqrt{2} \log \eta]^2 \\
&= [-\log \eta^{\sqrt{2}}]^2.
\end{aligned}
$$

Thus, by Assumption 1,

$$\eta(\langle n, s \rangle, \langle s, n \rangle) = \eta(\langle s, n \rangle, \langle n, s \rangle) = \eta^{\sqrt{2}},$$

and so, letting $b' = b(2)/b(1)$, the matrix of scale values reduces to

$$
\begin{array}{cc}
& \begin{array}{cc} 1 & \quad 2 \end{array} \\
\begin{array}{c} \langle s, n \rangle \\ \langle n, s \rangle \end{array} &
\begin{bmatrix} 1 & \eta^{\sqrt{2}}b' \\ \eta^{\sqrt{2}} & b' \end{bmatrix},
\end{array}
\qquad (14)
$$

where η is the Yes-No detection parameter. Note that $b' = 1$ corresponds to no response bias.

Again, there is no question about the model reproducing the data. What is not automatic is that the estimate of η from the Yes-No data will be the same as that from the forced-choice data, as is alleged by the theory.

Before turning to the threshold analysis of these two detection experiments, a possible objection to our analysis must be examined. It may be quite misleading to treat the Yes-No experiment as one in which an absolute identification of s or n is made, for in many studies the subject hears the noise background both before and after the marked interval in which the stimulus may occur. That being so, it seems more realistic to say that the two stimulus presentations are $\langle n_b, n, n_a \rangle$ and $\langle n_b, s, n_a \rangle$, where n_b denotes the noise before and n_a, the noise after the interval. If these three intervals are uncorrelated, we may invoke Assumption 4 as follows:

$$[-\log \eta(\langle n_b, s, n_a \rangle, \langle n_b, n, n_a \rangle)]^2$$
$$= d(\langle n_b, s, n_a \rangle, \langle n_b, n, n_a \rangle)^2$$
$$= d(n_b, n_b)^2 + d(s, n)^2 + d(n_a, n_a)^2$$
$$= [-\log \eta(n_b, n_b)]^2 + [-\log \eta(s, n)]^2 + [-\log \eta(n_a, n_a)]^2.$$

But $\eta(n_b, n_b) = \eta(n_a, n_a) = 1$, hence $\log \eta(n_b, n_b) = \log \eta(n_a, n_a) = 0$, and so

$$\eta(\langle n_b, s, n_a \rangle, \langle n_b, n, n_a \rangle) = \eta(s, n) = \eta.$$

Thus the more precise analysis leads to the same result as the simpler one, provided that the effects in successive intervals are uncorrelated.

2.3 Threshold Analysis

Let us suppose that when the stimulating conditions are held constant the two cut-offs k and k' of the threshold model are fixed quantities independent of the presentation probabilities, the payoffs, and the experimental design. So the true detection probabilities can be written simply as $q(s)$ and $q(n)$. For the Yes-No design, we may summarize the "internal" detection observations as

Observation

		D	$\overline{D}$
Stimulus	s	$q(s)$	$1 - q(s)$
Presentation	n	$q(n)$	$1 - q(n)$

These, however, are not the response probabilities.

Suppose that the subject wishes to reduce his false-alarm rate—Yes responses to noise—below the true rate $q(n)$; then we assume that in addition to saying No to all $\overline{D}$ observations he also falsely responds No to some proportion $1 - t$ of his D observations. This means, therefore, that he responds Yes to only a proportion t of his D observations, that is, if $p(Y \mid n) \leqslant q(n)$,

$$p(Y \mid s) = tq(s)$$
$$p(Y \mid n) = tq(n), \tag{15}$$

where $0 \leqslant t \leqslant 1$. Similarily, when he wishes to increase his rate of correct Yes responses above his true rate $q(s)$, albeit at the same time increasing his false-alarm rate above $q(n)$, he is assumed to say Yes to all D observations and to some proportion u of his $\bar{D}$ observations, that is, if $p(Y \mid n) \geqslant q(n)$

$$p(Y \mid s) = q(s) + u[1 - q(s)]$$
$$p(Y \mid n) = q(n) + u[1 - q(n)], \tag{16}$$

where $0 \leqslant u \leqslant 1$.

It is clear that even if we knew which of these processes, Eq. 15 or 16, a subject had used, we would still have no way of testing the model because there are three parameters, $q(s)$, $q(n)$, and t or u, to account for two independent probabilities. Moreover, going to the two-alternative forced-choice design as we did for the other two models does not provide us with a test; however, in the next section testable conclusions are derived.

Before describing one possible threshold analysis of the two-alternative forced-choice experiment, we examine the familiar technique to correct for guessing (see Blackwell, 1953; Swets, 1961b; and Tanner & Swets, 1954a). The so-called high-threshold model underlying this technique assumes that the true probability of a false alarm, $q(n)$, is zero but that the observed rate is positive because the subject inflates the number of Yes responses to s beyond its true value $q(s)$. Thus Eq. 16 represents the situation, and, with $q(n) = 0$, it follows that $u = p(Y \mid n)$. Substituting this into the expression for $p(Y \mid s)$ and solving yields

$$q(s) = \frac{p(Y \mid s) - p(Y \mid n)}{1 - p(Y \mid n)}. \tag{17}$$

This formula is frequently recommended to "correct" threshold data for guessing. Because this correction involves the rather strong assumption that $q(n) = 0$, which, as we shall see in the next section, is surely incorrect, I very much doubt that this "correction" should be made.

On each trial of a two-alternative forced-choice experiment, the subject is confronted with two Yes-No determinations—one for each time interval. This means that there are four possible observation states, $\langle D, \bar{D} \rangle$, $\langle \bar{D}, D \rangle$, $\langle D, D \rangle$, or $\langle \bar{D}, \bar{D} \rangle$, where D denotes a detection observation in the Yes-No situation and $\bar{D}$, a nondetection observation. The first, $\langle D, \bar{D} \rangle$, surely suggests making response 1; the second, response 2; but the last

two give him no hint how to respond. Presumably, these are the observations he should bias, at least when there is nothing to drive him to extreme
biases. We assume this.

To write the equations for the response probabilities, we need to know
the probabilities of each of these observation outcomes for each of the
presentations. As with the other two models, we assume that successive
stimulus effects are independent, so that, for example, the probability of a
$\langle D, \bar{D} \rangle$ observation when $\langle s, n \rangle$ is presented is simply $q(s)[1 - q(n)]$. The
other cases are similar:

$$p(1 \mid \langle s, n \rangle) = q(s)[1 - q(n)] + vq(s)\,q(n) + w[1 - q(s)][1 - q(n)]$$
$$p(1 \mid \langle n, s \rangle) = q(n)[1 - q(s)] + vq(n)\,q(s) + w[1 - q(n)][1 - q(s)], \tag{18}$$

where v and w are biasing parameters such that $0 \leqslant v, w \leqslant 1$. Again, the
model has too many parameters to permit any check on it with just
forced-choice data. In Sec. 3 we discuss experiments in which it, as well
as the other models, can be tested.

2.4 Comparison of Models with Data

Swets (1959) reported data for three subjects run in both Yes-No and
two-alternative forced-choice designs. The stimuli were 1000-cps tones
of 100-ms duration at several different energy levels in a background of
white noise. Five hundred observations were obtained from each subject
in each energy-design condition. The presentation probabilities were
approximately $\frac{1}{2}$ and a symmetric payoff matrix was used. The data,
which Professor Swets has kindly provided me, and the estimates of d'
for two different designs are shown in Table 1.

Shipley (1961) also ran three subjects in both designs, using a background of white noise and 500- and 1000-cps stimuli at one energy level
each. A total of 1600 observations were obtained in each condition for
each subject using presentation probabilities of $\frac{1}{2}$ and a symmetric payoff
matrix. The data and d' estimates are shown in Table 2. With the
exception of subject 3 on the 1000-cps stimulus, all pairs of estimates are
within 10 per cent of each other.

Shipley's estimates seem considerably more consistent than Swets's,
but in large part this is due to the increased number of observations. To
see this, suppose $d' = 1.2$ and $p(Y \mid n) = 0.2$, then $p(Y \mid s) = 0.640$. An
increase of 10 per cent in d' and $p(Y \mid n) = 0.2$ yields $p(Y \mid s) = 0.683$.
With 250 s presentations, a difference of $0.683 - 0.640 = 0.043$ corresponds to about 1.4 standard deviations, whereas with 800 presentations
it corresponds to about 2.5 standard deviations.

These same data are reanalyzed in terms of the choice model in Tables 3 and 4, and much the same pattern is exhibited as for the detectability model. For example, the largest difference in Table 4 is in the same place

Table 1   Yes-No and Two-Alternative Forced-Choice Acoustic Data (Swets, 1959) and the Corresponding Estimates of d'

Subject	S/N in db	$p(Y \mid s)$	$p(Y \mid n)$	$p(1 \mid \langle s, n \rangle)$	$p(1 \mid \langle n, s \rangle)$	Yes-No d'	Two-Alternative Forced-Choice d'
1	9.4	0.793	0.226	0.824	0.187	1.57	1.29
	14.5	0.872	0.180	0.931	0.060	2.05	2.15
	16.6	0.902	0.120	0.963	0.071	2.45	2.29
2	9.4	0.753	0.288	0.670	0.149	1.24	1.03
	11.7	0.771	0.254	0.777	0.194	1.40	1.14
	14.5	0.833	0.295	0.854	0.145	1.51	1.50
	16.6	0.867	0.232	0.855	0.078	1.83	1.83
3	9.4	0.731	0.195	0.835	0.149	1.48	1.43
	11.7	0.836	0.254	0.870	0.142	1.65	1.56
	14.5	0.816	0.169	0.959	0.125	1.85	1.96
	16.6	0.895	0.149	0.953	0.037	2.29	2.45

The stimuli were 1000-cps tones of 100-ms duration in noise of 50 db re 0.0002 d/cm²; 500 observations were made on each subject at each energy level for each condition. Presentation probabilities of about ½ and symmetric payoff matrices were used.

Table 2   Yes-No and Two-Alternative Forced-Choice Acoustic Data (Shipley, 1961) and the Corresponding d'

Stimulus 1

Subject	$p(Y \mid s)$	$p(Y \mid n)$	$p(1 \mid \langle s, n \rangle)$	$p(2 \mid \langle n, s \rangle)$	Yes-No d'	Forced-Choice d'
1	0.768	0.148	0.895	0.880	1.78	1.72
2	0.712	0.258	0.798	0.796	1.20	1.18
3	0.746	0.216	0.836	0.866	1.44	1.48

Stimulus 2

1	0.695	0.201	0.835	0.838	1.35	1.38
2	0.675	0.199	0.795	0.812	1.30	1.20
3	0.693	0.287	0.791	0.832	1.07	1.25

Each stimulus lasted for 100 ms in a 500-ms interval and was imbedded in wide band noise at 0.0435 volt across the terminals of the ear phones. Stimulus 1 was 500 cps at 0.0023 volt and Stimulus 2 was 1000 cps at 0.0026 volt. Each presentation of each condition occurred approximately 800 times. Presentation probabilities of ½ and symmetric payoff matrices were used.

and is of comparable magnitude. In both analyses the Yes-No parameters do not seem to be consistently larger or smaller than the forced-choice ones.

Thus, although the two theories differ in their approach, it is evident that they do not differ appreciably in their predictions from one simple detection design to another. To see this more vividly, we make the following calculation. For each of several different values of d', determine from Eq. 9 the values of $p(Y \mid s)$ and $p(Y \mid n)$ corresponding to different

Table 3   Estimates of η for Swets's (1959) Data

Subject	S/N in db	η Yes-No	η Forced-Choice
1	9.4	0.276	0.344
	14.5	0.180	0.151
	16.6	0.122	0.100
2	9.4	0.365	0.419
	11.7	0.319	0.394
	14.5	0.290	0.285
	16.6	0.216	0.201
3	9.4	0.299	0.304
	11.7	0.258	0.270
	14.5	0.214	0.164
	16.6	0.144	0.109

See Table 1 for a description of the experimental conditions.

Table 4   Estimates of η for Shipley's (1961) Data

Subject	Stimulus 1 Yes-No	Stimulus 1 Forced-Choice	Stimulus 2 Yes-No	Stimulus 2 Forced-Choice
1	0.238	0.242	0.332	0.317
2	0.375	0.369	0.347	0.370
3	0.305	0.290	0.421	0.356

See Table 2 for a description of the experimental conditions.

choices of c. Elliot's (1959) tables of d' are handy for this. For these pairs of probabilities, determine η from Eq. 13. A plot of the logarithm of η versus d' is shown in Fig. 5. It is evident that the relation is approximately linear and that the correlation is high. The points that differ the most from the main trend are those for which at least one of the probabilities is near 0 or 1.

As noted earlier, the threshold model has too many parameters to be tested with these data.

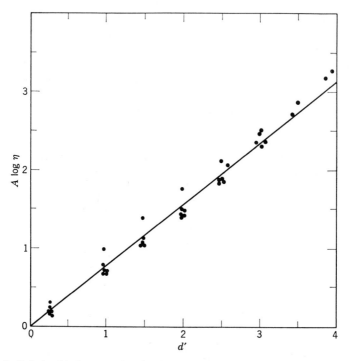

Fig. 5. Relationship between the stimulus parameters d' and η of the signal detectability and choice models for the Yes-No design.

3. ISOSENSITIVITY CURVES

It has been suggested that the parameters d', η, $q(s)$, and $q(n)$ of the three theories represent the subject's sensitivity to stimuli and that c, b, t, and u are biases more or less under his control. Among the experimental conditions that are thought to affect the biases, but not the stimulus parameters, are the presentation probabilities, the payoffs, and the names given to the response alternatives. It is, of course, necessary to show empirically that there is some justice to these interpretations and, if there is, to examine how the parameters are related to objective features of the experiment. The justification we consider here; the dependence of model parameters upon experimental parameters is treated in Secs. 5 and 6.

Suppose that we have a physiologically stable subject (no drugs, minimal fatigue, etc.), and suppose that d', η, or $q(s)$ and $q(n)$, as the case may be, depend only upon the stimulus and noise, then up to errors due to binomial variability our estimates of them should be the same no matter what instructions, presentation probabilities, and payoffs are used. This should be true in spite of the fact that varying these factors produces changes in the response probabilities. For example, if in a Yes-No design one of the two types of errors is very costly, we anticipate that subjects will bias their responses away from the one that makes this expensive error possible. In terms of the models, the payoffs affect either their choice of c, of b, or of t or u. Nevertheless, if one of these models is correct, then as the bias parameters change the response probabilities are constrained by one of the Eqs. 9, 12, 15, or 16. That is to say, each model establishes an exchange relation between the two probabilities so that if one probability is altered the other is also and in a predetermined way. To find the equation for this relation, one merely eliminates the biasing parameter from the pair of equations determining $p(Y \mid s)$ and $p(Y \mid n)$. The resulting function depends upon the stimulus parameters but not upon the biases. Plots of these relations I shall call *isosensitivity* curves.[4] In the literature they are commonly called R.O.C. curves, which stands for *receiver operating characteristic curves*, a term used in the original engineering publications. Because this seems an unfortunate psychological phrase, I suggest that it be changed.

The isosensitivity curves for the choice model can easily be written down. From Eq. 12, we know

$$p(Y \mid s) = \frac{1}{1 + \eta b}$$

$$p(Y \mid n) = \frac{\eta}{\eta + b},$$

and, eliminating b, we obtain

$$\left[\frac{1 - p(Y \mid s)}{p(Y \mid s)} \right] \left[\frac{p(Y \mid n)}{1 - p(Y \mid n)} \right] = \eta^2. \tag{19}$$

One cannot write an explicit function for the isosensitivity curves of the signal detectability model because Eq. 9 involves integrals of normal distributions, but it is easy to calculate them numerically. The curves for the two theories, along with detection data for a pure tone in noise (Tanner, Swets, & Green, 1956), are shown in Fig. 6. These data were generated by varying P from 0.1 to 0.9 in steps of 0.2; each point is based upon a total of 300 observations. It is clear that the theories produce substantially the same curves and that both are in reasonable accord with the data.

[4] Because "sensitivity" derives from Latin, one should use the term "equisensitivity," but the common use of "iso" in similar scientific contexts makes the term of mixed origin seem more natural to nonpurists.

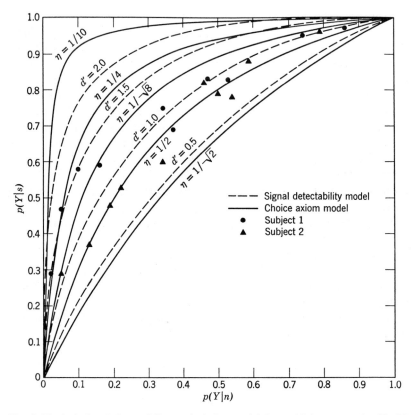

Fig. 6. Typical signal detectability and choice model isosensitivity curves for Yes-No design. The data points, reported in Tanner, Swets, & Green (1956), were obtained by presenting pure tones in noise, with P varied from 0.1 to 0.9 in steps of 0.2 and a fixed symmetric payoff matrix.

Note that the theoretical curves in Fig. 6 are symmetric about the main diagonal that runs from $\langle 0, 1 \rangle$ to $\langle 1, 0 \rangle$. Not all data are symmetric, however, as the visual ones shown in Fig. 7 for one of four subjects studied by Swets, Tanner, and Birdsall (1955, 1961) indicate. The empirical isosensitivity curve was swept out by varying the payoffs and holding $P = \frac{1}{2}$. The data for the other subjects are similar. It is evident that these data reject both the choice and the equal-variance signal detectability models. The theoretical curves of Fig. 7, one of which corresponds reasonably well with the data, were obtained from the detectability model by assuming that the stimulus plus noise standard deviation is $1 + \frac{1}{4}d'$ times the noise standard deviation. For these data, d' is in the range of 2 to 4, so the factor is 1.5 to 2. Thus a second stimulus parameter allows detectability theory to account for these data, but I am at a loss to understand why adding a faint tone to the noise should have such major repercussions on the variance of the distribution of effects.

In all likelihood, there is some plausible way to add a second stimulus parameter to the choice model so that it does just about as well, but none has yet been suggested.

The threshold theory isosensitivity curves are obtained by eliminating t from Eq. 15 and u from Eq. 16:

$$
p(Y \mid s) =
\begin{cases}
p(Y \mid n) \left[\dfrac{q(s)}{q(n)} \right], & \text{if } p(Y \mid n) \leqslant q(n) \\[2ex]
p(Y \mid n) \left[\dfrac{1 - q(s)}{1 - q(n)} \right] + \dfrac{q(s) - q(n)}{1 - q(n)}, & \text{if } p(Y \mid n) \geqslant q(n).
\end{cases}
\tag{20}
$$

This equation represents two line segments: one from $\langle 0, 0 \rangle$ to $\langle q(n), q(s) \rangle$, which is referred to as the *lower limb*, and the other, the *upper limb*, from $\langle q(n), q(s) \rangle$ to $\langle 1, 1 \rangle$.

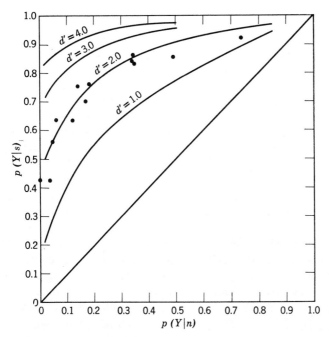

Fig. 7. Nonsymmetric signal detectability isosensitivity curves for the Yes-No design. The data points were obtained by presenting local increases in light intensity, with $P = \frac{1}{2}$ and different payoff matrices. See text for an explanation of the theoretical curves. Adapted with permission from Swets, Tanner, & Birdsall (1961, p. 319).

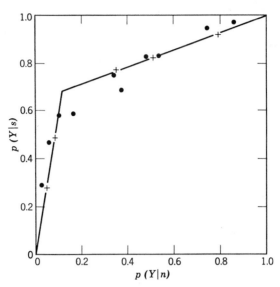

Fig. 8. Threshold isosensitivity curve fitted by eye to subject 1 acoustic data previously plotted in Fig. 6. The theoretical crosses are explained in Sec. 5.2.

The traditional "correction-for-guessing" procedure assumes that $q(n) = 0$, in which case the lower limb runs along the ordinate to $q(s)$ at which point the upper limb departs for $\langle 1, 1 \rangle$. It is abundantly clear that the $q(n) = 0$ model does not describe the data of Figs. 6 or 7; as a result, Tanner and Swets (1954a) concluded that these detection data reject the high-threshold hypothesis. Sometimes their conclusion has been interpreted as a rejection of all sensory thresholds, but the more general threshold model appears to be quite adequate. In Fig. 8, threshold curves are fitted to Tanner, Swets, and Green's (1956) subject 1 data and in Fig. 9 to those of Swets, Tanner, and Birdsall's (1955) subject 4. These theoretical curves are comparable to those of Fig. 7, not to the symmetric ones of Fig. 6, because the threshold model, like the unequal-variance signal-detectability model, has two estimated parameters. The threshold curves appear to be just as satisfactory as the signal-detectability ones.

I shall not carry out the parallel development of isosensitivity curves for the two-alternative forced-choice design using the detectability or choice models. Suffice it to say that the same equations result, except that $d'/\sqrt{2}$ replaces d' and $\eta^{\sqrt{2}}$ replaces η. The isosensitivity curve for the threshold model is obtained by subtracting the second expression in Eq. 18 from the first and rewriting the result as

$$p(1 \mid \langle s, n \rangle) = p(1 \mid \langle n, s \rangle) + q(s) - q(n). \tag{21}$$

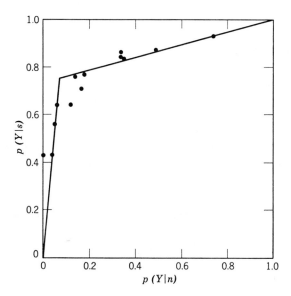

Fig. 9. Threshold isosensitivity curve fitted by eye to subject 4 visual data previously plotted in Fig. 7.

This represents a straight line with slope 1. By setting

$$v = w = \frac{q(s)\,q(n)}{q(s)\,q(n) + [1 - q(s)][1 - q(n)]}$$

in Eq. 18, we see that the isosensitivity curve passes through $\langle q(n), q(s) \rangle$. Thus, when the stimulating conditions are the same, the Yes-No and forced-choice isosensitivity curves must be related, as shown in Fig. 10; so,

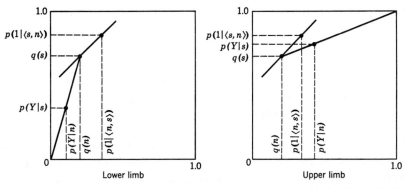

Fig. 10. The geometry relating the threshold Yes-No and two alternative forced-choice isosensitivity curves.

aside from the ambiguity about whether the Yes-No data point lies on the upper or lower limb of its isosensitivity curve, the data from the two experiments provide an estimate of the true detection probabilities. This method seems a suitable replacement for the incorrect correction-for-guessing procedure. Examples of such estimates can be found in Luce (1963), or they can be reconstructed from the raw data presented in Tables 1 and 2.

For some reason not apparent to me, no one has yet reported two-alternative forced-choice data where the presentation probabilities or payoff function are varied, and so we do not know what the empirical isosensitivity curves look like.

In summary, the following conclusions seem justified.

1. The models with but one stimulus parameter, including the threshold model that underlies the correction-for-guessing equation (17), are inadequate to account for existing visual data. In addition, the $q(n) = 0$ threshold model is incorrect for acoustic data.

2. The detectability and threshold models that have two estimated stimulus parameters both handle the visual data quite well.

3. The stimulus parameters for either of these models can be estimated from empirical Yes-No isosensitivity curves, which can be generated by varying the presentation probability, the payoffs, or both. In addition, a simple scheme exists to find the "true" threshold probabilities, which uses data from just one run in each of the Yes-No and two-alternative forced-choice designs.

4. COMPLEX DETECTION

Three somewhat more complex detection designs are our next concern. The first is the *multiple-look Yes-No design* in which there are m distinct intervals, all or none of which contain the stimulus. Thus $S = \{\langle s, s, \ldots, s \rangle, \langle n, n, \ldots, n \rangle\}$, $R = \{Y, N\}$, and $\iota(Y) = \langle s, s, \ldots, s \rangle$ and $\iota(N) = \langle n, n, \ldots, n \rangle$.

The second is the *k-alternative forced-choice design* in which there are k intervals, exactly one of which contains the stimulus. If we let s_i denote the presentation in which s occurs in the ith interval and n in all others, $S = \{s_1, s_2, \ldots, s_k\}$, $R = \{1, 2, \ldots, k\}$, and $\iota(r) = s_r$ for $r \in R$.

The third is the *multiple-look k-alternative forced-choice* design in which the k-alternative forced-choice presentation s_i is repeated a total of m times. Thus $S = \{\langle s_1, s_1, \ldots, s_1 \rangle, \langle s_2, s_2, \ldots, s_2 \rangle, \ldots, \langle s_k, s_k, \ldots, s_k \rangle\}$, $R = \{1, 2, \ldots, k\}$, and $\iota(r) = \langle s_r, s_r, \ldots, s_r \rangle$ for $r \in R$.

For each of these designs, we assume that the noise is uncorrelated on successive presentations, except when explicitly stated otherwise. In particular, this means that successive presentations cannot simply be tape recordings of the initial one. The reason for imposing this experimental limitation is to permit us to assume independence of effects in the analysis, as was done earlier in the discussions of the two-alternative forced-choice design.

4.1 Signal Detectability Analysis

Let X_i denote the logarithm of the likelihood ratio of the observation on the ith look of the multiple-look Yes-No experiment; then it is assumed that $X = \sum_{i=1}^{m} X_i$ is the random variable used to arrive at a decision. First, suppose noise is presented m times. If each presentation is independent and normally distributed with mean 0 and standard deviation σ, then X is normally distributed with mean 0 and standard deviation $\sigma_m = \sqrt{m}\sigma$. Similarly, if the stimulus is presented each time and the presentations are independent, then the mean is $d_m = md$ and the standard deviation is $\sigma_m = \sqrt{m}\sigma$. Thus the effective detection parameter is

$$d_m' = \frac{d_m}{\sigma_m} = \frac{md}{\sqrt{m}\sigma} = \sqrt{m}d', \qquad (22)$$

and so we can predict multiple-look data from simple Yes-No data (Swets, Shipley, McKey, & Green, 1959).

The generalization of the two-alternative signal detectability model to the k-alternative forced-choice design is comparatively complicated if response biases are included and very simple if they are not. I shall sketch the general idea of the former and carry out the latter in detail.

As presented in terms of differences, it is not easy to see how to generalize the two-alternative analysis; however, if we view it in a different but equivalent way, the outlines of the generalization become clear (Swets & Birdsall, 1956). As before, suppose that the observations in the two intervals are independent, in which case it is plausible to represent the two decision axes as orthogonal coordinates in the plane. Joint normal distributions for $\langle s, n \rangle$ and for $\langle n, s \rangle$ are assumed to exist and to have equal variances. When projected on either axis, these distributions generate the usual one-dimensional noise and signal distributions, the means of the noise distributions being at the origin. This is diagrammed in Fig. 11. The observational random variable is the pair (X_1, X_2), and the decision rule is no longer characterized by a point but by a division of the plane

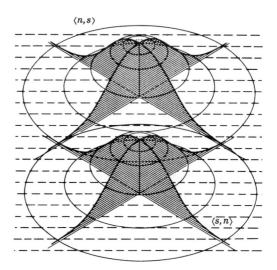

Fig. 11. The two-dimensional signal detectability representation of the two-alternative forced-choice experiment. The dotted lines represent the family of decision rules that correspond to the cutpoints in the decision axis representation.

into two nonoverlapping regions. Under reasonable assumptions about the subject's goals, it can be shown that the division of the plane must be by a line located at 45° between the two decision axes; typical ones are shown dotted. It is not difficult to see that our original representation in terms of differences is simply the projection of the present model onto a plane orthogonal both to this family of 45° lines and to the decision plane. The intersection of each 45° line with this plane corresponds to a possible cut-point c'.

The generalization to k-alternatives is now clear. There are k random variables, $X_1, X_2, \ldots, X_k$, corresponding to observations in each of the intervals. For each stimulus presentation, s_i, where the stimulus is in the ith interval and noise is in the others, there is a density function having the value $p(x_1, x_2, \ldots, x_k \mid s_i)$ at $X_1 = x_1$, $X_2 = x_2, \ldots$, and $X_k = x_k$. These are assumed to be independent multivariate normal distributions with equal variances. The decision rule is a partition of the k-dimensional Euclidean space into k response regions; the simplest rule involves a division of the space by hyperplanes. The mathematics required for specific numerical calculations is, of course, rather clumsy, and, so far as I know, no actual work has used this general form of the model.

If, however, we assume that the payoffs are symmetric and that the subject introduces no biases, matters are very much simpler. The subject makes an observation, X_i, in each interval, and he is assumed simply to say that the stimulus is located in the interval having the largest observation. Because there is no bias, it does not matter which interval actually contains the stimulus—the probability of a correct response, $p_k(C)$, is the same for all. The probability density that s generates an effect x that is the largest is simply $p(x \mid s)$ times the probability that all $k - 1$ of the noise observations are less than x, that is, $p(x \mid s) P(x \mid n)^{k-1}$, where $P(x \mid n) = \int_{-\infty}^{x} p(z \mid n) \, dz$. Because the particular value of the largest value is immaterial to the response made, we integrate over all x to obtain

$$p_k(C) = \int_{-\infty}^{\infty} P(x \mid n)^{k-1} p(x \mid s) \, dx. \tag{23}$$

Of course, we assume that $p(x \mid s)$ and $p(x \mid n)$ are normal, have the same variance, and are separated by an amount d, just as in the Yes-No model. That being so, an estimate of d' from either the Yes-No or two-alternative forced-choice data is sufficient to predict $p_k(C)$ from Eq. 23 (Tanner & Swets, 1954a).

The analysis of the multiple-look k-alternative forced-choice design is analogous to that for the multiple-look Yes-No design (Swets, Shipley, McKey, & Green, 1959). The subject is assumed to make observation $\mathbf{X}_{ij}$ in interval i on the jth observation. The sums $\sum_{j=1}^{m} \mathbf{X}_{ij}$ are calculated, and then the subject chooses the interval having the largest sum. Because the $\mathbf{X}_{ij}$ are assumed to be independent and normally distributed, $\sum_{j=1}^{m} \mathbf{X}_{ij}$ is normally distributed with mean 0 and standard deviation $\sqrt{m}\sigma$ when n is presented in interval i and with mean md and standard deviation $\sqrt{m}\sigma$ when s is presented. Thus Eq. 23 can be used to calculate the probability of a correct detection. Note that if $d'(k)$ denotes the value of d' estimated from the simple k-alternative forced-choice design and $d_m'(k)$ denotes that corresponding to the m-look design, they are related by

$$d_m'(k) = \sqrt{m} \, d'(k). \tag{24}$$

4.2 Choice Analysis

By repeated use of the independence Assumption 4, it is easy to see that the choice model matrix of scale values for the multiple look Yes-No design is

$$
\begin{array}{cc}
 & \begin{array}{cc} Y & N \end{array} \\
\begin{array}{c} \langle s, s, \ldots, s \rangle \\ \langle n\,n, \ldots, n \rangle \end{array} &
\left[\begin{array}{cc} 1 & \eta^{\sqrt{m}b} \\ \eta^{\sqrt{m}} & b \end{array} \right].
\end{array}
\tag{25}
$$

The argument is much the same as that used for the two-alternative forced-choice design.

Letting s_i denote the presentation in which the stimulus is in interval i, then by a similar argument we obtain as the matrix for the k-alternative forced-choice design

$$
\begin{array}{c}
 \quad 1 \quad\quad 2 \quad\; \cdots \quad k \\
\begin{array}{c} s_1 \\ s_2 \\ \cdot \\ \cdot \\ \cdot \\ s_k \end{array}
\left[
\begin{array}{cccc}
1 & \eta^{\sqrt{2}} & \cdots & \eta^{\sqrt{2}} \\
\eta^{\sqrt{2}} & 1 & \cdots & \eta^{\sqrt{2}} \\
& & & \\
& \cdots\cdots\cdots\cdots & & \\
& & & \\
\eta^{\sqrt{2}} & \eta^{\sqrt{2}} & \cdots & 1
\end{array}
\right] ,
\end{array}
\tag{26}
$$

where I have omitted writing the response biases. When the biases are equal—the assumption we shall make in analyzing data—the equation for the probability of a correct response is seen to be

$$
p_k(C) = \frac{1}{1 + (k - 1)\eta^{\sqrt{2}}} .
\tag{27}
$$

When the biases are not assumed equal, then it is easy to see from Eq. 26 that

$$
\prod_{i=1}^{k} \prod_{j=1}^{k} \frac{p(j \mid s_i)}{p(i \mid s_i)} = \eta^{\sqrt{2}\, k(k-1)}
$$

and

$$
\prod_{l=1}^{k} \frac{p(i \mid s_l)}{p(j \mid s_l)} = \left[\frac{b(i)}{b(j)} \right]^{k} ;
$$

these equations can be used to estimate the parameters η and $b(i)$.

Because $(\eta^{\sqrt{2}})^{\sqrt{m}} = \eta^{\sqrt{2m}}$, the matrix for the multiple-look k-alternative forced-choice design is

$$
\begin{array}{c}
 \quad 1 \quad\quad\; 2 \quad\;\; \cdots \quad\; k \\
\begin{array}{c} \langle s_1, s_1, \ldots, s_1 \rangle \\ \langle s_2, s_2, \ldots, s_2 \rangle \\ \cdots\cdots\cdots\cdots \\ \langle s_k, s_k, \ldots, s_k \rangle \end{array}
\left[
\begin{array}{cccc}
1 & \eta^{\sqrt{2m}} & \cdots & \eta^{\sqrt{2m}} \\
\eta^{\sqrt{2m}} & 1 & \cdots & \eta^{\sqrt{2m}} \\
\cdots\cdots & \cdots\cdots & & \cdots\cdots \\
\eta^{\sqrt{2m}} & \eta^{\sqrt{2m}} & \cdots & 1
\end{array}
\right] ,
\end{array}
\tag{28}
$$

where again I have not written the biases explicitly.

4.3 Threshold Analysis

In the multiple look Yes-No experiment the threshold model says that the subject will observe some sequence of D's and $\overline{D}$'s on the basis of which he must say Yes or No. We assume that these observations are independent and that he bases his response upon the number of D's that occur; specifically, that when there are m looks he says Yes if and only if the number of D's is k_m or greater. It is easy to see that

$$p(Y \mid s) = \sum_{i=k_m}^{m} q(s)^i [1 - q(s)]^{m-i} \binom{m}{i}$$

$$p(Y \mid n) = \sum_{i=k_m}^{m} q(n)^i [1 - q(n)]^{m-i} \binom{m}{i}.$$
(29)

The two most extreme cases are when $k_m = 1$, that is, when the subject says Yes if at least one D observation occurs, in which case

$$p(Y \mid s) = 1 - [1 - q(s)]^m \quad \text{and} \quad p(Y \mid n) = 1 - [1 - q(n)]^m,$$

and when $k_m = m$, that is, when the subject says Yes only if the D observation occurs for all presentations, in which case

$$p(Y \mid s) = q(s)^m \quad \text{and} \quad p(Y \mid n) = q(n)^m.$$

A more plausible assumption is something like majority rule (we suppose that he says Yes 50 per cent of the time when there is an equal number of D's and $\overline{D}$'s). No simple equation can be written for this case, but it is easy to calculate specific values from Eq. 29. Note that the response probabilities for successive odd-even m's are identical.

For the k-alternative forced-choice design, we assume that the responses are unbiased as in the other two models. If the subject obtains D observations in m of the k intervals, we assume that he chooses one of these intervals at random. Luce (1963) has shown that this implies

$$p_k(C) = \frac{1}{kq(n)} \{q(s) - [1 - q(n)]^{k-1}[q(s) - q(n)]\}.$$
(30)

Note that

$$p_2(C) = \tfrac{1}{2}[1 + q(s) - q(n)],$$

and so two-alternative forced-choice data determine $q(s) - q(n)$, but not $q(s)$ and $q(n)$. However, for $k > 2$, the value of $p_k(C)$ depends upon $q(s)$ and $q(n)$ separately, not just upon their difference. This is to be contrasted with the other two models in which the $p_2(C)$ data uniquely determine $p_k(C)$.

No threshold analysis for the multiple look k-alternative forced-choice design has yet been suggested.

4.4 Comparison of Models with Data

There do not appear to be any published raw data for the multiple-look Yes-No design, and so all we can do is attempt to compare the several theories. In all three cases there is a free parameter which gives one a good deal of freedom: neither the bias parameters in the detectability and choice models nor the value of k_m in the threshold model need be the same as the number of looks is changed. If we assume no bias in the first two models and suppose that, for $m = 1$, $p(Y \mid s) = \frac{2}{3}$ and $p(Y \mid n) = \frac{1}{3}$, then we get the solid points on the diagonal of Fig. 12. The two models differ so little that the separate points cannot be shown on a graph of this size. The majority rule for the threshold model also yields points on the diagonal, but they do not approach the corner quite so rapidly. The threshold $m = 7$ and 8 point is nearly the same as the detectability and choice $m = 5$. The other two sets of threshold points are for the extremes $k_m = 1$ and $k_m = m$, and it is clear that by other choices for k_m almost

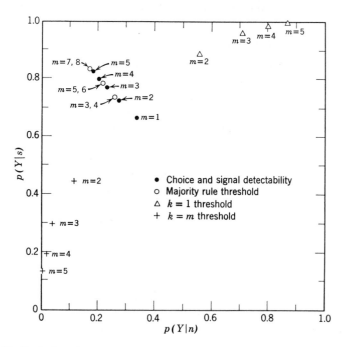

Fig. 12. Typical predictions of the several models for the multiple look Yes-No design. The parameter m denotes the number of independent repetitions of the stimulus plus noise or of the noise alone.

any other curve to the left and above these extremes can be generated. Much the same is true for the other two models because of the freedom in choosing the bias parameter.

In addition to the Yes-No and two-alternative forced-choice data given in Table 1, Swets (1959) collected four-alternative forced-choice data on the same subjects. Using Eq. 23, or Elliott's (1959) tables, $p_4(C)$ for the detectability model can be predicted from the observed values of $p_2(C)$ and

Table 5   Observed and Predicted Values of $p_4(C)$ for Swets's (1959) data

| Subject | Threshold Parameters | | Observed | | | Predicted | |
| | Upper Limb | Lower Limb | | | | Threshold | |
E/N_0 in db	q(n) q(s)	q(n) q(s)		Signal Detectability	Choice	Upper Limb	Lower Limb
1 9.4	0.13 0.77	0.25 0.89	0.623	0.66	0.60	0.67	0.62
14.5	0.00 0.87	0.13 1.00	0.823	0.87	0.83	0.90	0.82
16.6	0.00 0.89	0.11 1.00	0.883	0.89	0.86	0.92	0.85
2 9.4	0.19 0.72	0.33 0.86	0.524	0.57	0.52	0.58	0.53
11.7	0.17 0.74	0.28 0.86	0.626	0.61	0.55	0.62	0.57
14.5	0.07 0.78	0.29 1.00	0.750	0.71	0.66	0.75	0.64
16.6	0.02 0.83	0.19 1.00	0.792	0.80	0.75	0.84	0.75
3 9.4	0.00 0.69	0.25 0.94	0.677	0.70	0.64	0.76	0.65
11.7	0.07 0.80	0.27 1.00	0.734	0.73	0.68	0.77	0.66
14.5	0.00 0.83	0.17 1.00	0.847	0.83	0.79	0.88	0.80
16.6	0.00 0.92	0.08 1.00	0.895	0.91	0.88	0.94	0.88

See Table 1 for a description of experimental conditions.

for the choice model from Eq. 27. The predictions for the threshold model, Eq. 30, depend upon knowing both $q(n)$ and $q(s)$. These may be estimated from the Yes-No and two-alternative forced-choice data, with, however, the upper limb-lower limb ambiguity inherent in the Yes-No model. The details about how this was done can be found in Luce (1963). Both sets of estimates and the predictions for all three models are shown in Table 5. It is clear that there is little to choose between the detectability and choice models. The threshold model is adequate only if we admit the possibility that the subjects did not all operate on the same limb and that some may have shifted from one limb to the other as the stimulus energy was increased. Both seem like reasonable possibilities.

Swets (1959) also reported $p_k(C)$ estimates for three subjects and $k = 2$, 3, 4, 5, and 8. Assuming equal biases, so that Eqs. 23 and 27 can be used, the detectability and choice models can be compared. The results are shown in Fig. 13, and they clearly favor the detectability model. To what extent this conclusion depends upon the assumption of equal biases is not

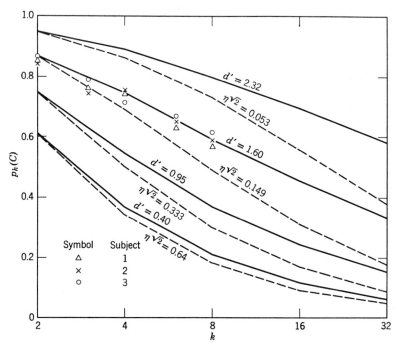

Fig. 13. Typical predictions of the signal detectability (solid curves) and choice (dotted curves) models for the unbiased *k*-alternative forced-choice design. The data points for these subjects are from Swets (1959).

clear. If, for example, the biases were U-shaped, so that the relative frequency of the first and last responses was in excess of $1/k$ and of the middle ones less than $1/k$, then it is quite possible that $p_3(C)$ would be artificially inflated and that $p_k(C)$, $k \geqslant 5$, would be artificially deflated. If that were the case, the data surely would not support the choice model and, depending upon the magnitude of the effect, might very well not support the signal detectability model. On the other hand, if the biases formed an inverted U, then $p_3(C)$ could easily be deflated and $p_k(C)$, $k \geqslant 5$, inflated. If the effect were large enough, this could cause us to accept the choice and reject the detection model. Swets does not indicate the nature of the biases in his data, but my best guess (based upon biases in recognition confusion matrices) is that they were of the first type, in which case the choice model is inadequate to account for these data. Until more detailed data are available, however, no very certain decision is possible.

Without Yes-No data on the same subjects under the same conditions, it is impossible to predict $p_k(C)$ uniquely using the threshold model. The best we can do is to calculate the extreme limits of Eq. 30 for several different values of $p_2(C)$. These are shown in Fig. 14 along with the data points again.

Swets, Shipley, McKey, and Green (1959) reported an acoustic study of the multiple-look four-alternative forced-choice design, using $m = 1$, 2, 3, 4, and 5. Assuming again that the biases are equal, η can be estimated from the probability of a correct response when $m = 1$, and then the other values are predicted from

$$p(r \mid \langle s_r, s_r, \ldots, s_r \rangle) = \frac{1}{1 + 3\eta^{\sqrt{2m}}},$$

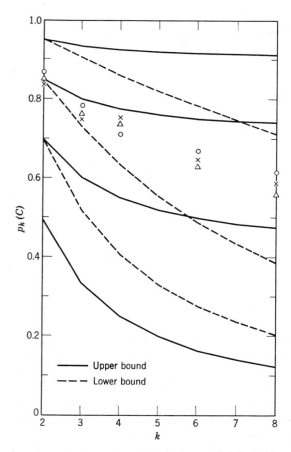

Fig. 14. Typical upper- and lower-bound predictions of the threshold model for an unbiased k-alternative forced-choice design. The data points for these subjects are the same as those shown in Fig. 13.

which follows from Eq. 28. The signal detectability analysis is similar, except that Eq. 24 is used. The results are shown in Table 6. The detectability model predicts a somewhat more rapid improvement in correct responses than is shown by the subjects; the choice model is closer to the behavior. Because each probability is estimated from 600 observations and because the theoretical probabilities are so near 1, some of the deviations of the detectability model are significant if not spectacular.

Table 6 Multiple-Look Four-Alternative Forced-Choice Data Reported by Swets, Shipley, McKey, and Green (1959)

Subject	Number of Observations	Observed Data	Predicted from $m = 1$ data	
			Signal Detectability	Choice Model
1	1	0.81	—	—
	2	0.92	0.937	0.925
	3	0.97	0.979	0.965
	4	0.99	>0.99	0.982
	5	0.99	>0.99	0.990
2	1	0.80	—	—
	2	0.89	0.930	0.918
	3	0.95	0.974	0.961
	4	0.96	>0.99	0.976
	5	0.98	>0.99	0.989
3	1	0.82	—	—
	2	0.95	0.942	0.931
	3	0.97	0.981	0.968
	4	0.98	>0.99	0.984
	5	0.99	>0.99	0.991

The noise was 35 db re 0.0002 d/cm² and the signal a 1000-cps tone at 12.5 db measured in terms of $10 \log_{10} E/N_0$.

In connection with the independence assumption that plays such a significant role in all three models, the following result is of considerable importance. Swets et al. repeated the last experiment using a tape recording of the stimulus plus noise or of the noise alone for the several presentations. Instead of gradually improving, as they do with uncorrelated noise (Table 6) and as is predicted by the theories, the subjects exhibited little or no improvement beyond two presentations. This suggests that it is perfectly possible experimentally to render the independence assumption incorrect to a degree that is quite noticeable.

In evaluating these studies, it should be kept in mind that none of them was designed to test among the three models but rather to decide about the adequacy of the signal detectability one. So far as these data are concerned, there is nothing in my opinion that clearly favors one model over another. There is some suggestion in the k-alternative forced-choice data that the choice model is inferior to the detectability one, but the reverse is true for the multiple-look four-alternative data. Because of the threshold model's larger number of parameters, none of these experiments adequately taxes it.

5. THEORIES OF THE BIAS PARAMETERS

To a traditional psychophysicist, what we have been doing so far in this chapter must seem strange, if not totally irrelevant to his interests. He wants to know the laws relating responses to well-controlled, specifiable stimuli, and yet nothing at all has been said about them. The reason is that many contemporary psychophysicists do not believe that this problem is nearly so straight-forward as it seems. The current view is that it should be divided into three distinct parts. The first is a theory of responses that relates responses to responses, not to stimuli. Such theories—they are what we have discussed so far—contain estimable parameters, such as η, d', or $q(s)$ and $q(n)$ and b, c, or t and u, which are thought to depend upon and to summarize the relevant decision-making effects of the stimulating and reward conditions of the experiment. Because such parameters can be estimated from the response data, there is actually no need to measure the physical properties of the stimuli or the characteristics of the outcome structure of the experiment; they need only be under control and reproducible at will. This sort of theory, as we have seen, uses the data from one experiment to predict the results of others having different designs but involving the same stimuli, background, and residual environment.

Once such a theory is developed and has received enough confirmation so that one feels that it may be approximately correct, one can begin to look into the other two problems: first, relations between the stimulus parameters of the theory and measurable properties of the stimuli, and second, relations between bias parameters and other aspects of the experimental conditions. There is precious little point, however, in trying to establish such relations until the response-response theory has been rather carefully tested.

If we are correct in supposing that parameters of the one class measure the subject's sensitivity to the stimuli and those of the other measure response biases that are under his control, then we must anticipate separate theories relating each to certain aspects of the experimental situation. This section presents two quite different theories for the bias parameters. The next discusses theories of the sensitivity parameters.

5.1 Expected Value

As we have seen in Sec. 3 on isosensitivity curves, experimental manipulations of either the presentation probability or of the payoff matrix appreciably affect the response probabilities, even when the stimulating conditions are fixed. This suggests that a theory of the bias parameters must involve at least these two experimental factors. Broadly speaking, mathematical psychologists have come up with two ideas about this dependence. The one that we look into in this subsection stems mainly from the economic and statistical literature. It says that subjects choose the parameters to optimize something. The other, which is discussed in the next subsection, says that subjects continually adjust the parameters in an "adaptive" fashion—they learn.

Suppose that the presentation and payoff structure in the Yes-No design is

Presentation Probability	Stimulus Presentation	Response Y	N
P	s	$\begin{bmatrix} o_{11} & o_{12} \\	
$1 - P$	n	o_{21} & o_{22} \end{bmatrix},$	

where the o_{ij} are sums of money. One reasonably sensible criterion that a subject might use is to select that bias parameter that maximizes his total expected money return during the course of the experiment. Because the trials are assumed to be independent and because the response probabilities are assumed to be constant, this is the same as selecting it to maximize the expected value of a single trial. This assumption is criticized later.

The expected outcome, $E(o)$, is simply the money value of each of the four possible presentation-response conditions weighted by their respective probabilities of occurring:

$$E(o) = Pp(Y \mid s)o_{11} + Pp(N \mid s)o_{12} + (1 - P)\,p(Y \mid n)o_{21} + (1 - P)\,p(N \mid n)o_{22}$$

$$= [p(Y \mid s) - \beta p(Y \mid n)]\,P(o_{11} - o_{12}) + Po_{12} + (1 - P)o_{22}, \quad (31)$$

where

$$\beta = \left(\frac{1 - P}{P}\right)\left(\frac{o_{22} - o_{21}}{o_{11} - o_{12}}\right). \quad (32)$$

If the response probabilities depend upon a single bias parameter z, then to find that value of z that maximizes $E(o)$ we set the derivative of $E(o)$ with respect to z equal to 0 and solve for z:

$$\frac{dE(o)}{dz} = 0 = \frac{dp(Y \mid s)}{dz} - \beta \frac{dp(Y \mid n)}{dz},$$

so

$$\beta = \frac{dp(Y \mid s)/dz}{dp(Y \mid n)/dz}. \tag{33}$$

For the signal detectability model, we simply calculate the derivative of Eqs. 8 with respect to c and find that

$$\beta = \frac{p(c \mid s)}{p(c \mid n)}. \tag{34}$$

Thus, given the payoffs and presentation probabilities, we can calculate β and from this determine c via Eq. 34, provided that we know the forms of $p(\cdot \mid s)$ and $p(\cdot \mid n)$. An exactly parallel development holds for the two-alternative forced-choice design, except that β equals the ratio of the difference density for $\langle s, n \rangle$ to the difference density for $\langle n, s \rangle$.

Equation 33 says that the slope of the isosensitivity curve should equal the optimum β defined in Eq. 32, so that one comparison we can make is between these two quantities, using, say, the theoretical signal detectability curve to estimate the slope. Green (1960) has done this, and the results are shown in Fig. 15. It is clear that the data depart considerably from the

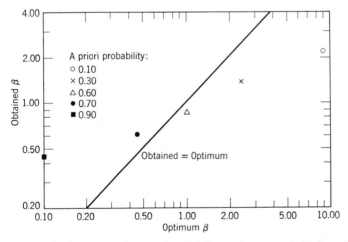

Fig. 15. Obtained versus optimum values of β assuming a maximization of expected value and the detectability Yes-No model. Adapted with permission from Green (1960, p. 1195).

theory. Green argues that the insensitivity of the expected value to changes in the response probabilities probably accounts for the poor predictions. For example, with $P = 0.5$, a symmetric payoff matrix, and $d' = 1$, the expected payoff is within 90 per cent of the maximum as long as $p(Y \mid n)$ is between 0.15 and 0.50. Nevertheless, the departure from the optimum β curve is systematic and needs to be explained.

Note that the quantity $p(c \mid s)/p(c \mid n)$ is the likelihood ratio of the stimulus density to the noise density; it is usually denoted by $l(c)$. It is a measure of the relative likelihood that a given observation is due to s or to n, and the decision rule that maximizes expected value is to say Yes if the observation x is such that $l(x) > \beta$ and to say No if $l(x) < \beta$. Thus, if we had simply postulated a decision axis, we would have been forced by this bias theory to the position that it is the likelihood ratio axis. So, this biasing model is a possible defense for the original assumption that likelihood ratios are involved.

A variety of other decision rules has been explored (Birdsall, 1955; Peterson, Birdsall, & Fox, 1954), all of which lead to the same general structure: the likelihood ratio is compared with some function of P and the o_{ij}. I shall not go into these here.

The analysis for the choice theory is little different. Through Eq. 33 no response theory is assumed. At that point we calculate the derivatives of the Yes-No choice model probabilities (Eq. 12)

$$p(Y \mid s) = \frac{1}{1 + \eta b} \quad \text{and} \quad p(Y \mid n) = \frac{\eta}{\eta + b}$$

with respect to b, substitute in Eq. 33, and solve for b:

$$b = \frac{\sqrt{\beta} - \eta}{1 - \eta\sqrt{\beta}}. \tag{35}$$

The forced choice solution is the same, except that η is replaced by $\eta^{\sqrt{2}}$.

Similar, but more complex, calculations can be made for designs having three or more responses. Partial differentiation with respect to each of the bias parameters results in a set of simultaneous equations for these parameters, which may be very difficult to solve explicitly, but numerical solutions can always be obtained when needed.

In both models the optimum bias parameter depends continuously upon β, which in turn is a continuous function of P and the o_{ij}, except when $P = 0$ or when $o_{11} = o_{12}$. The same maximization analysis leads to quite different results when it is applied to the threshold model. Because the response probabilities depend linearly upon the bias parameter—t on the lower limb and u on the upper—the maximum of $E(o)$ occurs either at $t = 0$ or 1 or at $u = 0$ or 1, depending upon the particular values of P and the o's. In terms of the isosensitivity curves, this means that the response data must fall at either $\langle 0, 0 \rangle$, $\langle q(n), q(s) \rangle$, or $\langle 1, 1 \rangle$, which is clearly not what happens in Figs. 8 and 9. Thus it is certain that the threshold model together with the maximization of expected money criterion is wrong, but which of the two is at fault is not certain.

No very serious testing of the expected value model has been carried out within the detection context, but we know from preference and utility studies (*see* Edwards, 1954, 1961) that to have any hope of predicting behavior we must convert it into a subjective expected utility model in which subjective presentation probabilities replace P and utilities of outcomes replace the o_{ij}. Whether or not this change results in an adequate bias theory for the detectability and choice models, it leaves unaffected the unacceptable results for the threshold model. So we must consider whether there is an acceptable alternative for the threshold theory.

5.2 Asymptotic Learning

It is well known that when information feedback is used a period of pretraining must be included before the responses settle down to their "asymptotic" values. Presumably, the subject is gaining some information relevant to his responses and he is using it to alter his behavior. One possibility is that he is discovering empirically, as it were, what the presentation probability P and his own response probabilities $p(Y \mid s)$ and $p(Y \mid n)$ are so that he can calculate an optimum bias parameter from Eq. 33 or something analogous to it. Another possibility, which some feel is a bit more likely, is that he is engaged in a learning process during which he alters his biases one way or the other, depending upon the trial-by-trial outcomes. This suggests that we set up a stochastic learning process of the sort discussed in Chapter 9 of Vol. II, in which different operators are applied to the biases, depending upon the outcomes. Its asymptotic properties describe the subject when we, as psychophysicists, observe his behavior.

In deciding on a given trial how to modify the bias—from the theorists' viewpoint, in deciding what learning operator to use—three classes of events might be taken into account: the stimulus presented, which is revealed to the subject by the information feedback, his internal observation (if any) resulting from the presentation, and the response made. It seems clear that the operator applied should depend upon the presentation. One might also suspect that it should depend upon the response—in the

choice model this is the only other possibility. If so, then the probability
of applying an operator depends upon the product of the presentation
probability, which is constant during the experimental run, and the
response probability, which is not. Because the probability that a particular operator will be applied is changing over trials, the resulting
stochastic process is exceedingly complicated. At present insufficient is
known about its asymptotic properties for it to be of any use to us. This
is, of course, a limitation in practice, not in principle.

So we confine our attention to models in which the subject decides how
to change his bias on the basis of the presentation and the internal observation resulting from it. These models are called experimenter-controlled
in learning theory. In many ways the internal observation seems a much
more relevant event than the subject's response, for it is these observations
that he must use in the future to decide what responses to make. By
assumption, the conditional probability of an internal effect occurring is
constant over trials, so the probability of applying a given learning operator
is also constant, which eliminates the major difficulty mentioned above.

With the signal detectability model, however, a problem still remains,
namely that there is a continuum of effects. Although Suppes (1959, 1960)
has begun work on such learning models, insufficient is currently known
about them to arrive at a theory of biasing. The choice model does not
suffer from this difficulty because there are no internal observations, nor
does the threshold model because there are only two observation states,
D and $\bar{D}$.

The choice theory learning model has already been presented in Sec. 1.2
as an argument for assuming the choice theory. As far as the biases are
concerned, we found that

$$b(r) = P[\iota(r)] \, \theta(r),$$

where ι is the identification function, P the presentation probability, and
θ a learning rate parameter. Assuming that this learning model is correct,
the major unsolved bias problem is how learning rates depend on the payoffs and whatever else they depend on.

A somewhat similar analysis can be given for the threshold model.
Suppose, first, that the subject is operating upon the lower limb of the
isosensitivity curve; that is, he is saying Yes only to a proportion t of the
D observations and No, otherwise. He is adjusting t on the basis of his
experiences. It is surely inappropriate for him to change it on those trials
when a $\bar{D}$ observation occurs. (Such an observation may, of course,
influence his decision to shift from the lower to the upper limb.) So
suppose a D observation occurs. If it resulted from an s presentation, he
should increase his tendency t to say Yes to D observations; whereas, if

it resulted from an n observation, he should decrease t. With this in mind and assuming linear operators, we postulate that

$$t_{i+1} = \begin{cases} t_i + \theta(1 - t_i), & \text{if } s \text{ and } D \text{ occur on trial } i \\ t_i - \theta't_i, & \text{if } n \text{ and } D \text{ occur on trial } i \\ t_i, & \text{if } \bar{D} \text{ occurs on trial } i, \end{cases} \quad (36)$$

where t_i is the bias on trial i. It follows that the expected value of t_{i+1} given t_i is

$$\begin{aligned} E(t_{i+1} \mid t_i) &= [t_i + \theta(1 - t_i)]\, Pq(s) + (1 - \theta')t_i(1 - P)\, q(n) \\ &\quad + t_i P[1 - q(s)] + t_i(1 - P)[1 - q(n)] \\ &= t_i\{(1 - \theta)\, Pq(s) + (1 - \theta')(1 - P)q(n) + P[1 - q(s)] \\ &\quad + (1 - P)[1 - q(n)]\} + \theta\, Pq(s). \end{aligned}$$

Because all of the probabilities on the right are trial-independent, we can take expectations over t_i:

$$E(t_{i+1}) = E(t_i)\{-Pq(s)\theta - (1 - P)\, q(n)\theta' + 1\} + \theta\, Pq(s). \quad (37)$$

If we assume that the asymptotic expectation of t_i, call it t_∞, exists, then by taking the limit of Eq. 37 as i goes to infinity we may solve for t_∞:

$$t_\infty = \frac{q(s)}{q(s) + q(n)b}, \quad (38)$$

where

$$b = \left(\frac{1 - P}{P}\right)\left(\frac{\theta'}{\theta}\right). \quad (39)$$

Note that, as in the choice model, the bias parameters are the product of the presentation probability and the corresponding learning rate parameters.

The parallel model for the upper limb assumes

$$u_{i+1} = \begin{cases} u_i + \theta(1 - u_i), & \text{if } s \text{ and } \bar{D} \text{ occur on trial } i \\ u_i - \theta'u_i, & \text{if } n \text{ and } \bar{D} \text{ occur on trial } i \\ u_i, & \text{if } D \text{ occurs on trial } i, \end{cases} \quad (40)$$

and it results in the asymptotic expectation of u_n

$$u_\infty = \frac{1 - q(s)}{1 - q(s) + [1 - q(n)]b}. \quad (41)$$

The quantity b is formally similar to β (Eq. 32) in that the presentation probability enters in the same way. Presumably, the learning-rate parameters depend in some fashion upon the payoffs, but no one has yet reported a theory for this dependence. Much research is needed to determine whether this sort of model is adequate and to understand the relation between learning rates and payoffs.

An interesting feature of these asymptotic results for the threshold model is that the response probabilities can approach the true detection probabilities only under very special conditions. If the subject is operating on the lower limb and b has a moderate value somewhere in the neighborhood of 1, then t_∞ approaches 1 only as $q(n)$ approaches 0. On the upper limb u_∞ approaches 0 only as $q(s)$ approaches 1. Thus, if, as in the data of Figs. 8 and 9, $q(n) > 0$ and $q(s) < 1$, the theory predicts that no data points lie in the immediate neighborhood of $\langle q(n), q(s) \rangle$, and none seems to. In other words, one effect of information feedback, according to this model, is to prevent the subject from revealing directly the true detection probabilities. It is not known what he does when there is no information feedback, but it certainly should not be assumed that $p(Y \mid s) = q(s)$ and $p(Y \mid n) = q(n)$ without careful investigation.

A second point of interest is that at asymptote the response probabilities are still fluctuating under the processes described by Eqs. 36 and 40. An expression can be derived for the variance of the response probability at asymptote which shows that the more rapid the learning, the larger the variance. Most experimenters feel that there is more than binomial variability in much psychophysical data, and learning may very well be one source. If so, considerable care must be exercised in applying the standard tests of significance that postulate constant underlying probabilities.

A similar learning model can be developed for the biases v and w of the two-alternative forced-choice design (see Luce, 1963). Suffice it to say that $v_\infty = w_\infty = 1/(1 + b)$. Note that, when $b = 1$, $v_\infty = w_\infty = \frac{1}{2}$, which implies $p(1 \mid \langle s, n \rangle) = p(2 \mid \langle n, s \rangle)$. For $P = \frac{1}{2}$, $b = 1$ if and only if $\theta = \theta'$. Thus the apparent tendency toward behavioral symmetry when $P = \frac{1}{2}$ and the payoff matrix is symmetric suggests that the learning rates corresponding to symmetric payoffs are approximately equal. In that case $b = (1 - P)/P$.

Assuming this, we may use Eqs. 38 and 41 to predict the data shown earlier in Fig. 8. The predicted values, which correspond to the points by pairs as one sweeps around the isosensitivity curve, are shown as crosses in Fig. 8 (p. 134).

6. THEORIES OF THE STIMULUS PARAMETERS

Relatively little is yet known about the way in which the stimulus parameters of the several theories depend upon physical measures of the stimuli. The research is scattered and incomplete. Tanner and his colleagues have worked intensively on this problem for detectability theory during the last three or four years, and considerable data have been collected, but in my view no adequate theory has yet evolved. Some indication of their direction is given in Sec. 6.1. No work at all has yet been done in connection with the choice theory. The quantal studies of Békésy (1930) and Stevens, Morgan, and Volkmann (1941) can, and I think should, be viewed as a stimulus-parameter theory for the threshold model when applied to situations in which the background and stimulus differ on only one physical dimension, such as energy or frequency. Although I shall avoid the details, it is not difficult to modify their model to give a threshold theory for the detection of a stimulus in noise. The neural quantum theory is examined in Secs. 6.2 and 6.3.

6.1 Ideal Observers

Peterson, Birdsall, and Fox (1954), in their presentation of detectability theory as a physical—not a psychophysical—theory, treated the question of the optimum detectability possible for physical signals in noise when one has different amounts of information about the signals and noise. They were not concerned with what people do but with what an optimum detection device can possibly do. The best known of the several sets of assumptions they looked into is the case of the so-called "signal-known-exactly." The signal and noise are both assumed to be limited to some band of frequencies, and the noise is assumed to have equal power at all of its frequencies and to have normally distributed amplitudes (so-called white Gaussian noise). The ideal detector knows everything there is to know about the signal: frequencies, phase relationships, amplitudes, time of onset, etc. Under these assumptions, they showed that the logarithm of the likelihood ratio is normally distributed with variance $2E/N_0$, where E denotes the stimulus energy and N_0 the noise power per unit bandwidth. When noise alone is presented, the mean is $-E/N_0$, and when stimulus plus noise is presented it is E/N_0. Thus we see that $d' = (2E/N_0)^{1/2}$. It was primarily this result that suggested the normality and equal variance assumptions typical of detectability theory. I shall not attempt to reproduce the argument leading to it. Peterson et al. explored a variety of other cases in which different assumptions are made about the information available to the detector.

Given that results of this sort can be found, a possible approach to the question of a stimulus-parameter theory is suggested. We suppose that the person is in fact an optimum detection device operating on certain of the information that he has available—*an ideal observer.*

Thus, if the human observer were to perform as an ideal observer the following would be necessary: (1) he would have no source of internal noise. That is, the input signal would have to be transformed to a different type of energy by the end organ and transmitted by the nervous system, all with perfect fidelity. (2) He would have perfect memory for the signal parameters and the noise parameters. At any time t within the observation interval he must know the exact amplitude of the signal waveform. (3) He would be capable of calculating likelihood ratio or some monotonic transformation of likelihood ratio.

These are some of the requirements which must be met by the human observer if he is to perform as well as the ideal observer. Clearly, the human observer does not meet these specifications. However, it is possible to determine experimentally the manner and degree to which the human observer fails to meet these requirements and thus obtain a better understanding of the human observer. (Tanner, Birdsall, & Clarke, 1960, pp. 19–20).

As well as I can make out, Tanner proposes to search for assumptions about the information that is available to the ideal observer until he finds a set for which the optimum behavior predicted is that of the human being. Although much of this work is not yet published, or published only in summary form (Tanner, 1960, 1961), it seems that two lines are being developed: modifications of the experiments to fit the model and modifications of the model to fit the experiments. For example, the signal-known-exactly model postulates that the subject knows, among other things, the frequency and time of onset of the stimulus. The poorer performance of the subject may reflect a failure of these assumptions, and so by various experimental devices information about frequency and onset are presented to the subject to see whether the availability of this information improves his performance. The comparison measure used is the square of the ratio of the observed d' to that of the ideal observer detecting a signal that is completely known. This ratio is called the *efficiency* of the observer. Unfortunately, considerable good data are being reported only in terms of efficiencies and d''s, which, it is conceivable, may one day be of little more than historical interest.

The other approach is to change the information assumptions about the ideal observer to see whether an ideal observer with a less perfect memory more nearly approaches human behavior. Examples of this approach can be found in Green (1960), where the whole notion of the ideal observer is carefully described, and in Tanner (1961), who summarizes some of the memory aspects now believed to be relevant.

As the signal detectability theorists recognize, this program may eventually run afoul of difficulties that cannot easily be overcome within the framework of the ideal observer. In addition to introducing restrictions upon the physical information that is usable, the subject may very well add his own noise and other distortions to the presented information, in which case it may be quite impossible to find an ideal observer that performs as he does—assuming that ideal observers continue to be defined to have properties such as those listed in the foregoing quotation. A somewhat cruder approach that nonetheless may merit attention involves parametric studies in which one or at most two physical variables are manipulated and the model parameters are calculated from the data to see what, if any, simple relations appear to exist.

6.2 The Neural Quantum Model

Suppose that we have a simple background, such as a tone, and that a stimulus involves a short duration change of the background on one dimension, such as energy. The Békésy-Stevens neural quantum model attempts to relate the change in the number of neural quanta excited by the stimulus to a physical measure of the increment (or decrement) introduced in the background. The model supposes that this physical dimension can be partitioned at any instant into nonoverlapping intervals that correspond to the neural quanta. Thus two different levels of stimulation lying within one interval excite the same number of quanta, whereas two in different intervals excite different numbers of quanta. We may think of the subject as imposing a quantal grid over the physical dimension.

Over time, the quantal grid is assumed to fluctuate slowly as the result of changes internal to the subject, and so the number of quanta excited by a constant stimulus also fluctuates, sometimes increasing, at other times decreasing. Although it is generally felt that it is the grid that shifts, it is more convenient mathematically to view the grid as fixed and to suppose that the physical measure corresponding to the stimulus does the fluctuating. The two ways of viewing the matter are completely equivalent as long as the grid is equally spaced, as we shall assume. In terms of a fixed grid, a given background will have some distribution, such as that shown in Fig. 16.

Suppose that just prior to presenting stimulus s, which, it will be recalled, is simply an increment (or decrement) in the background, the effect of the background is X. This effect is a random variable distributed in some manner, as shown in Fig. 16. The addition of s is assumed to change the effect from X to $X + \Delta(s)$, where $\Delta(s)$ depends only upon s. Thus, whenever s is presented, the same increment is always added. This is an important point. We are saying that the effect of the background just before stimulation and the effect of the background plus the stimulus are perfectly correlated. This assumption is quite different from the independence assumptions we have repeatedly made when discussing the detection of stimuli in noise. The correlation assumption is interlocked

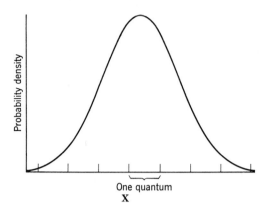

Fig. 16. A typical density of assumed stimulus effects in the quantal model.

with our earlier supposition that the grid fluctuates slowly—in order that a perfect correlation may exist, the stimulus presentation must be of sufficiently short duration so that little or no change in the grid location will take place during the presentation. In practice, a duration of the order of 100 ms has been deemed sufficiently short.

It will be recalled (Sec. 1.3) that we set up the decision rule that a change in stimulation is noted when it equals or exceeds some number k of quanta. Thus, if the physical increment corresponding to s, $\Delta(s)$, is less than the physical increment corresponding to $k - 1$ quanta, it fails to produce a detection observation. If, however, it equals or exceeds that corresponding to k quanta, then it will always be detected. And when it is between that corresponding to $k - 1$ and k quantal intervals, a detection observation may or may not occur. To be specific, suppose that $\Delta(s)$ corresponds to $\frac{1}{3}$ of a quantum interval more than $k - 1$ quanta; then, if the random variable X overflows an integral number of intervals by less than $\frac{2}{3}$, the stimulus cannot excite the necessary k quanta. However, if it overflows $\frac{2}{3}$ or more, then s excites the required k quanta. So the probability that a presentation of s produces a detection observation depends upon the probability that the background *residue*, as it is called, is greater than $\frac{2}{3}$.

It follows, then, that the probability of a detection observation occurring depends upon the distribution of residues. To talk about this distribution without specifying just how many quanta are excited by the background, as we have been doing, makes sense only if the physical measure we are using has the property that all quantal intervals are of the same size. It is not obvious that the usual physical measures have this property, but under very general conditions it is possible to find a continuous monotonic transformation that has. We assume that this is the measure we are using.

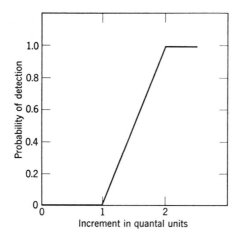

Fig. 17. Predicted true probability of detection versus a measure of the stimulus increment in quantal units (i.e., the true psychometric function) assuming the quantal model, a uniform distribution of residues, and a two-quantum criterion.

Now, if the distribution of residues is uniform in that measure, as has generally been assumed in discussions of neural quantum theory, then the probability of detection is easily seen to be rectilinear, as in Fig. 17.

Stevens, Morgan, and Volkmann (1941) attempted to argue verbally, and Corso (1956) alleged that it follows from Bayes's theorem, that the distribution of residues is uniform independent of the distribution of **X**. This is false. For example, suppose that **X** is distributed according to

$$\Pr\left(\mathbf{X} = x\right) = \frac{\lambda}{2}\, e^{-\lambda|x|}$$

and that the quantal boundaries are located at the points iq, where $i = 0$, ± 1, $\pm 2, \ldots$, and $q > 0$ is the size of one quantum. If **R** denotes the residue random variable, then its distribution for $0 \leqslant r \leqslant q$ is given by

$$\Pr\left(\mathbf{R} = r\right) = \sum_{i=-\infty}^{\infty} \Pr\left(\mathbf{X} = iq + r\right)$$

$$= \sum_{i=1}^{\infty} \left[\Pr\left(\mathbf{X} = iq + r\right) + \Pr\left(\mathbf{X} = -iq + r\right)\right] + \Pr\left(\mathbf{X} = r\right)$$

$$= \frac{\lambda}{2}\left(e^{-\lambda r} + e^{\lambda r}\right) \sum_{i=1}^{\infty} \left(e^{-\lambda q}\right)^i + \frac{\lambda}{2}\, e^{-\lambda r}$$

$$= \frac{\lambda}{2}\left(\frac{e^{-\lambda r} + e^{\lambda r}\, e^{-\lambda q}}{1 - e^{-\lambda q}}\right),$$

and elsewhere it is zero. It is simple to show that the nonzero portion of this function has a minimum at $r = q/2$; hence, to get an idea of the departure from uniformity, we look at the ratio

$$\frac{\Pr(\mathbf{R} = 0)}{\Pr(\mathbf{R} = q/2)} = \frac{1 + e^{-\lambda q}}{2(e^{-\lambda q})^{\frac{1}{2}}}.$$

Thus, if $e^{-\lambda q} = \frac{1}{4}$, the ratio is 5/4. It is clear that as the distribution of **X** becomes flat relative to the quantum size, that is, as λq approaches 0, the more nearly the distribution of the residues approaches the uniform.

In general, however, this distribution is not uniform, and, to the extent that it deviates from uniformity, the transition from 0 to 1 in Fig. 17 must deviate from linearity. This point is important because much of the controversy in the literature over the quantal hypothesis has centered on the prediction of linearity and whether or not appropriate statistical tests have been performed to decide between it and an ogive. In my view, the theory as presently stated does not really make this prediction. I have already given one reason, another will be given now, and a third is presented in the next section.

Suppose that x denotes the physical value of a stimulus in a measure for which the quantal increments are equal and suppose that the distribution of residues is uniform in that measure. Thus a plot of the detection probability versus stimulus increments in this measure is rectilinear. Because we do not know what measure this is, we use instead some "natural" physical measure for which that value corresponding to x is y, the functional relation being $f(x) = y$. In general, we must expect f to be nonlinear, and so the straight line plot is somewhat warped when the natural physical measure is used; however, because the estimated size of the neural quantum is small, this effect is hardly noticeable for moderately nonlinear functions such as the logarithm.

But if not the straight line prediction, what then is there to test? The only other prediction as far as I can see is that the $p = 1$ and $p = 0$ intercepts stand in the ratio $k:(k - 1)$, where k is an integer. This result is independent of the distribution of the residues, but, of course, it is not independent of the independent variable that we use. Fortunately, if the transformation f is moderate in the sense that its derivative is nearly constant over a k quantum interval, then it does not matter much whether we use x or y. To show this, we use the well-known mean-value theorem, namely that if f is differentiable then there exists an x^* such that

$$y = f(x_b) + f'(x^*)(x - x_b),$$

where x_b is the background level and $x_b \leqslant x^* \leqslant x$. Thus, if x_0 denotes the

$p = 0$ intercept and x_1, the $p = 1$ intercept, we have

$$\frac{y_1 - y_b}{y_0 - y_b} = \frac{f(x_1) - f(x_b)}{f(x_0) - f(x_b)}$$

$$= \frac{f'(x_1{}^*)(x_1 - x_b)}{f'(x_0{}^*)(x_0 - x_b)}$$

$$= \left[\frac{f'(x_1{}^*)}{f'(x_0{}^*)}\right]\left(\frac{k}{k-1}\right).$$

Hence, if $f'(x_1{}^*)/f'(x_0{}^*)$ is approximately 1, which we expect because the quantal increments are thought to be small, the integral relation between the two intercepts is little changed.

6.3 The Neural Quantum Experiment

The neural quantum hypothesis and the experimental studies under-taken to test it have generated considerable controversy, much of which is described by Corso (1956). As has been indicated, a good deal of it has centered on the linearity hypothesis, but this is not really an essential feature of the theory. Much of the rest centers on the design of the so-called quantal experiment.

The proponents of the theory have emphasized how easy it is not to confirm the theory, and anyone who has tried is only too aware of the difficulties. Anything in the experimental design that makes the contri-bution of the stimulus, $\Delta(s)$, a random variable, so that X and $X + \Delta(s)$ are not perfectly correlated, generates ogival detection functions that have no simple integral relation between intercepts. (It is easy to see this. The model is substantially the same as the detectability one with two independent random variables, the difference being that a response occurs only if the observations differ by some fixed amount corresponding to k quanta.) Apparently, any sort of distraction is likely to uncorrelate the presentations, and thus quantal results often are not found. This sort of vague notion of an acceptable experiment unfortunately makes the theory nearly immune to rejection. Any failure of the data to confirm it is likely to be taken as prima facie evidence that something was wrong with the experiment.

The feature of the "standard" quantal design that has received most criticism is the fact that the subject knows the presentation schedule. In order that the subject get properly "set," he is permitted to listen to repetitions of the same stimulus increment until he says he is ready, and then a run of identical increments is presented. The subject responds to each of these. Thus he knows in advance that Yes is the correct answer on every trial. The possibility for biasing seems great.

One school has argued as follows. Suppose that the true detection function is a smooth ogive. For a stimulus with a high detection probability, say 0.9, there is a tendency for the number of Yes responses to be inflated artificially because of two factors. One is that the subject knows that Yes is the correct response, and the other is that he is assumed to have a tendency to perseverate his responses, most of which have been Yes. This means, then, that the data function must be above the true function, and it intercepts the $p = 1$ line in much the same way as a linear function does. For a stimulus with a low true-detection probability, say 0.1, the argument is less clear because the perseveration tendency decreases the number of Yes's, whereas his knowledge of the presentation schedule tends to increase the number. So, according to this argument, we may expect the upper intercept to confirm the neural quantum model, but the lower one should vary from subject to subject and, on the whole, be more rounded. Although it is difficult to prove formally, inspection of the published as well as of considerable unpublished data suggests that just the opposite is true: the lower intercept seems more stable and more in line with the quantal model than the upper one.

Assuming that the rectilinear quantal model correctly describes the dependence of the true detection probability upon the stimulus magnitude, the learning model of Sec. 5.2 suggests that the observed responses should distort this function, especially at the upper intercept when there are no or only a few catch trials (Luce, 1963). Specifically, let us assume that a detection observation occurs when and only when a two-quanta change occurs, as suggested by the data. In addition, however, let us suppose that a conservative lower-limb bias is used by the subject when the detection observation is based upon a change of only two neural quanta, whereas with three or more he uses an upper-limb bias. Thus, for any stimulus of magnitude less than two quantal units, a lower-limb bias is in force, and so, by Eqs. 15 and 38,

$$P(Y \mid s) = t_\infty \, q(s)$$

$$= \frac{q(s)^2}{q(s) + q(n)b} \, .$$

For stimuli two quantal units or larger, $q(s) = 1$. For such stimuli, the foregoing equation yields $p(Y \mid s) = 1/[1 + q(n)b]$ for the lower limb and, by Eq. 16, $p(Y \mid s) = 1$ for the upper limb. The probability that a lower-limb bias is used decreases from 1 to 0 linearly as the stimulus magnitude increases from two to three quantal units. In summary, then, if s denotes the stimulus magnitude in quantal units, the response function is

$$p(Y \mid s) = \begin{cases} 0, & \text{if } 0 \leqslant s < 1 \\[2mm] \dfrac{(s-1)^2}{s-1+q(n)b}, & \text{if } 1 \leqslant s < 2 \\[3mm] \dfrac{1+(s-2)q(n)b}{1+q(n)b}, & \text{if } 2 \leqslant s < 3 \\[2mm] 1, & \text{if } 3 \leqslant s. \end{cases}$$

Plots of this function for three values of $q(n)b$ are shown in Fig. 18. We

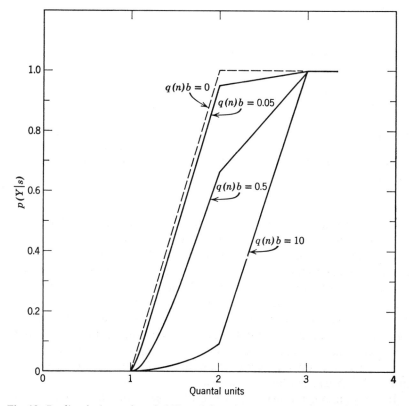

Fig. 18. Predicted observed probability of detection versus a measure of the stimulus increment in quantal units assuming a true underlying rectilinear function and the response biasing model described in the text. The parameter $q(n)$ is the true false alarm rate and b is a quantity that depends on the frequency of "catch" trials and the learning rates of the subject.

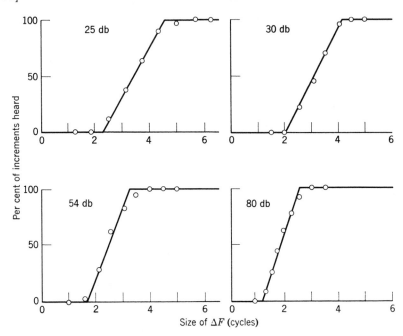

Fig. 19. Quantal data for the detection of frequency increments by one subject at four levels of sound intensity. Each data point is based on 100 observations. The theoretical curves were drawn subject to the condition that the intercepts stand in the relation of 2 to 1. Adapted with permission from Stevens, Morgan, and Volkmann (1941, p. 327).

see that for small values of $q(n)b$, which, for example, corresponds to a small proportion of catch trials, the only effect is a slight distortion of the true quantal function near the upper intercept. As $q(n)b$ becomes larger, we obtain a function that is approximately a straight line with 3:1 intercepts, and as $q(n)b$ becomes still larger the function approaches a 3:2 line.

In spite of all the arguments why the observed functions should not be rectilinear, the surprising thing is how linear they are. In Fig. 19 are data for one subject detecting frequency increments at different levels of intensity. The theoretical lines have 2:1 intercepts. Similar data for the detection of intensity differences of a pure tone for two subjects are shown in Fig. 20. Again 2:1 lines are shown.

In my opinion, the main challenge of these results for those who do not believe that thresholds exist is to explain, using a continuous theory, why the apparent intercepts should exhibit a 2:1 ratio. This has yet to be done.

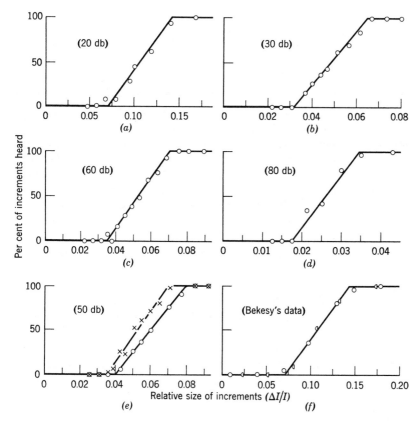

Fig. 20. Quantal data for the detection of intensity increments of a 1000-cps tone by one subject at five levels of sound intensity and in plot f Bekesy's intensity data for both increments and decrements. Each data point is based on 50 to 100 observations. The theoretical curves were drawn subject to the condition that the intercepts stand in the relation of 2 to 1. Adapted with permission from Stevens, Morgan, and Volkmann (1941, p. 323).

7. PURE RECOGNITION

7.1 Introduction

As mentioned at the beginning of this chapter, a recognition experiment is a complete identification design in which the presentation set has at least two stimuli in addition to the null one. We make the further distinction that it is a *pure recognition experiment* when $\emptyset \notin S$, and that it is a *simultaneous detection and recognition experiment* when $\emptyset \in S$.

Given a set of stimuli, it is the experimenter's decision whether to perform a pure recognition or a simultaneous detection and recognition study. To be sure, he would be considered foolish to use a simultaneous detection and recognition design with perfectly detectable stimuli, but it has not been uncommon to use pure recognition designs when the stimuli are difficult to detect. In such experiments there are bound to be trials when the subject would prefer, if permitted, to say that no stimulus was presented. That not being allowed, what happens? Broadly speaking, there are two possibilities. Either the subject has some information about the stimulus which he then uses when forced to recognize, in which event he is more often correct than not, even though he does not believe a stimulus was presented; or he does not have any information at all, and so he can only choose arbitrarily, possibly with a bias, among the recognition responses. If the first possibility is correct, then the pure recognition experiment may well tell us directly about his ability to recognize the stimuli, but if the second is correct, these simple experiments cannot produce simple data. The response frequencies are a compound of his ability to recognize when he has detected and of his arbitrary assignment of undetected presentations to the recognition responses.

The necessary data to decide this point are included in Shipley's (1961) thesis. On each trial stimulus s, stimulus s', or noise n was presented, and the subjects were required both to detect, Y or N, and, no matter what the detection response, to recognize s or s'. The stimuli were tones differing both in frequency and intensity. (Because it is conceivable that there is an interaction between the detection and forced-recognition responses, the same experiment was run except that the subjects were not required to recognize when they failed to detect. No interaction was found.) We look to see whether the recognition of "No stimulus" responses depends upon the stimulus presentation. The conditional percentages of s responses when no detection is reported and, for comparison, when detection is reported are shown in Table 7 for each of the three presentations. Also shown are the comparable data for recognition in the two-alternative forced-choice design. Apparently these three subjects were unable differentially to recognize the stimuli when they failed to detect them. There are strong biases, but there is no correlation with the stimulus presented (except possibly a slight negative one for subject 3 in the Yes-No design).

It is important before proceeding further to assess the significance of these data. Above all, they suggest that a recognition experiment involving barely detectable stimuli should not employ a forced-choice design. Two such studies performed in different laboratories with slightly different levels

Table 7   Percentage of Detected and of Undetected Responses
Recognized as Stimulus s (Shipley, 1961)

Stimulus Presentation	Subject					
	1		2		3	
	Detected	Undetected	Detected	Undetected	Detected	Undetected
s	90.3	77.5	88.7	73.8	87.8	31.2
s'	7.6	75.7	19.7	74.7	11.7	41.5
n	40.8	72.2	56.8	78.6	47.9	31.5

Yes-No Design

Stimulus Presentation	Subject					
	1		2		3	
	Correct Detection	Incorrect Detection	Correct Detection	Incorrect Detection	Correct Detection	Incorrect Detection
s	87.6	43.4	87.2	63.3	87.3	42.7
s'	14.3	46.6	24.6	62.8	12.7	40.9

Forced-Choice Design

of detectability could easily lead to apparent differences in recognition, even when none existed. The relative stability, both experimentally and theoretically, of the forced-choice as against the three-response category scheme in discrimination studies (see Chapter 4, Sec. 5.2) must not be interpreted as a blanket recommendation for forced-choice designs in other types of experiments.

These data raise again the question of a threshold, for, when symmetric payoffs are used, the "no stimulus" response contains no residual information about the identity of the presented stimulus. This is certainly consistent with the notion of a detection threshold. It does not, however, prove that one exists. Another interpretation is that all information about the presentation is lost once the subject decides that no stimulus was presented. It should be possible to decide between these two hypotheses by running a simultaneous detection and recognition experiment with various asymmetric payoff matrices. If there is a threshold, the recognition of detected stimuli will be degraded in a predictable fashion as the detection frequency is increased by changing the payoffs; whereas, if we are witnessing a decision phenomenon, the recognition of detected stimuli will be independent of the frequency of detection responses. This study has not been performed.

Having made clear that the two types of recognition experiments must be treated separately, the remainder of this section is devoted to pure recognition studies.

7.2 Information Theory Analysis

Aside from traditional statistics of contingency tables, the main mathematical tool that has come to be used to study pure recognition with more than two or three stimulus presentations is information theory. It is impossible to devote the space needed for a complete review of Shannon's theory (Shannon & Weaver, 1949) or even of its varied uses in psychophysics, but fortunately several suitable summaries with extensive bibliographies already exist (Attneave, 1959; Luce, 1960; Miller, 1953, 1956).

Except for the words used, the description of a communication system assumed by the information theorists is identical to our complete identification design. They interpret S as the set of elementary signals that can be transmitted by the system, R as the set of signals that can be received, and ι as a given one-to-one correspondence between them. Thus S might be the ordinary alphabet, R the sequences of dots and dashes used in the Morse code, and ι the code relating them. A probability distribution p over $S \times R$ is assumed to exist—$p(s, r)$ is interpreted as the joint probability that signal s is transmitted and r is received. If we define

$$P(s) = \sum_{r \in R} p(s, r),$$

$$p(r) = \sum_{s \in S} p(s, r),$$

and

$$p(r \mid s) = \frac{p(s, r)}{P(s)},$$

then $P(s)$ is the probability that signal s is transmitted, $p(r)$ the unconditional probability that r is received, and $p(r \mid s)$ the conditional probability that r is received when s is transmitted. In a complete identification experiment, $P(s)$ is the probability that s is presented, $p(r)$, the unconditional probability of response r, and $p(r \mid s)$, the conditional probability of response r given stimulus s. In the communication terminology the matrix of conditional probabilities $p(r \mid s)$ is called a *noise matrix*, for by definition that which prevents communication from being perfect is *noise*; in a complete identification experiment it is called a confusion matrix.

Information theorists undertook to state by means of a single summary number the average information-transmitting characteristics of such a system. It was to be a measure that would satisfy certain a priori criteria and permit one to capture in precise theorems certain known empirical results concerning channel capacity, information transmission, and error correction. The major a priori requirement imposed by Shannon was this. Suppose that several signals are, in the statistical sense, independently selected and transmitted; then the average amount of information created by their joint selection shall be the sum of the average amounts of information created by their separate selections, that is, average information is postulated to be additive when the selections are independent. He showed that this coupled with other much weaker conditions implies that the measure must be of the form

$$H(S) = -\sum_{s \in S} P(s) \log P(s). \tag{42}$$

Usually, the base of the logarithm is chosen to be 2, thereby setting the unit of measure. Following a suggestion by J. Tukey, this unit is called a *bit*. A choice between two equally likely alternatives creates one bit; among 4, two bits; among 8, three bits; etc.

Two features of this measure should be noted. First, it is nonnegative and has the value 0 when and only when one of the probabilities is 1 (and so all the rest are 0). That is to say, no information is generated by the selection of an alternative that is certain to be selected; this agrees, for example, with the view that little or no information is transmitted by the conventional replies to conventional greetings. Second, the measure has its maximum value when all of the probabilities are equal; if there are k alternatives, the maximum is $\log_2 k$.

In like manner, we have as the information measure of the responses

$$H(R) = -\sum_{r \in R} p(r) \log_2 p(r), \tag{43}$$

and, as the conditional measure of the response given the stimulus,

$$H(R \mid S) = \sum_{s \in S} \sum_{r \in R} p(s, r) \log_2 p(r \mid s). \tag{44}$$

The quantity

$$T(S; R) = H(R) - H(R \mid S) \tag{45}$$

is called the *information transmitted* from the stimulus to the response. It not only plays a significant role in information theory itself, but it has proved to be a useful measure in psychology. It is not difficult to show that

$0 \leqslant T(S; R) \leqslant H(S)$; that T is 0 when and only when the responses are statistically independent of the stimuli, that is, when $p(r \mid s) = p(r)$; and that it is equal to $H(S)$, its maximum, when there is no confusion, that is, when $p[r \mid \iota(r)] = 1$ for all $r \in R$. Thus T is an inverse measure of how much degrading, on the average, is introduced by the subject.

The principal empirical results stemming from information analyses of recognition experiments are described in an excellent survey article by Miller (1956), so we need only summarize them very briefly here. Suppose that we select k stimuli on some unidimensional continuum, such as sound energy, so that they cover most of the sensible range and are more or less equally spaced; then $T(S; R)$ is approximately equal to $H(S)$ (which equals $\log_2 k$ when the stimuli are equally likely) in the range from 0 to roughly 2 bits. For $H(S)$ greater than 2 bits, the rate of increase of the transmitted information diminishes sharply, reaching a peak between 1.6 and 3.9 bits, depending upon the continuum. Increasing $H(S)$ beyond that point may in fact cause $T(S; R)$ to decrease. Moreover, for pitch at least, Pollack (1952) has shown that the range of frequencies can be varied by a factor of at least 20 with relatively little effect on the maximum amount of information transmitted by a fixed number of equally spaced stimuli.

If the stimuli are multidimensional, the maximum value of T can be increased considerably from what it is for any one of their dimensions, but the maximum is always less than the sum of the values of the separate component dimensions. Nonetheless, more seems to be gained by adding another dimension than by refining the categories per dimension. (See Beebe-Center, Rogers, & O'Connel, 1955; Halsey & Chapanis, 1954; Klemmer & Frick, 1953; Pollack, 1953; Pollack & Ficks, 1954).

The regularity and generality of these results is impressive, and much has been made of the relatively small values of transmitted information. On the one hand, it is well to know such facts when designing certain types of systems in which men must interact with information generating or receiving machines, and, on the other hand, they stand as summary statements in need of detailed scientific explanation and, thereby, refined restatement. Some writers have, I believe, taken the view that the behavioral regularities expressed in terms of the information measures themselves constitute a theory, but I am inclined to class them simply as empirical generalizations requiring theoretical analysis. It is often not easy to know when a particular relation stemming from experiments should be considered a generalization in need of explanation and when it should be introduced as an unanalyzed assumption of a theoretical system, but two features of these relations lead me to class them as generalizations. First, they are not really simple, certainly not in the sense that linearity, additivity, and independence assumptions are simple.

Second, they are statements about averages—not just averages of data, which are often used as estimates of probabilities, but averages over distinct classes of responses—and so the observed regularities are bound to mask much of the possibly interesting fine detail of the behavior.

McGill (1954, 1955a,b) and Garner and McGill (1956) extended the decomposition of transmitted information (Eq. 45) to more complex stimulus presentations. McGill's idea was, roughly, to ascertain how much each of the various possible determiners of the response, such as previous responses and stimulus presentations, contribute to the total information transmitted. He devised an additive decomposition in terms of the contributions of each variable and the various possible interactions among them. This constitutes an information theoretic, and hence nonparametric, analogue of the analysis of variance, and as such it is a useful device in the study of sequential dependencies among the responses and in discovering which events are determiners of the responses. For a summary of the ideas and applications, see Luce (1960).

7.3 A Choice Analysis of the Results of Information Theory

Little has been published attempting to account for the information theory findings in terms of the three response theories we have been considering. To show that work of this sort is possible, a choice theory analysis is given here. Also, see Luce (1959).

Consider stimuli that differ on only one physical dimension, such as energy. In terms of the distance measure (Eq. 6) introduced in Sec. 1.2, it is plausible that distance is simply additive for such stimuli. In terms of the η-scale, this amounts to assuming that

$$\eta(s, s'') = \eta(s, s') \, \eta(s', s'') \qquad (46)$$

when s, s' and s'' differ on one physical dimension and $s < s' < s''$. Let us suppose further that we choose k stimuli that are ordered $s_1 < s_2 < \ldots < s_k$ and spaced on that dimension so that successive pairs are equally recognizable in the sense that

$$\eta(s_i, s_{i+1}) = \eta, \qquad \text{for } i = 1, 2, \ldots, k - 1. \qquad (47)$$

Performing a simple induction on Eqs. 46 and 47, it is easy to see that

$$\eta(s_i, s_j) = \eta^{|i-j|}.$$

Thus the confusion matrix of scale values is of the form

$$
\begin{array}{c}
\text{Response} \\[4pt]
\begin{array}{cccccc}
& 1 & 2 & 3 & \cdots & k \\[4pt]
s_1 & 1 & \eta & \eta^2 & \cdots & \eta^{k-1} \\[4pt]
s_2 & \eta & 1 & \eta & \cdots & \eta^{k-2} \\[4pt]
s_3 & \eta^2 & \eta & 1 & \cdots & \eta^{k-3} \\
& \cdot & & & & \\
& \cdot & \cdots\cdots\cdots\cdots\cdots\cdots\cdots & & & \\
& \cdot & & & & \\
s_k & \eta^{k-1} & \eta^{k-2} & \eta^{k-3} & \cdots & 1
\end{array}
\end{array} \tag{48}
$$

Stimulus
Presentation

where the bias parameters are omitted.

The first thing to note is that the model has the often observed U-shape when the probabilities $p(r \mid s_r)$ are plotted against r. In Table 8 the predicted probabilities for the end and middle stimuli are presented for several small k's and for several plausible values of η. The dip is evident. Of course, the bias parameters affect the exact form of this U-shaped function.

Table 8   Comparison of the Theoretical Probability of Correct Identification for End and Middle Stimuli

k		η 0.50	0.25	0.10
2	$p(1 \mid s_1)$	0.667	0.800	0.909
3	$p(1 \mid s_1)$	0.571	0.762	0.901
	$p(2 \mid s_2)$	0.500	0.667	0.833
5	$p(1 \mid s_1)$	0.547	0.751	0.900
	$p(3 \mid s_3)$	0.400	0.615	0.820
7	$p(1 \mid s_1)$	0.546	0.750	0.900
	$p(4 \mid s_4)$	0.381	0.604	0.820

Next we look into the question of transmitted information. By what we have assumed for our stimuli, we know that the matrix of scale values for the $k = 2$ recognition design is

$$
\begin{array}{cc}
 & \begin{array}{cc} s_i & s_{i+1} \end{array} \\
\begin{array}{c} s_i \\ s_{i+1} \end{array} & \left[\begin{array}{cc} 1 & \eta \\ \eta & 1 \end{array} \right],
\end{array}
$$

again omitting biases. Assuming the independence condition, Assumption 4 on p. 114, the parallel forced-choice design has the matrix of scale values

$$
\begin{array}{cc}
 & \begin{array}{cc} 1 & \quad 2 \end{array} \\
\begin{array}{c} \langle s_i, s_{i+1} \rangle \\ \langle s_{i+1}, s_i \rangle \end{array} & \left[\begin{array}{cc} 1 & \eta^{\sqrt{2}} \\ \eta^{\sqrt{2}} & 1 \end{array} \right].
\end{array}
$$

In the light of our discussion of the quantal model, it is not clear whether the independence assumption is justified, but in order to continue the discussion we accept it. In discrimination work (see Chapter 4, Sec. 1.2) two stimuli are said to be one jnd (one just noticeable difference) apart if $p(1 \mid \langle s_i, s_{i+1} \rangle) = \frac{3}{4}$, in which case the forced-choice model yields

$$
\eta = (\tfrac{1}{3})^{1/\sqrt{2}}.
$$

For stimuli that are m-jnds apart in the sense that $m - 1$ stimuli can be found between them such that successive ones are one jnd apart, Eq. 46 implies

$$
\eta = (\tfrac{1}{3})^{m/\sqrt{2}}. \tag{49}
$$

For our calculations, let us consider k stimuli so spaced that successive ones are m jnds apart; thus the total range of stimuli is $(k - 1)m$ jnds. Specifically, let us fix the range at $2^6 = 64$ jnds and let $k = 5, 9, 17$, and 33 stimuli, which means that successive ones are separated by $m = 16, 8, 4$, and 2 jnds, respectively. For each k the confusion matrix of probabilities can be determined from the scale values given in Eq. 48, using Eq. 49 to determine η. Assuming that the stimuli are equally likely, the information transmitted is calculated using the formulas in Sec. 7.2. The results are shown in the last column of Table 9. Up to something just over three bits presented, the information transmitted is nearly equal to the stimulus information. Increasing the stimulus information further, the transmitted information increases less rapidly, reaching a maximum of about 3.6 bits. Not only does this correspond qualitatively to the data, but it is in about the right range of values. The data, however, appear to have arisen from a somewhat broader range of stimulus values and to have resulted in

Table 9   Choice Theory Predictions of Information Transmitted versus Information Presented

Number of Equally Likely Alternatives	Bits Presented	Bits Transmitted for Stimulus Range in jnds	
		16	64
3	1.58	1.56	1.58
5	2.32	1.90	2.32
9	3.17	1.53	3.12
17	4.09		3.59
33	5.04		3.45

somewhat smaller maxima, which suggests that we are using too small a value for η. It is obvious that we could select a value of η that would yield quantitatively the same summary results as the data; it is a much more subtle question whether this model can reproduce the whole confusion matrix in detail, and that has not been thoroughly investigated.

A second major information result is that the increase in information transmitted is relatively slight as the range is increased (Pollack, 1952). Two ranges, differing by a factor of four, are shown in columns 3 and 4 of Table 9. A considerable difference in the maximum exists, strongly suggesting that the present model is inadequate to explain these results.

A third information theory result concerns the less than additive increase of the transmitted information as the number of dimensions per stimulus is increased. We consider the simplest possible case of two perfectly detectable stimuli differing on two equally recognizable dimensions. Suppose s and s' are the stimulus values on one dimension and t and t' on the other and that their confusion matrices of scale values are

$$
\begin{array}{cc}
& \text{Response} \\
& \begin{array}{cc} s & s' \end{array} \\
\begin{array}{c} \text{Stimulus} \\ \text{Presentation} \end{array}
\begin{array}{c} s \\ s' \end{array}
& \begin{bmatrix} 1 & \eta \\ \eta & 1 \end{bmatrix}
\end{array}
\qquad
\begin{array}{cc}
& \text{Response} \\
& \begin{array}{cc} t & t' \end{array} \\
\begin{array}{c} t \\ t' \end{array}
& \begin{bmatrix} 1 & \eta \\ \eta & 1 \end{bmatrix}
\end{array}.
$$

For the choice model with Assumption 4, the scale values for the composite stimuli are

$$
\begin{array}{cc}
& \begin{array}{cc} \langle s, t \rangle & \langle s', t' \rangle \end{array} \\
\begin{array}{c} \langle s, t \rangle \\ \langle s', t' \rangle \end{array}
& \begin{bmatrix} 1 & \eta^{\sqrt{2}} \\ \eta^{\sqrt{2}} & 1 \end{bmatrix}.
\end{array}
$$

The ratio of the information transmitted in the composite case to that in the unidimensional case, assuming equally likely stimulus presentations, is shown in Table 10 for three values of η. The ratio is always less than 2, and it approaches 1 as the stimuli become more recognizable.

Table 10   Predicted Ratio of Information Transmitted for Two-Alternative Two-Dimensional Case to Two-Alternative One-Dimensional Case

η	0.50	0.25	0.10
ratio	1.90	1.66	1.38

Although there are some tentative indications that the recognition choice model may account for the information theory results, the only really satisfactory test is whether it accounts for the whole confusion matrix. Assuming that the stimuli are physically ordered and that i is the correct response for stimulus presentation s_i, we have the matrix of scale values

$$
\begin{array}{c}
\\
s_1 \\
s_2 \\
\cdot \\
\cdot \\
\cdot \\
s_k
\end{array}
\begin{bmatrix}
\eta(1,1)b(1) & \eta(1,2)b(2) & \cdots & \eta(1,k)b(k) \\
\eta(2,1)b(1) & \eta(2,2)b(2) & \cdots & \eta(2,k)b(k) \\
\multicolumn{4}{c}{\dotfill} \\
\eta(k,1)b(1) & \eta(k,2)b(2) & \cdots & \eta(k,k)b(k)
\end{bmatrix}
\begin{array}{c}
1 \quad\quad 2 \quad \cdots \quad k \\
\end{array}.
$$

Assuming that Eq. 46 holds, then for $i < j$,

$$\eta(i,j) = \eta(i, i+1)\eta(i+1, i+2) \ldots \eta(j-1, j),$$

and, recalling that $\eta(i,j) = \eta(j,i)$ and that $\eta(i,i) = 1$, it follows that there are only $k - 1$ independent stimulus parameters, the $\eta(i, i+1)$, and $k - 1$ bias parameters, the $b(i)$, to be estimated.

In practice, we can only be certain that the conditional probabilities on and near the main diagonal are appreciably larger than zero, and so any estimation scheme had better rely heavily upon these entries. One possibility—one that has no known statistical properties but that uses entries only from the main diagonal and adjacent cells—is

$$\eta(i, i + 1)^2 = \left[\frac{\eta(i, i + 1)b(i + 1)}{b(i)}\right]\left[\frac{\eta(i, i + 1)b(i)}{b(i + 1)}\right]$$

$$= \frac{p(i + 1 \mid i)}{p(i \mid i)} \frac{p(i \mid i + 1)}{p(i + 1 \mid i + 1)}$$

and

$$\left[\frac{b(i + 1)}{b(i)}\right]^2 = \left[\frac{\eta(i, i + 1)b(i + 1)}{b(i)}\right]\left[\frac{b(i + 1)}{\eta(i, i + 1)b(i)}\right]$$

$$= \frac{p(i + 1 \mid i)}{p(i \mid i)} \frac{p(i + 1 \mid i + 1)}{p(i \mid i + 1)}.$$

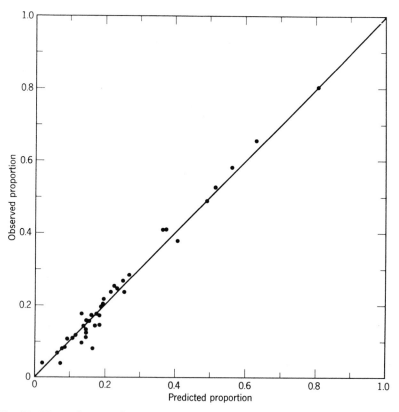

Fig. 21. Observed proportion versus proportions predicted by the choice model for McGuire's (Shepard, 1958b) size recognition data. The estimation scheme and the collapsing of the data are described in the text.

We apply this estimation scheme to McGuire's data on size recognition (reported in Shepard, 1958b), although they are not ideal because ten subjects are averaged together. Each subject responded to 80 presentations of each of nine circular areas. A χ^2 comparison of the predicted and observed proportions yields a value of 96.3 which with $8 \times 9 - 16 = 56$ degrees of freedom is highly significant. This is none too surprising because the estimation scheme completely ignores the small entries in the table, which, of course, contribute heavily to χ^2. That the estimates are probably nonoptimal is indicated, for example, by the fact that about half the total contribution to χ^2 comes from the first column. In the light of the failings of the estimation procedure, a more reasonable test of the model is to lump together all entries to the left of cell $i - 1$ in row i and all of those to the right of the $i + 1$ entry. This reduces χ^2 to 15.6 and the degrees of freedom to 14, yielding $0.2 < p < 0.5$. The observed versus predicted proportions for this collapsing are shown in Fig. 21. These results suggest that a better estimation method might very well result in a nonsignificant over-all χ^2.

8. SIMULTANEOUS DETECTION AND RECOGNITION

Even restricting our attention to the simplest simultaneous detection and recognition designs, namely $S = \mathscr{S} = \{s, s', \emptyset\}$, we find that relatively little work has been reported. Because the ideas are adaptations of those we have already discussed, it will suffice simply to outline them.

8.1 Signal Detectability Analysis

Following the general structure of the signal detectability model, there is a decision axis relating stimulus s to stimulus s', another relating s to noise, and a third relating s' to noise. Tanner (1956) assumed that they can be represented in the plane, as in Fig. 22. The three intersections are supposed to occur at the means of the distributions projected on the several axes. The noise and each of the stimulus-plus-noise distributions are assumed to be independent and normal, all with equal variance. The two detection axes are separated by some angle θ, not necessarily $90°$.

Tanner (1956) used this structure to analyze the pure recognition experiment $\mathscr{S} = \{s, s'\}$. I did not present this in the last section because no testable conclusions seem to derive from it. Swets and Birdsall (1956) discussed the simultaneous detection and recognition experiment, proposing

DETECTION AND RECOGNITION

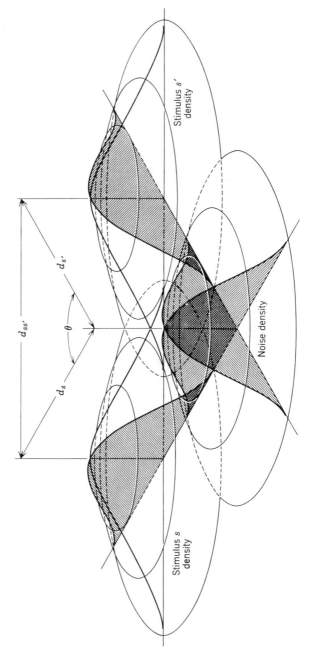

Fig. 22. Representation of stimulus effects in the signal detectability model for simultaneous detection and recognition of two stimuli s and s'. The two decision axes of the simple Yes-No design are assumed to be separated by an angle θ, not in general 90°.

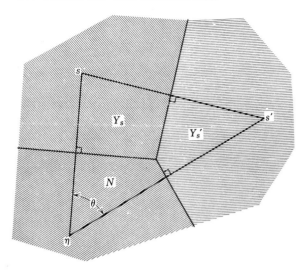

Fig. 23. A decision rule proposed by Swets and Birdsall (1956) for the two-stimulus simultaneous detection and recognition experiment.

the decision rule shown in Fig. 23. The three straight lines meet at a point in the triangle formed by connecting the means of the three distributions; each line is orthogonal to a side of the triangle.

8.2 Choice Analysis

The choice model analysis follows immediately from Eq. 5 and Assumptions 1 to 3:

$$
\begin{array}{c}
\begin{array}{ccc} Y_s & Y_{s'} & N \end{array} \\
\begin{array}{c} s \\ s' \\ n \end{array}
\left[
\begin{array}{ccc}
1 & \lambda b & \eta c \\
\lambda & b & \eta' c \\
\eta & \eta' b & c
\end{array}
\right]
\end{array}
\qquad (50)
$$

where $\eta = \eta(s, n)$, $\eta' = \eta(s', n)$, and $\lambda = \eta(s, s')$.

The adequacy of the choice model for this simultaneous identification design can be tested, using Shipley's (1961) data. The parameters η and η' are estimated as the mean of those obtained from the simple Yes-No and two-alternative forced-choice experiments (Table 2). The remaining

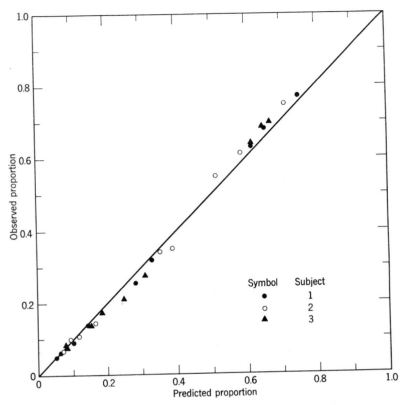

Fig. 24. Observed proportions versus those predicted by the choice model for a two-stimulus simultaneous detection and recognition design. The data are from Shipley (1961). The parameter values used were

Subject	η	η'	λ	b	c
1	0.240	0.325	0.089	1.068	1.785
2	0.372	0.358	0.139	0.767	1.610
3	0.298	0.389	0.124	0.958	1.241

three parameters are estimated from the data in question by

$$\lambda = \left[\frac{p(Y_{s'} \mid s)}{p(Y_s \mid s)} \frac{p(Y_s \mid s')}{p(Y_{s'} \mid s')} \right]^{\frac{1}{2}}$$

$$b = \left[\frac{p(N \mid s)}{p(Y_s \mid s)} \frac{p(Y_{s'} \mid s)}{p(Y_s \mid s)} \frac{p(Y_{s'} \mid s')}{p(Y_s \mid s')} \frac{p(Y_{s'} \mid s')}{p(N \mid s')} \frac{p(Y_{s'} \mid n)}{p(Y_s \mid n)} \right]^{\frac{1}{4}}$$

$$c = \left[\frac{p(N \mid s)}{p(Y_s \mid s)} \frac{p(Y_{s'} \mid s)}{p(Y_s \mid s)} \frac{p(N \mid s')}{p(Y_s \mid s')} \frac{p(N \mid n)}{p(Y_s \mid n)} \frac{p(N \mid n)}{p(Y_{s'} \mid n)} \right]^{\frac{1}{4}},$$

which follow immediately from Eq. 50. This leaves three degrees of freedom. The observed versus predicted proportions are shown in Fig. 24. Although the prediction is really quite good, the errors appear to be not entirely random: the predicted values are consistently less than the observed for the larger probabilities and consistently more for the middle values. Whether better estimates would eliminate this deviation is not known.

9. DETECTION OF AN UNKNOWN STIMULUS

A simple Yes-No detection experiment in which the stimulus presentation can be one of two or more different stimuli is said to involve the detection of an unknown stimulus. It is, of course, a partial identification experiment—the first to be examined in this chapter. For simplicity we restrict our attention to the case in which the unknown stimulus is one of two possibilities, s or s'. The existing data (Creelman, 1959; Green, 1958; Swets, Shipley, McKey, & Green, 1959; Tanner, Swets, & Green, 1956; Veniar, 1958a,b,c) indicate that the detectability of an unknown stimulus is less than that of either stimulus singly and that the decrement is an increasing function of the recognizability of the stimuli. Why?

One theory, suitable for pure tones, assumes that a subject can listen at any instant to only a narrow band of frequencies and that, when the signal is unknown, he must continually shift from filter to filter (Tanner, Swets, & Green, 1956). Because he sometimes listens through the wrong filter, the probability of detecting an unknown stimulus must be less than that for a known one.

A second acoustic theory, proposed by Green (1958), assumes that the subject can listen through as many filters as needed, each being centered on a different frequency. The effect of increasing the number of frequencies is to increase the total amount of noise heard without affecting the detectability of the stimulus in a single band. This produces an over-all reduction in the detectability. The theory states precisely how the detectability reduces with the number of unknown frequencies, the band width of the filter being a parameter in the model.

Detailed statements of these theories and some relevant acoustic data are given in Swets, Shipley, McKey, & Green (1959); on the whole, the scanning model comes off better than the multiband model. Veniar (1958a,b,c) suggests that neither is completely adequate. Whichever may be better for pure tones, neither is readily generalizable to other classes of stimuli for which, presumably, the same decrease in detectability occurs. Possibly each stimulus modality requires its own explanation, but, in the absence of any compelling data or arguments, one hopes that the phenomenon is of a more general response character and that it requires fewer specific assumptions than those made in the filter theories.

Shipley (1960) suggested such an idea, one that is applicable to any response model. She supposed that the subject is covertly recognizing the stimuli as well as overtly detecting them, even though he makes no recognition response. If so, and if we assume the choice model, the matrix of scale values is simply Eq. 50 with the two detection responses combined.

To show that this predicts results qualitatively similar to those observed, consider the special case in which the stimuli are equally detectable and there is no recognition bias, that is, $\eta = \eta'$ and $b = 1$. Then we can combine the two stimulus presentations into one because the two rows are the same:

$$\begin{array}{cc} & \text{Response} \\ & Y \quad N \end{array}$$

$$\begin{array}{cc} \text{Stimulus} & s \text{ or } s' \\ \text{Presentation} & n \end{array} \begin{bmatrix} 1 + \lambda & \eta c \\ 2\eta & c \end{bmatrix}.$$

This is equivalent, in the sense of generating the same probabilities, to a matrix of scale values of the form

$$\begin{array}{cc} & Y \quad N \end{array}$$

$$\begin{array}{cc} s \text{ or } s' \\ n \end{array} \begin{bmatrix} 1 & \zeta c' \\ \zeta & c' \end{bmatrix},$$

where

$$\zeta = \frac{\eta}{[(1 + \lambda)/2]^{\frac{1}{2}}}. \tag{51}$$

This is the form of the simple Yes-No matrix discussed in Sec. 2.2, and so ζ is an apparent detection parameter and

$$c' = \frac{c/2}{[(1 + \lambda)/2]^{\frac{1}{2}}}. \tag{52}$$

is an apparent bias parameter.

The probability of detecting an unknown stimulus is smaller than that of a known stimulus if and only if $\zeta > \eta$, and that in turn holds if and only if $\lambda < 1$, as it must be for distinct stimuli. Moreover, as the stimuli become more recognizable, that is, as λ gets smaller, ζ gets larger and so detectability becomes poorer, as has been observed.

A parallel development exists for the forced-choice design. Omitting the biases, the simultaneous detection-recognition matrix of scale values is seen to be

Responses

$$
\begin{array}{c}
\text{Stimulus} \\
\text{Presentation}
\end{array}
\quad
\begin{array}{c}
 \\
\langle s, n\rangle \\
\langle s', n\rangle \\
\langle n, s\rangle \\
\langle n, s'\rangle
\end{array}
\begin{array}{cccc}
1s & 1s' & 2s & 2s' \\
\left[\begin{array}{cccc}
1 & \lambda & \eta^{\sqrt{2}} & \delta \\
\lambda & 1 & \delta & \eta'^{\sqrt{2}} \\
\eta^{\sqrt{2}} & \delta & 1 & \lambda \\
\delta & \eta'^{\sqrt{2}} & \lambda & 1
\end{array}\right]
\end{array},
$$

where δ is given by

$$(\log \delta)^2 = (\log \eta)^2 + (\log \eta')^2$$

and the other symbols have their previous meanings. To see what happens qualitatively, again suppose $\eta = \eta'$ and that the biases all equal 1; then we can collapse on both rows and columns:

$$
\begin{array}{c}
 \\
\langle s \text{ or } s', n\rangle \\
\langle n, s \text{ or } s'\rangle
\end{array}
\begin{array}{cc}
1 & 2 \\
\left[\begin{array}{cc}
1 + \lambda & 2\eta^{\sqrt{2}} \\
2\eta^{\sqrt{2}} & 1 + \lambda
\end{array}\right]
\end{array}.
$$

The standard form for the unbiased forced-choice matrix of scale values is

$$
\begin{array}{c}
 \\
\langle s, n\rangle \\
\langle n, s\rangle
\end{array}
\begin{array}{cc}
1 & 2 \\
\left[\begin{array}{cc}
1 & \xi^{\sqrt{2}} \\
\xi^{\sqrt{2}} & 1
\end{array}\right]
\end{array},
$$

so the effective stimulus parameter is

$$\xi = \frac{\eta}{[(1 + \lambda)/2]^{1/\sqrt{2}}}. \tag{53}$$

As for the Yes-No design, there is an increasing reduction in detectability as the stimuli are made more identifiable, that is, as λ is made smaller. We observe that the apparent loss in detectability is greater in the forced-choice than in the Yes-No design because

$$\zeta = \frac{\eta}{[(1 + \lambda)/2]^{1/2}} < \frac{\eta}{[(1 + \lambda)/2]^{1/\sqrt{2}}} = \xi.$$

To see whether Shipley's idea has any possibility of being correct, I turn again to her (1961) data. Both the simultaneous detection-recognition and the detection of an unknown stimulus conditions were run, so we can collapse the first data matrix on the recognition responses and compare it with the second. This is done in Table 11 for the Yes-No experiment and in Table 12 for the forced-choice experiment. Although there are some differences, which may very well be due to different response biases, they seem in sufficient accord to warrant more study of the idea.

Table 11   Per Cent Yes Responses in the Yes-No Design When the Signal Is Unknown

Stimulus Presentation	Subject					
	1		2		3	
	Observed	Calculated	Observed	Calculated	Observed	Calculated
s	77.5	74.4	69.2	67.6	73.3	78.9
s'	65.2	68.0	70.4	65.2	55.1	72.2
n	27.8	23.1	33.3	25.1	34.6	31.6

The calculated columns are obtained by collapsing the recognition responses in the corresponding detection and recognition experiment (Shipley, 1961). See Table 2 for a description of the experimental conditions.

Table 12   Per Cent Correct Responses in Forced-Choice Design When Stimulus Is Known and When It Is Unknown

Stimulus Presentation	Subject								
	1			2			3		
	Stimulus Known	Stimulus Unknown	Calculated	Stimulus Known	Stimulus Unknown	Calculated	Stimulus Known	Stimulus Unknown	Calculated
$\langle s, n \rangle$	89.5	81.8	83.9	79.8	70.9	66.7	83.6	78.1	72.2
$\langle s', n \rangle$	83.5	76.2	76.8	79.5	73.8	67.7	79.1	61.7	67.8
$\langle n, s \rangle$	88.0	83.0	83.1	79.6	70.7	81.9	86.6	78.3	84.2
$\langle n, s' \rangle$	83.8	78.2	77.8	81.2	78.1	81.0	83.2	80.5	83.1

The calculated columns are obtained by collapsing the recognition responses for the four response detection and recognition experiment (Shipley, 1961). See Table 2 for a description of the experimental conditions.

10. CONCLUSIONS

Although detection and recognition experiments have long been performed—not always under those names—interest in them in theoretical circles has increased considerably during the last ten or fifteen years, and a healthy interaction of theory and experiment has evolved. There is every reason to expect a continued rapid accretion in our knowledge of these basic processes during the 1960's. Perhaps a brief indication of some of the possible paths of work is a good way to summarize the progress we have made.

1. As I have been at pains to point out, there are now at least three different response theories designed to account for detection behavior. One task, therefore, is to decide among them or, if need be, to develop better theories for at least several of the more important modalities, including visual and acoustic intensity.

2. No matter what response model is ultimately judged best, questions of the dependence and independence of effects are bound to exist. For example, we must know when a forced-choice design can be treated as an independent combination of several Yes-No designs. At present, we make *ad hoc* assumptions that apply only to certain extreme cases: a white noise background is assumed to result in independent effects, whereas a pure tone background is assumed to result in a perfect correlation of effects. Just why we should make these assumptions and what we should assume in intermediate cases is unclear; hence we need a detailed characterization, stated in terms of the physical nature of the stimulation, of the dependencies that are introduced.

3. Again, no matter how we resolve the question of the best response theory, we shall need a theory to relate the stimulus parameters to the physical properties of the stimuli and one to relate the bias parameters to various other objective features of the experiments, especially the payoffs. Considerable research is currently under way to uncover the stimulus-parameter relations for both the signal detectability and threshold models. Rather less effort is being devoted to the biasing problem, partly because it strikes a number of workers as less interesting than the stimulus problem, which they feel deals with the fundamental mechanisms of hearing and vision. Without questioning the importance of theories about the stimuli, it should not be forgotten that theories about the bias parameters are likely to get at fundamental issues in learning and cognition and so, in my view, deserve as much careful attention.

4. The theoretical analysis of stimulus recognition is less developed than that of detection, despite all of the interesting work that has resulted from applications of the information-theoretic measures. No one has yet effectively accounted for the information-theory findings in terms of any of the response theories we have discussed. My attempts to apply the choice theory are incomplete and are not entirely satisfactory. No really serious attempts have been made using the other theories, mainly because

of the severe conceptual difficulties that seem to arise when there are more than two or at most three stimuli.

Substantively, recognition seems to be somewhat different from detection, even though both are studied experimentally by means of complete identification designs. This apparent difference should not be forgotten by theorists, for it may mean that quite different response theories are needed. It would not surprise me if detection were a discrete threshold phenomenon, whereas recognition might turn out to be a continuous process or, at least, well approximated by one.

References

Attneave, F. *Applications of information theory to psychology.* New York: Holt, 1959.

Beebe-Center, J. B., Rogers, M. S., & O'Connel, D. N. Transmission of information about sucrose and saline solutions through the sense of taste. *J. Psychol.*, 1955, **39**, 157–160.

Békésy, G. von. Über das Fechner'sche Gesetz und seine Bedeutung für die Theorie der akustischen Beobachtungsfehler und die Theorie des Hörens. *Ann. Phys.*, 1930, **7**, 329–359.

Birdsall, T. G. The theory of signal detectability. In H. Quastler (Ed.), *Information theory in psychology*, Glencoe, Ill.: The Free Press, 1955. Pp. 391–402.

Birdsall, T. G. *Detection of a signal specified exactly with a noisy stored reference signal.* T.R. 93, Electronic Defense Group, Univer. of Mich., Ann Arbor, 1959.

Blackwell, H. R. *Psychophysical thresholds: experimental studies of methods of measurement.* Engineering Research Bulletin 36, Ann Arbor: Univer. of Michigan, 1953.

Bradley, R. A. Incomplete block rank analysis: on the appropriateness of the model for the method of paired comparisons. *Biometrics*, 1954, **10**, 375–390.(a)

Bradley, R. A. Rank analysis of incomplete block designs. II. Additional tables for the method of paired comparisons. *Biometrika*, 1954, **41**, 502–537.(b)

Bradley, R. A. Rank analysis of incomplete block designs. III. Some large sample results on estimation and power for a method of paired comparisons. *Biometrika*, 1955, **42**, 450–470.

Bradley, R. A., & Terry, M. E. Rank analysis of incomplete block designs. I. The method of paired comparisons. *Biometrika*, 1952, **39**, 324–345.

Bush, R. R., Luce, R. D., & Rose, R. M. Learning models for psychophysics. In R. C. Atkinson (Ed.), *Studies in mathematical psychology*, Vol. I. Stanford: Stanford Univer. Press, in press, 1963.

Clarke, F. R. Constant-ratio rule for confusion matrices in speech communication. *J. acoust. Soc. Amer.*, 1957, **29**, 715–720.

Clarke, F. R., Birdsall, T. G., & Tanner, W. P., Jr. Two types of R.O.C. curves and definitions of parameters. *J. acoust. Soc. Amer.*, 1959, **31**, 629–630.

Corso, J. F. The neural quantum theory of sensory discrimination. *Psychol. Bull.*, 1956, **53**, 371–393.

Creelman, C. D. *Detection of signals of uncertain frequency.* T.M. 71, Electronic Defense Group, Univer. of Mich., Ann Arbor, 1959.

Creelman, C. D. *Detection of complex signals as a function of signal band width and duration.* T.R. 99, Electronic Defense Group, Univer. of Mich., Ann Arbor, 1960.

Edwards, W. The theory of decision making. *Psych. Bull.*, 1954, **51**, 380–417.

Edwards, W. Behavioral decision theory. In *Annual Reviews of Psychology*, Vol. 12. Palo Alto, Calif.: Annual Reviews, Inc. 1961. Pp. 473–498.

Egan, J. P., Schulman, A. I., & Greenberg, G. Z. Operating characteristics determined by binary decisions and by ratings. *J. acoust. Soc. Amer.*, 1959, **31**, 768–773.

Elliott, P. B. *Tables of d'.* T.R. 97, Electronics Defense Group, Univer. of Mich., Ann Arbor, 1959.

Garner, W. R., & McGill, W. J. Relation between uncertainty, variance, and correlation analysis. *Psychometrika*, 1956, **21**, 219–228.

Green, D. M. Detection of multiple component signals in noise. *J. acoust. Soc. Amer.*, 1958, **30**, 904–911.

Green, D. M. Psychoacoustics and detection theory. *J. acoust. Soc. Amer.*, 1960, **32**, 1189–1203.

Green, D. M., Birdsall, T. G., & Tanner, W. P., Jr. Signal detection as a function of signal intensity and duration. *J. acoust. Soc. Amer.*, 1957, **29**, 523–531.

Halsey, R. M., & Chapanis, A. On the number of absolutely identifiable spectra hues. *J. opt. Soc. Amer.*, 1954, **41**, 1057–1058.

Klemmer, E. T., & Frick, F. C. Assimilation of information from dot and matrix patterns. *J. exp. Psychol.*, 1953, **45**, 15–19.

Licklider, J. C. R. Three auditory theories. In S. Koch (Ed.), *Psychology: a study of a science*, Vol. 1. New York: McGraw-Hill, 1959. Pp. 41–144.

Luce, R. D. *Individual choice behavior.* New York: Wiley, 1959.

Luce, R. D. The theory of selective information and some of its behavioral applications. In R. D. Luce (Ed.), *Developments in mathematical psychology.* Glencoe, Ill.: The Free Press, 1960.

Luce, R. D. A threshold theory for simple detection experiments. *Psychol. Rev.*, in press, 1963.

McGill, W. J. Multivariate information transmission. *Psychometrika*, 1954, **19**, 97–116.

McGill, W. J. Isomorphism in statistical analysis. In H. Quastler (Ed.), *Information theory in psychology.* Glencoe, Ill.: The Free Press, 1955. Pp. 56–62.(a)

McGill, W. J. The relation between uncertainty and variance. *Proc. 1954 Conf. Test Probl. Educ. Test. Serv.*, 1955, 37–42.(b)

Miller, G. A. What is information measurement? *Amer. Psychol.*, 1953, **8**, 3–11.

Miller, G. A. The magical number seven, plus or minus two: some limits on our capacity for processing information. *Psychol. Rev.*, 1956, **63**, 81–97.

Neisser, U. R. G. *A methodological study of the quantal hypothesis in auditory psychophysics.* Unpublished doctoral dissertation, Harvard University, 1955.

Peterson, W. W., Birdsall, T. G., & Fox, W. C. The theory of signal detectability. *IRE Trans. Professional Group on Information Theory*, 1954, **4**, 171–212.

Pollack, I. Information of elementary auditory displays. *J. acoust. Soc. Amer.*, 1952, **24**, 745–750.

Pollack, I. The information of elementary auditory displays. II. *J. acoust. Soc. Amer.*, 1953, **25**, 765–769.

Pollack, I., & Ficks, L. Information of elementary multidimensional auditory displays. *J. acoust. Soc. Amer.*, 1954, **26**, 155–158.

Restle, F. *Psychology of judgment and choice.* New York: Wiley, 1961.

Senders, Virginia L. Further analysis of response sequences in the setting of a psychophysical experiment. *Amer. J. Psychol.*, 1953, **66**, 215–228.

Senders, Virginia L., & Sowards, A. Analysis of response sequences in the setting of a psychophysical experiment. *Amer. J. Psychol.*, 1952, **65**, 358–374.

Shannon, C. E., & Weaver, W. *The mathematical theory of communication*. Urbana: Univer. of Illinois Press, 1949.

Shepard, R. N. Stimulus and response generalization: a stochastic model relating generalization to distance in a psychological space. *Psychometrika*, 1957, **22**, 325–345.

Shepard, R. N. Stimulus and response generalization: deduction of the generalization gradient from a trace model. *Psychol. Rev.*, 1958, **65**, 242–256.(a)

Shepard, R. N. Stimulus and response generalization: tests of a model relating generalization to distance in psychological space. *J. exp. Psychol.*, 1958, **55**, 509–523.(b)

Shipley, Elizabeth F. A model for detection and recognition with signal uncertainty. *Psychometrika*, 1960, **25**, 273–289.

Shipley, Elizabeth F. *Detection and recognition with uncertainty*. Unpublished doctoral dissertation, Univer. of Pennsylvania, 1961.

Smith, M., & Wilson, Edna A. A model of the auditory threshold and its application to the problem of the multiple observer. *Psychol. Monogr.*, 1953, **67** (9, Whole No. 359).

Speeth, S. D., & Mathews, M. V. Sequential effects in the signal detection situation. *J. acoust. Soc. Amer.*, 1961, **33**, 1046–1054.

Stevens, S. S., Morgan, C. T., & Volkmann, J. Theory of the neural quantum in the discrimination of loudness and pitch. *Amer. J. Psychol.*, 1941, **54**, 315–335.

Suppes, P. A linear model for a continuum of responses. In R. R. Bush, & W. K. Estes (Eds.), *Studies in mathematical learning theory*. Stanford: Stanford Univer. Press, 1959. Pp. 400–414.

Suppes, P. Stimulus-sampling theory for a continuum of responses. In K. J. Arrow, S. Karlin, & P. Suppes (Eds.), *Mathematical methods in the social sciences*, 1959. Stanford: Stanford Univer. Press, 1960. Pp. 348–365.

Swets, J. A. Indices of signal detectability obtained with various psychophysical procedures. *J. acoust. Soc. Amer.*, 1959, **31**, 511–513.

Swets, J. A. Detection theory and psychophysics: a review. *Psychometrika*, 1961, **26**, 49–63.(a)

Swets, J. A. Is there a sensory threshold? *Science*, 1961, **134**, 168–177.(b)

Swets, J. A., & Birdsall, T. G. The human use of information III. Decision making in signal detection and recognition situations involving multiple alternatives. *IRE Trans. Professional Group on Inform. Theory*, **2**, 1956, 138–165.

Swets, J. A., Shipley, Elizabeth F., McKey, Molly J., & Green, D. M. Multiple observations of signals in noise. *J. acoust. Soc. Amer.*, 1959, **31**, 514–521.

Swets, J. A., Tanner, W. P., Jr., & Birdsall, T. G. *The evidence for a decision-making theory of visual detection*. T.R. 40, Electronic Defense Group, Univer. of Mich., Ann Arbor, 1955.

Swets, J. A., Tanner, W. P., Jr., & Birdsall, T. G. Decision processes in perception. *Psychol. Rev.*, 1961, **68**, 301–340.

Tanner, W. P., Jr. On the design of psychophysical experiments. In H. Quastler (Ed.), *Information theory in psychology*, Glencoe, Ill.: The Free Press, 1955. Pp. 403–414.

Tanner, W. P., Jr. Theory of recognition. *J. acoust. Soc. Amer.*, 1956, **28**, 882–888.

Tanner, W. P., Jr. Theory of signal detectability as an interpretive tool for psychophysical data. *J. acoust. Soc. Amer.*, 1960, **32**, 1140–1147.

Tanner, W. P., Jr. Physiological implications of psychophysical data. *Ann. N.Y. Acad. Sci.*, 1961, **89**, 752–765.

Tanner, W. P., Jr., & Birdsall, T. G. Definitions of d' and η as psychophysical measures. *J. acoust. Soc. Amer.*, 1958, **30**, 922–928.

Tanner, W. P., Jr., Birdsall, T. G., & Clarke, F. R. *The concept of the ideal observer in psychophysics.* T.R. 98, Electronic Defense Group, Univer. of Mich., Ann Arbor, 1960.

Tanner, W. P., Jr., & Norman, R. Z. The human use of information. II. Signal detection for the case of an unknown signal parameter. *IRE Trans. Professional Group on Information Theory*, 1954, **4**, 222–226.

Tanner, W. P., Jr., & Swets, J. A. A decision making theory of visual detection. *Psychol. Rev.*, 1954, **61**, 401–409.(a)

Tanner, W. P., Jr., & Swets, J. A. The human use of information. I. Signal detection for the case of the signal known exactly. *IRE Trans. Professional Group on Information Theory.* 1954, **4**, 213–221.(b)

Tanner, W. P., Jr., Swets, J. A., & Green, D. M. *Some general properties of the hearing mechanism.* T.R. 30, Electronic Defense Group, Univer. of Mich., Ann Arbor, 1956.

Van Meter, D., & Middleton, D. Modern statistical approaches to reception in communication theory. *IRE Trans. Professional Group on Information Theory*, 1954, **4**, 119–145.

Veniar, Florence A. Effect of auditory cue on discrimination of auditory stimuli. *J. acoust. Soc. Amer.*, 1958, **30**, 1079–1081.(a)

Veniar, Florence A. Signal detection as a function of frequency ensemble. I. *J. acoust. Soc. Amer.*, 1958, **30**, 1020–1024.(b)

Veniar, Florence A. Signal detection as a function of frequency ensemble. II. *J. acoust. Soc. Amer.*, 1958, **30**, 1075–1078.(c)

Wald, A. *Statistical decision functions.* New York: Wiley, 1950.

4

Discrimination[1,2,3]

R. Duncan Luce
University of Pennsylvania

Eugene Galanter
University of Washington

1. *This work was supported in part by grant NSF G-8864 from the National Science Foundation to the University of Pennsylvania and by the Office of Naval Research Contract NONR-551(37). Reproduction in whole or part is permitted for any purpose of the United States Government.*
2. *We wish to thank Francis W. Irwin, G. A. Miller, and Elizabeth F. Shipley and our students for their thoughtful comments on drafts of this material.*
3. *Although some of the basic ideas introduced here are the same as or similar to those involved in the analysis of detection and recognition experiments, we have purposely restated them so that the two chapters are independent.*

Contents

Discrimination

"To note the differences between. To set apart as different; differentiate; distinguish. To observe a difference; distinguish. To make a distinction; treat unequally or unfairly." These are the ordinary meanings of *discriminate*. Traditionally, in psychophysics, it has had a special meaning which we take up first; later, in Sec. 5, we consider experiments in which the responses are more nearly coordinate with the dictionary meaning.

In many early discrimination experiments the stimuli differed on only one physical dimension, and the subject judged not only whether the two stimuli of a presentation differed but which he believed to be the larger, or more intense, etc. Thus his possible responses were "larger," "same," and "smaller," or something equivalent. Later studies deviated even more from the usual meaning of discriminate in that the "same" response was omitted, for evidence accumulated that subjects were quite unstable in their definition of that category (Thompson, 1920; Boring, 1920). When the only permitted responses are "larger" and "smaller," or the like, we call it a *forced-choice* procedure—"forced" because the subject is not permitted to say that two stimuli are the same, even when they are or seem to be. The models we discuss first are designed to account for forced-choice data.

The exact responses used, words or other signals, depend upon how the experiment is implemented, but there must be just two when pairs of stimuli are presented and they must be unambiguously related to the physical characteristics of the stimuli. For example, if one stimulus is presented after the other, then the subject can be asked to designate whether the first or the second is the larger or, equivalently, whether the second is larger or smaller than the first.[4] If the stimuli, for example, color patches, are presented simultaneously, then spatial designations such as "up" and "down" or "right" and "left" are used or the patches are labeled 1 and 2 or A and B, etc. In any event, a label that is unambiguous to both the subject and the experimenter is used.

In terms of the notation described in Chapter 2, we have a set $\mathscr{S}$ composed of stimuli that are assumed to differ on only one continuous physical dimension. This dimension can be anything we choose—mass, energy, frequency, etc.—as long as there is a physical measure that defines a weak

---

[4] The logical equivalence of these responses does not imply that two experiments which differed only in this way would yield identical data. See pp. 194, 224 ff.

ordering $\geqslant$ over $\mathscr{S}$, that is, $\geqslant$ must be a connected, reflexive, and transitive binary relation. In the following we shall say that $\varDelta$ is "larger than" $\varDelta'$ if $\varDelta > \varDelta'$ under the given physical ordering. In the simplest case the presentation set S is a subset of $\mathscr{S} \times \mathscr{S}$, and the abstract response set R is simply $\{1, 2\}$ (or any other pair of symbols). If we let

$$I_1 = \{\langle \varDelta^1, \varDelta^2 \rangle \mid \varDelta^1, \varDelta^2 \in \mathscr{S} \text{ and } \varDelta^1 > \varDelta^2\}$$

$$I_2 = \{\langle \varDelta^1, \varDelta^2 \rangle \mid \varDelta^1, \varDelta^2 \in \mathscr{S} \text{ and } \varDelta^2 > \varDelta^1\},$$

then the identification function is

$$\iota(1) = I_1$$

$$\iota(2) = I_2.$$

This, as we pointed out in Chapter 2, is an example of a partial identification experiment.

The most inclusive two-alternative, forced-choice design is called *pair comparisons*, and it is characterized by $S = \mathscr{S} \times \mathscr{S}$. If $\mathscr{S}$ consists of k stimuli, a total of k^2 ordered pairs can be formed. For example, when $\mathscr{S} = \{\varDelta, \varDelta', \varDelta''\}$, then there are the nine ordered pairs: $\langle \varDelta, \varDelta \rangle$, $\langle \varDelta, \varDelta' \rangle$, $\langle \varDelta, \varDelta'' \rangle$, $\langle \varDelta', \varDelta \rangle$, $\langle \varDelta', \varDelta' \rangle$, $\langle \varDelta', \varDelta'' \rangle$, $\langle \varDelta'', \varDelta \rangle$, $\langle \varDelta'', \varDelta' \rangle$, $\langle \varDelta'', \varDelta'' \rangle$. To say that the first stimulus is larger than the second when $\langle \varDelta, \varDelta' \rangle$ is presented seems to be equivalent to saying that the second is larger than the first when $\langle \varDelta', \varDelta \rangle$ is presented, and so one might be tempted to present only one of the two pairs. It is not, however, empirically true that the results are the same: the order of presentation affects the behavior. Just how it affects behavior is a question we study later; at present we need only realize that it does.

For an interesting number of stimuli, say 10 to 100, there are quite a few ordered pairs, 100 to 10,000. What makes these numbers unpleasant is that it is insufficient to present each pair just once, for subjects do not always respond the same way each time a pair is presented. To get reasonably stable relative frequencies of these choices, we must present each pair many times—"many" being of the order of 100 to 1000. Thus a modest pair comparison experiment entails 10,000 observations and a big one, 10 million. The need to reduce these numbers, at least the second one, is evident.

The clue to doing so lies in the fact that inconsistencies exist only when two stimuli are physically not very different—just what we mean by "not very different" will become clear later. There is surely little point, then, in presenting pairs hundreds of times when the response is certain. This suggests that we pick one or more stimuli, which are called *standards*, and study only pairs formed from other stimuli, called *comparison* stimuli, in the near neighborhood of each standard. A standard stimulus has, therefore, its own set of comparison stimuli. Usually, though not always, the standard is presented first, and a comparison, second, and the subject is asked to judge whether the second is greater or less than the first. Although it is not necessary, in most studies an odd number of comparison stimuli are used, with the physically middle one often being identical to the standard. This type of design is known as the *method of constant stimuli*, although a more appropriate name seems to be the "method of standard stimuli."

1. RESPONSE MEASURES AS FUNCTIONS OF STIMULUS MEASURES

1.1 The Psychometric Function

So that subjects are not free to indulge their taste for consistency—which most seem to have—we are careful in most constant stimuli experiments not to group all like presentations together. Some irregular presentation schedule, often a simple random one, is used. When it comes to data analysis, however, we want to deal with the responses to each pair as a unit, and so from now on our problem is to account for these sets of responses to presentation pairs.

Changing notation slightly, let x denote the numerical value of the relevant physical dimension of a typical comparison stimulus and s, the numerical value of the standard. Suppose, to be specific, that each $\langle s, x \rangle$ pair is responded to 100 times. It will surprise no one that, when x is sufficiently smaller (on whatever physical variable differentiates them) than s, then all or almost all of the subject's responses are that it is smaller. He is equally correct when x is sufficiently larger than s. As we move up the series of comparison stimuli from the smallest to the largest, we find that his reports first decrease in consistency, reach a peak at which roughly half his responses are that the comparison stimulus is larger, and then become increasingly more consistent until he always says that it is larger. What is interesting is the patterning to the inconsistency: the proportion of "larger" responses changes rather smoothly from 0 to 1.

To see this, we may plot the proportion as a function of the physical measure of the stimulus. Although we could plot the physical measure as the independent variable, it is more usual to use either the dimensionless linear scale $(x - s)/s$ or the dimensionless logarithmic scale $\log(x/s) = \log x - \log s$. Both have the virtue of setting the zero at s, which is sensible because we are studying the neighborhood of s. A typical data plot is shown in Fig. 1.

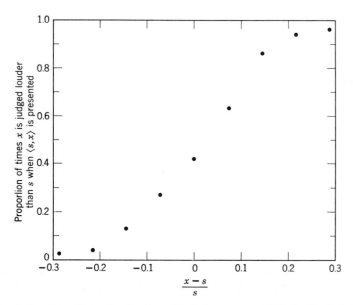

Fig. 1. Loudness discrimination data (E. Galanter, unpublished). Each data point is based upon 105 observations collected over three sessions. The standard stimulus was at 50 db *re* 0.0002 dynes/cm².

The S (or sigmoidal or ogival) shape of these points is typical of discrimination data, as are the slight irregularities. Were we to introduce another comparison stimulus between two actually used, we anticipate that the new proportion would usually fall between the two old data points, approximately on a smooth S-curve faired to the original data points. Of course, we cannot be sure exactly where it will fall. In two different runs of 100 observations we do not generally get exactly the same proportions, but we would be surprised if they were very different from each other or from the faired curve. And data confirm such conjectures.

These considerations lead us to postulate that for each value x, $x > 0$ of the comparison stimulus and for each s, $s \geqslant s_0 > 0$ there exists a probability $p(2 \mid \langle s, x \rangle)$ governing the response that x is judged larger than s. Clearly, $p(1 \mid \langle s, x \rangle) = 1 - p(2 \mid \langle s, x \rangle)$. The number s_0 is interpreted as a thresholdlike quantity, somewhat larger than the usual absolute or detection threshold. Moreover, we postulate that these probabilities satisfy:

Assumption I. *Strict Monotonicity: if* $x < y$, *then* $p(2 \mid \langle s, x \rangle) \leqslant p(2 \mid \langle s, y \rangle)$, *and, when* $p(2 \mid \langle s, x \rangle)$ *and* $p(2 \mid \langle s, y \rangle) \neq 0$ *or* 1, *then* $p(2 \mid \langle s, x \rangle) < p(2 \mid \langle s, y \rangle)$.

Assumption 2.   *Differentiability:* $p(2 \mid \langle s, x \rangle)$ *is a differentiable and, therefore, continuous function of each of its arguments* x *and* s *except, possibly, at a finite number of points.*

Assumption 3.   *Limiting behavior:*

$$\lim_{x \to \infty} p(2 \mid \langle s, x \rangle) = 1 \quad and \quad \lim_{x \to 0} p(2 \mid \langle s, x \rangle) = 0.$$

Such a function, assuming that it exists, is called a *psychometric function* (Urban, 1907).

The usual and unbiased estimate of $p(2 \mid \langle s, x \rangle)$ is the proportion of times that the subject responded x is larger when the pair $\langle s, x \rangle$ was presented.

The reader should be fully aware that these three assumptions about the psychometric function are not easily tested. The inherent binomial variability of the data means that the observed proportions can have the opposite order from the actual probabilities and that they can be rather widely separated when the probabilities are actually quite close. A numerical example is revealing. We know that when N independent observations are made, each with probability p of success, then the expected proportion of successes is p and the standard deviation of the proportion is $\sqrt{p(1 - p)/N}$. If $p = 0.50$ and $N = 100$, the standard deviation is 0.05. If $p' = 0.55$, the standard deviation is nearly the same. Therefore, we should not be unduly surprised to observe proportions of 0.56 and 0.53, respectively, which is an apparent violation of mono-tonicity, or of 0.43 and 0.59, which might suggest a violation of continuity. Only by very careful experimentation and statistical analysis can one detect such violations, unless they are quite gross, which they are not. In the absence of contrary evidence, experimental or theoretical, mono-tonicity and continuity seem to be sensible assumptions.

1.2 The PSE, CE, and jnd

Let $p_y(2 \mid \langle s, y \rangle)$ be the partial derivative of $p(2 \mid \langle s, y \rangle)$ with respect to y, which by Assumption 2 exists. Thus

$$p(2 \mid \langle s, x \rangle) = \int_0^x p_y(2 \mid \langle s, y \rangle) \, dy,$$

where the constant of integration is 0 by Assumption 3. The monotonicity assumption implies

$$p_x(2 \mid \langle s, x \rangle) \geqslant 0,$$

and Assumption 3 implies

$$\int_0^\infty p_y(2 \mid \langle s, y \rangle) \, dy = \lim_{x \to \infty} p(2 \mid \langle s, x \rangle) = 1.$$

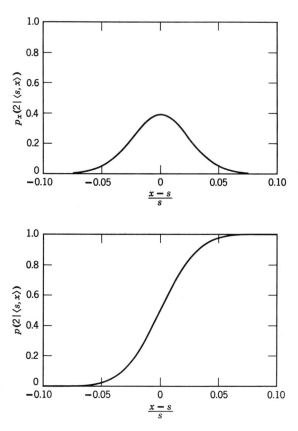

Fig. 2. Typical plots of $p_x(2 \mid \langle s, x \rangle)$ versus $(x - s)/s$ and of its cumulative $p(2 \mid \langle s, x \rangle)$ versus $(x - s)/s$. The density function is normal and its cumulative is, in this context of a psychometric function, often called a normal ogive.

Thus p_y is a probability density function and p is its distribution function. Moreover, p is an S-shaped function if and only if p_y is unimodal. An example of this relation is shown in Fig. 2.

Two important features of a density function, especially a unimodal one, are a measure of central tendency, such as the mean or median, and a measure of dispersion, such as the standard deviation or the interquartile range. In discrimination studies it has been customary to use the median and interquartile range rather than the mean and standard deviation because the former pair makes weaker assumptions about the metric properties of the independent variable (Urban 1907, Boring 1917).

The median, $x_{1/2}$, of the distribution p_y is by definition that point such that half the area under p_y lies to the left of it. Because the total area is 1, this means that $x_{1/2}$ is characterized by

$$p(2 \mid \langle s, x_{1/2} \rangle) = \int_0^{x_{1/2}} p_y(2 \mid \langle s, y \rangle) \, dy = \tfrac{1}{2}. \tag{1}$$

In the discrimination context, $x_{1/2}$ is often called the *point of subjective equality* and is abbreviated PSE. As we noted earlier, order of presentation matters, so in general $x_{1/2} \neq s$. The difference, $x_{1/2} - s$, is called the *constant error*, or CE, which is in a way a misnomer because it can be altered by certain experimental manipulations.

The interquartile range is the interval $x_{3/4} - x_{1/4}$, where $x_{3/4}$ is the stimulus value above $x_{1/2}$ such that $\tfrac{1}{4}$ of the area under p_y lies between these two points and $x_{1/4}$ is the corresponding point below $x_{1/2}$. More succinctly, they are defined by

$$p(2 \mid \langle s, x_{3/4} \rangle) = \tfrac{3}{4} \quad \text{and} \quad p(2 \mid \langle s, x_{1/4} \rangle) = \tfrac{1}{4}.$$

Most often, psychophysicists work with half the interquartile range, that is,

$$\text{jnd} = \frac{x_{3/4} - x_{3/4}}{2}, \tag{2}$$

which is called the *just noticeable difference* or the *difference limen* (DL). We use the first term.[5] The jnd is really an algebraic approximation to a probabilistic structure, as was first emphasized by Urban. We go into its structure as an algebraic entity in Sec. 3.3.

Graphically, the several quantities just defined are shown in Fig. 3.

It should be realized that the cutoffs of $\tfrac{3}{4}$ and $\tfrac{1}{4}$ in the definition of the jnd are arbitrary; other values, π and $1 - \pi$, where $\tfrac{1}{2} < \pi < 1$, could have been used, and we would speak of the π-jnd at s. When the value of π is not specified, it is taken for granted that it is $\tfrac{3}{4}$.

1.3 Estimating the PSE and jnd

To estimate the PSE and the jnd when the mathematical form of the psychometric function is known, it seems appropriate first to find that function of the given class which gives the "best" fit to the data and then to calculate these quantities according to these definitions. Various definitions of "best," such as least squares and maximum likelihood, can

---

[5] Classically, the jnd and the DL were distinguished as a theoretical term and a statistic of data, respectively. However they are now often used interchangeably, and so we adopt the first term to refer to the statistic because of its mnemonic value.

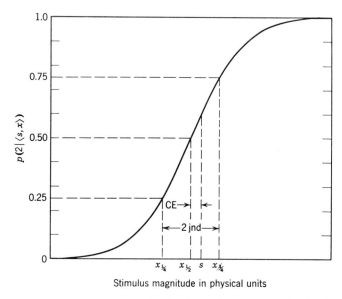

Fig. 3. A typical psychometric function $[p(2 \mid \langle s, x \rangle)$ versus $x]$ showing the CE and the jnd.

be used, and solutions are known for certain classes of functions (see Chapter 8). In practice, however, these calculations are usually tedious, and a rather simpler procedure can be used, which, although not optimal, seems quite satisfactory for many purposes.

The data uniformly suggest that the psychometric function is very nearly a straight line in a region approximately one jnd, or a little more, above and below the PSE. So, instead of using a more precise psychometric function, we may calculate a best-fitting straight line to those data points between about 0.2 and 0.8; usually a least squares procedure is used, although with practice one can become quite skillful doing it graphically by eye. If the equation of this line is $p = ax + b$, then it is easy to see that

$$\hat{x}_{1/2} = \frac{1 - 2b}{2a}$$

and that

$$\widehat{jnd} = \frac{1}{4a}.$$

Thus the jnd and the slope are inversely related: good discrimination means a small jnd and a large slope; poor discrimination, a large jnd and a small slope.

1.4 Study of the jnd: Weber functions and Weber's law

The psychometric function tells us something about local behavior, namely, about the nature of discrimination in the neighborhood of the standard s. One can ask: how does this function vary with experimental manipulation, with, among other things, changes in the standard? Because it is difficult to describe how an entire function varies, the question is usually reduced to asking how the CE and the jnd vary with experimental conditions; however, somewhat different questions are posed in the two cases. In this section we take up the jnd and postpone discussing the CE until Sec. 4.

Of two techniques to determine the jnd, the one giving the smaller value is considered the better, for the primary interest has been the absolute limits of discrimination. For this reason, modifications of equipment, instructions, outcomes, or procedures are deemed desirable and are incorporated into the experiment if they reduce the size of the jnd, but for the most part their effects, as such, upon the size of the jnd are not studied. This does not mean that such questions are meaningless or even uninteresting but only that other problems have seemed more important. This leaves us only one major manipulation for studying the jnd, the value of the standard stimulus.

If we estimate the jnd at s, $\widehat{jnd}$ (s), for several different values of s, we may then construct a plot such as that shown in Fig. 4. Actually, it is not easy to find reports of jnds estimated at different values of s using the method of constant stimuli. For example, the data of Fig. 4 (Miller, 1947) for the intensity of random noise were obtained by the quantal method described in Sec. 6.3 of Chapter 3, with the jnd being defined as that increment in intensity which is detected 50 per cent of the time. The curves shown in Fig. 6 below were obtained by the method of limits in which the variable stimulus is systematically increased and decreased until a difference is found that is noted 50 per cent of the time. Most experimentalists assume that, aside from a constant factor, the same function would be obtained by the method of constant stimuli or by one of the other, somewhat more convenient methods, but this assumption has yet to be adequately checked. For present purposes, we will assume that it is correct.

The regularity of the data points in Fig. 4 suggests that a continuous, monotonically increasing function underlies them. This function we denote by jnd (s) and call it the jnd-function (of the stimulus variable).

Such functions were first studied by E. H. Weber in the second quarter

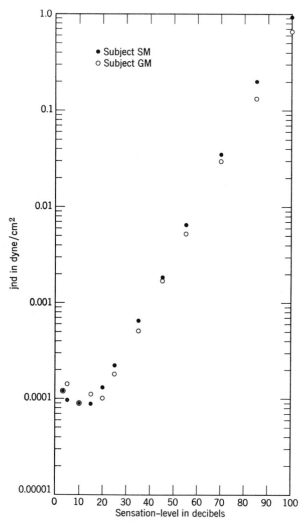

Fig. 4. Intensity discrimination of random noise for two subjects using the quantal method. The jnd is measured in dynes/cm² and is plotted on a logarithmic scale. The stimulus is measured in so-called sensation level units which is decibels re subject's threshold (which is approximately 10 db re 0.0002 dynes/cm²). Adapted by permission from Miller (1947, p. 612).

of the nineteenth century for cutaneous sensitivity discrimination. On the basis of his data, Weber suggested that for intensity variables, at least, the jnd-function is of the form

$$\text{jnd } (s) = Ks, \qquad (3)$$

where the constant $K > 0$ is called the *Weber fraction* and the proposed empirical relation is called *Weber's law*. Usually one plots the data as $\widehat{\text{jnd}}\,(s)/s$ versus s or $\log s$, in which case the points lie on a horizontal line K units above the x-axis when Weber's law is correct. Actually, most data show an initial drop, then a relatively flat region, and sometimes a final rise for very "large" stimuli (Cobb, 1932, Holway & Pratt, 1936). The final rise has been debated, and some believe that it can be accounted for by difficulties in the experimental procedure or equipment, but there is little doubt about the initial dip.

To cope with the dip, Fechner proposed and G. A. Miller (1947) later revived a *generalized Weber's law* of the form

$$\text{jnd}\,(s) = Ks + C, \tag{4}$$

where $K > 0$. In Fig. 5 Miller's jnd-data for intensity discrimination of white noise are shown along with a fitted curve of the form of Eq. 4. The approximation is good.

Guilford (1932) proposed as a substitute for Eq. 3 or 4,

$$\text{jnd}\,(s) = Ks^n,$$

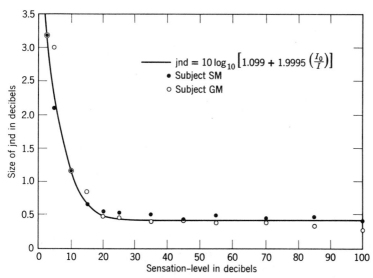

Fig. 5. The data of Fig. 4 are replotted with the jnd measured in decibels, i.e., if at intensity I the jnd measured in dynes/cm^2 is $\Delta(I)$, then the jnd in db $= 10 \log_{10}\left[1 + \dfrac{\Delta(I)}{I}\right]$.

The theoretical curve is the generalized Weber law with the numerical constants shown. Adapted by permission from Miller (1947, p. 612).

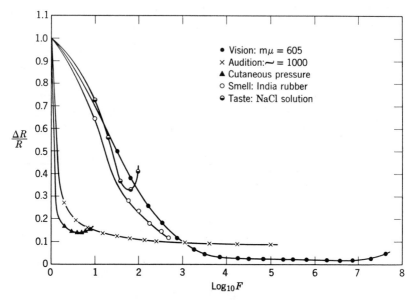

Fig. 6. Weber fractions versus sensation-level of the stimulus (in logarithmic units) for five senses obtained by the method of limits. The Weber fractions have been normalized to be unity at threshold. Adapted by permission from Holway & Pratt (1936, p. 337).

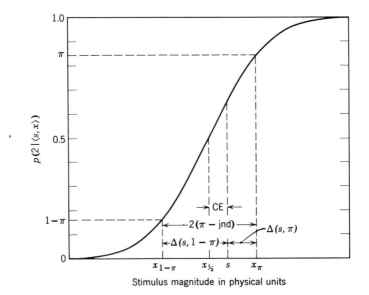

Fig. 7. A typical psychometric function showing the values of the Weber functions $\Delta(s, 1 - \pi)$ and $\Delta(s, \pi)$ at s as well as the CE and the π-jnd.

where $n > 0$. Hovland (1938) presented data for which this is a somewhat better approximation than Eq. 4. Householder and Young (1940) point out, however, that the law that holds depends upon the physical measure of the stimulus used. Under very general mathematical conditions it is possible to find a measure for which Weber's law is correct for a single subject, but such a transformation will work for all subjects only under very special circumstances.

Table 1   Values of the Weber Fraction

	Weber Fraction
Deep pressure, from skin and subcutaneous tissue, at about 400 grams	0.013
Visual brightness, at about 1000 photons	0.016
Lifted weights, at about 300 grams	0.019
Tone, for 1000 cps, at about 100 db above absolute threshold	0.088
Smell, for rubber, at about 200 olfacties	0.104
Cutaneous pressure, on an isolated spot, at about 5 grams/mm	0.136
Taste, for saline solution at about 3 moles/liter concentration	0.200

Taken from Boring, Langfeld, & Weld (1948) p. 268.

It hardly need be mentioned that such jnd-functions are empirically defined only from the absolute threshold up to either the upper threshold, as for pitch, or just short of intensity levels that damage the receptors, as for sound and light intensity.

Table 1 presents estimates of the Weber fraction K for several continua, and Fig. 6 presents plots of several Weber functions.

For the theoretical work to follow, it is convenient to use a somewhat different measure of dispersion than the jnd. Let π be a number such that $0 < \pi < 1$. We define the function $\Delta(s, \pi)$ by the property

$$p[2 \mid \langle s, s + \Delta(s, \pi)\rangle] = \pi,$$

that is,

$$\Delta(s, \pi) = x_\pi - s. \tag{5}$$

Depending upon the value of π, $\Delta(s, \pi)$ may be positive or negative. For a fixed π, we shall call $\Delta(s, \pi)$ a *Weber function* of s.

It should be noted that CE $= \Delta(s, \frac{1}{2})$ but that for other values of π, $\Delta(s, \pi)$ is a measure of dispersion. In fact, if the CE $= 0$, then jnd $(s) = \frac{1}{2}[\Delta(s, \frac{3}{4}) - \Delta(s, \frac{1}{4})]$, and in general π-jnd $(s) = \frac{1}{2}[\Delta(s, \pi) - \Delta(s, 1 - \pi)]$. (See Fig. 7.)

No one has paid much heed to the fact that the empirically calculated jnd and the Weber functions used in theoretical work are defined slightly differently. When, for example, the jnd is found to satisfy the generalized Weber law, one usually takes for granted that the Weber function does too, that is,

$$\Delta(s, \pi) = K(\pi)s + C(\pi).$$ (6)

But, if this is true, then

$$CE = \Delta(s, \tfrac{1}{2}) = K(\tfrac{1}{2})s + C(\tfrac{1}{2}),$$ (7)

which is more than is usually intended. Possibly this CE relation is correct—we know of no relevant data—but, if it is not, then, because $\Delta(s, \pi) - CE$ plays a closer role to the jnd for symmetric psychometric functions than does $\Delta(s, \pi)$, we should assume Weber's law for the former and not for the latter.

2. FECHNERIAN SCALING[6]

2.1 The Problem of Scaling

With the publication of *Elemente der Psychophysik* in 1860, G. T. Fechner not only founded psychophysics as a science but introduced a theoretical idea which has dominated the field in the intervening years. It is this. As the magnitude of stimulation is varied, for example, as the sound energy of a tone is varied, we appreciate the change as a closely parallel subjective change, in this case in what is called loudness. We say that stimulation produces a sensation peculiar to it, and most of us allege that sensations vary continuously and monotonically with the usual physical magnitudes involved. They do not, however, seem to vary linearly: a 10-unit change of intensity at low levels does not seem to be the same size as a 10-unit change at high intensities.

Fechner, and many after him, wanted to know exactly how "sensation intensity" varies with physical magnitude. The problem is not one of straight-forward experimentation because the question is not an empirical one until we know how to define and measure sensation. The question of definition, and therefore of measurement, is, we should judge, still unsettled and probably will not be finally resolved until psychophysics is a more nearly perfected chapter of science than it is today; nonetheless, we shall explore a number of different answers that have been proposed and seriously entertained. It may be well to pause a moment here to sketch our general view of the matter, to make our biases known, before we discuss the views of others.

[6] To many, the problems of this section are of no more than historical interest. But they certainly are that, and so we feel it worthwhile to devote space to their careful analysis. If one wishes, the section can be omitted with little loss of continuity.

First, it is not clear what behavioral observations constitute a measure of sensation. This role has been claimed for one or another class of observations, but none has had such clear face validity that it has not been vigorously questioned by some careful students of the field. Second, although it seems reasonable to suppose that physiological measures of sensation may one day be found, little is known about them today. Third, in several mathematical theories of discrimination (and other choice behavior) it is not particularly difficult to introduce numerical scales that, on the one hand, allow us to reconstruct the behavioral data rather efficiently and, on the other hand, are monotonically, but not usually linearly, related to physical intensity. Fourth, although each of these scales is a possible candidate for the unknown measure of sensation, no clear criterion for choice yet exists. It is probably unwise for scientific purposes (engineering applications are another matter) to attempt to make any terminological decision until more is known. Aside from a question of terms, it is by no means certain which, if any, of these scales is truly useful. If a scale serves no purpose other than as a compact summary of the data from which it was calculated, if it fails to predict different data or to relate apparently unrelated results, that is, if it is not an efficient theoretical device, then it is worth but little attention and surely we should not let it appropriate such a prized word as "sensation." If, however, a scale is ever shown to have a rich theoretical and predictive role, then the scientific community can afford to risk the loss of a good word. At present, no scale meets this criterion.

The scales of this section are the most traditional in psychology, and at the same time the most unlikely. What we shall be doing is to take highly local information, as given by the psychometric function, and from it attempt to generate scales over the whole range of the physical variable. In recent years a school of thought, led by S. S. Stevens, has condemned this processing of confusion (or noise or variability) as, on the face of it, irrelevant to measures of magnitude. We take up his alternative method, magnitude estimation, more fully in Chapter 5; here it suffices to describe Fechner's idea. Earlier critiques of Fechner's whole scheme of psycho- physics can be found in Cobb (1932), James (1890), and Johnson (1929, 1930, 1945).

2.2 Fechner's Problem

Let a particular value π be chosen and suppose that $\Delta(s, \pi)$ is the resulting Weber function. Fechner posed the question: for what (reasonably smooth) transformations of the physical scale is the transformed

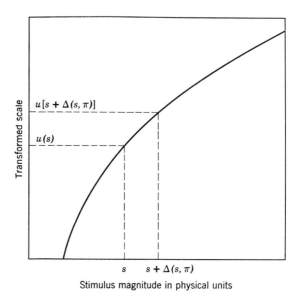

Fig. 8. A typical monotonic transformation showing the interval on the transformed scale corresponding to the value $\Delta(s, \pi)$ of the Weber function at s on the original scale.

Weber function a constant independent of s? This defining property of the "sensation" scale is sometimes loosely phrased by saying that at the level of sensations jnds are all equal. Mathematically, if $u(s)$ is a transformation of the physical scale, then in terms of the u-variable the Weber function is simply $u[s + \Delta(s, \pi)] - u(s)$. This is easily seen in Fig. 8.

Fechner's Problem. *For a fixed π, $0 < \pi < 1$, find those "smooth" strictly monotonic functions u such that for all $s > s_0$*

$$u[s + \Delta(s, \pi)] - u(s) = g(\pi), \tag{8}$$

where g is a strictly monotonic increasing function of π and is independent of s.

Two comments. First, we have explicitly included the vague word "smooth," its exact definition to be decided upon later when we see how the problem develops. Second, the assumption that g is a strictly monotonic function follows from the assumption that the psychometric function is strictly monotonic for $0 < p < 1$.

Is this characterization of the unknown scale u a self-evident truth, an empirical assumption, or a definition? Fechner, we believe, believed it to be the first or possibly the second. The era of self-evident truths having largely passed, some today regard it as an assumption, and the remainder, a definition (Boring, 1950; Cobb, 1932). Without an independent measure of u, it is difficult for us to see how it can be considered an assumption. But no matter, let us accept the problem as it stands without worrying about its philosophic status.

The task Fechner faced was to solve the functional equation (8). The method he attempted to use—see Boring (1950) or Luce & Edwards (1958)—involved certain approximations which allow Eq. 8 to be transformed into a first-order linear differential equation. Such differential equations are well known to have solutions which are unique except for an additive constant of integration provided that certain weak assumptions are met. However, because $g(\pi)$ is unspecified, the unit of u is also free, so by this argument u is an interval scale (i.e., it is unique up to positive linear transformations). Certainly, such reasoning would be acceptable had the problem been initially cast as the differential equation, but it was not, and for other classes of functional equations one must investigate carefully both the questions of the existence and uniqueness of solutions. Neither can ever be taken for granted with unfamiliar equations.

Because π is a fixed quantity in Fechner's problem, we drop it from the notation. The following result solves the uniqueness question.

Theorem 1. *Let u^* be a strictly monotonic solution to Eq. 8; then u is another solution to Eq. 8 if and only if*

$$u(s) = u^*(s) + F[u^*(s)],$$

where F is a periodic function of period g, that is, $F(x + g) = F(x)$ for all x.

PROOF. First, suppose F is periodic with period g; then by the definition of u,

$$u[s + \Delta(s)] - u(s) = u^*[s + \Delta(s)] + F\{u^*[s + \Delta(s)]\} - u^*(s) - F[u^*(s)].$$

Because u^* is a solution to Eq. 8, we know that

$$u^*[s + \Delta(s)] = g + u^*(s),$$

and because F is periodic with period g

$$F\{u^*[s + \Delta(s)]\} = F[u^*(s) + g]$$
$$= F[u^*(s)].$$

Thus

$$u[s + \Delta(s)] - u(s) = u^*[s + \Delta(s)] + F[u^*(s)] - u^*(s) - F[u^*(s)]$$
$$= g,$$

as was to be shown.

Now, suppose u and u^* are both solutions to Eq. 8, and let $w = u - u^*$. Then

$$w[s + \Delta(s)] - w(s) = u[s + \Delta(s)] - u^*[s + \Delta(s)] - u(s) + u^*(s)$$
$$= g - g$$
$$= 0.$$

Because u^* is strictly monotonic, its inverse $u^{*^{-1}}$ exists, so we may write

$$s + \Delta(s) = u^{*^{-1}}[u^*(s) + g]$$

by Eq. 8 and

$$s = u^{*^{-1}}[u^*(s)]$$

by the definition of an inverse. Define $F = w(u^{*^{-1}})$. Substituting, we have

$$0 = w[s + \Delta(s)] - w(s)$$
$$= w\{u^{*^{-1}}[u^*(s) + g]\} - w\{u^{*^{-1}}[u^*(s)]\}$$
$$= F[u^*(s) + g] - F[u^*(s)].$$

Thus F is periodic with period g, and

$$u = u^* + w$$
$$= u^* + w[u^{*^{-1}}(u^*)]$$
$$= u^* + F(u^*),$$

as was to be shown.

There is trouble. The class of solutions to Eq. 8 is, according to Theorem 1, much too heterogeneous to be acceptable as a scale. If, for example, u^* is a nice smooth function, then $u^* + F(u^*)$ may be quite a lumpy function, such as that shown in Fig. 9. It is difficult to consider these two functions as merely two different representations of the same "subjective scale."

We need a recasting of the problem that permits us to narrow down the set of solutions to, say, an interval scale. This is not difficult to find. Our first phrasing of the problem involved an arbitrary cutoff π. Now, either the value of the cutoff is completely inessential or the problem holds no scientific interest. If we get one scale for one cutoff, another for a different one, and so on, we can hardly believe that some one of these scales has any inherent importance, whereas the others have none. So we rephrase the problem.

The Revised Fechner Problem. *For every π, $0 < \pi < 1$, find those "smooth" strictly monotonic functions u that are independent of π such that for all $s \geqslant s_0$*

$$u[s + \Delta(s, \pi)] - u(s) = g(\pi), \tag{9}$$

where g is a strictly monotonic increasing function of π and is independent of s.

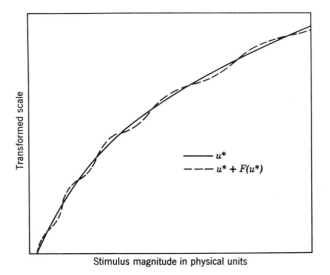

Fig. 9. Examples of solutions to Fechner's problem that are related by a periodic function.

Theorem 2. *If u and u* are two continuous strictly monotonic solutions to Eq. 9, then there exists a constant b such that u = u* + b.*
PROOF. By the preceding theorem, we know that

$$u = u^* + F(u^*),$$

where F must be periodic with period $g(\pi)$ for all π, $0 < \pi < 1$. Because g is a strictly monotonic function, F has a nondenumerable set of periods which together with its continuity (implied by that of u and u^*) means that F must be a constant, as asserted.

Because the unit of u^* is arbitrary, Theorem 2 implies that the solutions to the revised Fechner problem constitute an interval scale.

Before turning to some discussion of the existence of solutions, we show that the revised Fechner problem is identical to a condition that has gone under the lengthy title "equally often noticed differences are equal, unless always or never noticed."

The Equally-Often-Noticed-Difference Problem. *Let $p(2 \mid \langle s, x \rangle)$ be a psychometric function which, for $0 < p < 1$, is strictly monotonic in the x-argument. Find those strictly monotonic functions h and u, if any, such that for all $x > 0$ and $s \geqslant s_0$ for which $p(2 \mid \langle s, x \rangle) \neq 0$ or 1*

$$p(2 \mid \langle s, x \rangle) = h[u(x) - u(s)]. \tag{10}$$

Theorem 3. *The equally-often-noticed-difference problem has a solution if and only if the revised Fechner problem has a solution and both problems have the same set of scales.*

PROOF. Suppose the Fechner problem has the solution u. For x and s such that $p(2 \mid \langle s, x \rangle) = \pi \neq 1$ or 0, we know that $x = s + \Delta(s, \pi)$ by the definition of the Weber function. Because u solves the Fechner problem, $u(x) - u(s) = g(\pi)$. Because g is strictly monotonic, it has an inverse h, hence

$$h[u(x) - u(s)] = h[g(\pi)]$$
$$= \pi$$
$$= p(2 \mid \langle s, x \rangle),$$

so u solves the equally-often-noticed-difference problem.

Conversely, suppose u solves the equally-often-noticed-difference problem. Let $\pi \neq 0$ or 1 be given; then by definition of $\Delta(s, \pi)$,

$$p[2 \mid \langle s, s + \Delta(s, \pi) \rangle] = \pi = h\{u[s + \Delta(s, \pi)] - u(s)\}.$$

Because h is strictly monotonic, its inverse, g, exists, and so

$$g(\pi) = u[s + \Delta(s, \pi)] - u(s),$$

as was to be shown.

2.3 Fechner's Law

It is by no means obvious under what conditions the revised Fechner problem has a solution and, when it has, what its mathematical form is. A variety of sufficient conditions is known, two of which are described in later sections and one here. Moreover, a general expression, in terms of a limit (but not an integral, as Fechner thought) is known for the solution when it exists (see Koenigs, 1884, 1885, or Luce & Edwards, 1958). We shall not present it here.

If the generalized Weber law, $\Delta(s, \pi) = K(\pi)s + C(\pi)$, is empirically correct, then, of course, we are interested in solutions only for that case; fortunately, it is quite well understood.

Theorem 4. *If the generalized Weber law holds, a solution exists to the revised Fechner problem provided that $C(\pi)/K(\pi)$ is a constant, γ, independent of π; the solution is*

$$u(s) = A \log (s + \gamma) + B,$$

when $A > 0$ and B are constants.

PROOF. $u[s + \Delta(s, \pi)] - u(s) = u[s + K(\pi)(s + \gamma)] - u(s)$

$$= A \log [s + K(\pi)(s + \gamma) + \gamma] + B - A \log (s + \gamma) - B$$

$$= A \log [1 + K(\pi)].$$

Because u is strictly monotonic, and $\Delta(s, \pi) = K(\pi)(s + \gamma)$, it follows easily that $A > 0$.

Observe that this restriction $C(\pi)/K(\pi) = \gamma$ is strong: it means that $\Delta(s, \pi) = K(\pi)(s + \gamma)$, which is tantamount to Weber's original law with the origin of the physical variable shifted to $-\gamma$.

The logarithmic scale is sometimes called *Fechner's law*, although it is not a law in any usual sense of the term—the scale u is not independently defined. Frequently, the set of ideas that we have discussed in this section are grouped together as the *Weber-Fechner problem*, but, as has been repeatedly emphasized in the literature, Weber's and Fechner's laws are independent of one another (e.g., Cobb, 1932).

As we turn to later work, we should keep in mind that Fechner attempted to establish a scale by demanding that subjective jnds on that scale all be equal. In doing this, he made no attempt to specify anything about the form of the psychometric function. When, because of uniqueness problems, we revised his problem to get rid of its dependence upon an arbitrary probability cutoff, it became apparent that solutions exist only when the psychometric functions satisfy rather stringent conditions. It is not surprising, therefore, that we devote considerable attention to the form of these functions.

3. UNBIASED RESPONSE MODELS

Partly because of historical interest and partly because it is easier to begin this way, we first take up models that apply only when the order of presentation of the stimuli does not matter. Specifically, we assume that for all $x, y \in \mathscr{S}$, such that $\langle x, y \rangle, \langle y, x \rangle \in s$,

$$p(1 \mid \langle x, y \rangle) = p(2 \mid \langle y, x \rangle). \tag{11}$$

Because in both cases the response designates a particular stimulus, namely x, as larger, it is possible and convenient to speak as if the subject had chosen x from the unordered set $\{x, y\}$ and to write $p(x \mid \{x, y\})$ for the common value of Eq. 11. Usually this notation is simplified further by letting $p(x, y) = p(x \mid \{x, y\})$.

3.1 The Equation of Comparative Judgment

In 1927 L. L. Thurstone, in his papers "Psychophysical analysis" and "A law of comparative judgment,"[7] took up Fechner's approach from a new point of view, one which has since dominated theoretical work in psychophysics and, even more, psychometrics. Unlike Fechner, Thurstone was concerned with why there is any confusion at all between two stimuli or, to put it another way, why the psychometric function is not a simple jump function from 0 to 1. This surely is what we would expect if repeated presentations of a stimulus always produce the same internal effect and if the same decision rule is always applied to the internal information generated by the two stimuli of a presentation. The facts being otherwise, these cannot both be correct assumptions. A varying decision rule, although a real possibility, is most distasteful because it seems so unmanageable; hence the other assumption is the first to be abandoned.

The problem, then, is to develop a model for the information to which the simple decision rule is applied. Thurstone postulated that the "internal effect" of each stimulus can be summarized by a number, but not necessarily the same number each time the stimulus is presented. Although we need not say why this should happen, plausible reasons exist. Undoubtedly there are small uncontrolled variations in the experimental conditions as well as some internal to the subject himself which affect the appearance of the stimulus. Put in statistical language, the presentation of stimulus x is assumed to result in a random variable X whose range is the real numbers. Thurstone called these random variables *discriminal processes;* their distribution he called the *discriminal dispersion* in (1927b), but in (1927a) he used this term for the standard deviation of the distribution and that has come to be the accepted usage.

It should be noticed that this is exactly the same postulate made by Tanner and his colleagues when analyzing detection and recognition problems (see Chapter 3, Sec. 1.1 for a more complete discussion of this idea).

Thurstone then assumed the following decision rule:

$$Stimulus\ x\ is\ judged \begin{Bmatrix} larger \\ smaller \end{Bmatrix} than\ y\ if\ X \begin{Bmatrix} > \\ < \end{Bmatrix} Y. \qquad (12)$$

[7] These papers, along with many others of Thurstone's, have recently been reprinted in Thurstone (1959). To some extent, Thurstone's ideas stem from those of Müller (1879), Solomons (1900), and Urban (1907). For other expositions of Thurstone's work, see Gulliksen (1946) and Torgerson (1958).

Thus the probability that x is judged larger than y is the same as the probability that $X - Y > 0$, that is,

$$p(x, y) = \Pr(X - Y > 0). \tag{13}$$

To calculate this, we need to know the distribution of the differences $X - Y$, which quantities Thurstone referred to as *discriminal differences*. To get at this distribution, we consider the single random variable X. We suggested that the range of X is not a unique number because of a variety of minor uncontrolled disturbances. If these perturbations are independent and random, and if their number is large, then their over-all sum will be approximately normally distributed. So we assume that X is normally distributed with mean $u(x)$, which Thurstone called the *modal discriminal process*, and standard deviation $\sigma(x)$. Similarly, Y is normally distributed with mean $u(y)$ and standard deviation $\sigma(y)$. Because x and y are usually presented in close spatial and temporal contiguity, it is quite possible that the random variables X and Y are correlated;[8] let the correlation coefficient be $r(x, y)$. It is a well known statistical result that under these conditions $X - Y$ is normally distributed with mean $u(x) - u(y)$ and variance $\sigma^2(x, y) = \sigma^2(x) + \sigma^2(y) - 2r(x, y)\,\sigma(x)\,\sigma(y)$. Thus, by Eq. 12, the form of the psychometric function is

$$p(x, y) = \frac{1}{\sqrt{2\pi}} \int_{-\infty}^{[u(x)-u(y)]/\sigma(x,y)} e^{-t^2/2}\, dt.$$

$$= \int_0^\infty N[u(x) - u(y), \sigma(x, y)], \tag{14}$$

where $N(\mu, \sigma)$ is the normal distribution with mean μ and standard deviation σ.

---

[8] The question of a correlation between stimulus effects arose a number of times in the discussion of detection (see especially Secs. 1, 2 and 6.2 of Chapter 3), and in all cases it was handled in one of two extreme ways. When the presentation consisted of the null stimulus followed by a tone (both in a background of noise), the correlation was assumed to be zero; when it was the null stimulus followed by an increment in a background such as a tone, the correlation was assumed to be perfect. One might anticipate that we would again postulate a correlation coefficient of one because the two stimuli of a discrimination experiment differ on only one physical dimension; however, that assumption, coupled with the decision rule given in Eq. 12, leads to perfect discrimination, which is contrary to fact. The reason that the assumption of perfect correlation worked in the analysis of detection but does not work here lies in the difference between the two psychophysical models that are assumed. There we used a threshold (quantal) model, whereas here we are assuming a continuous one. Presumably it is possible to develop a threshold model for discrimination, and it would be interesting to see how it differs from existing models.

Note that this model, as it stands, cannot handle the constant-error problem, for, when $x = y$, $[u(x) - u(y)]/\sigma(x, y) = 0$, and $p(x, x) = \frac{1}{2}$. This is because we have supposed that the order of presentation does not matter. A generalization that includes biases is given in Sec. 4.1.

If we let $Z(x, y)$ denote the normal deviate corresponding to $p(x, y)$, that is, $p(x, y) = \int_{-\infty}^{Z(x,y)} N(0, 1)$, then Eq. 14 can be written

$$u(x) - u(y) = Z(x, y)\, \sigma(x, y)$$
$$= Z(x, y)\{\sigma(x)^2 + \sigma(y)^2 - 2\sigma(x)\, \sigma(y)\, r(x, y)\}^{\frac{1}{2}}, \quad (15)$$

which is what Thurstone sometimes called the *law* and sometimes the *equation of comparative judgment*. Because its status as a law is far from certain, we prefer the more neutral word *equation*.

We notice, first, that the function u, which gives the means of the random variables associated with the stimuli, is a scale of the sort that interested Fechner. Second, the equally-often-noticed-difference problem has a solution if and only if the variances $\sigma(x, y)$ of the discriminal differences are all equal. Third, without some further assumptions, even with complete pair-comparison data, there are more unknowns than there are equations. With k stimuli, there are $k - 1$ unknown means (fixing one arbitrarily determines the zero of the scale), $k - 1$ unknown variances (fixing one sets the unit), and, including the $\langle x, x \rangle$ presentations, $k(k + 1)/2$ unknown correlations, but there are only $k(k - 1)/2$ equations.

To cope with this indeterminancy, Thurstone singled out five special cases of increasingly strong assumptions, of which Case V is the most familiar. It assumes that the discriminal dispersions are all the same, $\sigma^2(x) = \sigma^2$ for all x, and that the correlations are all the same (usually assumed to be 0), $r(x, y) = r$. If we choose $\sigma = 1/\sqrt{2(1 - r)}$, as we may because it merely determines the unit of our scale, then for Case V the equation of comparative judgment, Eq. 15, reduces to just

$$u(x) - u(y) = Z(x, y). \quad (16)$$

Thus the data in the form of the deviates $Z(x, y)$ give the scale when one of the scale values is chosen arbitrarily. Of course, the system of equations is now overdetermined: it consists of $k(k - 1)/2$ linear equations in $k - 1$ unknowns. It is easy to see that this imposes severe internal constraints on the data, among them

$$Z(x, z) = u(x) - u(z)$$
$$= u(x) - u(y) + u(y) - u(z)$$
$$= Z(x, y) + Z(y, z), \quad (17)$$

which amounts to saying that, if $p(x, y)$ and $p(y, z)$ are given, then $p(x, z)$ is determined.

Methods for using all the data to determine scale values are described in Green (1954), Guilford (1954), and Torgerson (1958), and procedures for evaluating the adequacy of the model in Mosteller (1951a,b,c).

Suppose that the data satisfy the conditions of Case V. If Weber's law is true, then by Theorem 4 u must be a logarithmic function of stimulus intensity, which suggests plotting the psychometric function as a function of the logarithm of intensity. This is frequently done, the independent variable being 10 $\log_{10}$ of the relative energy—the so-called decibel (db) scale. The data are usually well approximated by a cumulative normal distribution, as assumed indirectly by Thurstone and as Fechner suggested in his work. The assumption that the psychometric function is a cumulative normal of the physical stimulus was referred to as the "phi-gamma hypothesis" by Urban (1907, 1910), but, as Boring (1924) pointed out, this is not really a hypothesis until the physical measure is specified.

Thurstone's psychophysical theory is like Fechner's in that an underlying scale plays a crucial role; however, in the general case, the scale does not meet the equal-jnd property central to Fechner's work. It is a more specific theory than Fechner's in that the form of the psychometric function is taken to be a cumulative normal distribution. Finally, in the important Case V, in which the two theories overlap, the observed data must satisfy the strong constraint given in Eq. 17.

3.2 The Choice Axiom

A second approach to these questions of the form of the psychometric function and a scale of "sensation" has recently been suggested (Luce, 1959). The tack is a bit different from Thurstone's in that one begins with an assumption about the choice probabilities and from that derives a scaling model. This model is extremely similar to that described in Sec. 1.2 of Chapter 3.

So far, we have confined our attention to presentations of stimulus pairs; however, it is clear that we can generalize our experiments in several ways so that three or more stimuli are presented. Suppose that $T \subseteq \mathcal{S}$ has k stimuli and that $\sigma(T)$ is a simple ordering of T. Thus $\sigma(T) \in \mathcal{S} \times \mathcal{S} \times \ldots \times \mathcal{S}$ (k times) and $\sigma(T)$ is a possible presentation of k stimuli. By $\sigma_r(T)$ we denote the element of T that is in the rth position of the k-tuple $\sigma(T)$. If $R = \{1, 2, \ldots, k\}$, then the identification function, which can be stated formally if one wishes, simply says that response r means that the largest element is believed to have been in the rth position of the ordering.

In this section we are supposing that order of presentation does not matter, that is, if $\sigma_r(T) = \sigma_{r'}{}'(T) = x$, then

$$p[r \mid \sigma(T)] = p[r' \mid \sigma'(T)]. \qquad (18)$$

Because the response in both cases designates the same stimulus as the largest, it is again convenient to speak as if the subject made the choice x from the unordered set T and to denote the common value in Eq. 18 by $p_T(x)$. Note that the basic choice set T is written as a subscript; this is done in order to simplify writing other conditional probabilities later. To conform to the previous notation, we denote $p_{\{x,y\}}(x)$ by $p(x, y)$.

The probability that the subject's choice is an element from the subset $U \subseteq T$ is given by

$$p_T(U) = \sum_{x \in U} p_T(x).$$

The usual probability axioms are assumed to hold for each T.

The question of empirical interest is what, if any, added relations that are not logical consequences of the probability axioms are imposed by the organism. One suspects that the probability measure associated with the presentation of one set T cannot be totally independent of that governing the behavior when sets overlapping T are presented—that the organism is unable or unwilling to generate totally unrelated choices in two related situations. If there are no such relations, a whole range of possible scientific questions has no significance; if there are relations, their statement is a piece of a theory of behavior.

It may well be that, although they exist, these relations are very complicated; however, it seems best to begin with the simplest conditions that are not completely at variance with known facts. The one suggested by Luce and, in another context, by Clarke (1957), states, in essence, that if some alternatives are removed from consideration then the relative frequency of choices among the remaining alternatives is preserved. Put another way, the presence or absence of an alternative is irrelevant to the relative probabilities of choice between two other alternatives, although, of course, the absolute value of these probabilities will generally be affected. To cast this in mathematical language, we need the definition of *conditional probability*, namely

$$\text{if } p_T(U) \neq 0, \quad \text{then } p_T(V \mid U) = \frac{p_T(U \cap V)}{p_T(U)}.$$

We assume the following:

The Choice Axiom. *If $x \in U \subseteq T$ and if $p_T(x \mid U)$ exists, then*

$$p_T(x \mid U) = p_U(x).$$

We first prove Theorem 5 and then discuss its significance.

Theorem 5. *Suppose that the choice axiom holds for all U, $x \in U \subseteq T$.*

1. *If $p_T(x) \neq 0$, then $p_U(x) \neq 0$.*
2. *If $p_T(x) = 0$ and $p_T(U) \neq 0$, then $p_U(x) = 0$.*
3. *If $p_T(y) = 0$ and $y \neq x$, then $p_T(x) = p_{T-\{y\}}(x)$.*
4. *If, for all $y \in T$, $p_T(y) \neq 0$, then $p_T(x) = p_U(x)\, p_T(U)$.*

PROOF. 1. Because $p_T(x) \neq 0,\quad p_T(U) = p_T(x) + \sum_{y \in U-\{x\}} p_T(y) \neq 0.$

Therefore, the conditional probability $p_T(x \mid U) = p_T(x)/p_T(U)$ is defined, and it is not 0 because $p_T(x) \neq 0$. By the choice axiom, it equals $p_U(x)$.

2. If $p_T(x) = 0$ and $p_T(U) \neq 0$, then by the definition of conditional probability and by the choice axiom

$$p_U(x) = p_T(x \mid U) = \frac{p_T(x)}{p_T(U)} = 0.$$

3. Because $p_T(y) = 0$,

$$p_T(T - \{y\}) = p_T(y) + \sum_{x \in T-\{y\}} p_T(x)$$
$$= p_T(T)$$
$$= 1.$$

Using this,

$$p_T(x \mid T - \{y\}) = \frac{p_T(\{x\} \cap [T - \{y\}])}{p_T(T - \{y\})}$$
$$= p_T(x).$$

So, by the choice axiom,

$$p_{T-\{y\}}(x) = p_T(x \mid T - \{y\})$$
$$= p_T(x).$$

4. By assumption, $p_T(y) \neq 0$ for $y \in U$, so $p_T(U) \neq 0$, and the choice axiom and the definition of conditional probability yield

$$p_U(x) = p_T(x \mid U)$$
$$= \frac{p_T(x)}{p_T(U)}.$$

Multiplying by $p_T(U)$ yields the result.

What does this tell us? If we have an alternative y that is never chosen, Part 3 tells us that we may delete it from the set of alternatives. That we may keep repeating this process with no concern about the order in which it is done until all the choice probabilities are positive is guaranteed by Parts 1 and 2. The final part tells us how the various probabilities are related when we have only positive probabilities. The next theorem makes this relation more vivid.

Theorem 6. *If, for all $x \in T$, $p_T(x) \neq 0$ and if the choice axiom holds for all x and U such that $x \in U \subseteq T$, then*

1. *for $x, y, z \in T$,*

$$p(x, z) = \frac{p(x, y)\, p(y, z)}{p(x, y)\, p(y, z) + p(z, y)\, p(y, x)} \tag{19}$$

and

2.
$$p_T(x) = \frac{1}{1 + \sum\limits_{y \in T - \{x\}} p(y, x)/p(x, y)}. \tag{20}$$

PROOF. We begin by showing that

$$\frac{p(x, y)}{p(y, x)} = \frac{p_T(x)}{p_T(y)}. \tag{21}$$

By Part 4 of Theorem 5,

$$p_T(x) = p(x, y)p_T(\{x, y\})$$
$$= p(x, y)[p_T(x) + p_T(y)].$$

Rewrite this as

$$p_T(x)[1 - p(x, y)] = p(x, y)\, p_T(y),$$

and note that $p(y, x) = 1 - p(x, y)$. By Part 1 of Theorem 5 none of these probabilities is 0, so we may cross divide to get the assertion.

To prove Part 1, we note that

$$1 = \frac{p_T(x)\, p_T(y)\, p_T(z)}{p_T(y)\, p_T(z)\, p_T(x)}$$
$$= \frac{p(x, y)\, p(y, z)\, p(z, x)}{p(y, x)\, p(z, y)\, p(x, z)}. \tag{22}$$

Substitute $p(z, x) = 1 - p(x, z)$ and solve for $p(x, z)$ to get Eq. 19.

To prove Part 2, consider

$$1 + \sum_{y \in T - \{x\}} \frac{p(y, x)}{p(x, y)} = \frac{p_T(x)}{p_T(x)} + \sum_{y \in T - \{x\}} \frac{p_T(y)}{p_T(x)}$$
$$= \frac{1}{p_T(x)} \sum_{y \in T} p_T(y)$$
$$= \frac{1}{p_T(x)},$$

because $P_T(T) = 1$. Solve for $p_T(x)$ to get Eq. 20.

This excursion completed, let us now see what implications the choice axiom has for two-alternative discrimination. First, as with Thurstone's Case V, we find that there is a strong constraint on the psychometric functions: if $p(x, y)$ and $p(y, z)$ are known, then $p(x, z)$ is determined by Eq. 19. It is obvious that Eq. 19 establishes a relation different from Thurstone's Eq. 17, which hints at an experiment to decide between the models. Unfortunately, a few calculations show that such an experiment is probably not practical. Table 2 presents representative predictions of the

Table 2   Comparison of Predicted $p(x, z)$ from Known $p(x, y)$ and $p(y, z)$ Using Choice Axiom and Thurstone's Case V

		$p(y, z)$				$p(y, z)$		
	0.6	0.7	0.8	0.9	0.6	0.7	0.8	0.9
0.6	0.692	0.778	0.857	0.931	0.695	0.782	0.864	0.938
$p(x, y)$ 0.7		0.845	0.903	0.954		0.853	0.915	0.965
0.8			0.941	0.973			0.954	0.983
0.9				0.988				0.995

$p(x, z)$ from the choice axiom $p(x, z)$ from Thurstone's Case V

two models; the differences are simply not large enough to be detectable in practice. Presently, we shall see in another way how similar the two models are.

Part 2 of Theorem 6 suggests a way of introducing a scale into this model. To an arbitrary stimulus s assign the scale value $v(s) = k$, where k is some positive number. To any other stimulus x assign the value $v(x) = kp(x, s)/p(s, x)$. Optimal procedures for estimating these v-scale values from data are discussed in Abelson & Bradley (1954), Bradley (1954a,b, 1955), Bradley & Terry (1952), Ford (1957). Now, consider

$$\frac{v(y)}{v(x)} = \frac{kp(y, s) \, p(s, x)}{p(s, y) \, kp(x, s)}.$$

Using Eq. 19 in the form of Eq. 22, we see that the right side can be replaced by $p(y, x)/p(x, y)$, so

$$\frac{v(y)}{v(x)} = \frac{p(y, x)}{p(x, y)}. \tag{23}$$

Substituting this into Eq. 21, we get the basic equation relating choice probabilities to the v-scale:

$$p_T(x) = \frac{1}{1 + \sum_{y \in T-\{x\}} v(y)/v(x)}$$

$$= \frac{v(x)}{\sum_{y \in T} v(y)}. \tag{24}$$

In the two-alternative case, this reduces simply to

$$p(x, y) = \frac{1}{1 + v(y)/v(x)}.$$

A number of authors (Bradley & Terry, 1952; Ford, 1957; Gulliksen, 1953; Thurstone, 1930) have proposed and studied this model. Now, if we define

$$u(x) = a \log v(x) + a' \tag{25}$$

then

$$p(x, y) = \frac{1}{1 + \exp \{[u(y) - u(x)]/a\}}, \tag{26}$$

which shows that the choice axiom is a sufficient condition to solve the revised Fechner problem. It also shows the form of the psychometric function in terms of the Fechnerian scale u; this is known as the logistic curve. It is well known that the logistic is quite a good approximation to the cumulative normal so again we see the close similarity of this model to Thurstone's Case V.

If the data satisfy the generalized Weber law (Eq. 6) and if $C(\pi)/K(\pi) = \gamma$, then we know by Theorem 4 that

$$u(x) = A \log (x + \gamma) + B. \tag{27}$$

Thus, solving for $v(x)$ by eliminating $u(x)$ from Eqs. 25 and 27, we obtain

$$v(x) = \alpha(x + \gamma)^{\beta},$$

where α and β are constants. The former is a free, positive constant, but β can be determined as follows. We know that

$$p(x, y) = \pi = \frac{1}{1 + [(y + \gamma)/(x + \gamma)]^{\beta}}$$

if and only if $x = y + K(\pi)(y + \gamma)$. Thus,

$$\beta = \frac{\log [(1 - \pi)/\pi]}{\log [(y + \gamma)/(x + \gamma)]}$$

and

$$\frac{y + \gamma}{x + \gamma} = \frac{1}{1 + K(\pi)}.$$

So,

$$\beta = \frac{\log [\pi/(1 - \pi)]}{\log [1 + K(\pi)]}.$$

Note that β is a constant independent of π and that this equation states how $K(\pi)$ varies with π if the model is correct. Typically, for $\pi = 0.75$,

$K(\pi)$ is in the range for 0.01 to 0.10 (see Table 1, p. 205) in which case β is in the range from 10 to 100.

It should be stressed again that this model, like Thurstone's, has $CE = 0$, for, when $x = y$, $p(x, y) = \frac{1}{2}$. In Sec. 4.2 a generalized choice model is presented in which nonzero CE's are possible.

3.3 Semiorders

The notion of a jnd, introduced in Sec. 1.2, is a summary of some of the information included in the psychometric function. It is an algebraic rather than probabilistic notion. Although nothing was said then about properties it might exhibit as an algebraic entity, they are of interest whether jnds are treated as behavioral data in their own right or as simple approximations to the psychometric functions.

One way to state such properties is to introduce two binary relations, their "boundary" coinciding with the notion of a π-jnd. For $\pi, \frac{1}{2} < \pi < 1$, define

$$xL(\pi)y \quad \text{if and only if} \quad p(x, y) > \pi$$
$$xI(\pi)y \quad \text{if and only if} \quad 1 - \pi \leqslant p(x, y) \leqslant \pi, \tag{28}$$

where L is used to suggest "larger" and I, "indifference." If $xL(\pi)y$, then x is more than one π-jnd larger than y, and, if $xI(\pi)y$, then x is less than or equal to one π-jnd from y.

On a priori grounds, Luce (1956) suggested that such relations might satisfy the following axiom system:

A pair of binary relations $I(\pi)$ and $L(\pi)$ over $\mathscr{S}$ form a semiordering of $\mathscr{S}$ if for all $x, y, z,$ and $w \in \mathscr{S}$:

1. *exactly one of $xI(\pi)y$, $xL(\pi)y$, or $yL(\pi)x$ holds;*
2. *$xI(\pi)x$;*
3. *when $xL(\pi)y$, $yI(\pi)z$, and $zL(\pi)w$, then $xL(\pi)w$;*
4. *when $xL(\pi)y$ and $yL(\pi)z$, then not both $xI(\pi)w$ and $wI(\pi)z$*

Some of the main features of a semiorder are much like those of a weak order: $L(\pi)$ is transitive and asymmetric and $I(\pi)$ is reflexive and symmetric. The important difference is that $I(\pi)$ need not be transitive. It is constrained, however, by Axioms 3 and 4 to have the feature that an indifference interval can never "span" a larger-than interval. For other discussions of semiorders, including an axiomatization in terms of the single relation L, see Scott & Suppes (1958), Gerlach (1957), and Sec. 3.2 of Chapter 1.

In Luce (1959) it is shown that if the probabilities satisfy the choice model, then $L(\pi)$ and $I(\pi)$ as defined in Eq. 28 form a semiordering of $\mathscr{S}$. We shall not reproduce the proof here. Rather, we shall show that the same is true for Thurstone's Case V model. Let $Z(\pi)$ be defined by

$$\pi = \int_{-\infty}^{Z(\pi)} N(0, 1),$$ where $N(0, 1)$ is the normal distribution with zero mean and unit variance. By Eqs. 14 and 28,

$$xL(\pi)y \quad \text{if and only if} \quad u(x) - u(y) > \sigma Z(\pi)$$

$$xI(\pi)y \quad \text{if and only if} \quad -\sigma Z(\pi) \leqslant u(x) - u(y) \leqslant \sigma Z(\pi).$$

It is obvious that properties 1 and 2 of a semiorder are met. If $xL(\pi)y$, $yI(\pi)z$, and $zL(\pi)w$, then $u(x) - u(y) > \sigma Z(\pi)$, $u(y) - u(z) \geqslant -\sigma Z(\pi)$, and $u(z) - u(w) > \sigma Z(\pi)$. So $u(x) - u(w) = u(x) - u(y) + u(y) - u(z) + u(z) - u(w) > \sigma Z(\pi) - \sigma Z(\pi) + \sigma Z(\pi) = \sigma Z(\pi)$, which implies $xL(\pi)w$. Thus condition 3 is met. Suppose condition 4 is false, that is, for some $x, y, z, w \in \mathscr{S}$, $xL(\pi)y$, $yL(\pi)z$, $xI(\pi)w$, and $wI(\pi)z$, then $u(x) - u(y) > \sigma Z(\pi)$ and $u(y) - u(z) > \sigma Z(\pi)$ imply $u(x) - u(z) > 2\sigma Z(\pi)$. But $u(x) - u(w) \leqslant \sigma Z(\pi)$ and $u(w) - u(z) \leqslant \sigma Z(\pi)$ imply $u(x) - u(z) \leqslant 2\sigma Z(\pi)$. This contradiction shows that condition 4 is met.

For the more general Thurstone models, the relations defined by Eqs. 28 need not satisfy the semiorder axioms.

4. BIASED RESPONSE MODELS

It is a curious historical fact that the CE has not received nearly the attention that the jnd has. Possibly, this is because the jnd is, in fact, a measure of discriminability, whereas, from the point of view of one interested in discrimination, the CE is after all a nuisance factor—albeit an ubiquitous one. Moreover, because psychologists have by their designs and procedures tried to achieve maximum discriminability and have not been concerned how the jnd varies with experimental manipulations, there has really been only the single question: how does the jnd depend upon the physical measures of the stimuli under study? With the CE, matters are not so simple, and in the past interest seems not to have been great. In the last few years, however, theorists have begun to give it more attention, and we anticipate increased experimental interest. There is, for example, the result of Eq. 7 in Sec. 1.4, which suggests that the CE may follow Weber's generalized law when the jnd does; this needs to be tested, but more interesting are questions that can be raised about the impact of payoffs and other experimental variables on the CE (see Sec. 4.3). As early as 1920, Thompson discussed this problem, but evidently this did not lead to empirical research. Boring (1920) expressed the attitude of the time that these are matters for experimental control, not investigation.

Whether or not we study the CE as such, its mere existence shows that the two response models just discussed cannot be correct and suggests that we introduce response biases in some fashion. We now look into this question.

4.1 The Equation of Comparative Judgment

The most obvious way to introduce response biases into Thurstone's model is to modify the decision rule, Eq. 12. We do so as follows:

When $\langle x, y \rangle$ is presented, the first stimulus, x, is judged $\begin{Bmatrix} larger \\ smaller \end{Bmatrix}$ than the second, y, if $\mathbf{X} \begin{Bmatrix} > \\ < \end{Bmatrix} \mathbf{Y} + c$, where c is some positive or negative number. (29)

With this rule, we have, as before,

$$p(1 \mid \langle x, y \rangle) = \Pr\,(\mathbf{X} > \mathbf{Y} + c)$$
$$= \Pr\,(\mathbf{X} - \mathbf{Y} - c > 0)$$
$$= \int_{-\infty}^{\frac{u(x)-u(y)-c}{\sigma(x,y)}} N(0,\ 1)$$
$$= \int_{c}^{\infty} N[u(x) - u(y), \sigma(x, y)], \qquad (30)$$

where $N(\mu, \sigma)$ is the normal distribution with mean μ and standard deviation σ. This modification of Thurstone's model was first suggested by Harris (1957). (If we had simply assumed an additive bias so that the mean of the effect of stimulus x is $u(x) + a(1)$ when x is presented first and $u(x) + a(2)$ when it is presented second, then setting $c = a(2) - a(1)$ yields Eq. 30. As we shall see in Eq. 32, this means that the way biases are introduced into the choice model is substantially the same as this way of introducing them into Thurstone's model, except for a logarithmic transformation.)

Consider a pair-comparison design involving k stimuli. The unknowns are c, the k means $u(x)$, the k standard deviations, $\sigma(k)$, and the $k(k + 1)/2$ correlations, $r(x, y)$, a total of $1 + k + k + k(k + 1)/2 = 1 + k(k + 5)/2$ variables. If we set one of the means equal to 0 and one of the standard deviations equal to 1, which only fixes the zero and unit of the scale, this reduces the number of unknowns to $k(k + 5)/2 - 1$. There are, of course,

k^2 equations. The number of unknowns is easily seen to be less than or equal to the number of equations for $k \geqslant 5$, and if we are willing to introduce the constraints of the form

$$[u(x) - u(y)] + [u(y) - u(z)] = u(x) - u(z)$$

as assumptions rather than use them to test the model then the minimum number of stimuli needed to estimate the parameters is reduced to 4.

Thus, introducing the cutoff c not only makes the model more realistic but, in principle, at least, renders the model determinant, which we recall it was not in Thurstone's original formulation. Just how to solve for the unknowns appears, however, to be an extremely formidable problem, involving as it does 25 unknowns in 25 nonlinear equations.

Certain special cases are amenable to solution and, as in Thurstone's work, may serve as useful first approximations. For example, suppose $r(x, y) = 0$ for all x and y. For some particular stimulus s, we may arbitrarily set $u(s) = 0$ and $\sigma(s) = 1/\sqrt{2}$, and equating the relative frequencies of choices to the theoretical probabilities we estimate c from

$$p(1 \mid \langle s, s \rangle) = \int_{\hat{c}}^{\infty} N(0, 1).$$

With $\hat{c}$ so determined, we estimate $\sigma(x)$ from

$$p(1 \mid \langle x, x \rangle) = \int_{\hat{c}}^{\infty} N[0, \sqrt{2}\, \hat{\sigma}(x)].$$

Finally, with $\hat{c}$ and $\hat{\sigma}(x)$ known for all x, we estimate $u(x) - u(y)$ from

$$p(1 \mid \langle x, y \rangle) = \int_{\hat{c}}^{\infty} N\{\hat{u}(x) - \hat{u}(y), [\hat{\sigma}(x)^2 + \hat{\sigma}(y)^2]^{\frac{1}{2}}\}.$$

There are various internal checks on the adequacy of the model, including the two estimates of $u(x) - u(y)$ from $p(1 \mid \langle x, y \rangle)$ and from $p(1 \mid \langle y, x \rangle)$ and the additivity condition on triples of stimuli mentioned earlier.

As far as we know, no empirical research has been carried out using this generalization of the Thurstone model in the context of discrimination, although for a similar model in detection there are considerable data (see Chapter 3).

It follows immediately from Eq. 30 that $p(1 \mid \langle s, x_{1/2} \rangle) = \frac{1}{2}$ if and only if $u(s) - u(x_{1/2}) - c = 0$. If we suppose that Fechner's law is correct so that $u(s) = A \log (s + \gamma) + B$ and define b so that $c = -A \log b$, then

$$A \log (s + \gamma) + B - A \log (x_{1/2} + \gamma) - B + A \log b = 0$$

implies $x_{1/2} = b(s + \gamma) - \gamma$. Thus, $\text{CE} = x_{1/2} - s = (b - 1)(s + \gamma)$, which again is the generalized Weber law for the CE.

4.2 A Choice Model

A generalization of the unbiased choice model (Sec. 3.2), but not of the choice axiom itself, was described by Luce (1959). Although the argument leading to the model is somewhat indirect and to some people not entirely satisfactory, the model itself is easily stated. Let $s = \langle \mathcal{A}_1, \mathcal{A}_2, \ldots, \mathcal{A}_k \rangle$ $\in S$, where $\mathcal{A}_r \in \mathcal{S}$, and $R = \{1, 2, \ldots, k\}$, then there are two numerical ratio scales

$$\eta : \mathcal{S} \to \text{positive reals}$$
$$b : R \to \text{positive reals}$$

such that

$$p(r \mid s) = \frac{\eta(\mathcal{A}_r) \, b(r)}{\sum_{r' \in R} \eta(\mathcal{A}_{r'}) \, b(r')} . \tag{31}$$

This representation is closely similar to that given in Eq. 24, except that now the order of presentation of the stimuli matters. Both the stimulus and the response used to designate it contribute multiplicatively and independently to the response probability in Eq. 31. It is appropriate to think of $\eta(\mathcal{A})$ as a stimulus parameter associated with stimulus $\mathcal{A}$, which is independent of the response used to designate it, and to think of $b(r)$ as a response parameter, or bias, associated with the response, which is independent of the stimulus to which the response refers. If there is no differential tendency to use the responses, that is, if $b(r)$ is a constant independent of $r \in R$, then the b terms drop out and Eq. 31 reduces to Eq. 24.

This representation is also similar to the choice model for complete identification experiments described in Sec. 1.2 of Chapter 3. The only formal difference is that the stimulus parameters here depend upon single stimuli, whereas there they depend upon pairs of stimuli. This difference may well be more apparent than real, as we shall see shortly.

One way to arrive at Eq. 31 is via a learning argument similar to that given in Sec. 1.2 of Chapter 3 (see Bush, Luce, & Rose, 1963). Consider the special but important design in which $\mathcal{S}$ has k elements and each presentation includes every element of $\mathcal{S}$. Put another way, the presentations are just orderings of $\mathcal{S}$. Let $\mathcal{A}^* \in \mathcal{S}$ denote the "correct" element— the one meeting the discriminative criterion. In terms of the identification function, $\iota(r) = \{s \mid \mathcal{A}_r = \mathcal{A}^*\}$. Suppose that s' is presented and $s' \in \iota(r')$; then the response probabilities are assumed to be transformed linearly by

$$p_{n+1}(r \mid s) = p_n(r \mid s) + \eta(\mathcal{A}_{r'}, \mathcal{A}^*) \, \theta(r')[\delta_{rr'} - p_n(r \mid s)].$$

As in the complete identification situation, θ is a basic learning rate parameter associated with the correct response and η is a generalization parameter. Note that by our assumptions the generalization is not between presentations but between the stimuli corresponding to the correct response, one of these stimuli, of course, being $\varDelta^*$.

Paralleling the argument used in Sec. 1.2 of Chapter 3, it is easy to show that

$$\lim_{n \to \infty} E[p_n(r \mid s)] = \frac{\eta(\varDelta_r, \varDelta^*) \, b(r)}{\sum\limits_{r' \in R} \eta(\varDelta_{r'}, \varDelta^*) \, b(r')} \, ,$$

where $b(r) = P(r) \, \theta(r)$, and $P(r)$ denotes the a priori probability that r is the correct response, that is, $P(r)$ is the sum of all the presentation probabilities $P(s)$ for which $s \in \iota(r)$. This equation has the same form as Eq. 31, except that $\eta(\varDelta_r)$ is replaced by $\eta(\varDelta_r, \varDelta^*)$. Because $\varDelta^*$ is fixed throughout, this is a purely notational difference. Thus, the discrimination choice model for at least this special case is not as different from the complete identification model as it first seems.

If one does not assume that the presentations are orderings of $\mathscr{S}$, then different stimuli are correct for different presentations and matters are more complicated. In particular, the asymptotic form is not Eq. 31, and so, for example, the analysis of the method of constant stimuli given below in terms of Eq. 31 may very well be wrong.

It is not difficult to see that Eq. 31 implies: for any $s, s' \in S$ and any $r, r', r'' \in R$ such that $\varDelta_r = \varDelta_{r'}$, then $[p(r \mid s)/p(r'' \mid s)][p(r'' \mid s')/p(r' \mid s')]$ is a function of only $r, r', \varDelta_{r''}$, and $\varDelta_{r''}'$. It has been shown that this property, which involves only observable quantities, is in fact equivalent to Eq. 31 (Luce, 1962).

The empirical adequacy of Eq. 31 is readily tested because the number of parameters increases linearly with the number of stimuli used and with the number of response categories, whereas the number of probabilities to be accounted for increases much more rapidly. For example, if three stimuli are used, they may be presented in six different orders when the subject is to select one out of three and also in six ordered pairs when he is to select one out of two, yielding a total of 18 independent conditional probabilities. Because we can, and must, arbitrarily choose the unit of the η and b scales in Eq. 31, there are two, not three, stimulus parameters and, assuming different biases in the two- and three-choice situations, a total of three bias parameters. So there are $18 - 5 = 13$ degrees of freedom even in this simple situation.

Such an experiment was performed on lifted weights by Shipley and Luce (1963) and on visual brightness by van Laer (undated). As an example of

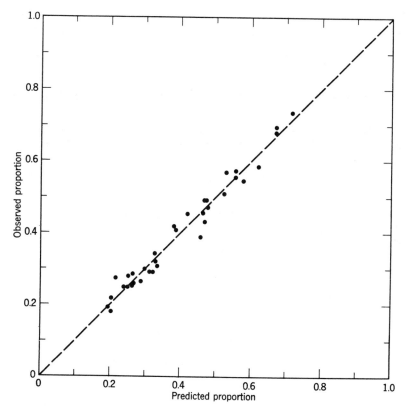

Fig. 10. Observed versus expected proportions predicted by the choice model for lifted weight data collected under two procedures. In one, each of the six orderings of three weights plus three repetitions of the intermediate weight were presented 400 times. In the other, each of the six orderings of two of the three weights plus two repetitions of the intermediate weight were presented 400 times. Stimulus and bias parameters were estimated from the data for each condition using a technique suggested in Luce (1959). The geometric means of the two estimates of the stimulus parameters were used to calculate the expected proportions. For this subject, $\chi^2 = 24.00$, df $= 16$, and $0.05 < p < 0.10$. These data were collected by Shipley and Luce (1963).

the adequacy of the model, Fig. 10 shows the predicted versus observed proportions for one subject in the weight-lifting experiment.

Consider, now, the method of constant stimuli, where the standard stimulus s is presented first, the comparison x, second, and the response categories are 1 and 2. Then

$$p(1 \mid \langle s, x \rangle) = \frac{1}{1 + \eta(x)/\eta(s)b}, \tag{32}$$

where $b = b(1)/b(2)$. If we let $u(s) = a \log \eta(s) + a'$ and $c = -a \log b$, then it is easy to see that Eq. 32 can be rewritten in the logistic form

$$p(1 \mid \langle s, x \rangle) = \frac{1}{1 + \exp \{[u(x) - u(s) + c]/a\}} .$$

Questions of estimating the parameters a and c from data are discussed in Chapter 8.

By setting $p(1 \mid \langle s, x_{1/2} \rangle) = p(2 \mid \langle s, x_{1/2} \rangle) = \frac{1}{2}$, it is easy to see that $\eta(x_{1/2}) = b\eta(s)$. If the η-scale is a power function, $\eta(x) = \alpha(x + \gamma)^\beta$, then

$$x_{1/2} = b^{1/\beta}(s + \gamma) - \gamma,$$

so

$$\text{CE} = x_{1/2} - s = (b^{1/\beta} - 1)(s + \gamma),$$

which is again the generalized Weber law for the CE. A similar calculation with $p[2 \mid \langle s, s + \Delta(s, \pi) \rangle] = \pi$ yields

$$\Delta(s, \pi) = \left[\left(\frac{b\pi}{1 - \pi} \right)^{1/\beta} - 1 \right] (s + \gamma), \quad \cdot$$

and so

$$\pi\text{-jnd} = (\tfrac{1}{2})[\Delta(s, \pi) - \Delta(s, 1 - \pi)]$$

$$= (\tfrac{1}{2})(s + \gamma)b^{1/\beta} \left[\left(\frac{\pi}{1 - \pi} \right)^{1/\beta} + \left(\frac{1 - \pi}{\pi} \right)^{1/\beta} \right],$$

which is a generalized Weber law.

Note that both the CE and the jnd depend upon the factor $b^{1/\beta}$ but that the jnd also depends upon a factor involving only β, namely $[\pi/(1 - \pi)]^{1/\beta} + [(1 - \pi)/\pi]^{1/\beta}$. It is really only the second term that measures discriminability if this model is correct. This suggests considering the quantity

$$\frac{\text{jnd}}{x_{1/2} + \gamma} = \frac{1}{2} \left[\left(\frac{\pi}{1 - \pi} \right)^{1/\beta} + \left(\frac{1 - \pi}{\pi} \right)^{1/\beta} \right]$$

as a measure of discrimination rather than the Weber fraction $\text{jnd}/(s + \gamma)$, which depends upon b.

4.3 Payoffs

Little or no experimental work has been carried out to determine the effects of payoffs in discrimination designs. Some workers have used symmetric payoff matrices in an attempt to motivate the subjects to reduce the size of the jnd, but in contrast to the extensive use of payoffs to manipulate the response probabilities in detection research, the effects of payoffs upon the psychometric function have not been investigated. It is difficult not to believe that analogous manipulations are possible and that, in particular, the magnitude and sign of the CE are a function of the payoffs used. All we can do at present is to carry out some theoretical calculations, which we do for the choice model. The parallel calculations for the Thurstone model are possible, but they are somewhat messier in detail.

Suppose we consider a constant stimulus experiment with the standard s and variable stimuli $x_{-k} < x_{-k+1} < \ldots < x_{-1} < s < x_1 < \ldots < x_{k-1} < x_k$. Suppose that each presentation $\langle s, x_i \rangle$, $i = 0, \pm 1, \ldots, \pm k$, where $s = x_0$, occurs equally often, that is, with probability $1/(2k + 1)$. The subject is to say whether the first or second stimulus is larger, and after each trial he is paid off according to the following monetary payoff matrix:

$$
\begin{array}{cc}
 & \begin{array}{cc} 1 & \quad 2 \end{array} \\
\begin{array}{l} \text{Relation between} \\ \text{Stimuli in the} \\ \text{Presentation} \end{array}
\begin{array}{l} x_i < s \\ x_i = s \\ x_i > s \end{array}
\left[
\begin{array}{cc}
o_{11} & o_{12} \\
0 & 0 \\
o_{21} & o_{22}
\end{array}
\right],
\end{array}
$$

where $o_{11} > o_{12}$ and $o_{22} > o_{21}$.

The expected monetary return on a typical trial is

$$
E(o) = \frac{1}{2k + 1} \left\{ \sum_{i=-1}^{-k} [o_{11}p(1 \mid \langle s, x_i \rangle) + o_{12}p(2 \mid \langle s, x_i \rangle)] \right.
$$

$$
\left. + 0 + \sum_{i=1}^{k} [o_{21}p(1 \mid \langle s, x_i \rangle) + o_{22}p(2 \mid \langle s, x_i \rangle)] \right\}.
$$

If the choice model is correct, then Eq. 32 applies. Writing η_i for $\eta(s)/\eta(x_i)$, we see that

$$
E(o) = \frac{1}{2k + 1} \left\{ \sum_{i=-1}^{-k} \left[\frac{o_{11}b\eta_i + o_{12}}{1 + b\eta_i} \right] + 0 \right.
$$

$$
\left. + \sum_{i=1}^{k} \left[\frac{o_{21}b\eta_i + o_{22}}{1 + b\eta_i} \right] \right\}.
$$

Assuming that the subject selects the value of the bias parameter to maximize $E(o)$, we calculate the derivative of $E(o)$ with respect to b and set it equal to 0:

$$
\frac{dE(o)}{db} = 0 = \frac{1}{2k + 1} \left\{ \sum_{i=-1}^{-k} \left[\frac{(o_{11} - o_{12})\eta_i}{(1 + b\eta_i)^2} \right] + \sum_{i=1}^{k} \left[\frac{(o_{21} - o_{22})\eta_i}{(1 + b\eta_i)^2} \right] \right\}. \tag{33}
$$

If the payoff matrix is symmetric in the sense that $o_{11} = o_{22}$ and $o_{12} = o_{21}$, then

$$\sum_{i=1}^{k} \frac{\eta_i}{(1 + b\eta_i)^2} = \sum_{i=-1}^{-k} \frac{\eta_i}{(1 + b\eta_i)^2} = \sum_{i=1}^{k} \frac{\eta_{-i}}{(1 + b\eta_{-i})^2} . \tag{34}$$

In general this equation is satisfied only if $b \neq 1$. Thus, even with symmetric payoffs, a bias may be needed to optimize the expected payoff. An important exception is when the stimuli are located symmetrically around s in the sense that $\eta_{-i} = 1/\eta_i$ or in terms of $\log \eta$ when $\log s - \log \eta(x_{-i}) = \log \eta(x_i) - \log s$. If this is so and if $b = 1$, then

$$\frac{\eta_{-i}}{(1 + \eta_{-i})^2} = \frac{1/\eta_i}{(1 + 1/\eta_i)^2} = \frac{\eta_i}{(\eta_i + 1)^2} ,$$

and so Eq. 34 is satisfied.

When the pairs are not presented equally often, when the o_{ij} must be treated as utilities that are nonlinear with money so that the payoff matrix is not really symmetric even if the money outcomes are, or when the stimuli are not symmetric about the standard in the sense that $\eta(x_{-i})/\eta(s) = \eta(s)/\eta(x_i)$, in all these cases the expected payoff is a maximum only if a bias is introduced. Thus it may not be surprising that we so often find nonzero CE's. The empirical question remains whether or not the CE varies as predicted when we use different payoff matrices. It should not be forgotten that some detection studies cast doubt upon the maximization-of-expected-value model, and, if it is inadequate there, probably it is inadequate here as well.

5. UNORDERED DISCRIMINATION

The responses used in what we may call an *unordered discrimination experiment* are like those ordinarily used when speaking of discrimination. The subject simply reports whether he believes the pair of stimuli presented to be different, without specifying just how they differ. Aside from its more specific responses, any forced-choice discrimination design is equally suited to the study of unordered discrimination, but the converse is not true. Same-different responses make sense for many pairs of stimuli for which larger-smaller judgments are meaningless: for example, color patches that differ in hue, brightness, and saturation or, more generally, any stimuli that differ on two or more physical variables. In this section we shall look into models that have been proposed for studies of this type.

5.1 The Matching Experiment

In what we call a matching experiment, the set $\mathscr{S}$ of stimuli can be anything that we can control with an acceptable error. Because they need not be physically ordered, as in the forced-choice discrimination design, a whole new range of possibilities opens up, including stimuli that we cannot easily characterize in detail as physical objects: photographs, samples of handwriting, patches of textured material, etc.

The set S of stimulus presentations is usually a subset of $\mathscr{S} \times \mathscr{S}$, although the possibility of presenting k-tuples of stimuli certainly exists. Because all existing research concerns pairs, we shall confine our attention to them. As with forced-choice discrimination, we can use either the method of pair comparisons, where $S = \mathscr{S} \times \mathscr{S}$, or methods (e.g., constant stimuli) in which S is a proper subset of $\mathscr{S} \times \mathscr{S}$.

The response set R consists of two elements, "match" and "not match," "same" and "different," or some equivalent terms, which we denote by M and $\bar{M}$, respectively.

To get at the identification function, we must first consider ways in which terms such as "same" and "different" might be used, for there is an inherent ambiguity in their meanings. Certainly when a subject says two stimuli are the same he cannot mean that they are strictly the same in all respects, for two things cannot occur in the same place at the same time and still be designated by the subject. Just how much "sameness" is required differs from study to study, ranging from the stringent demand that the two stimuli be identical in all measurable aspects, except for their space-time location, to the weaker requirement that they be the same with respect to some one physical measure, such as sound energy, to the considerably weaker request that they be of the same "subjective loudness." The last of these examples differs from the other two in that the experimenter has no independent measure with which to decide whether the subject's response is correct or incorrect; that is, there is no identification function.

We shall confine our attention to stimuli such that there is an equivalence relation $\sim$ defined over them in terms of their physical properties. In some experiments it may denote identity; in others, equivalence with respect to sound energy or the like. This defines the partition

$$I_M(S) = \{\langle x, y \rangle \mid \langle x, y \rangle \in S \text{ and } x \sim y\}$$
$$I_{\bar{M}}(S) = S - I_M(S),$$

hence the identification function is

$$\iota(M) = I_M(S)$$
$$\iota(\bar{M}) = I_{\bar{M}}(S).$$

We shall suppose that the payoff matrix is compatible with the identification function in the sense that for $\langle x, y \rangle \in S$, it is

Response

$$
\begin{array}{c}
 \\
x \sim y \\
\text{not } (x \sim y)
\end{array}
\begin{array}{cc}
M & \bar{M} \\
\begin{bmatrix} o_{11} & o_{12} \\ o_{21} & o_{22} \end{bmatrix}
\end{array},
$$

where $o_{11} > o_{12}$ and $o_{22} > o_{21}$.

The final ingredient in the design of a matching experiment is the schedule that assigns a presentation to each trial. As is customary in most of psychophysics, the assignment is random; however, equal probabilities for the several presentations are not generally used. The reason is simple. In a pair-comparison design with 10 stimuli and a criterion of strict identity there are 10 presentations, the $\langle x, x \rangle$ ones, for which "match" is the correct response, and 90 for which it is wrong. Thus, if the presentations were equiprobable, the subject would be wise to bias his responses strongly, possibly exclusively, to "not match." To avoid this bias, one can either increase the frequency of the $\langle x, x \rangle$ presentations, decrease the number of different $\langle x, y \rangle$ pairs presented, or use some mixture of these two that results in each response being correct half the time. If the outcomes are money and symmetric in the sense that $o_{11} = -o_{12} = -o_{21} = o_{22}$ and the subject responds entirely at random, then his expected outcome is zero for such schedules.

5.2 A Thurstonian Model

As far as we know, no probability model has been stated in the literature for the matching experiment. We do not see how to extend the choice model to unordered discrimination, but as it is easy to do so for the Thurstone model, we include that.

As in the forced-choice discrimination model, we suppose that to each stimulus $x \in \mathscr{S}$ there is a random variable $\mathbf{X}$ assuming values on the real line; it is again interpreted as the momentary effect of the presentation of x. We assume that $\mathbf{X}$ is normally distributed with mean $u(x)$ and standard deviation $\sigma(x)$ and that, when x and y are presented successively, the correlation between $\mathbf{X}$ and $\mathbf{Y}$ is $r(x, y)$. In forced-choice discrimination the choice between x and y was made by comparing $\mathbf{X} - \mathbf{Y}$ with some fixed cutoff c (Sec. 4.1). Here the decision is between saying that the stimuli are the same or that they are different, and the plausible decision rule is that the subject selects two cutoffs, $-c$ and d, where $-c < d$, and that

$$
he\ responds \begin{Bmatrix} M \\ \bar{M} \end{Bmatrix} \quad if \quad \begin{Bmatrix} -c \leqslant \mathbf{X} - \mathbf{Y} \leqslant d \\ otherwise \end{Bmatrix}. \tag{35}
$$

In other words, if the effects are sufficiently close, he says the stimuli do not differ; otherwise, he says they do.

Because the distribution of the difference $X - Y$ is normal, with mean $u(x) - u(y)$ and standard deviation,

$$\sigma(x, y) = [\sigma^2(x) + \sigma^2(y) - 2\sigma(x)\, \sigma(y)\, r(x, y)]^{\frac{1}{2}},$$

the decision rule yields the representation

$$p(M \mid \langle x, y \rangle) = \int_{-c}^{d} N[u(x) - u(y), \sigma(x, y)], \tag{36}$$

where $N(\mu, \sigma)$ denotes the normal distribution with mean μ and standard deviation σ.

Note that the often assumed, but probably incorrect, property of response symmetry $p(M \mid \langle x, y \rangle) = p(M \mid \langle y, x \rangle)$ is equivalent to $d = c$.

An equations-and-unknowns count similar to that carried out in Sec. 4.1 yields the same number of equations and one more unknown, still leaving five as the smallest number of stimuli for which the number of equations is not less than the number of unknowns. Again, nothing is known about solving this general case.

Previously we were able to solve the special case $r(x, y) = 0$, for all x and y, by setting $u(s) = 0$ and $\sigma(s) = 1/\sqrt{2}$. Doing this here, we obtain from Eq. 36

$$p(M \mid \langle s, s \rangle) = \int_{-c}^{d} N(0, 1),$$

$$p(M \mid \langle x, x \rangle) = \int_{-c}^{d} N[0, \sqrt{2}\, \sigma(x)],$$

$$p(M \mid \langle x, s \rangle) = \int_{-c}^{d} N\{u(x), [\tfrac{1}{2} + \sigma^2(x)]^{\frac{1}{2}}\},$$

$$p(M \mid \langle s, x \rangle) = \int_{-c}^{d} N\{- u(x), [\tfrac{1}{2} + \sigma^2(x)]^{\frac{1}{2}}\},$$

which is a system of four equations in four unknowns, c, d, $u(x)$, and $\sigma(x)$. Although we do not know how to solve this system, mainly because there are two unknowns—c and d—in the first equation, at least the number is sufficiently small so that one can hope that usable techniques for calculating the solutions can be found.

If we assume both $r(x, y) = 0$, for all x and y, and that $d = c$, then solutions are easy to find:

$$p(M \mid \langle s, s \rangle) = \int_{-c}^{c} N(0, 1)$$

determines c,

$$p(M \mid \langle x, x \rangle) = \int_{-c}^{c} N[0, \sqrt{2}\,\sigma(x)]$$

determines $\sigma(x)$, a similar equation determines $\sigma(y)$, and

$$p(M \mid \langle x, y \rangle) = \int_{-c}^{c} N\{u(x) - u(y), [\sigma^2(x) + \sigma^2(y)]^{1/2}\}$$

determines $u(x) - u(y)$.

To get some idea about the effects of payoffs in this model, consider the simplest experiment and the simplest model. The experiment involves the presentation of either $\langle s, s \rangle$ with probability P or $\langle s, s' \rangle$ with probability $1 - P$, and the payoff matrix is

		Response	
		M	$\bar{M}$
Stimulus	$\langle s, s \rangle$	o_{11}	o_{12}
Presentation	$\langle s, s' \rangle$	o_{21}	o_{22}

Thus the expected outcome is

$$E(o) = [p(M \mid \langle s, s \rangle) - \beta p(M \mid \langle s, s' \rangle)]P(o_{11} - o_{12}) + Po_{12} + (1 - P)o_{22},$$

where

$$\beta = \left(\frac{1 - P}{P}\right)\left(\frac{o_{22} - o_{21}}{o_{11} - o_{12}}\right).$$

The model is the one just stated in which $d = c$, with the added assumption that all of the variances are equal, so that the variance of the difference distribution may be taken to be 1. Differentiating $E(o)$ with respect to c and setting that equal to zero yields

$$\frac{dE(o)}{dc} = 0 = \frac{dp(M \mid \langle s, s \rangle)}{dc} - \beta \frac{dp(M \mid \langle s, s' \rangle)}{dc}$$

$$= 2\exp\left(\frac{-c^2}{2}\right) - \beta\left(\exp\left\{\frac{-[u(s) - u(s') - c]^2}{2}\right\}\right.$$

$$\left. + \exp\left\{\frac{-[u(s) - u(s') + c]^2}{2}\right\}\right)$$

$$= 2\exp\left(\frac{-c^2}{2}\right) - \beta 2\exp\left\{\frac{-[u(s) - u(s')]^2}{2}\right\}$$

$$\times \exp\left(\frac{-c^2}{2}\right)\cosh[u(s) - u(s')]c$$

$$= 2\exp\left(\frac{-c^2}{2}\right)\left(1 - \beta\exp\left\{\frac{-[u(s) - u(s')]^2}{2}\right\}\cosh[u(s) - u(s')]c\right).$$

So

$$\cosh [u(s) - u(s')]c = \frac{1}{\beta} \exp \left\{ \frac{[u(s) - u(s')]^2}{2} \right\}.$$

This last equation, which determines c, depends not only upon the payoff conditions through the parameter β but also on the spacing of the stimuli $u(s) - u(s')$. In more complicated experiments the dependence upon the spacing of the stimuli remains but is, of course, more complex. It is evident from these considerations that the subject's definition of the match category is highly sensitive to the distribution of the stimuli, and one would guess that it is likely to be unstable in a given experiment unless the subject is well practiced. This may well be the theoretical counterpart of the empirical observation that indifference categories are very tricky to use and that, on the whole, it is better in discrimination work to use forced-choice procedures. (See Sec. 7.1 of Chapter 3 for a caution about extending this recommendation outside discrimination work.)

It appears that a series of experiments needs to be performed on the same subjects and with the same stimuli in which both forced-choice and unordered discrimination designs are used and the payoffs varied. The data should then be analyzed in terms of the Thurstonian models which, if they are correct, will yield approximately the same estimates of u and σ from all conditions. If that is verified, then the dependence of the cutoffs on the payoffs should be investigated, for maximization of expected money is not obviously the correct decision mechanism.

5.3 An Algebraic Model

In Chapter X of *The Structure of Appearance* Goodman (1951) presented an algebraic model for unordered discrimination. This model was later restated in slightly modified form and applied to data in visual psychophysics by Galanter (1956). Both presentations used the language of symbolic logic; we restate it in set terminology.

Goodman's work was not motivated by psychophysics, as such, but by philosophical considerations. To what extent can an ordering of stimuli be constructed from what in Goodman's view is the most primitive observing response: matching? The criticisms we are forced to make of Goodman's model considered as a possible description of behavior may very well not be appropriate when it is considered as a philosophical contribution.

Suppose that when two stimuli s and s' are presented the subject says either that they match (are the same) or that they do not and that he is

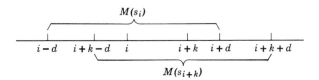

Fig. 11. Manors of stimuli that can be represented as points on a line.

consistent in his reports. Thus his behavior may be summarized as a matching relation M over $\mathscr{S}$. In terms of a probability model, this is the same as supposing that all of the probabilities are either 0 or 1. By analogy to the probability models, we might suppose that there is a distance measure $d(s, s')$ [paralleling, e.g., $u(s) - u(s')$ in the Thurstone models] and a criterion d such that the decision rule is

$$sMs' \quad \text{if and only if} \quad d(s, s') \leqslant d. \tag{37}$$

Accepting the heuristic argument, it follows immediately that M is a reflexive and symmetric relation but is not, in general, transitive. Goodman assumes that M is reflexive and symmetric.

Now, suppose that instead of working with a sample of stimuli we have all possible stimuli of a given type, such as all 1000-cps tones of different intensities; suppose that the world is discrete in the sense that there is only a finite number of different stimuli, and suppose that they are ordered psychologically $s_1 < s_2 < \ldots < s_m$. Because these are supposed to be the only stimuli, the simplest possible distance measure is the number of intervening stimuli plus one: $d(s_i, s_j) = |j - i|$. If this is so and Eq. 37 is the decision rule, then there is a simple way to discover the distances between pairs of stimuli. We define the *manor* of stimulus s to be the set of stimuli $M(s) = \{s' \mid sMs'\}$. For stimuli s_i and s_{i+k}, where s_iMs_{i+k}, that is, where $k \leqslant d$, the manors are shown in Fig. 11. If $N(X)$ denotes the number of elements in a set X, then we see that

$$N[M(s_i) - M(s_{i+k})] = (i + k - d) - (i - d) = k,$$

and

$$N[M(s_{i+k}) - M(s_i)] = (i + k + d) - (i + d) = k,$$

hence

$$d(s_i, s_{i+k}) = k = \tfrac{1}{2}\{N[M(s_i) - M(s_{i+k})] + N[M(s_{i+k}) - M(s_i)]\}; \tag{38}$$

that is, the distance is one half the number of elements in the symmetric difference of the manors of the two stimuli.

Having the notion of distance given in Eq. 38, Goodman suggested that it can be used to reconstruct the ordering of the stimuli using the following three definitions:

1. *If s, s', and s" ∈ 𝒮 are all different and sMs', s'Ms", and sMs", then s' is between s and s" if and only if d(s, s") > d(s, s') and d(s, s") > d(s', s"), where d is defined by Eq. 38.*
2. *Stimulus s is said to be* beside *s' if and only if s ≠ s', sMs', and no s" exists between s and s'.*
3. *A finite set of stimuli over which a reflexive and symmetric relation M is defined form a* linear array *if two of the stimuli are each beside just one other stimulus and all others are beside exactly two others.*

It seems to us that for the empirical scientist this scheme to organize stimuli into linear arrays has a fatal flaw. The scheme rests crucially upon the assumption that one has all possible stimuli, for only in that case does Eq. 38 give the underlying distance measure. When subsets of stimuli are used, as must be the case in practice, Eq. 38 does not define an invariant distance measure. Thus there may be arrays that are nonlinear by Goodman's definition which have subsets that are linear. An example is shown in Fig. 12. In the basic underlying two-dimensional grid each point matches itself and each adjacent point in its row and column. This array is clearly nonlinear, but the subset of darkened points and lines forms a linear array in Goodman's sense.

The results given below regarding Goodman's definition of a linear array are of interest. Suppose that by his method a set of stimuli form a linear array, ordered $s_1 \leqslant s_2 \leqslant \ldots \leqslant s_m$. Assume, in addition to

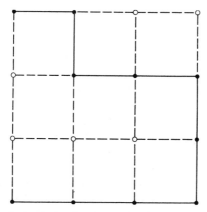

Fig. 12. An example of a nonlinear array having a subset which is linear.

reflexiveness and symmetry, that M satisfies this condition which follows from the basic decision rule:

Weak Mapping Assumption. If $s_i < s_j < s_k < s_l$ and $s_i M s_l$, then $s_j M s_k$.

Suppose we define the distance measure $\delta(s_i, s_j) = |j - i|$. It should be noted that in general this definition of distance differs from that given by Eq. 38, which is the one used to organize the stimuli into a linear array.

Three concepts are now introduced. The first is, essentially, the decision rule we have been assuming, but applied to the distance δ.

1. *A linear array is* uniform *provided that a number δ can be found such that sMs' if and only if $\delta(s, s') \leqslant \delta$.*
2. *A linear array is* regular *provided that when sMs' and $\delta(t, t') \leqslant \delta(s, s')$ then tMt'.*
3. *In a linear array s is* just noticeably different *from s', denoted sJs', if not sMs' and there exists an s'' such that s'' is beside s and $s''Ms'$.*

Fine (1954) has proved the following theorem:

Theorem 7. *If a linear array satisfies the weak mapping assumption, then the following are equivalent:* (1) *it is uniform,* (2) *it is regular, and* (3) *sJs' implies $s'Js$.*

In a later paper Fine and Harrop (1957) showed that it is always possible to embed a linear array that satisfies the weak mapping assumption into a uniform linear array. The motive for proving this is, evidently, to show that we can always consider the set of stimuli actually used as a subset of a set of stimuli for which the decision rule (Eq. 37) holds. It does not, however, overcome the lack of invariance in Goodman's scheme for arranging the stimuli into an array in the first place.

6. CONCLUSIONS

It came as a surprise to us when preparing this chapter, as it may have to the reader, that in spite of a long history of experimental work on discrimination there are relatively few data available that are suitable to test existing mathematical theories. This is in striking contrast to the abundance of detection and recognition data that have been collected specifically to test and guide the recent flurry of theoretical research in that area. It is evident that a program of empirical work needs to be developed to parallel that now under way on detection.

Although there are currently three different response theories in the detection studies, only two have been worked out for discrimination. We are at present totally lacking a true threshold theory of discrimination.

As in the detection work, the most fully developed theories establish relations among response probabilities. Each of these theories defines numerical parameters, some of which are thought to be stimulus-determined and others, response biases. Adequate theories are still lacking to account for how these depend, respectively, upon the stimulus measures and upon payoffs, presentation probabilities, and the like. It is clear that much work needs to be done, especially on the way in which the response biases are determined. The possibility of treating the biases as the end product of a learning process, as was done with the choice and threshold models in detection, needs investigation.

References

Abelson, R. M., & Bradley, R. A. A 2 × 2 factorial with paired comparisons, *Biometrics*, 1954, **10**, 487–502.

Boring, E. G. Urban's tables and the method of constant stimuli. *Amer. J. Psychol.*, 1917, **28**, 280–293.

Boring, E. G. The control of attitude in psychophysical experiments. *Psychol. Rev.*, 1920, **27**, 440–452.

Boring, E. G. Is there a generalized psychometric function? *Amer. J. Psychol.*, 1924, **35**, 75–78.

Boring, E. G. *A history of experimental psychology*. (2nd ed.) New York: Appleton-Century-Crofts, 1950.

Boring, E. G., Langfeld, H. S., & Weld, H. P. *Foundations of psychology*. New York: Wiley, 1948.

Bradley, R. A. Incomplete block rank analysis: on the appropriateness of the model for a method of paired comparisons. *Biometrics*, 1954, **10**, 375–390.(a)

Bradley, R. A. Rank analysis of incomplete block designs. II. Additional tables for the method of paired comparisons. *Biometrika*, 1954, **41**, 502–537.(b)

Bradley, R. A. Rank analysis of incomplete block designs. III. Some large-sample results on estimation and power for a method of paired comparisons. *Biometrika*, 1955, **42**, 450–470.

Bradley, R. A., & Terry, M. E. Rank analysis of incomplete block designs. I. The method of paired comparisons. *Biometrika*, 1952, **39**, 324–345.

Bush, R. R., Luce, R. D., & Rose, R. Learning models for psychophysics. In R. C. Atkinson (Ed.), *Studies in mathematical psychology*. Vol. I. Stanford: Stanford Univer. Press, 1963, in press.

Clarke, F. R. Constant-ratio rule for confusion matrices in speech communication. *J. acoust. Soc. Amer.*, 1957, **29**, 715–720.

Cobb, P. W. Weber's law and the Fechnerian muddle. *Psychol. Rev.*, 1932, **39**, 533–551.

Fechner, G. T. *Elemente der Psychophysik*. Leipzig: Breitkopf und Hartel, 1860.

Fine, N. J. Proof of a conjecture of Goodman. *J. Symbolic Logic*, 1954, **19**, 41–44.

Fine, N. J., & Harrop, R. Uniformization of linear arrays. *J. Symbolic Logic*, 1957, **22**, 130–140.

Ford, L. R., Jr. Solution of a ranking problem from binary comparisons. *Amer. Math. Mon.* Herbert Ellsworth Slaught Memorial Papers, 1957, 28–33.

Galanter, E. An axiomatic and experimental study of sensory order and measure. *Psychol. Rev.*, 1956, **63**, 16–28.

Gerlach, Muriel W. *Interval measurement of subjective magnitudes with subliminal differences.* Stanford: Applied Mathematics and Statistics Laboratory, 1957, Technical Report 7.

Goodman, N. *The structure of appearance.* Cambridge: Harvard Univer. Press, 1951.

Green, B. F. Attitude measurement. In G. Lindzey (Ed.), *Handbook of social psychology.* Cambridge: Addison-Wesley, 1954. Pp. 335–369.

Guilford, J. P. A generalized psychophysical law. *Psychol. Rev.*, 1932, **39**, 73–85.

Guilford, J. P. *Psychometric methods.* New York: McGraw-Hill, 1954.

Gulliksen, H. Paired comparisons and the logic of measurement. *Psychol. Rev.*, 1946, **53**, 199–213.

Gulliksen, H. A generalization of Thurstone's learning function. *Psychometrika*, 1953, **18**, 297–307.

Harris, W. P. A revised law of comparative judgment. *Psychometrika*, 1957, **22**, 189–198.

Holway, A. H., & Pratt, C. C. The Weber-ratio for intensive discrimination. *Psychol. Rev.*, 1936, **43**, 322–340.

Householder, A. S., & Young, G. Weber laws, the Weber law, and psychophysical analysis. *Psychometrika*, 1940, **5**, 183–193.

Hovland, C. I. A note on Guilford's generalized psychophysical law. *Psychol. Rev.*, 1938, **45**, 430–434.

James, W. *The principles of psychology.* New York: Holt, 1890.

Johnson, H. M. Did Fechner measure "introspectional" sensation? *Psychol. Rev.*, 1929, **36**, 257–284.

Johnson, H. M. Some properties of Fechner's intensity of sensation. *Psychol. Rev.*, 1930, **37**, 113–123.

Johnson, H. M. Are psychophysical problems genuine or spurious? *Amer. J. Psychol.*, 1945, **58**, 189–211.

Koenigs, M. G. Recherches sur les intégrales de certaines équations fonctionnelles. *Ann. Scientifiques de l'Ecole Normale Supérieure* (3), 1884, **1**, Supplement Sl-S41.

Koenigs, M. G. Nouvelles recherches sur les équations fonctionnelles. *Ann. Scientifiques de l'Ecole Normale Supérieure* (3), 1885, **2**, 385–404.

Luce, R. D. Semiorders and a theory of utility discrimination. *Econometrica*, 1956, **24**, 178–191.

Luce, R. D. *Individual choice behavior.* New York: Wiley, 1959.

Luce, R. D. An observable property equivalent to a choice model for discrimination experiments. *Psychometrika*, 1962, **27**, 163–167.

Luce, R. D., & Edwards, W. The derivation of subjective scales from just noticeable differences. *Psychol. Rev.*, 1958, **65**, 222–237.

Miller, G. A. Sensitivity to changes in the intensity of white noise and its relation to masking and loudness. *J. acoust. Soc. Amer.*, 1947, **19**, 609–619.

Mosteller, F. Remarks on the method of paired comparisons: I. The least squares solution assuming equal standard deviations and equal correlations. *Psychometrika*, 1951, **16**, 3–11.(a)

Mosteller, F. Remarks on the method of paired comparisons: II. The effect of an aberrant standard deviation when equal standard deviations and equal correlations are assumed. *Psychometrika*, 1951, **16**, 203–206.(b)

Mosteller, F. Remarks on the method of paired comparisons: III. A test of significance for paired comparisons when equal standard deviations and equal correlations are assumed. *Psychometrika*, 1951, **16**, 207–218.(c)

Müller, G. E. Über die Massbestimmung des Ortsinnes der Haut mittels der Methode der richtigen und falschen Fälle. *Arch. f. d. ges. Physiol.*, 1879, **19**, 191–235.

Scott, D., & Suppes, P. Foundational aspects of theories of measurement. *J. Symbolic Logic*, 1958, **23**, 113–128.

Shipley, Elizabeth F., & Luce, R. D. Discrimination among two- and three-element sets of weights. In R. C. Atkinson (Ed.), *Studies in mathematical psychology*. Vol. I. Stanford: Stanford Univer. Press, 1963, in press.

Solomons, L. M. A new explanation of Weber's law. *Psychol. Rev.*, 1900, **7**, 234–240.

Thompson, G. H. A new point of view in the interpretation of threshold measurements in psychophysics. *Psychol. Rev.*, 1920, **27**, 300–307.

Thurstone, L. L. A law of comparative judgment. *Psychol. Rev.*, 1927, **34**, 273–286.(a)

Thurstone, L. L. Psychophysical analysis. *Amer. J. Psychol.*, 1927, **38**, 368–389.(b)

Thurstone, L. L. The learning function. *J. gen Psychol.*, 1930, **3**, 469–493.

Thurstone, L. L. *The measurement of values*. Chicago: Univer. of Chicago Press, 1959.

Torgerson, W. S. *Theory and methods of scaling*. New York: Wiley, 1958.

Urban, F. M. On the method of just perceptible differences. *Psychol. Rev.*, 1907, **14**, 244–253.

Urban, F. M. The method of constant stimuli and its generalizations. *Psychol. Rev.*, 1910, **17**, 229–259.

van Laer, J. Response biases in psychophysical judgments: a test of Luce's model. Northwestern Univer., dittoed, undated.

5

Psychophysical Scaling[1,2]

R. Duncan Luce
University of Pennsylvania

Eugene Galanter
University of Washington

1. This work was supported in part by grant NSF G-17637 from the National Science Foundation to the University of Pennsylvania and by the Office of Naval Research, Contract NONR-551(37). Reproduction in whole or part is permitted for any purpose of the United States Government.
2. We are indebted to Francis W. Irwin, Elizabeth F. Shipley, and S. S. Stevens for their helpful criticisms of a preliminary draft of this chapter. A special word of thanks is due Dr. Stevens, who, in addition to discovering several errors of fact and a number of stylistic blunders, forced us to reconsider some of our views on various aspects of scaling. His comments coupled with our own misgivings resulted in a complete revision of the section on magnitude estimation and the addition of some new theoretical work. Hopefully, this has produced some convergence of viewpoint.

Contents

Psychophysical Scaling

In the preceding two chapters we have examined models for asymptotic choice behavior in a number of common psychophysical identification experiments. By the definition of an identification experiment, the perceptual problem was partly prejudged: certain physical orderings of the stimuli were assumed to correspond to the subject's perceptual orderings of them. For example, in loudness discrimination experiments the usual measure of physical intensity is assumed to order tones in the same way that the subject's perception of loudness does. The main effect of this assumption is to permit us to say whether or not a response to a stimulus presentation is correct, and so it seems acceptable to feed back information and to use payoffs.

The response theories so far proposed to describe behavior in such experiments all have two distinct classes of numerical parameters, one reflecting the effects of stimuli and the other, motivational biases. In testing these theories, it is necessary, among other things, to show that the stimulus parameters are in fact stimulus determined in the sense that they do not change when payoffs, presentation probabilities, and experimental designs are varied in certain ways. Once such a response theory is accepted, one must next determine just how the bias parameters depend upon the payoffs, the presentation probabilities, and whatever else they depend upon, and how the stimulus parameters depend upon physical properties of the stimuli. The latter relation is often called a *psychophysical scale*.

To some extent, we have already examined psychophysical scaling theories (Sec. 6, Chapter 3, and Sec. 2, Chapter 4), and in Sec. 2.1 of Chapter 4 we expressed some views on the general scaling problem which should be reread as background for this chapter. In addition to what we have already described, a number of other methods and models exist which attempt to treat the scaling of stimuli rather more directly and completely. These methods differ in two important respects from identification experiments. First, they can be used to organize a large part, if not all, of the sensible range of stimulation within a modality, not just some local region such as the neighborhood of the threshold or a two- or three-jnd interval about stimuli well above threshold. Second, the perceptual problem is no longer prejudged, and so neither payoff nor identification functions are involved. As a result, attention is directed almost exclusively to how subjects "organize" the stimuli according to some verbal instructions given by the experimenter and not to other features of the behavior. The philosophy underlying this approach is succinctly summarized in the following comments of S. S. Stevens.

In a sense there is only one problem of psychophysics, namely, the definition of the stimulus. In this same sense there is only one problem in all of psychology —and it is the same problem. The definition of the stimulus is thus a bigger problem than it appears to be at first sight. The reason for equating psychology to the problem of defining stimuli can be restated thus: the complete definition of the stimulus to a given response involves the specification of all the transformations of the environment, both internal and external, that leave the response invariant. (1951, pp. 31–32.)

One consequence of not prejudging the perceptual problem is implicit in this quotation, namely a de-emphasis of the motivational factors which also influence behavior. Although Stevens mentions the "internal . . . environment," the fact of the matter is that people who do scaling experiments have not explicitly treated motivational questions. Yet, in the theories developed for identification experiments, stimuli and outcomes play complementary and equally important roles in determining the response. It is a little difficult to believe that the motivational factors have suddenly dropped from view just because we are certain that we do not understand the perceptual organization of the stimuli. Indeed, exactly the opposite seems more plausible. When the criterion for organizing the stimuli is uncertain to the experimenter, as for example when he asks a subject to make similarity judgments, it is probably equally vague to the subject, in which event his motives are likely to influence significantly his responses.

A closely related point is the fact that the experiments in question have to be somewhat modified before we can study the similarity perception of animals. We can ask a human subject which of two stimuli is more similar to a third or require him to group a set of stimuli into k equally spaced categories and usually he will comply without too much fuss, but with animals our only means of instruction is differential outcomes. For example, to study similarity judgments, we might first train the animal according to some more or less arbitrary identification function and then test their generalization to new stimuli during extinction trials (Herrnstein & van Sommers, 1962). Just how the results of such an experiment are related to those that we usually obtain from human beings in nonidentification experiments is an important research question about which little is known.

Given the data from a nonidentification, "perceptual" choice experiment, the usual procedure of analysis is this. One of the simpler response models for identification experiments, that is, one having no response bias parameters, is selected and is assumed to apply to a nonidentification design. The reasons for using the simpler models are that they are older and therefore better known, that they are easier to work with mathematically, and that an extra set of parameters for which there are no experimental counterparts can be a trifle embarrassing. On the assumption that the chosen response model is correct—often this can only be assumed because there are no experimental manipulations available with which to generate adequate tests—the stimulus parameters are calculated from the data. With these known for a number of stimuli from some extensive, homogeneous class of stimuli, the central question then is: what sort of "natural" organization do the scale values exhibit? If, for example, each stimulus is assigned a scale value, then we may ask, do these values, aside from sampling errors, stand in a simple functional relation to some physical measure of the stimuli? If scale values are assigned to pairs of stimuli, then we inquire whether the individual stimuli can be treated as points in some multidimensional space—Euclidean or otherwise—in such a way that distances in the space correspond approximately to the response-theory scale values.

This is what is done and what we shall describe in some detail in much of this chapter. What is not clear is why we have not yet evolved a somewhat more subtle approach using payoffs. For example, one might proceed in the following way. Let us assume that the effect of the vague instructions is to induce an unknown identification function in the subject and that part of our problem is to discover it. In general, any payoff function we use is going to be incompatible with it (see Sec. 3.3, Chapter 2, for a precise definition of compatibility), but different functions will be incompatible in different ways. These differences may give us some leverage on the problem. If we knew how incompatible payoffs and identification functions combine to generate responses, then the response data from a sufficient number of different payoff functions should permit us to "solve" for the unknown identification function. Just how many different experiments are needed to get a determinate solution depends, of course, upon the exact mathematical nature of the response theory, that is, upon exactly how the subject compromises his perceptions and his motivations.

The only difficulty in carrying out this program is that we do not know what response theory to use when the identification function and the payoffs are incompatible. Having noted this, however, it is clear what to do: we must perform identification experiments with incompatible payoffs, the goal being to work out suitable response theories that parallel those we now have for compatible situations. In all likelihood these theories will generalize the ones for compatible payoffs. Once such a theory is developed and tested, we can assume it applies when the identification function is unknown, solve for this unknown function, and then test the adequacy of the theory in the new context by predicting behavior for the other payoff functions.

Although this approach seems sensible, no work along these lines appears to have been reported. In the existing scaling studies identification functions are not defined, and neither payoffs nor information feedback are employed. Several quite different methods are of current interest and are discussed in the remainder of the chapter. We present them in what, it seems to us, is an order of decreasing familiarity. No other more compelling organization is apparent. At first we deal with experiments and theories that closely parallel those discussed in the preceding chapters, and then we move on to others that are more novel and less well understood.

1. SIMILARITY SCALES

1.1 The Method of Triads

Certain identification experiments are thought to yield information about the subjective similarity of pairs of stimuli, even though no direct judgments of similarity are made. For example, the choice theory analysis of complete identification experiments (Sec. 1.2, Chapter 3) led to scale values $\eta(\varDelta, \varDelta')$, which were interpreted as a possible measure of the similarity between pairs of stimuli. In addition to these theoretical interpretations, one can ask the subjects to make explicit similarity judgments. Because we have no precise, nonarbitrary notion about what psychological similarity might mean in terms of physical properties of the stimuli, we are forced to use nonidentification experimental designs. In this section we discuss in detail the one known as the method of triads; save for the absence of an identification function, it resembles the forced-choice discrimination design.

Let a, x, $y \in \mathscr{S}$. A typical stimulus presentation is $\langle x, y, a \rangle$, and the subject is instructed to report which of the first two stimuli in the presentation seems to him "more similar" to the third, the so-called *reference stimulus*. (Of course, the reference stimulus can be located in any of the three positions, and where it is may very well alter the experimental findings to some degree. For our purposes it will be convenient to locate it in the last position, realizing that this is merely a notational convenience.) In general, then,

$$S \subseteq \mathscr{S}^3 \quad \text{and} \quad R = \{1, 2\}.$$

If we confine our attention to those experiments, or to those parts of one, in which there is a single reference stimulus a, then

$$S \subseteq \mathscr{S}^2 \times \{a\}.$$

Now the close parallel to simple discrimination experiments is obvious; the only differences are that the reference stimulus is added to each presentation and, of course, that the subject is asked to make a judgment of similarity, not relative magnitude.

Obviously, the triad design is readily generalized to one of choosing which of k stimuli is most similar to a, in which case

$$S \subseteq \mathscr{S}^k \times \{a\} \quad \text{and} \quad R = \{1, 2, \ldots, k\}.$$

The word "similar" used in the instructions is vague, and it is left that way because neither the experimenter nor the subject can verbalize very precisely what he means by it. Nonetheless, subjects respond nonrandomly when instructed in this way. That reproducible data can arise from a vague criterion should not surprise us when we think of how often we use equally vague criteria in everyday life, but in the long run a science is not likely to let reproducibility alone substitute for well analyzed and controlled experimental designs.

The responses in the triad design are assumed to be generated from a probabilistic process having the basic conditional probabilities

$$p(i \mid \langle x, y, a \rangle), \qquad (i = 1, 2),$$

where

$$p(1 \mid \langle x, y, a \rangle) + p(2 \mid \langle x, y, a \rangle) = 1.$$

If the order of presentation does not matter, then as in discrimination work we can write

$$p(x, y; a) = p(1 \mid \langle x, y, a \rangle) = p(2 \mid \langle y, x, a \rangle).$$

The generalization to more stimuli is clear.

A somewhat more general procedure used to study similarity is the method of tetrads in which

$$S \subseteq \mathscr{S}^4 \quad \text{and} \quad R = \{1, 2\},$$

and the subject is asked to judge whether the first or second pair of stimuli presented is more similar. Suppes and Zinnes discuss models for this experiment in Secs. 3.3, 3.4, and 4.4, of Chapter 1; we shall not go into them here.

1.2 A Comparative Judgment Analysis: Multidimensional Scaling

Assume for the moment that, as in previous Thurstonian models we have examined, there is a random variable X in the real numbers which represents the effect of stimulus x and that the random variables associated with different stimuli assume values on the same numerical scale. If the order of presentation does not matter, the obvious decision rule for the method of triads is the following:

Stimulus x rather than y is judged to be more similar to the reference stimulus a if and only if $|X - A| < |Y - A|$, where the vertical bars denote the absolute value of the number between them.

Thus

$$p(x, y; a) = \text{Pr} \left(|X - A| < |Y - A) \right|.$$

Note that the quantity $|X - A|$ can be interpreted as a distance random variate, $D(x, a)$, that represents the momentary psychological distance between x and a on the decision continuum. This immediately suggests a multidimensional generalization of the Thurstone model, in which the random variables assume values in a k-dimensional Euclidean vector space of effects. As early as 1938 M. W. Richardson suggested that such models would be necessary to provide adequate representations of complex stimulus domains.

Let X denote a random vector assuming values in a k-dimensional Euclidean vector space and let its components be X_i, $i = 1, 2, \ldots, k$. If the usual Euclidean distance measure is assumed,

$$D(x, a)^2 = \sum_{i=1}^{k} (X_i - A_i)^2,$$

then the decision rule becomes

Stimulus x rather than y is judged to be more similar to the reference stimulus a if and only if $D(x, a) < D(y, a)$.

So

$$p(x, y; a) = \text{Pr} \left[D(x, a) < D(y, a) \right].$$

As pointed out by Suppes and Zinnes in Sec. 4.4 of Chapter 1, the square of the distance $D(x, a)$ has a noncentral χ^2 distribution, provided that the components X_i and A_i have normal distributions with the same variance. This fact, which makes matters rather more complicated than in previous Thurstonian models that we have examined, seems to have been overlooked in the published literature.

Torgerson (1952, 1958) attempted to bypass this complication by stating directly an analogue of the equation of comparative judgment, namely,

$$d(x, a) - d(y, a) = Z(x, y; a), \tag{1}$$

where $Z(x, y; a)$ is the unit normal deviate corresponding to $p(x, y; a)$.

Implicitly, this postulates that the difference $\mathbf{D}(x, a) - \mathbf{D}(y, a)$ is a normally distributed random variable with mean $d(x, a) - d(y, a)$ and unit variance. Just where Eq. 1 comes from, aside from being the purely formal analogue of the discrimination model, is not clear. As Suppes and Zinnes point out, it certainly does not make sense to assume that $\mathbf{D}(x, a)$ is normally distributed, because it must have the distance property $\mathbf{D}(x, a) \geqslant 0$. Thus Torgerson's multidimensional scaling model is *ad hoc* in the sense that it does not derive from the same basic considerations as the other Thurstonian models.

Given that Eq. 1 holds, Torgerson (1952, 1958) presented a least squares solution to the problem of estimating the values $d(x, a) - d(y, a)$. Because only differences of mean distances are estimated, the individual means are determined up to a positive linear transformation. This creates what is known as the problem of the additive constant. Because distances must form a ratio scale, the additive constant of the linear transformation is not in fact a free parameter, but rather it must have a fixed value, which, for some purposes, we must estimate.

Messick and Abelson (1956) proposed a general iterative solution to the problem, which is based, in part, upon an embedding theorem of Young and Householder (1938) (see Sec. 5.2). The details of the method are described in Torgerson (1958). For the unidimensional case, Torgerson (1952) gave a simple least squares solution which rests upon the following observation. Because the true distances must satisfy

$$d(x, z) = d(x, y) + d(y, z),$$

the calculated distances

$$d'(x, y) = d(x, y) + c,$$

which differ from the true ones by the additive constant c, must satisfy

$$d'(x, y) + d'(y, z) - d'(x, z) = d(x, y) + c + d(y, z) + c - d(x, z) - c$$
$$= c.$$

Thus, if the data were error free, c would be determined. When they are not error free, Torgerson's procedure gives a "best" estimate of c in the least squares sense.

1.3 A Choice Theory Analysis

Because of the formal parallel between discrimination and similarity designs (Sec. 1.1), a choice theory analysis follows almost immediately if we reinterpret the unbiased discrimination model described in Sec. 3.2 of Chapter 4. Specifically, if a denotes the reference stimulus, T, the set of comparison stimuli, and $x \in T$, then the basic response probabilities of the similarity experiment are of the form $p_T(x, a)$. Thus, with a held fixed, the choice axiom may be written as before, and so a ratio scale v exists for each a. The typical scale value can be written in the form $v(x, a)$. This dependence upon two stimuli makes these parameters formally similar to those that arose in the choice analysis of complete identification experiments (Sec. 1.2, Chapter 3), and Luce (1961) proposed that the same assumptions be investigated:

Assumption 1.   For all $x, y \in \mathscr{S}$, $v(x, y) = v(y, x)$.
Assumption 2.   For all $x \in \mathscr{S}$, $v(x, x) = 1$.
Assumption 3.   For all $x, y, z \in \mathscr{S}$, $v(x, z) \geqslant v(x, y)\, v(y, z)$.

Put another way, he suggested assuming that $-\log v$ is a distance measure.

The first of these assumptions, that concerning symmetry, is most important because it says that there is a single scale, not a collection of unrelated ones. If we let $p(x, y; z)$ denote $p_{\{x,y\}}(x, z)$, it is easy to show that Assumption 1 is equivalent to the (in principle) testable statement

$$p(x, y; z)\, p(y, z; x)\, p(z, x; y) = p(x, z; y)\, p(z, y; x)\, p(y, x; z).$$

The situation most carefully examined by Luce involves a strengthening of Assumption 3 so that $-\log v$ acts like distance on a line; presumably this restricted model can, at best, apply to physically unidimensional continua. Let us say that stimulus y is *between* stimuli x and z if, when z is the reference stimulus, z is more often judged similar to y than to x and, when x is the reference stimulus, x is judged more similar to y than to z, that is,

$$p(y, x; z) > \tfrac{1}{2} \quad \text{and} \quad p(y, z; x) > \tfrac{1}{2}.$$

Assumption 3'.   For all $x, y, z \in \mathscr{S}$ such that y is between x and z, then $v(x, z) = v(x, y)\, v(y, z)$.

The main conclusion that has been derived from Assumptions 1, 2, and 3', concerns the plot of $p(a, b; x)$ as a function of x, assuming that the stimuli differ only along one physical dimension. Note the reversal of viewpoint that has occurred. We began by thinking of the reference stimulus as a fixed quantity and the comparison stimuli as experimental variables; now we propose to think of the comparison stimuli as fixed and the reference as the variable. Suppose on the physical continuum that $a < b$. The result says that for $x \leqslant a$, $p(a, b; x)$ has a constant value, say K, and that for $x \geqslant b$ it has the constant value $1 - K$. For $a \leqslant x \leqslant b$, there is some (presumably continuous) transition from K to $1 - K$ (see Fig. 1). This transition function does not depend upon a and b independently but rather is associated with what may be called their midpoint. Specifically, we say that stimulus $\overline{ab}$ is the *midpoint* of a and b if $p(a, b; \overline{ab}) = \tfrac{1}{2}$. Now, if c

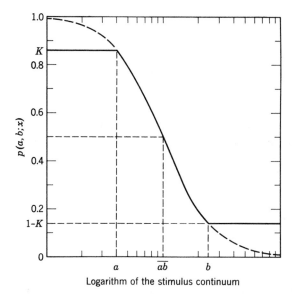

Fig. 1. The transition function derived from a choice theory analysis of similarity judgments. Adapted by permission from Luce (1961, p. 158).

and d, $c < d$, are two different stimuli such that $\overline{cd} = \overline{ab}$, it can be shown that when a, $c < x < b$, d, then $p(a, b; x) = p(c, d; x)$. That is to say, if two pairs of comparison stimuli have the same midpoint, then the two functions coincide in the region of overlap defined by the pairs of stimuli.

No empirical research has yet been performed to test this model. Whether or not it is correct, it will be interesting to develop empirical plots of $p(a, b; x)$ versus x simply to see what they are like.

It is of interest also to inquire about the relation between the stimulus-scale values obtained from the analysis of recognition data (Chapter 3) and those obtained from the analysis of similarity data gathered under the same experimental conditions and their relation to the scale values calculated from discrimination data. From a rather questionable assumption, Luce (1961) showed that

$$v(x, y) = \begin{cases} \dfrac{v(x)}{v(y)} & \text{if} \quad v(x) \leqslant v(y) \\[2mm] \dfrac{v(y)}{v(x)} & \text{if} \quad v(x) \geqslant v(y), \end{cases}$$

where the two-place v denotes the similarity scale value and the one-place v, the discrimination value. Formally, this same assumption was invoked in Sec. 7.3 of Chapter 3 in an attempt to account for some of the information theory results. The only difference is that the two-place scale value there denoted the recognition experiment scale value $\eta(x, y)$. We suspect that the weaker assumption

$$v(x, y) = \begin{cases} \left[\dfrac{v(x)}{v(y)}\right]^{\beta} & \text{if} \quad v(x) \leqslant v(y) \\[2ex] \left[\dfrac{v(y)}{v(x)}\right]^{\beta} & \text{if} \quad v(x) \geqslant v(y), \end{cases}$$

in which β is a parameter to be estimated from the data, is far more likely to receive support. Note that for x, y, and z, with $v(x) < v(y) < v(z)$, then either assumption implies:

$$v(x, z) = v(x, y) \, v(y, z).$$

2. BISECTION SCALES

2.1 The Method

The bisection design is uniquely different from anything else in psychophysics that we have discussed. As it is usually performed, the response literally involves the selection of a stimulus. Consider a stimulus set in which the stimuli differ on one physical dimension, such as sound intensity. An ordered pair of stimuli is presented to the subject, who adjusts the gain of a third presentation until, in his opinion, this variable tone has a subjective loudness that "bisects" the loudnesses of the fixed pair of tones. In practice, there are various ways to make this adjustment. In one of the most common the subject first chooses a gain setting and then listens to the ordered triplet $\langle a, x, b \rangle$, in which a and b are the fixed tones and x is the one he selected. Having heard the triplet, the subject decides whether he likes his setting; if he does not, he resets x, listens, and so on, until he is satisfied that his response stimulus "bisects" a and b. Observe that this selection of a stimulus is utterly different from that in any experiment previously described; in some that we have studied the responses identified one of the presented stimuli as larger, more similar, etc., than the others, but the subjects's choice was restricted to one of the stimuli presented. The whole stimulus set was not available.

In another method of studying bisection the experimenter selects the triples and asks the subject whether the test stimulus is above or below his bisection point. The 50 per cent point on the resulting psychometric function is taken to be the bisection stimulus. It is not clear that the two methods will yield the same results, but on the assumption that they do, then bisection can be interpreted as a special case of a similarity judgment. An analysis based upon this assumption is given in Sec. 2.2.

It should be noted in passing that bisection can also be considered as a special case of what S. S. Stevens (1958a) has called category production, which is the logical counterpart of category estimation discussed in Sec. 3. Because we know of no theory for the general case, we shall confine our attention to bisection.

If $\mathscr{S}$ denotes the set (usually a continuum) of stimuli, physically ordered by the relation $\geqslant$, then $S \subseteq \mathscr{S}^2$ and $R = \mathscr{S}$ in this design. The basic response data are presumed to be generated by conditional probabilities (or densities, as the case may be) of the form $p(x \mid \langle a, b \rangle)$, where $x \in R = \mathscr{S}$ and $\langle a, b \rangle \in S$. If $\mathscr{S}$ is made discrete by the design of the equipment, then in principle it is feasible to estimate these probabilities; if $\mathscr{S}$ is continuous, then parameters of the density function can be estimated.

As in much psychophysical work, the order of presentation matters. For intensive (prothetic) continua, the mean bisection value $\bar{x}$ in the ascending series $\langle a, x, b \rangle$, is consistently and appreciably different from the mean $\bar{y}$ in the descending series $\langle b, y, a \rangle$. Because of a superficial analogy to a well-known physical phenomenon, this response bias has been called *hysteresis*. Examples of it are shown in S. S. Stevens (1957).

No truly probabilistic model has yet been proposed for bisection data, the main reason being that three stimuli are involved—two in the presentation and one in the response. For the choice model, this leads to scale values of the form $v(x; a, b)$, and so some drastic simplifying assumptions are needed. For the discriminal dispersion model, one has to deal with the three random variables, **A**, **X**, and **B**. Presumably the decision rule would be something of the form: there exist positive constants c and d such that whenever

$$\frac{\mathbf{A} + \mathbf{B}}{2} - c \leqslant \mathbf{X} \leqslant \frac{\mathbf{A} + \mathbf{B}}{2} + d$$

the subject accepts x as the bisection value. If one were willing to postulate how the subject would alter his setting of the response stimulus as a function of the previously observed **A**, **X**, and **B**, then it would be possible to calculate the distribution of adjustments until the process terminated. Because the number of adjustments made is just as observable as the actual choice, such a model could be tested in some detail.

The only models we discuss here are essentially deterministic in nature.

2.2 A Similarity Analysis

If we assume that the subject interprets "bisect" to mean "equally similar to," in the sense of the method of triads, then any model for that method also is a model for bisection. What is assumed is that the subject adjusts the reference stimulus until he is satisfied that it is equally similar to both a and b. Because of the probabilistic nature of the similarity models, his choice of a bisection point must vary from trial to trial, but the mean value $\bar{x}$ might be defined by the property

$$p(a, b; \bar{x}) = \tfrac{1}{2}.$$

Assuming a similarity model with no response biases, which we know cannot be precisely correct because of the hysteresis effect, the bisection point then coincides with what we called the midpoint $\overline{ab}$ in Sec. 1.3. If in the choice model we suppose that there exists a constant β such that

$$v(x, y) = \begin{cases} \left(\dfrac{x}{y}\right)^{\beta} & \text{if } x \leqslant y \\[2mm] \left(\dfrac{y}{x}\right)^{\alpha} & \text{if } x \geqslant y, \end{cases}$$

then from

$$p(a, b; \overline{ab}) = \tfrac{1}{2}$$
$$= \frac{1}{1 + v(b, \overline{ab})/v(a, \overline{ab})},$$

and from the assumption that $a < \overline{ab} < b$ it follows that

$$\left(\frac{a}{\overline{ab}}\right)^{\beta} = v(a, \overline{ab})$$
$$= v(b, \overline{ab})$$
$$= \left(\frac{\overline{ab}}{b}\right)^{\beta}.$$

If $b < \overline{ab} < a$, then similarly

$$\left(\frac{\overline{ab}}{a}\right)^{\beta} = \left(\frac{b}{\overline{ab}}\right)^{\beta}.$$

Thus, in either case, $\overline{ab} = (ab)^{\frac{1}{2}}$, that is, the midpoint is predicted to be the geometric mean of the stimulus values that are bisected. In logarithmic—for example, decibel—measures the midpoint is predicted to be the arithmetic mean of the given stimulus values. This is empirically incorrect (S. S. Stevens, 1957), both because of the hysteresis effect and because both midpoints are above the geometric mean.

In Luce (1961) the similarity model of Sec. 1.3 is generalized to one having response biases, which overcomes the difficulties just described.

Although it seems plausible that bisection is a special case of a similarity judgment, experiments are definitely needed to test this hypothesis.

2.3 A Measurement Analysis

Pfanzagl (1959a,b), extending and reinterpreting Aczél's (1948) axiomatization of mean values, has created an interesting measurement axiom
system, specializations of which yield a number of familiar measurement
models for different subject matters. For example, it includes the classic
models for the measurement of mass and of length, the von Neumann-
Morgenstern axioms for utility, as well as a possible model for the measurement of sensation based upon bisection. We first present the bisection
specialization of Pfanzagl's axioms and the resulting representation and
uniqueness theorem; then we discuss the interpretation. Let $\mathscr{S}$ denote
the set of stimuli, physically weakly ordered by $\geqslant$.

Axiom 1 (Existence). *For every $x, y \in \mathscr{S}$ there exists a unique element
$B(x, y) \in \mathscr{S}$, which is interpreted as the bisection point of x and y.*

Axiom 2 (Monotonicity). *If $x \lessgtr x'$, then, for all $y \in \mathscr{S}$, $B(x, y) \lessgtr B(x', y)$.*

Axiom 3 (Continuity). *B is a continuous function in both of its arguments,
which is to say that $\{x \in \mathscr{S} \mid B(x, b) > a\}$, $\{x \in \mathscr{S} \mid B(x, b) < a\}$,
$\{x \in \mathscr{S} \mid B(b, x) > a\}$, and $\{x \in \mathscr{S} \mid B(b, x) < a\}$ are all topologically
open sets for every $a, b \in \mathscr{S}$.*

Axiom 4 (Bisymmetry). *For all w, x, y, $z \in \mathscr{S}$, $B[B(w, x), B(y, z)] =
B[B(w, y), B(x, z)]$.*

Axiom 5 (Reflexivity). *For all $x \in \mathscr{S}$, $B(x, x) = x$.*

Axioms 1 and 3 are largely technical in nature and need not be discussed.
Axioms 2 and 5 are most plausible, and it seems unlikely that empirically
they will be shown to be false. This leaves in doubt only Axiom 4, which
contains most of the mathematical power of the system. Graphically, the
various quantities involved in Axiom 4 are shown in Fig. 2. The assertion
is that the two bisections of bisection points are the same. No thorough
experimental investigation of this axiom has ever been made, but Pfanzagl
(1959b) refers to studies of special cases for pitch, in which it seems to be
sustained, and for loudness, in which it may not be.

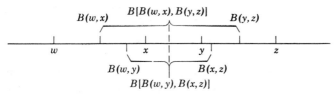

Fig. 2. A graphical representation of the quantities involved in Pfanzagl's Axiom 4.

Theorem 1. *If Axioms 1 to 5 hold, then there exists a real valued
function u on $\mathscr{S}$ and a real number δ, $0 < \delta < 1$, such that*

1. *u is a continuous function;*
2. *u is a strictly monotonic function, that is, if $x < y$, $u(x) < u(y)$;*
3. *$u[B(x, y)] = \delta u(x) + (1 - \delta)u(y)$;*
4. *u is unique up to a positive linear transformation, that is, it is an interval scale.*

If, in addition, B is symmetric (commutative) in the sense that $B(x, y) = B(y, x)$, then $\delta = \frac{1}{2}$.

We shall not attempt to prove this result here; see Pfanzagl (1959a) for a full proof and (1959b) for a less complete one.

Because interval scales of "sensation" previously have appeared to be logarithmic functions of physical intensity, it is reasonable again to investigate the assumption that

$$u(x) = \alpha \log x + \beta,$$

where x is now both the physical magnitude and the name of the stimulus. It is easy, then, to show that

$$B(x, y) = x^{\delta}y^{1-\delta},$$

and so

$$B(x, y) = B(y, x)\left(\frac{x}{y}\right)^{2\delta-1}$$

Thus, for $\delta \neq \frac{1}{2}$, this model permits a hysteresis effect. For $\delta = \frac{1}{2}$, the bisection point is again the geometric mean of the given stimulus value.

This treatment of bisection has two major drawbacks. First, the data strongly suggest that a probabilistic, not a deterministic, model is needed. Of course, one can treat the deterministic analysis as an approximation to the probabilistic, for example, by letting

$$B(x, y) = \int_{0}^{\infty} zp(z \mid \langle x, y \rangle) \, dz,$$

but then the full probability process remains unanalyzed. Second, it is questionable whether the behavior is sufficiently invariant under various experimental manipulations to treat the phenomenon as a form of fundamental measurement, as this axiom system does. There is little doubt that the behavior can be altered by means of payoffs, and it is far from evident that the axioms will hold up under such changes. The most critical one, of course, is Axiom 4, and we suspect that it will not fare well when strong experimentally induced response biases exist. Despite the fact that many psychophysicists believe that they are in the business of discovering fundamental measures of sensation, response models, yielding derived measures, rather than fundamental measurement models, seem much more appropriate for psychophysical phenomena. The reason simply is that factors intrinsic to the experiment other than the stimuli importantly influence the responses. It is as though one tried to measure current without being aware of factors such as the area and temperature of a conductor, both of which affect its resistance and so the current flow. A good theory stating the relations among the relevant factors makes the accurate measurement of any one feasible; without such a theory, one only can try to hold the other variables constant, which may not be easy to do.

3. CATEGORY SCALES

3.1 The Method

In much the same sense that similarity experiments are analogous to discrimination designs, category experiments have some formal resemblance to those of recognition. Most of the recognition experiments that we discussed in Chapter 3 were complete identification designs, but it is clear what one would mean by a partial recognition design: $S = \mathscr{S}$ and certain responses are correct identifications for more than one stimulus presentation. The category experiments are analogous to this, except that no identification function, partial or otherwise, is specified by the experimenter.

Category methods are generally employed only when the stimuli can reasonably be considered to be ordered; for example, when they differ on only one physical dimension. Because the stimuli are ordered, it is reasonable to use responses that are also ordered in some way. Often the first m integers are used for the responses and the ordering is the natural one. Other response labels, such as the first m letters of the alphabet or descriptive adjectives, are sometimes employed. The subject is instructed to assign the "smallest" (weakest, lightest, darkest, etc.) stimulus to the first category, the "largest" to the mth category, and to use the other response categories so that his subjective impressions of the distances between successive categories is the same, that is, so that the categories are *equally spaced subjectively*. Because these instructions are vague, just as the similarity and bisection ones are, no identification function is assumed to be known.

It is generally felt that we are not demanding much more of the subject when we ask for category judgments rather than for similarity ones. If we believe that he can tell whether a is more similar to x than it is to y, then it should be possible for him to group stimuli into classes of comparable similarity. One suspects, however, that the meaningfulness of

the obtained data depends upon the degree to which the subject under-
stands what it is that he is being asked to do. Therefore, in testing the
feasibility, reliability, and coherence of methods of this type, experimenters have generally first worked with simple physical dimensions,
such as sound intensity, which they feel are relatively well understood
both by the subjects and themselves. Later, the methods were extended
to stimuli that have no known ordering other than a subjective one.
Examples are the degrees of favorableness toward the church which are
exhibited by certain statements and the degrees of intelligibility which are
exhibited by handwriting samples. Formally, the nature of the stimuli
makes no difference: once the relative frequencies are obtained, the models
proceed without reference to the meaningfulness of the data. Substantively,
there may well be important differences. For our purposes, it suffices and
simplifies matters to consider only relatively simple physical stimuli.

The initial exploration of category methods was undertaken by experimenters primarily interested in discrimination (Titchener, 1905, Wever &
Zener, 1928). They introduced, as a modification of the method of
constant stimuli, what is called the *method of single stimuli*. It amounts
to omitting the standard stimulus, so that only a single stimulus is presented
on each trial. The subject's task is to judge whether a presentation is
"loud" or "soft" or, in a variant, whether it is "loud," "medium," or
"soft." After a few trials, during which the subject becomes acquainted
with the range of stimuli involved, his responses settle down to "asymptotic" levels. It was found that psychometric functions generated in this
way are quite similar to those generated by the method of constant stimuli
(Fernberger, 1931). It is almost as if a subject defined his own standard
stimulus for the given set of comparisons and that he was able to hold
this image reasonably well fixed during the course of the experiment.

No identification functions were assumed in these studies, hence no
information feedback or payoffs were used. Payoffs could have been used
had the experimenter selected an arbitrary point on the continuum to
separate loud from soft, but at the time this was considered inappropriate.
Today, it is not so clear that payoffs should not be used. To be sure, the
data for just one arbitrary cutpoint would not hold much interest, but
those for several cutpoints from subjects judging the same set of stimuli
could very well reveal what compromise the subject is making between his
perceptions and the arbitrary feedback.

The method of single stimuli, although initially introduced only as a
more rapid version of the method of constant stimuli, has certain important
features of its own. It is easily adapted to yield nontrivial information
over large ranges of stimulation by increasing the number of response
categories. As early as 1898, E. P. Sanford (see Titchener, 1905, p. 82) had

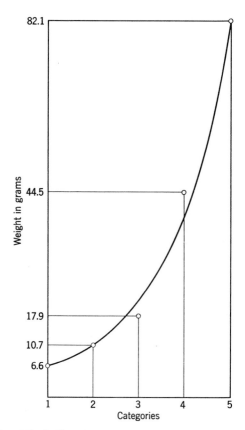

Fig. 3. The results of Sanford's weight-lifting experiment. Observe that the category judgments are plotted as the abscissa and the stimulus values are plotted as the ordinate. Adapted by permission from Titchener (1905).

experimental psychology students sort envelopes containing different weights into five categories of increasing weights. Category 1 was to be used for those that were lightest and 5 for those that were heaviest. The resulting plot of average stimulus weight against category number, shown in Fig. 3, was interpreted as a demonstration of Fechner's law. The observed curve is so close to Fechner's logarithmic law that Titchener claimed that the students had defined the categories so that they contained equal numbers of jnds. This idea for the definition of the categories was later adapted to serve as the basis of a Thurstonian theory of category judgments (Sec. 3.3).

Today, the following general procedure is used. The experimenter selects a set of *m* stimuli—usually *m* is about 20 but sometimes it is as large as 100—which he presents in random order to the subject. (Sometimes they are presented simultaneously, when this is feasible, but we shall confine our attention to trial-by-trial presentations of single stimuli.) To each presentation the subject responds by choosing one of k categories. Usually k is an odd number in the range from 5 to 11. When the stimuli differ in only one physical dimension, the instructional problem is relatively simple. The smallest stimulus is presented, and the subject is told that it is the smallest and is therefore a member of category 1; the largest is presented, and he is told that it is the largest and is therefore a member of category k; finally, he is told that he is to use the remaining categories as if they were equally spaced along the sensation continuum between these two extreme stimuli. Just what this means to subjects is not clear; there is some indication that they may interpret it to mean that the categories should be used equally often. For example, the assignments to categories are far from invariant when everything else is held fixed and the presentation probabilities are varied.

The data are the relative frequencies that response category r is used when stimulus presentation s is presented, and these frequencies are treated as estimates of underlying conditional probabilities $p(r \mid s)$. When the response categories are the first k integers and the stimuli are ordered, we usually denote a typical response by j and a typical stimulus by i and write $p(j \mid i)$.

3.2 The Mean Category Scale

The simplest analysis of the data involves calculating the mean category assignment for each stimulus and calling this number a "sensation scale value." At a theoretical level the scale is $u(s) = \sum_{j=1}^{k} jp(j \mid s)$. When the stimuli are presented many times to individual subjects, the mean can be calculated over presentations for each subject separately, as shown in Fig. 4 for an $m = 14$, $k = 7$ design, using white noise stimuli separated by five decibel steps of intensity. When each stimulus is presented just once to each subject, the mean is calculated over subjects. By and large, the data for individual subjects differ so little that means calculated over groups of subjects are considered adequate (see below, however, for an objection to this procedure).

The variety of stimulus domains that can be quickly explored and the ease with which various experimental manipulations can be evaluated by category methods has made this analysis into mean category judgments very popular. To the theorist, however, the whole business is a bit

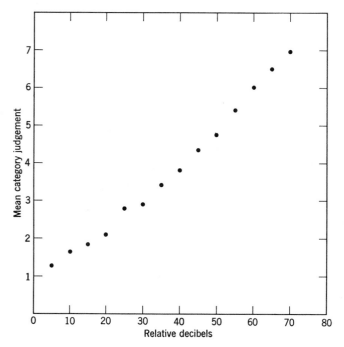

Fig. 4. The mean category judgments for a single subject for 20 independent irregular presentations of 14 white noise stimuli. The abscissa is labeled in relative decibels. Unpublished data of Eugene Galanter.

hair-raising. To calculate the means of category *labels*, to plot them against physical measures of the stimuli, and then to discuss the form of the resulting function strikes him as close to meaningless. Because there is nothing about the procedure to prevent one from labeling the categories by any other increasing sequence of numbers, we can by our choice of labels produce any arbitrary monotonic function of the physical stimuli we choose. What then can a particular one of these scales mean?

Although we do not think that the absolute form of the obtained function using the first k integers as labels has any meaning, the occurrence or nonoccurrence of changes in that function when various experimental parameters are changed may be a convenient way to summarize this class of empirical results.

If we use different ordered sets to label the responses, for example, names like soft, medium, and loud, letters of the alphabet, or different buttons in a line to depress, then we can make the natural identifications with the first k integers to calculate scale values. If everything save the labeling is held constant, then in general the data suggest that the function

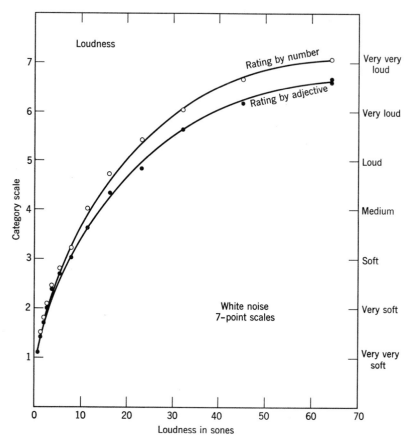

Fig. 5. Category rating scales for two different labelings of the responses. Adapted by permission from Stevens & Galanter (1957, p. 391).

is independent of the labeling (Stevens & Galanter, 1957). For example, scales computed from the first seven integers and from an equal number of adjectives are shown in Fig. 5. The similarity of the two functions is clear.

Varying the number of categories used has some effect, but it is small (Stevens & Galanter, 1957). The data shown in Fig. 6 compare $k = 3$ with $k = 100$.

There is considerable freedom in choosing instructions, and were they to affect the results appreciably the method would be judged poor. In general, however, the exact instructions used seem to have little effect as long as they ask the subject to make the intervals subjectively equal. The initial judgments seem to be somewhat influenced by the instructions, but if one permitted the subject to continue judging until his behavior stabilized, the functions would all be about the same (Stevens & Galanter, 1957). For this reason, most experimenters attempt to find and use instructions that cause subjects to achieve asymptotic stability rapidly. This result does, however, argue against averaging single judgments from a number of subjects.

The variables that have really important effects are those concerning the stimuli. The spacing of the stimuli along the physical continuum has noticeable consequences on the mean scale values because subjects tend to devote more categories to a stimulus interval as the density of stimuli in that interval is increased. It is as though the subjects were trying to spread out stimuli that are in fact close together, or, what is the same thing, to name the categories about equally often. This affects the apparent slope

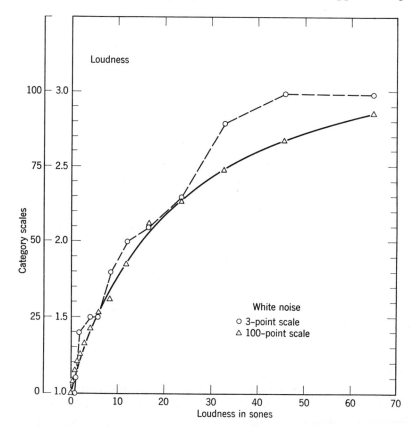

Fig. 6. Category scales of loudness with 3 and 100 categories. Adapted by permission from Stevens & Galanter (1957, p. 391).

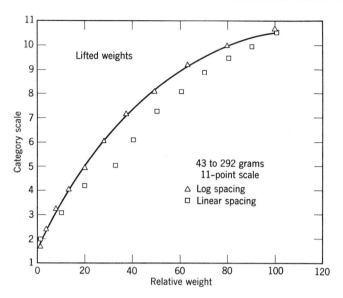

Fig. 7. Category scale of weight for two different stimulus spacings. Adapted by permission from Stevens & Galanter (1957, p. 384).

of the function: when the stimuli are closely packed, the function tends to be appreciably steeper in that region than when they are less dense (Stevens & Galanter, 1957). Examples are shown in Fig. 7. Essentially the same finding occurs if the spacing of the stimuli is held fixed and their presentation frequencies are varied. The function is steepened in regions of high presentation probability (Parducci, 1956). Together, these results suggest that the controlling variable is motivational, namely the relative use of the response categories.

Possibly related to this spacing effect is the so-called "anchoring effect." If a particular stimulus is selected as an anchor and is presented prior to every trial, then the function is always steeper in the vicinity of the anchor than when none is used (Michels & Doser, 1955). Alternatively, this has been interpreted as a purely stimulus effect, the anchor affecting the sensitivity of the subject in its neighborhood.

A full understanding of these effects cannot be expected until we have a sophisticated theory of category judgments. Unfortunately, what is now available is not fully satisfactory. Basically, the problem is to find a response theory which defines a scale of sensation that is invariant under the various experimental manipulations we have just described and does not depend upon an arbitrary, albeit conventional, labeling of the responses.

3.3 Successive Intervals and Related Scaling Models

The most widely known *model* for the analysis of category judgments is an adaptation of Thurstone's equation of comparative judgment for discrimination. Various versions have been discussed, the first by Saffir (1937) for what is known as successive intervals scaling and the most general by Torgerson (1954). The special cases that have been examined in detail are described by Torgerson (1958).

As before, each presentation s_i is assumed to result in a number on a subjective decision continuum, this number being a normally distributed random variable $\mathbf{S}_i$ with mean $\bar{s}_i$ and standard deviation σ_i. The subject's problem is assumed to be the assignment of the presentation to one of the k ordered response categories on the basis of this observation. The assumed decision rule is that the subject partitions the decision continuum into k intervals which are in one-to-one correspondence with the responses and that he responds r_j if and only if $\mathbf{S}_i$ lies in the jth interval. This partition is characterized by the $k - 1$ boundary values of the intervals ($-\infty$ and $+\infty$ need not be explicitly included as boundary values). The upper boundary point of interval j, $j < k$ is assumed to be a normally distributed random variable $\mathbf{T}_j$ with mean $\bar{t}_j$ and standard deviation τ_j.

The basic relative frequencies are assumed to estimate underlying probabilities $p(r_j \mid s_i)$. The cumulative

$$P(r_j \mid s_i) = \sum_{h=1}^{j} p(r_h \mid s_i)$$

is the probability that stimulus presentation s_i is assigned to one of the first j categories. By the decision rule, we see that

$$P(r_j \mid s_i) = \Pr(\mathbf{T}_j - \mathbf{S}_i \geqslant 0).$$

Paralleling the argument of Sec. 3.1 of Chapter 4, if $Z(j, i)$ is the normal deviate corresponding to $P(r_j \mid s_i)$ and if r_{ij} is the correlation between the two random variables $\mathbf{S}_i$ and $\mathbf{T}_j$, then

$$\bar{t}_j - \bar{s}_i = Z(j, i)(\sigma_i^2 + \tau_j^2 - 2r_{ij}\sigma_i\tau_j)^{\frac{1}{2}}. \tag{2}$$

This is known as the *equation* (or sometimes law) *of categorical judgment*.

The general model cannot be solved because there are $2(k + m - 2) + (k - 1)m$ unknowns (the $\bar{s}_i$, $\bar{t}_j$, σ_i, τ_j, r_{ij}) and only $(k - 1)m$ equations (not km because the last cumulative must be 1 for each stimulus). Various simplifying assumptions, similar to those for the equation of comparative judgment, have been explored and corresponding computational schemes

have been worked out (see Torgerson, 1958). Before the general availability of high-speed computers, attention was largely confined to equal
variance models, even though many workers suspected them to be wrong.
Recently, a computer program for the case of zero correlations and
unequal variances was described by Helm (1959).

By and large, the scale values found from this model are closely similar
to those found simply by calculating the mean category number except
that the calculated function has somewhat more curvature against the
physical measure. This can be seen, for example, in Galanter and Messick's
(1961) study of the loudness of white noise. They found that the scale
values were approximately a logarithmic function of the energy level of the
noise. Moreover, we suspect that this "processed category" scale is more
invariant under changes in stimulus spacing, presentation probabilities,
category labels, etc., than the mean category judgments, but we know of
no research to prove it.

In an important special case of the equation of categorical judgment
the category boundaries are assumed to be fixed, not random variables.
This is known as the *successive intervals model*, and it has been carefully
investigated by Adams and Messick (1958). Their main results are quoted
by Suppes and Zinnes in Section 4.5 of Chapter 1. For this model, Eq. 2
reduces to

$$t_j - \bar{s}_i = Z(i,j)\sigma_i. \tag{3}$$

It is clear from Eq. 3 that

$$Z(i,j) = \frac{t_j - \bar{s}_i}{\sigma_i}$$

$$= \frac{t_j - \bar{s}_{i'} + \bar{s}_{i'} - \bar{s}_i}{\sigma_i}$$

$$= \alpha(i, i') \, Z(i', j) + \beta(i, i'), \tag{4}$$

where

$$\alpha(i, i') = \frac{\sigma_{i'}}{\sigma_i}$$

$$\beta(i, i') = \frac{\bar{s}_{i'} - \bar{s}_i}{\sigma_i}.$$

Thus the linear equation (4) is a necessary condition for the successive
intervals model to hold; Adams and Messick also showed that it is a
sufficient condition.

We note that there are $2m + k - 3$ unknowns in this model, which is
not greater than $m(k - 1)$, the number of equations, when $k \geqslant 3$, which
it always is.

3.4 A Choice Analysis

The other published models for category data (see Chapters 12 and 13 of Torgerson, 1958) all assume data from a group of subjects. A simultaneous analysis of responses and subjects based upon an assumed common scale is then performed. These methods belong to psychometrics, not psychophysics. Rather than go into them, we conclude this section by describing a simple choice model. No work has yet been done on the estimation of its parameters and, therefore, on its ability to account for data.

In essence, the idea is to collapse implicit responses into response categories just as was done in the analysis of the detection of an unknown stimulus (Sec. 9 of Chapter 3). Specifically, we suppose that underlying the observed category judgments are implicit recognition responses t_j which satisfy the choice model described in Sec. 1.2 of Chapter 3; the matrix of scale values is of the form

$$
\begin{array}{c}
\quad t_1 \dots\dots\dots\dots t_j \dots\dots\dots\dots t_m \\
\begin{array}{c}
s_1 \\ \cdot \\ \cdot \\ \cdot \\ s_i \\ \cdot \\ \cdot \\ \cdot \\ s_m
\end{array}
\left[
\begin{array}{ccccc}
\eta(s_1, s_1)b_1 & \dots & \eta(s_1, s_j)b_j & \dots & \eta(s_1, s_m)b_m \\
 & & & & \\
 & & & & \\
\eta(s_i, s_1)b_1 & \dots & \eta(s_i, s_j)b_j & \dots & \eta(s_i, s_m)b_m \\
 & & & & \\
 & & & & \\
\eta(s_m, s_1)b_1 & \dots & \eta(s_m, s_j)b_j & \dots & \eta(s_m, s_m)b_m
\end{array}
\right].
\end{array}
\tag{5}
$$

We assume that the subject's overt category responses are formed by partitioning the implicit responses into k classes in some unknown way. If we confine our attention to simply ordered stimuli and implicit responses, it seems reasonable to postulate partitions that can be defined in terms of $k - 1$ boundary points. We suppose that the set R_1 of implicit responses corresponding to category 1, that is, to response r_1, consists of all implicit responses $t_1, t_2 \dots$ up to and including some last one, whose index we label r_1. The set R_2 of implicit responses corresponding to category 2 consists of the next implicit response after r_1 and all others up to and including a last one, whose index we label r_2; and so on. Thus the name of a response category and the index of the largest implicit response in that category have the same symbol.

Working again with cumulative response probabilities, we see from Eq. 5 that the fundamental equations are

$$
\begin{aligned}
P(r_j \mid s_i) &= \sum_{h=1}^{j} p(r_h \mid s_i) \\
&= \sum_{h=1}^{j} \sum_{l \in R_h} p(t_l \mid s_i) \\
&= \sum_{l=1}^{r_j} p(t_l \mid s_i) \\
&= \frac{\displaystyle\sum_{l=1}^{r_j} \eta(s_i, s_l) b_l}{\displaystyle\sum_{h=1}^{m} \eta(s_i, s_h) b_h} .
\end{aligned}
$$

The unknowns are the $k - 1$ category boundary indices r_j, the $m - 1$ implicit response biases b_h, and the $m(m - 1)$ stimulus parameters $\eta(s_i, s_j)$, a total of $(m + 1)(m - 1) + k - 1$ unknowns. There are only $m(k - 1)$ independent equations, and so, like the general Thurstonian model, the general choice model cannot be solved, even in principle.

Because we assumed that the stimuli were ordered, it is just as plausible here as it was in the study of similarity to suppose that the analogues of Assumptions 1, 2, and 3' of Sec. 1.3 are satisfied. Then there are only $m - 1$ independent stimulus parameters, namely the $\eta(s_{i+1}, s_i)$ between adjacent pairs of stimuli. In that case the number of unknowns, $2m + k - 3$, does not exceed the number of equations provided that $k \geqslant 3$, which it always is. No workable scheme to find these unknowns is yet available.

Note that the unknown partition of the implicit responses into k classes has the same form as an identification function for a partial identification experiment, and so this choice analysis amounts to treating the category experiment as a recognition experiment of the partial identification variety in which the identification function is unknown. At the beginning of this chapter we suggested that ultimately this may be the way that all problems of this general type will be handled.

We observed earlier that the category methods are sensitive to the presentation probabilities, and, although we know of no relevant data, they are undoubtedly sensitive to payoffs. In terms of the foregoing model, these observed alterations in the response probabilities could correspond to adjustments in the response biases, b_h, in the category boundaries (i.e., the unknown identification function), or in both. It would be interesting to know which is affected. A reasonable conjecture is that the instructions fix the identification function and that the presentation probabilities and payoffs influence only the response biases in the underlying recognition model. Unfortunately, little can be done to answer these questions until we learn how to estimate the parameters, and that appears to be difficult.

4. MAGNITUDE ESTIMATION SCALES

4.1 The Method

Magnitude estimation and a number of allied methods evolved mainly from a program of research begun in the 1930's by S. S. Stevens to find better psychophysical scaling procedures than those of Fechner and Thurstone. One difficulty with the classical schemes is their reliance upon confusion among stimuli. They generate scales only for regions within which behavioral inconsistencies exist. If scales of wider range are desired, the local ones have to be pieced together in some fashion, usually by assuming that the subjective impression of a jnd is the same throughout the continuum or something nearly equivalent to that. This assumption Stevens doubted. A second difficulty is that these traditional methods at best yield interval scales, that is, they are unique only up to positive linear transformations, so that neither the zero nor the unit can be specified in a nonarbitrary way. For dimensions of intensity, such as sound intensity, it is difficult to believe that the subjective attribute, loudness, has an unspecified zero; there seems to be a reasonably well-specified level of stimulation below which there is no sensation and certainly negative loudnesses do not exist. Frequently, the threshold is chosen to be the zero, but this is an afterthought, not an integral part of the scaling model itself.

Among the methods that Stevens and others explored were fractionation and multiplication in which a stimulus is presented and the subject is asked to adjust a variable stimulus to a value that is either half or twice as loud. On the assumption that the subjective scale value of the stimulus chosen is indeed half or twice that of the one first presented, it was established empirically that the subjective scale would have to be approximately a power function of the usual physical measure of the stimulus, not the logarithmic function arising from Fechner's and Thurstone's models. Of course, the important and totally untested assumption of this model is the way in which the terms "one half" and "twice" in the instructions are assumed to be used by the subject in arriving at his judgments.

Having introduced "numbers" at all, it was not much of a leap to employ them in a much more massive way. In the resulting *method of magnitude estimation* the subject is instructed to assign a number to each stimulus presentation so that the numbers are proportional to the subjective magnitudes produced by the stimuli. Thus, for example, if one stimulus has been called 50 and another one seems subjectively one fifth as intense, it is to be called 10 = 50/5. One stimulus is sometimes designated a standard and assigned a particular response value by the experimenter; usually 1, 10, or 100 is chosen so that fractional computations are easier for subjects. As early as 1956, however, S. S. Stevens showed that by not using a standard one can avoid certain local perturbations. Other methods that give essentially identical results have been described by S. S. Stevens (1958a). We shall confine our attention to magnitude estimation on the reasonable assumption of first-order experimental equivalence among these methods.

In some ways magnitude estimation and recognition experiments are alike. In both, the subject is more or less explicitly urged to make a unique response to each different stimulus presentation, that is, to act as if there were a one-to-one correspondence between stimuli and responses. A major difference between the two experiments is the size of the presentation and response sets. As far as the subject knows in a magnitude estimation experiment, any possible stimulus magnitude may be presented, although in practice the experimenter uses only relatively few. The subject's responses are restricted by the instructions only to the positive real numbers, although subjects seldom if ever use numbers other than integers and simple fractions.

As in recognition experiments, subjects do not consistently assign the same number to a particular stimulus. The inconsistencies are large enough that, in our opinion, they cannot be dismissed as analogous to the errors of measurement familiar in physics. The standard deviation[3] of the responses to a particular stimulus is somewhere in the neighborhood of 20 to 40 per cent of the mean response value, whereas, in good physical measurement the errors are usually reduced to less, often considerably less, than one per cent of the mean. The variability of magnitude estimation data appears to be due mostly to the subject, not to our equipment or

[3] There is a problem of conventional usage here. The subject's responses are not numbers but rather utterances or marks that conventionally name numbers. These names can no more be manipulated as numbers than can, say, responses that are color names. Numerical manipulations do, however, make sense if the responses are converted into random variables by establishing a one-to-one correspondence between the possible responses and a set of real numbers. We can then speak of the expectation of various functions of these random variables. Because the obvious one-to-one correspondence, namely, the assignment to a response of the number usually designated by the utterance made, is always used when analyzing magnitude estimation data, it is conventional to drop any reference to this correspondence and to treat the responses as if they were actually numbers. We shall follow this convention throughout the rest of this section.

recording procedures, and so it is an inherent part of the phenomena under study.

These observations suggest that the process can be effectively described only by a probabilistic model. But, in contrast to the models up to this point, we cannot hope to estimate in detail the relevant conditional probabilities, namely, the probabilities that particular numbers are emitted in response to a given stimulus presentation. There are simply too many possible responses to make that practical. We may, of course, postulate that such probabilities exist, but in tests of any such model we shall have to content ourselves with summary properties that can be easily estimated from data. Such a probabilistic model is described in Sec. 4.4, but as background we need to know more about experimental practice.

When studying a single subject, each of several (usually 10 to 20) stimuli are presented a number of times, and some "average" value of the responses to each is taken to be its "magnitude scale" value. The median, mean, and geometric mean have all been used at one time or another. Because the mean is the unbiased estimate of the expected value of the response, one might expect it to be favored; however, the data are almost always plotted in logarithmic coordinates, and, because the distribution of responses is approximately symmetrical and the geometric mean is the unbiased estimate of the quantity plotted, Stevens has recommended that it be used.

Most of the published data have not, however, been for single subjects. Rather, one or two responses per stimulus have been obtained from each subject, and an "average" over subjects is taken as the magnitude scale. The defense for averaging over subjects is that we are interested in central tendencies, not individual differences, and so the typical scale is what we want. Moreover, there are very practical engineering reasons for having standardized social scales for certain important dimensions such as loudness. Without disputing either point, we hope that more data for individual subjects will be published, because until it is decided just what it is that is invariant from subject to subject it will be difficult to be sure just what sort of averaging is permissible.

However the averaging is done, the resulting magnitude scale values are plotted against a physical measure of the stimuli; usually, both scales are shown in logarithmic coordinates. For continua involving changes of intensity, or what Stevens and Galanter (1957) called prothetic ones, the magnitude scale ψ is to a fair approximation a power function of the physical energy s of the stimulus, that is, there are constants α and β such that for stimulus values not too near threshold

$$\psi(s) = \alpha s^{\beta},$$

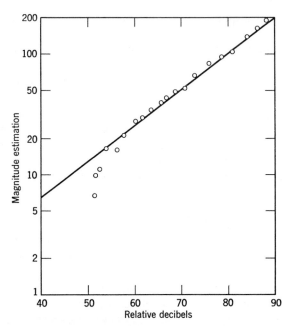

Fig. 8. Magnitude estimation judgments of loudness plotted in log-log coordinates. The straight line represents the power relation of loudness to intensity that has been accepted by the International Standards organization; the exponent is 0.3. Adapted by permission from Galanter & Messick (1961, p. 366).

or in logarithmic coordinates the relation is approximately a straight line with slope β (see Fig. 8). The departure from a straight line for small stimulus values is discussed later.

For each modality the exponent β is a reproducible quantity, not an unestimable parameter arbitrarily selected by the experimenter, whereas the constant α is a free parameter, whose value depends upon the units of both the physical and response scales. A listing of typical exponents for several different modalities is given in Table 1.

4.2 The Psychophysical Law

Historically, the relation between a measure of the subjective magnitude of sensation and a physical measure of the corresponding physical variable has been called the *psychophysical law*. There have been but two major contenders for the form of this relation. The first to appear, and the more dominant one throughout the history of psychophysics, was Fechner's logarithmic function, which we discussed at some length in Sec. 2 of

Chapter 4. Various modifications of his procedures and theory have evolved over the years, but with the exception of the relatively unsatisfactory mean category scale, all of them have rested upon some assumption that permits one to piece together the function from relatively local inconsistencies in the data. Neither a direct measurement of the subjective scale nor a satisfactory test of these assumptions has ever been suggested.

Table 1   Power Function Exponents of Magnitude Scales for Various Continua

Attribute	Exponent	Stimulus Conditions
Loudness	0.30	Binaural, 1000-cps tone, measured in energy units
Loudness	0.27	Monaural, 1000-cps tone, measured in energy units
Brightness	0.33	5° target, dark-adapted eye
Vibration	0.95	60 cps, finger
Vibration	0.6	250 cps, finger
Duration	1.1	White noise stimulus
Heaviness	1.45	Lifted weights
Electric shock	3.5	60 cps, through finger

Adapted from S. S. Stevens (1961b). Each exponent was determined by averaging data from at least ten subjects.

The alternative relation, the power function, was early suggested as a substitute to Fechner's proposal; it was briefly debated and then was forgotten for many decades until Stevens developed the method of magnitude estimation and discovered that it, not the logarithm, was consistent with his data. Buttressed by extensive experimentation, Stevens has argued that the power function is the correct form for the psychophysical law.

It is not our business here to recount these experimental studies nor to recapitulate all of Stevens' arguments; detailed summaries can be found in Stevens (1957, 1960, 1961a,b), where references are given to the numerous relevant experimental papers. Suffice it to say that he has repeatedly shown for a variety of prothetic continua that the magnitude scale is to a good approximation a power function of the physical scale and that he has created an elaborate network of consistent, interrelated results matched neither in detail nor in scope by those who adhere to the logarithmic form for the psychophysical law.

If this is so—and we suspect that most psychophysicists will agree that Stevens has amassed an impressive pattern of results—can there be any question about the form of the psychophysical law? His methods are direct, they do not involve Fechner's untested—and quite possibly untestable—assumption about the relation between magnitude and variability, and they have led to a structure of empirical relations which has few rivals for scope in psychophysics. Can there be doubt that the power function is the psychophysical law? Yet there is.

There are many detailed questions, but in our view the central one is: what meaning can we attach to an average of the numerical responses that a subject emits to a stimulus? Is it defensible or not to treat this as a measure of subjective sensation? Because this question seems so essential in resolving the debate between Stevens and his critics and because it is just the sort of question to which a mathematical theory might be brought to bear, we shall focus the rest of our discussion upon it.

4.3 The Invariance of the Scale

Averaging of one sort or another is certainly a legitimate way to condense and summarize one's observations, but that does not necessarily justify treating these numbers as a measure of anything—in particular, as scale values or as estimates of scale values. For example, in Sec. 3.2 we criticized an analogous averaging procedure in category scaling, and we might be expected to apply the same objections here with only a slight rewording. We shall not, however, for this reason. The trouble there was that the category numbers were assigned by the experimenter in a way that is arbitrary except for their ordering. Assuming that the subject's responses are independent of the labeling used, the experimenter can generate any monotonic function he wishes to by his choice of numbers to relate the mean category judgments to the physical scale. Magnitude estimation differs in that the subject, not the experimenter, chooses the numbers, and so they cannot be considered arbitrary in the same sense; it requires empirical evidence to know just how arbitrary they are.

The essence of the matter is probably the degree of arbitrariness of the responses, not the fact that they are utterances of number names. To be sure, one of the first objections to magnitude estimation was the numerical responses; there was an uneasy feeling that they must reflect more about the subject's number habits than about his sensory processes. To counter this view, Stevens (1959) argued in the following way that numerical responses are not essential to his results.

Let stimuli from one dimension, such as sound intensity, be presented, and during or just after each presentation let the subject adjust stimulation from another modality, such as skin vibration, until it "matches" the first in intensity. (The concept of a cross-modality match is left undefined, as are, of course, the matching operations basic to most physical measurement. The difference is that physical matching usually involves two stimuli on the same physical dimension, not from two different ones, and it is generally conceded that the former is a far simpler judgment.) Let us suppose that values of the two physical scales are s and t, that the two subjective scales are power functions

$$\psi(s) = \alpha s^{\beta} \quad \text{and} \quad \psi^*(t) = \alpha^* t^{\beta^*},$$

and that matching is defined as meaning equal subjective values, that is, s is the matching stimulus to t if and only if

$$\psi(s) = \psi^*(t).$$

It follows immediately that

$$s = \left(\frac{\alpha^*}{\alpha}\right)^{1/\beta} t^{\beta^*/\beta}.$$

These assumptions imply that the matching relation is a power function with the exponent β^*/β. Thus, if the magnitude scales represent subjective sensation, we predict not only that the matching data will follow a power function, but we also predict the value of the exponent. Both predictions have been confirmed in a variety of cases (see Stevens 1959, 1961b); sample data for vibration and sound intensity are shown in Fig. 9, where the theoretical line is a parameter-free prediction based upon the magnitude estimation data for each modality separately. The confirmation of the exponent is impressive. Comparable data for individual subjects have not been published.

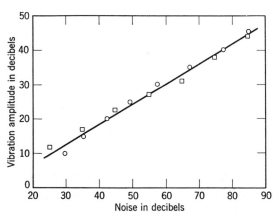

Fig. 9. The observed matching relation between the noise intensity and vibration amplitude. The theoretical line is predicted from magnitude estimation data on each modality separately. Adapted by permission from S. S. Stevens (1959, p. 207).

Critics have argued that this outcome of cross-modality matching is not really an argument supporting the power law, because if

$$\psi(s) = a \log \frac{s}{b} \quad \text{and} \quad \psi^*(t) = a^* \log \frac{t}{b^*},$$

then

$$a \log \frac{s}{b} = a^* \log \frac{t}{b^*},$$

or, taking exponentials,

$$s = ct^{a^*/a} \quad \text{where} \quad c = b \left(\frac{1}{b^*}\right)^{a^*/a}.$$

Thus both the power function and logarithmic hypotheses predict a power relation for the matching data, and so, it is argued, either is equally acceptable. This overlooks the fact that the two hypotheses differ in what they say about the exponent of the matching relation. If the magnitude scales are power functions, then the exponent of the matching data is given as the ratio of the estimable exponents of the magnitude functions; whereas, if they are logarithmic, the exponent is nothing but the ratio of the arbitrary units of the two scales, and so it is not predicted. The fact that the obtained exponents are well predicted by those from magnitude estimation leads us to favor the power function over the logarithm.

This last argument, however, somewhat prejudges the issue in question by assuming that we know the number of free parameters, and that is what is uncertain. Stevens has frequently referred to magnitude estimation as a "ratio scaling method" (e.g., Stevens, 1957, 1961b), which in this context is an unhappily ambiguous phrase. On the one hand, it might be purely descriptive of his method, referring to the fact that the subjects are asked to use numbers so that subjective ratios are preserved. On the other hand, it might be and usually is interpreted to mean that the resulting scale is technically a ratio scale, that is, it is completely specified except for its unit (see Chapter 1). No one can object to the descriptive use of the phrase except to the extent that it automatically suggests the second, much more significant, meaning. This extent seems to be great.

As Suppes and Zinnes point out in Chapter 1, the decision about the type of scale—ratio, interval, ordinal, etc.—is ultimately a theoretical one. One states certain axioms, for example, about some primitive concatenation operation and some binary relation corresponding to the judgments made. If these axioms are not empirically falsified in a few tests, they are assumed to be generally true. One then shows mathematically that a certain numerical representation exists which is isomorphic to the axiom system, and the scale type is determined by showing the group of transformations that characterizes all isomorphic representations into the same numerical system. If that is what is meant by constructing a scale of a particular type, then it is clear that we can be certain neither that the numbers obtained by magnitude estimation form a scale in this sense nor, if they do, what their scale type is until an explicit measurement theory is stated.

One can, however, hardly expect the empirical scientist to discard a method that seems to give regular and reproducible results just because no satisfactory theory exists to account for them. Rather, he will attempt to show by various experimental manipulations that the magnitude scale for a given physical dimension appears to have the invariances attributed to it. This Stevens has done. See Stevens (1960, 1961a,b) for summaries of this work. We examine several aspects that seem particularly relevant to the invariance question.

It was early noted that in log-log coordinates the functions are not quite straight lines and that they rise more rapidly for low stimulus levels than for the medium and high ones, where they are straight. This can be seen in Fig. 8. Moreover, if the subject's threshold is artificially inflated by introducing a masking background, the effect becomes more pronounced, as shown in Fig. 10. This lack of invariance in the form of the function can be interpreted either as showing that the magnitude scale simply is not a ratio scale or as showing that the relevant variables are not being used. The simple power relation states that the scale value approaches its zero as the physical variable approaches its zero, but we know perfectly well that stimuli cannot be detected for energy levels up to what is called the subject's threshold—absolute or artificial, as the case may be. This suggests that one of the two scales is wrong. One possibility suggested by a number of writers is to modify the equation to read

$$\psi(s) = \alpha(s - \gamma)^{\beta}, \qquad s \geqslant \gamma > 0, \qquad (6)$$

where α is again an unspecified parameter (namely, the unit of the magnitude scale) and β and γ are estimable parameters which supposedly depend upon the conditions of stimulation—the nature of the stimulus presentations, the background, etc.

An alternative, suggested by McGill (1960), is to add the new parameter to the scale values, that is,

$$\psi(s) = \alpha(s^{\beta} - \delta), \qquad s \geqslant \delta^{1/\beta} > 0. \qquad (7)$$

The variability of magnitude estimation data is such that both functions fit equally well, and so the decision will probably have to be reached indirectly. An example of such an attempt is the fairly elaborate argument

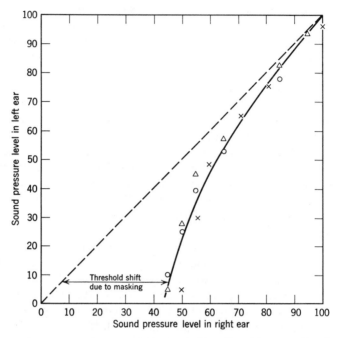

Fig. 10. The apparent increase of the threshold produced by a masking background. Adapted by permission from Stevens (1958, p. 519); the data were originally reported by Steinberg and Gardner (1937).

given by Galanter and Messick (1961), based in part upon some more or less philosophical considerations of Luce (1959), which suggests that Eq. 6 may be more appropriate than Eq. 7. In our opinion, however, the matter remains open.

It is now generally conceded that no matter where the "threshold" constant, γ or δ, is placed, the scale should be viewed as involving two estimated parameters—the threshold constant and the exponent β—and one unestimable parameter—the unit α—rather than treated as something weaker than a ratio scale. By weaker, we mean an interval scale or any other type in which there are two or more unestimable parameters. Incidentally, the previous arguments about the matching data are unaffected by the addition of such a "threshold" parameter.

Other empirical attempts to show that it is reasonable to treat the magnitude values as numbers on a ratio scale have involved showing that the form and the estimates of β and γ are invariant under modifications of the wording of the instructions, use of different number assignments to the standard stimulus, different locations of the standard, and variations in the number and spacing of the stimuli (Stevens & Galanter, 1957; J. C. Stevens, 1958). In all cases the data have been interpreted as supporting, to a first approximation, the desired invariance.

In spite of all this favorable experimental evidence, we still doubt that the magnitude scale is completely specified except for its unit. To anticipate the coming argument, we suspect that a psychophysical ratio scale exists which under certain conditions is well estimated by the magnitude scale. Nevertheless, just as in the rest of psychophysics, we suspect that a subject's responses, and therefore the magnitude scale, are some composite of his sensations and of other factors which, for lack of a better term, we call motivational. Our problem, therefore, is to attempt to construct a theory that makes these dependencies explicit and then to ask under what conditions is it reasonable to view the magnitude scale as a satisfactory estimate of the underlying, invariant psychophysical scale.

4.4 A Probabilistic Response Theory

As pointed out earlier, a magnitude estimation or a cross-modality matching experiment is much like the complete identification experiments discussed in Chapter 3. If we label stimuli by their physical magnitudes, then for a continuous dimension the set S of stimuli can be identified with the set of positive real numbers. Similarly, whether the responses are actual numbers or the physical measures of a matching variable, R can also be treated as the positive real numbers. Aside from the fact that S and R are no longer small finite sets, a magnitude estimation experiment also differs from a complete identification experiment in that no identification function ι is specified by the experimenter. Such a function we shall assume is induced in the subject by the instructions, and that function is just what one hopes to discover from the data.

This point is crucial in the development of a theory for magnitude estimation. Recall that in an identification experiment the identification function $\iota: R \to S$ is established by the experimenter and is communicated to the subject by the instructions and information feedback. Such an experiment is not considered under proper control until the identification function is specified. If, however, we are dealing with a situation in which we believe that the subject has what amounts to his own identification function and if we want to know what it is, then introducing our own arbitrary one would only help to conceal the unknown one of interest. Rather, we must let the subject be free to reveal the one he has. Magnitude estimation is one way that has been proposed for him to do this.

On the surface, there seems to be an inconsistency, for now we are saying that magnitude estimation is designed to get at the unknown identification function, whereas earlier we suggested that the unknown function is the psychophysical scale. If, however, we postulate that $\iota: R \to S$ is a strictly monotonic increasing function, then its inverse $\psi: S \to R$ exists, and so determining one is equivalent to determining the other. We shall suppose that ψ is the psychophysical scale, whereas its inverse ι is the identification function.

Because we know that subjects often fail to give the same response when a stimulus is repeated, more than ψ must be involved in relating responses to stimuli. Previously, we have had to invoke some notion both of response bias and of stimulus generalization to account for psychophysical data, and so we do it again using a continuous analogue of the choice model for complete identification experiments (Sec. 1.2, Chapter 3).

Let $p(r \mid s)$ denote the conditional probability density of response r to stimulus s, let b be a real-valued function defined over R, which represents the response bias, and let $\eta(s, t)$ denote a measure of generalization from stimulus s to stimulus t. The model postulates that

$$p(r \mid s) = \frac{\eta[s, \iota(r)] \, b(r)}{\displaystyle\int_0^\infty \eta[s, \iota(x)] \, b(x) \, dx} \, . \tag{8}$$

Observe that if we define a real-valued function ζ over $R \times R$ in terms of η, namely

$$\zeta(x, y) = \eta[\iota(x), \iota(y)], \quad x, y \in R,$$

then, by a simple substitution and taking into account that $\psi = \iota^{-1}$, Eq. 8 can be rewritten as

$$p(r \mid s) = \frac{\zeta[\psi(s), r] \, b(r)}{\displaystyle\int_0^\infty \zeta[\psi(s), x] \, b(x) \, dx} \, . \tag{9}$$

Thus it is immaterial whether we view the generalization as over stimuli or over responses, but for certain later computations it is more convenient to use the second form.

In words, Eq. 8 assumes that when stimulus s is presented it has some chance, which is proportional to $\eta(s, t)$, of seeming like stimulus t, and the subject responds to t according to his psychophysical function ψ. Thus the response is $r = \psi(t)$. In Eq. 9 s leads to the sensation $\psi(s)$, but because of response generalization the response r is emitted with some probability proportional to $\zeta[\psi(s), r]$. Overlying this purely psychophysical structure is a response bias $b(r)$ which differentially influences the responses that occur. The crude, unnormalized measure of the strength of connection between stimulus s and response r is simply $\eta[s, \iota(r)] \, b(r)$ or, equivalently, $\zeta[\psi(s), r] \, b(r)$. The total measure is $\int_0^\infty \zeta[\psi(s), x] \, b(x) \, dx$, so that dividing the measure of the strength of connection by the total measure yields a probability, just as in the discrete choice models.

(For those familiar with Stieltjes integrals, it should be noted that Eqs. 8 and 9 should properly be written as integrals with respect to a cumulative bias B. When that is done, discrete choice models are simply special cases in which the cumulative bias is a step-function.)

Three general comments about this model are in order. First, although we have viewed it as a continuous generalization of the choice theory for recognition experiments, it is also much like the response mechanism that Thurstone postulated to explain discrimination data and Tanner used in his analysis of detection and recognition data. The principal differences are the multiplicative biasing function and the fact that the generalization function is not assumed to be normal. These differences in the continuous case are minor compared with those that develop when the models are applied to finite stimulus presentation and response sets. There the choice theory involves only those values of the generalization function for the specific stimuli employed, whereas in the Thurstonian theories whole sets of stimuli, or their corresponding responses, are treated as equivalent, and integrals of the generalization measure over these sets are treated as the needed discrete probabilities.

Second, the three functions $\psi = \iota^{-1}$, η or ζ, and b, which enter into Eqs. 8 and 9, have no necessary relation to one another. In particular, the measure of generalization, η or ζ, which is of paramount importance in the choice theory analyses of detection, recognition, and discrimination, need have no particular connection with the psychophysical scale ψ, which characterizes how sensation grows with stimulus energy. This point has been repeatedly emphasized by Stevens (e.g., 1961a, p. 83) in his criticisms of the classic attempts to derive the psychophysical function from discrimination data (Sec. 2, Chapter 4). Shortly, however, we shall see certain theoretical reasons why, in a sense, both points of view may be correct and why it has proved so difficult using only confusion data to disentangle the psychophysical and generalization functions.

Third, a formal analogue of the asymptotic learning argument given in Sec. 1.2 of Chapter 3 yields Eq. 8. Of course, the discrete probabilities of the model for complete identification experiments must be replaced by probability densities. It seems doubtful, however, that this learning model can be taken as a serious argument for the continuous choice model because no payoffs are used in magnitude estimation experiments. It may, however, suggest a way of analyzing data in which payoffs are used.

As mentioned earlier, there is little hope of estimating $p(r \mid s)$ from data, but various of its parameters can be estimated. Of particular relevance to magnitude estimation are the expected response and the "geometric expected response," that is, the exponential of the expectation of the logarithm of the response. These are defined by

$$\psi_m(s) = E(r \mid s)$$

$$= \int_0^\infty r p(r \mid s)\, dr$$

$$= \frac{\int_0^\infty r \zeta[\psi(s), r]\, b(r)\, dr}{\int_0^\infty \zeta[\psi(s), r]\, b(r)\, dr}, \tag{10}$$

and

$$\psi_g(s) = \exp E(\log r \mid s)$$

$$= \exp \int_0^\infty (\log r)\, p(r \mid s)\, dr$$

$$= \exp \frac{\int_0^\infty (\log r)\zeta[\psi(s), r]\, b(r)\, dr}{\int_0^\infty \zeta[\psi(s), r]\, b(r)\, dr}, \tag{11}$$

respectively.

Assuming that the model is correct, the most important question is: when is the theoretical magnitude scale ψ_m or ψ_g approximately proportional to the psychophysical function ψ? It is evident that we can choose ζ and b so that they are quite different. In Theorem 2 we state one set of sufficient conditions leading to proportionality, but first we show two ways of stating one of the conditions.

Lemma I. *Suppose that ζ has the property that there exist positive continuous functions f and g such that for all $x, y, z > 0$, $\zeta(xz, yz) = f(x, y)\, g(z)$; then there exists a constant γ such that $\zeta(x, y) = x^\gamma \zeta(1, y/x)$. Conversely, if h is any positive, continuous function, then $\zeta(x, y) = x^\gamma h(y/x)$ has the foregoing property.*

PROOF.   By setting $z = 1$, we see that $f(x, y) = \zeta(x, y)/g(1)$. Using this and the hypothesis three times, we obtain

$$\zeta\left(1, \frac{yz}{xz}\right) \frac{g(xz)}{g(1)} = \zeta(xz, yz)$$

$$= \zeta(x, y) \frac{g(z)}{g(1)}$$

$$= \zeta\left(1, \frac{y}{x}\right) g(x) \frac{g(z)}{g(1)^2}.$$

Setting $u(x) = g(x)/g(1)$ and dividing by $\zeta(1, y/x)$, we get $u(xz) = u(x)\,u(z)$. Because g is positive and continuous, so is u; hence the functional equation has the solution $u(x) = x^\gamma$ for some constant γ. Thus $g(x) = g(1)x^\gamma$. Substituting,

$$\zeta(x, y) = f\left(1, \frac{y}{x}\right) g(x)$$

$$= \zeta\left(1, \frac{y}{x}\right) x^\gamma.$$

Conversely, if $\zeta(x, y) = h(y/x)x^\gamma$, then

$$\zeta(xz, yz) = h\left(\frac{yz}{xz}\right) (xz)^\gamma$$

$$= h\left(\frac{y}{x}\right) x^\gamma z^\gamma$$

$$= \zeta(x, y)z^\gamma.$$

Theorem 2. *If ζ has the property that $\zeta(x, y) = x^\gamma \zeta(1, y/x)$ and if $b(r) = br^c$ for all $r \in R$, then $\psi_m(s) = \mu\psi(s)$ and $\psi_g(s) = \mu_g\psi(s)$ for all $s \in S$, where μ and μ_g are, respectively, the mean and geometric mean of*

$$r^c\zeta(1, r)\Big/ \int_0^\infty x^c\zeta(1, x)\, dx.$$

PROOF. We prove this only for the mean; the other case is similar. If we let $x = r/\psi(s)$ and substitute our assumptions in Eq. 10, we obtain

$$\psi_m(s) = \frac{\displaystyle\int_0^\infty \psi(s)x\zeta[\psi(s), \psi(s)x]bx^c\,\psi(s)^c\,\psi(s)\,dx}{\displaystyle\int_0^\infty \zeta[\psi(s), \psi(s)x]bx^c\,\psi(s)^c\,\psi(s)\,dx}$$

$$= \psi(s) \frac{\displaystyle\int_0^\infty x^{1+c}\,\psi(s)^\gamma\zeta(1, x)\,dx}{\displaystyle\int_0^\infty x^c\,\psi(s)^\gamma\zeta(1, x)\,dx}$$

$$= \psi(s)\mu,$$

where

$$\mu = \frac{\displaystyle\int_0^\infty x^{1+c}\zeta(1, x)\,dx}{\displaystyle\int_0^\infty x^c\zeta(1, x)\,dx}.$$

The conclusion, then, is that both the expected response and the geometric expected response are proportional to the psychophysical function, provided that the response bias is a power function and that the generalization function has a particular form, the simplest case of which (i.e., $\gamma = 0$) postulates that generalization depends upon the ratio of the psychophysical function values of the two stimuli. Note that this conclusion is completely independent of the form of the psychophysical function ψ; therefore, if we can convince ourselves that the two assumptions of Theorem 2 are met in a magnitude estimation or matching experiment, then the observed magnitude scale estimates the underlying psychophysical function—which is what we want to measure.

In the next two sections we turn to questions about the mathematical form of the generalization and psychophysical functions. Some of the results about the generalization function appear to be helpful in deciding whether the conditions of Theorem 2 are met for a given set of data.

4.5 Form of the Generalization Function

To show that the expected response is proportional to the psychophysical function, we found it necessary to constrain the generalization function. This constraint is, however, quite different from those we seemed to need in analyzing detection and recognition experiments (Chapter 3). There we assumed that the negative logarithm of the generalization function has the properties of a distance function. Moreover, when the stimuli differ on only one physical dimension, we assumed that the distance measure was additive. Because these postulates have received some indirect support, it seems worthwhile to find out what they imply when added to the present constraint. The answer is given in the following theorem

Theorem 3. *If the generalization function ζ is such that*

1. $\zeta(x, y) = \zeta(1, y/x)x^{\gamma}$, *for all $x, y > 0$,*
2. $\zeta(x, z) = \zeta(x, y)\, \zeta(y, z)$, *for all x, y, z for which either $x \geqslant y \geqslant z$ or $x \leqslant y \leqslant z$,*
3. $\zeta(x, y) = \zeta(y, x)$, *for all $x, y > 0$, and*
4. *ζ is continuous in each of its arguments,*

then there exists a constant δ such that

$$
\zeta(x, y) = \begin{cases} \left(\dfrac{x}{y}\right)^{\delta} & \text{if } x \leqslant y \\[2ex] \left(\dfrac{x}{y}\right)^{-\delta} & \text{if } x \geqslant y. \end{cases}
$$

PROOF. By condition 2, $\zeta(x, y) = \zeta(x, x)\,\zeta(x, y)$, so $\zeta(x, x) = 1$. Using this and condition 1, $\zeta(x, x) = 1 = \zeta(1, 1)x^\gamma$, hence $\gamma = 0$. If $x, y \geqslant 1$, then conditions 1 and 2 imply

$$\zeta(1, x)\,\zeta(1, y) = \zeta(1, x)\,\zeta(x, xy)$$
$$= \zeta(1, xy).$$

Because, by (4), $\zeta(1, x)$ is continuous, this functional equation is known to have the solution $\zeta(1, x) = x^{-\delta}$ for some δ. A similar argument holds when $x, y \leqslant 1$, leading to $\zeta(1, x) = x^\epsilon$, for some ϵ. It is easy to see that condition 3 implies $\epsilon = \delta$, thus proving the theorem.

We examine next how one might study the form of the generalization function empirically. If we assume that there is no response bias, that is, $c = 0$, and that the generalization function depends only upon response ratios, then by Theorem 2 we see that

$$\frac{r}{\psi_m(s)} = \frac{1}{\mu}\frac{r}{\psi(s)}.$$

Thus the distribution ζ^* of $r/\psi_m(s)$ is simply the distribution ζ of $r/\psi(s)$, except that the independent variable is stretched by a factor μ, that is, $\zeta^*(x) = \mu\zeta(\mu x)$. So, if we estimate $\psi_m(s)$ from the mean empirical response curve, then we can develop the empirical frequency distribution corresponding to ζ^*, which except for a constant multiplicative factor is the generalization function.

If we wish to test the hypothesis that the generalization function has the form derived in Theorem 3, we can use a χ^2 test once δ is estimated. At the moment we have only *ad hoc* techniques for estimating δ under the assumption of no response bias. Because the mean of ζ^* is easily seen to be 1 in this case, it cannot be used to estimate δ, but either the median or variance can be. Let M and M^* denote, respectively, the medians of ζ and ζ^*; then it is clear that $M^* = M/\mu$. For the generalization function of Theorem 3, if $\delta > 2$, the mean μ is given by

$$\mu = \frac{\displaystyle\int_0^\infty x\,\zeta(x)\,dx}{\displaystyle\int_0^\infty \zeta(x)\,dx}$$

$$= \frac{\displaystyle\int_0^1 x^{\delta+1}\,dx + \int_1^\infty x^{1-\delta}\,dx}{\displaystyle\int_0^1 x^\delta\,dx + \int_1^\infty x^{-\delta}\,dx}$$

$$= \frac{\delta^2 - 1}{\delta^2 - 4}.$$

The median is defined by

$$\frac{1}{2} = \frac{\displaystyle\int_0^M \zeta(x)\,dx}{\displaystyle\int_0^\infty \zeta(x)\,dx}$$

$$= \frac{\displaystyle\int_0^1 x^\delta\,dx + \int_1^M x^{-\delta}\,dx}{\displaystyle\int_0^1 x^\delta\,dx + \int_1^\infty x^{-\delta}\,dx}$$

$$= \frac{\delta - 1}{2\delta} - \frac{\delta + 1}{2\delta}\,[M^{(1-\delta)} - 1].$$

Solving,

$$M = \left(\frac{\delta + 1}{\delta}\right)^{1/(\delta-1)}.$$

Thus,

$$M^* = \left(\frac{\delta + 1}{\delta}\right)^{1/(\delta-1)}\left(\frac{\delta^2 - 4}{\delta^2 - 1}\right). \tag{12}$$

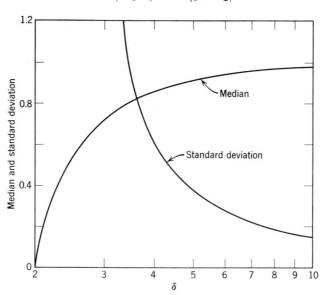

Fig. 11. The standard deviation and median of the generalization function

$$\zeta(x) = \begin{cases} \dfrac{\delta^2 - 1}{2\delta}\,x^\delta & \text{if } 0 < x < 1 \\[2ex] \dfrac{\delta^2 - 1}{2\delta}\,x^{-\delta} & \text{if } 1 < x. \end{cases}$$

So an empirical estimate of the median provides an estimate of δ. Equation 12 relating δ to M^* is plotted in Fig. 11.

Similarly, if $c = 0$ and $\delta > 3$,

$$\text{var}(\zeta^*) = \frac{\text{var}(\zeta)}{\mu^2}$$

and

$$\text{var}(\zeta) = \frac{\delta^2 - 1}{\delta^2 - 9} - \mu^2,$$

hence

$$\text{var}(\zeta^*) = \frac{(\delta - 4)^2}{(\delta^2 - 9)(\delta^2 - 1)} - 1. \tag{13}$$

The square root of Eq. 13 is also plotted in Fig. 11.

4.6 Form of the Psychophysical Function

If, as in Theorem 2, we assume that the magnitude scale is (approximately) proportional to the underlying psychophysical function ψ, then Stevens' results clearly suggest that ψ must be a power function for intensive continua. The question facing the theoretician is whether this empirical result can be arrived at from some more primitive considerations. We shall present two theories, neither of which we feel is really satisfactory.

The first is suggested by a study that Plateau (1872) reported in which he gave a pair of painted disks, one black and one white, to each of eight artists and asked them to return to their studios and paint a grey "midway" between the two. The resulting productions were "presque identique" in spite of the fact that they were painted under widely varying conditions. The range of reflectances from the two patches must have been great, yet "midway" was about the same for all eight artists. What had remained fixed, of course, was the ratio of the reflectances from the patches, and so the identical greys suggested that equal stimulus ratios must have induced equal sensation ratios. Given this generalization from one observation, it follows that sensation must be a power function of intensity. The formal statement and proof are the following:

Theorem 4. *If ψ is a positive, real-valued, continuous function of a positive real variable and if for any s, s', t, t' for which $s/t = s'/t'$, it follows that $\psi(s)/\psi(t) = \psi(s')/\psi(t')$; then $\psi(s) = \alpha s^\beta$, where $\alpha > 0$.*

PROOF. The second part of the hypothesis is clearly equivalent to saying that there is a function f such that when $s/t = z$ then $\psi(s)/\psi(t) = f(z)$. Rewriting, if $s = tz$, then $\psi(s) = \psi(tz) = \psi(t)f(z)$. Note that for $t = 1$,

$\psi(z) = \psi(1) f(z)$. If we define $u(s) = \psi(s)/\psi(1)$, then this condition can be restated as

$$
\begin{aligned}
u(sz) &= \frac{\psi(sz)}{\psi(1)} \\
&= \frac{\psi(s) f(z)}{\psi(1)} \\
&= \frac{\psi(s)\, \psi(z)}{\psi(1)^2} \\
&= u(s)\, u(z).
\end{aligned}
$$

It is well known that the only continuous solutions to this functional equation are of the form s^β; setting $\alpha = \psi(1) > 0$, we have

$$
\begin{aligned}
\psi(s) &= \psi(1)\, u(s) \\
&= \alpha s^\beta.
\end{aligned}
$$

This argument is subject to exactly the same criticisms as Fechner's equal jnd assumption (Sec. 2, Chapter 4); it merely replaces an untested postulate about equal differences by an equally untested one about equal ratios. For this reason we do not believe that it is a satisfactory rationalization of the power function.

A second argument that has sometimes been interpreted as a theory for the psychophysical function is given in Luce (1959). He points out that if (1) the stimulus scale is a ratio scale, (2) the sensation scale is also a ratio scale, (3) the function ψ relating them is single valued and continuous, (4) stimulus values are not multiplied by a dimensional constant in such a way that their product is independent of the unit chosen, and (5) an admissible change of scale for the stimulus variable produces only an admissible change of scale for the sensation variable, then ψ must satisfy the functional equation

$$
\psi(ks) = K(k)\, \psi(s),
$$

where k represents the unit of s and $K(k)$, the corresponding unit of the sensation scale. From this it is easy to show that ψ must be a power function.

This argument seems unsatisfactory in two respects: it prejudges the question whether sensations form a ratio scale—which, however, is certainly suggested by the data and must be the case if the generalization function depends only upon ratios of sensation values—and, more important, it assumes that the psychophysical function can be stated in terms of the physical scale without bringing in dimensional constants that cancel out the physical units. This is simply not true of many physical laws (e.g., the decay laws), although it is of some (e.g., Ohm's and Newton's laws), and so it seems unwise to invoke it as an a priori assumption here.

In our opinion, therefore, theoretical work on why the psychophysical function seems so often to be the power relation continues to be needed. It must be kept in mind that the reasoning should not be too pervasive because it is not at all clear that the power function is the correct psychophysical function for nonprothetic (metathetic) continua.

4.7 Relations to Other Experiments

If we are correct in supposing that the same fundamental response mechanism underlies all psychophysical experiments, it should be possible to predict aspects of one set of data from any of the others. Many of these connections have not yet been explored, but a few theoretical results can be derived about the connections between recognition and magnitude estimation experiments and some experimental-theoretical results are known about the relation between category and magnitude scales.

Following Stevens, let us suppose that

$$\psi(s) = \alpha(s - \gamma)^\beta$$

and, as suggested by Theorem 3, that

$$\zeta(x, y) = \begin{cases} \left(\dfrac{x}{y}\right)^\delta, & x \leqslant y \\[2ex] \left(\dfrac{x}{y}\right)^{-\delta}, & x > y. \end{cases}$$

Then, by the definition of η,

$$\eta(s, t) = \zeta[\psi(s), \psi(t)]$$

$$= \begin{cases} \left[\dfrac{\psi(s)}{\psi(t)}\right]^\delta, & s \leqslant t \\[2ex] \left[\dfrac{\psi(s)}{\psi(t)}\right]^{-\delta}, & s > t \end{cases}$$

$$= \begin{cases} \left(\dfrac{s - \gamma}{t - \gamma}\right)^{\beta\delta}, & s \leqslant t \\[2ex] \left(\dfrac{s - \gamma}{t - \gamma}\right)^{-\beta\delta}, & s > t. \end{cases}$$

Here we have a possible hint why it has proved so difficult to separate the psychophysical function from the generalization function. If both are power functions, as assumed above, then so is their composite, and so no single class of experiments is likely to suggest that two distinct functions are involved.

Assuming a two-stimulus, two-response recognition experiment with no bias, the probability of a correct response is given by

$$p(C) = \frac{1}{1 + \eta(s, t)}.$$

If $s < t$ and if we choose the probability cutoff of π, the equation $p(C) = \pi$ yields

$$\eta(s, t) = \left(\frac{s - \gamma}{t - \gamma}\right)^{\beta\delta} = \frac{1 - \pi}{\pi},$$

and so the recognition π-jnd is given by

$$t - s = (s - \gamma)\left[\left(\frac{\pi}{1 - \pi}\right)^{1/\beta\delta} - 1\right], \tag{14}$$

or in logarithmic (db) measure

$$10 \log_{10}\left(\frac{t - \gamma}{s - \gamma}\right) = \frac{10}{\beta\delta} \log_{10}\left(\frac{\pi}{1 - \pi}\right). \tag{15}$$

To get an idea of the size of the recognition jnd predicted from magnitude estimation data, let us suppose that we are working with 1000-cps tones. From Table 1 we see that β is approximately 0.3. If the standard deviation of the response generalization function lies between 0.2 and 0.4, then we see from the standard deviation curve in Fig. 11 that $5 < \delta < 8$. By taking $\pi = 0.75$ as the usual cutoff and assuming stimuli well above threshold so that we can forget about γ, substitution in Eq. 15 yields a predicted stimulus difference of 2.0 to 3.2 db. Relevant data to check this prediction do not seem to exist.

As Rosner (1961) first pointed out in a closely related context, there may be some difficulties with this argument. We see that it leads to a generalized Weber law (Sec. 1.4, Chapter 4) for the recognition jnd (Eq. 14); however, because γ is always positive for magnitude estimation data, the extra constant in the Weber law is subtracted. This is just opposite to what is needed to fit Weber's law to discrimination data (Sec. 1.4, Chapter 4). No one has reported recognition jnd data, and we cannot be sure that they behave in the same way as discrimination data, but it certainly seems to be a reasonable conjecture. If so, something must be wrong with our argument, at least for very small stimuli. Incidently, use of McGill's correction to the power function (Eq. 7) does not materially alter these remarks.

Concerning the relation between category and magnitude estimation data, it has been well known for some time that the simple mean category scale (Sec. 3.2) is moderately like the logarithm of the corresponding magnitude scale, but there are consistent deviations from a simple logarithmic relation. Recently, Galanter, and Messick (1961) have shown that for the loudness of bursts of noise the Thurstonian category scale based on the equation of categorical judgment and using unequal variances is, to a good approximation, the logarithm of the magnitude scale. Torgerson (1960b) presented similar results for estimations of greyness using the simple mean category scale.

On the basis of his data, Torgerson (1960a) suggested that there is but one psychophysical function underlying both category and magnitude estimation scales—whether you ask the subject to judge differences or ratios, he does the same thing, but depending upon what you ask he does or does not make a logarithmic transformation. This is an interesting hypothesis, but we do not believe that any existing data really prove it. Moreover, our attempts to work out theoretical predictions for the mean category scale from the magnitude estimation model have led to messy equations that are not very revealing.

Assuming that Torgerson's hypothesis is confirmed and that some appropriate category scale is in fact the logarithm of the psychophysical function, as obtained from magnitude estimation data, does this mean that the two methods are equally good? Some seem to feel that it does, but, even if we ignore the instability of category data, we cannot agree. The category scales involve two free parameters, corresponding to a zero and unit, whereas the psychophysical function estimated by the magnitude scale appears to have only one unestimable parameter. The other parameters, the exponent β and "threshold" γ, can be estimated from the data. To be sure, we do not yet understand just what the exponent means or what it is related to, but there can be no doubt that an estimated constant reveals more about a subject than does our arbitrary selection of a zero.

5. DISTANCES

In a number of the response models that we have discussed in the preceding two chapters as well as in this one, parameters arose that were attached to pairs of stimuli rather than to single stimuli. For the simpler stimulus parameters, the scaling problem is, in principle, straightforward: how do the scale values depend upon physical measures of the stimuli? When parameters are associated with pairs of stimuli, matters are somewhat more complicated. There is still nothing like the same understanding of these structures as there is of the simpler scales.

Without exception, we have assumed that either the parameters them-selves (in the case of Thurstonian models) or their negative logarithms (in the case of the choice models) behave like measures of distance in the following sense:

Definition I. *A function d: $\mathscr{S} \times \mathscr{S} \rightarrow$ real numbers is said to be a distance measure if for all x, y, z $\in \mathscr{S}$,*

1. $d(x, y) = d(y, x)$,
2. $d(x, y) \geqslant 0$ and $d(x, y) = 0$ *if and only if* $x = y$,
3. $d(x, z) \leqslant d(x, y) + d(y, z)$.

Two broad classes of questions come to mind. First, is there really any reason to expect measures of distance to arise when subjects make judgments about stimuli? Second, if so, what more can be said about such a measure; for example, can it be treated as the natural distance metric of an Euclidean *r*-space for some value of *r*? Given that it can, how can we determine the value of *r* and the coordinates of the points in the space that correspond to particular stimuli?

The question of a rationalization has been attacked by Restle (1959) following a point of view that is familiar from stimulus sampling theory in learning (Chapter 10, Vol. II). We turn to it first.

5.1 A Rationalization for Distance

Restle supposes that a finite set $\mathscr{A}$ of possible stimulus aspects exists. These aspects can be thought of as a list of the various properties that stimuli may possess and that are relevant to the organism under considera-tion. Each stimulus *x* has and is characterized by its set *X* of aspects ($X \subseteq \mathscr{A}$); by "characterize" we mean that stimuli *x* and *y* have the same set of aspects if and only if they are the same stimulus, that is, $X = Y$ if and only if $x = y$. Because the aspects may differentially influence the judgment being made, it is reasonable to suppose that each type of judg-ment generates its own measure function over the subsets of $\mathscr{A}$.

Definition 2. *A function m:* $2^{\mathscr{A}} \rightarrow$ *real numbers, where* $2^{\mathscr{A}}$ *is the set of subsets of* $\mathscr{A}$, *is said to be a* measure *if*

1. *for all* $X \subseteq \mathscr{A}, m(X) \geqslant 0$,
2. $m(\emptyset) = 0$, *where $\emptyset$ is the empty set*,
3. *for all* $X, Y \subseteq \mathscr{A}, m(X \cup Y) = m(X) + m(Y) - m(X \cap Y)$.

Let it be clear that from a formal, axiomatic point of view it does not matter what, if any, intuitions we have about the set of aspects and the measure function over them, but that from the point of view of the psychology assumed it matters a great deal. We feel that this scheme, like the stimulus-sampling theory which it closely resembles, is evasive at the intuitive level. Various assumptions other than Restle's are possible, and they are not clearly inferior to his. Moreover, it seems no more intuitively acceptable to us to assume the existence of sets of aspects and a measure over them than to assume directly the existence of distances between pairs of stimuli, which is what the aspects and measure are intended to justify. Apparently, not everyone feels as we do.

Definition 3. *Let $x, y \in S$ and let $X, Y \subseteq \mathscr{A}$ be their associated aspect sets. If m is a measure over $2^{\mathscr{A}}$, the quantity[4]*

$$d(x, y) = m[(X - Y) \cup (Y - X)] \tag{16}$$

is called the aspect distance *between x and y.*

This appears to be a sensible measure of the dissimilarity between x and y because it is the aspect-measure of the set of aspects in which the two stimuli differ.

Lemma 2

$$d(x, y) = m[(X \cap \bar{Y}) \cup (Y \cap \bar{X})] \tag{17}$$

$$= m(X \cap \bar{Y}) + m(Y \cap \bar{X}) \tag{18}$$

$$= m(X - Y) + m(Y - X) \tag{19}$$

$$= m[(X \cup Y) - (X \cap Y)] \tag{20}$$

$$= m(X) + m(Y) - 2m(X \cap Y). \tag{21}$$

PROOF.   Equation 17 is equivalent to Eq. 16 by the definition of difference.

Equation 18 is equivalent to Eq. 17 by applying property 3 of a measure, noting that the measure of the intersection term is 0 because $(X \cap \bar{Y}) \cap (Y \cap \bar{X}) = (X \cap \bar{X}) \cap (Y \cap \bar{Y}) = \emptyset$ and then using property 2.

Equation 19 is equivalent to Eq. 18 by the definition of difference.

Equation 20 is equivalent to Eq. 17 because $(X \cup Y) - (X \cap Y) = (X \cap \bar{Y}) \cup (Y \cap \bar{X})$ by simple set transformations.

Equation 21 is equivalent to Eq. 20 because $X \cap Y \subseteq X \cup Y$, and so $m[(X \cup Y) - (X \cap Y)] = m(X \cup Y) - m(X \cap Y) = m(X) + m(Y) - 2m(X \cap Y)$.

Theorem 5. *The aspect distance is a distance measure.*

PROOF.   By Eq. 21,

$d(x, y) + d(y, z)$

$= m(X) + m(Y) - 2m(X \cap Y) + m(Y) + m(Z) - 2m(Y \cap Z)$

$= m(X) + m(Z) - 2m(X \cap Z) + 2[m(X \cap Z)$

$\qquad\qquad\qquad\qquad + m(Y) - m(X \cap Y) - m(Y \cap Z)]$

$= d(x, z) + 2[m(X \cap Z) + m(Y) - m(X \cap Y) - m(Y \cap Z)]$

$\geqslant d(x, z)$

[4] $X - Y = X \cap \bar{Y}$ denotes the set theoretic difference of X and Y.

provided that $m(X \cap Z) + m(Y) - m(X \cap Y) - m(Y \cap Z) \geqslant 0$. To show this, define the following pairwise disjoint sets (see Fig. 12):

$$A = X \cap \bar{Y} \cap Z$$
$$B = X \cap Y \cap Z$$
$$C = X \cap Y \cap \bar{Z}$$
$$D = \bar{X} \cap Y \cap Z.$$

Clearly,

$$X \cap Z = A \cup B$$
$$X \cap Y = B \cup C$$
$$Y \cap Z = B \cup D$$
$$Y \supseteq B \cup C \cup D.$$

Thus,

$$m(X \cap Z) + m(Y) - m(X \cap Y) - m(Y \cap Z)$$
$$\geqslant m(A) + m(B) + m(B) + m(C) + m(D)$$
$$- m(B) - m(C) - m(B) - m(D)$$
$$\geqslant 0,$$

as was to be shown.

Observe from this last proof that

$$d(x, y) + d(y, z) = d(x, z) \tag{22}$$

if and only if

$$m(A) = 0 \quad \text{and} \quad m[Y - (B \cup C \cup D)] = 0. \tag{23}$$

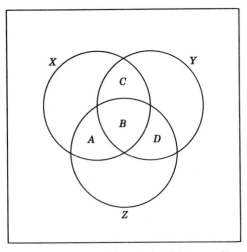

Fig. 12. A graphic representation of the eight pairwise disjoint sets discussed in Theorem 5.

If we suppose, with no psychological loss of generality, that for any $U \subseteq \mathscr{A}, m(U) = 0$ implies $U = \emptyset$, then Eq. 23 implies

$$A = \emptyset \quad \text{and} \quad Y = B \cup C \cup D.$$

It is not difficult to see that this is equivalent to

$$X \cap Z \subseteq Y \subseteq X \cup Z,$$

which in a certain reasonable sense can be interpreted as meaning that Y is between X and Z. This leads to the following definition:

Definition 4. *For stimuli x, y, and z which are all different, y is said to be* between x and z, *written $x |y| z$, if and only if*

$$X \cap Z \subseteq Y \subseteq X \cup Z. \tag{24}$$

We have already proved the following theorem.

Theorem 6. *If $x |y| z$, then Eq. 22 holds; the converse is true if and only if $U = \emptyset$ whenever $m(U) = 0$.*

Corollary. *If $x |y| z$, then $d(x, z) > d(x, y)$ and $d(x, z) > d(y, z)$.*

PROOF. Equation 22 and property 1 of a distance measure.

Care must be taken not to overrespond to Theorem 6, which seems to suggest that betweenness acts in the same way here as it does on an ordinary one-dimensional mathematical continuum. Because Eq. 22 holds only for triples of stimuli, we cannot conclude anything about larger sets of stimuli until we have shown it to hold. Unfortunately, not everything we would like to be true is true. For example, a usual form of extrapolation is the following:

Conjecture: *If $w |x| y$ and $x |y| z$, then $w |x| z$ and $w |y| z$.*

Counter Example. Let $W = \{1, 2\}$, $X = \{2, 3\}$, $Y = \{3, 4\}$, $Z = \{4, 5\}$, then $w |x| y$ because $W \cap Y = \emptyset \subseteq X \subseteq W \cup Y$ and $x |y| z$ because $X \cap Z = \emptyset \subseteq Y \subseteq X \cup Z$. But not $w |x| z$ because $X = \{2, 3\} \nsubseteq \{1, 2, 4, 5\} = W \cup Z$ and not $w |y| z$ because $Y = \{3, 4\} \nsubseteq \{1, 2, 4, 5\} = W \cup Z$.

We next show that a form of interpolation is true.

Theorem 7. *If $w |x| z$ and $x |y| z$, then $w |y| z$.*

PROOF. Because $w |x| z$, $W \cap Z \subseteq X$ and because $x |y| z$, $X \cap Z \subseteq Y$, so $W \cap Z = W \cap Z \cap Z \subseteq X \cap Z \subseteq Y$. Because $x |y| z$, $Y \subseteq X \cup Z$ and because $w |x| z$, $X \subseteq W \cup Z$, so $Y \subseteq X \cup Z \subseteq W \cup Z \cup Z = W \cup Z$. Thus, by definition, $w |y| z$.

Another result of interest is this one:

Theorem 8. *If $x |y| z$, then $z |y| x$ but not $y |x| z$ or any of the other permutations of the three symbols.*

PROOF. $z |y| x$ follows immediately from the definition of $x |y| z$ and the commutativity of union and intersection.

Suppose $y \, |x| \, z$ as well as $x \, |y| \, z$, then we know that

$$X \cap Z \subseteq Y \subseteq X \cup Z$$
$$Y \cap Z \subseteq X \subseteq Y \cup Z.$$

From the first we have

$$X \cap Z = X \cap Z \cap Z \subseteq Y \cap Z$$

and from the second

$$Y \cap Z = Y \cap Z \cap Z \subseteq X \cap Z,$$

so $X \cap Z = Y \cap Z$. In like manner,

$$Y \cap \bar{Z} \subseteq (X \cup Z) \cap \bar{Z} = (X \cap \bar{Z}) \cup (Z \cap \bar{Z}) = X \cap \bar{Z}$$

and

$$X \cap \bar{Z} \subseteq (Y \cup Z) \cap \bar{Z} = (Y \cap \bar{Z}) \cup (Z \cap \bar{Z}) = Y \cap \bar{Z},$$

so $X \cap \bar{Z} = Y \cap \bar{Z}$. Thus

$$X = (X \cap Z) \cup (X \cap \bar{Z}) = (Y \cap Z) \cup (Y \cap \bar{Z}) = Y,$$

that is, $x = y$, contrary to the definition of $x \, |y| \, z$.

Although, in the general case, the betweenness relation is not strong enough to patch together sets of ordered stimuli, there are special assumptions about the aspect sets for which it is possible. The simplest case is a set of stimuli $x_1, x_2, \ldots, x_n$ such that $X_1 \subset X_2 \subset \ldots \subset X_n$. This is known as a *monotone sequence of sets*, and it obviously has the property that if $i < j < k$ then $x_i \, |x_j| \, x_k$. The aspect set of a stimulus higher than another in the series is obtained from the lower one by adding new aspects. This appears to correspond to the definition of stimuli on what Stevens and Galanter (1957) have called *prothetic continua*, for in their terms stimulation is added to stimulation to give rise to a growth in sensation. Typical prothetic continua are those that are sometimes called intensive: sound intensity which gives rise to loudness, light intensity which gives rise to brightness, etc. In the model, aspect distance is additive when the aspect sets form a monotone sequence of sets (Theorem 6).

A somewhat more general notion, which includes monotone sequences of sets as a special case, is a sequence of sets generated in the following way from any three mutually disjoint sets of aspects, A, B, and C. The first stimulus in the array has the aspect set $A \cup B$. The second is obtained by removing some elements from B, but not from A, and adding some from C. The third is obtained by removing more from B, but not from A or those added from C, and by adding more from C, and so on. The ith aspect set is of the form $A \cup B_i \cup C_i$, where $B_i \subseteq B$ and $C_i \subseteq C$. The formal definition can be given as follows:

Definition 5. *A sequence of distinct sets $X_1, X_2, \ldots, X_n$ form a* linear array of sets *if there exist sets $A, B_1, \ldots, B_n, C_1, \ldots, C_n$, such that*

1. $A \cap B_1 = A \cap C_n = B_1 \cap C_n = \emptyset$,
2. for $i < j$, $B_j \subseteq B_i$, and $C_i \subseteq C_j$,
3. $X_i = A \cup B_i \cup C_i$.

In terms of the betweenness notion, the following seems to capture what we might mean by a linear array of stimuli.

Definition 6. *A sequence of distinct stimuli $x_1, x_2, \ldots, x_n$ form a* linear array of stimuli *if for all i, j, k such that $i < j < k$, then $x_i \,|x_j|\, x_k$.*

Theorem 9. *A sequence of stimuli form a linear array of stimuli if and only if their aspect sets form a linear array of sets.*

PROOF. Suppose, first, that the aspect sets form a linear array, and consider $i < j < k$. Because $B_k \subseteq B_j \subseteq B_i$ and $C_i \subseteq C_j \subseteq C_k$, we have

$$
\begin{aligned}
X_i \cap X_k &= (A \cup B_i \cup C_i) \cap (A \cup B_k \cup C_k) \\
&= A \cup B_k \cup C_i \\
&\subseteq A \cup B_j \cup C_j \\
&= X_j
\end{aligned}
$$

and

$$
\begin{aligned}
X_i \cup X_k &= (A \cup B_i \cup C_i) \cup (A \cup B_k \cup C_k) \\
&= A \cup B_i \cup C_k \\
&\supseteq A \cup B_j \cup C_j \\
&= X_j.
\end{aligned}
$$

Thus, by Def. 4, $x_i \,|x_j|\, x_k$.

Now, suppose that $x_1, x_2, \ldots, x_n$ form a linear array of stimuli. Define

$$
A = X_1 \cap X_n, \quad B_i = X_i \cap X_1 \cap \bar{A}, \quad \text{and} \quad C_i = X_i \cap X_n \cap \bar{A}.
$$

Observe that

$$
B_1 = X_1 \cap \bar{A} = X_1 - A \quad \text{and} \quad C_n = X_n \cap \bar{A} = X_n - A,
$$

and so

$$
B_i = X_i \cap B_1 \quad \text{and} \quad C_i = X_i \cap C_n.
$$

We show that these sets satisfy the conditions of Def. 5.

1. $A \cap B_1 = A \cap X_1 \cap \bar{A} = \emptyset$,
   $A \cap C_n = A \cap X_n \cap \bar{A} = \emptyset$,
   $B_1 \cap C_n = (X_1 \cap \bar{A}) \cap (X_n \cap \bar{A}) = X_1 \cap X_n \cap \bar{A} = A \cap \bar{A} = \emptyset$.

2. Suppose $i < j$. For $i = 1$, $B_1 \supseteq X_j \cap B_1 = B_j$. For $i > 1$,

$$B_j = X_1 \cap \bar{A} \cap X_j$$
$$= (X_1 \cap \bar{A}) \cap (X_1 \cap X_j)$$
$$\subseteq X_1 \cap \bar{A} \cap X_i$$
$$= B_i,$$

because, for $1 < i < j$, $x_1 \, |x_i| \, x_j$, which in turn implies $X_1 \cap X_j \subseteq X_i$. A similar argument shows that $C_i \subseteq C_j$.

3. Consider

$$A \cup B_1 \cup C_n = A \cup (X_1 - A) \cup (X_n - A)$$
$$= X_1 \cup X_n$$
$$\supseteq X_i,$$

because, for $1 < i < n$, $x_1 \, |x_i| \, x_n$. Thus

$$X_i = X_i \cap (A \cup B_1 \cup C_n)$$
$$= (X_i \cap A) \cup (X_i \cap B_1) \cup (X_i \cap C_n)$$
$$= A \cup B_i \cup C_i,$$

because $X_i \cap A \supseteq X_1 \cap X_n \cap X_1 \cap X_n = X_1 \cap X_n = A$.

Corollary. *If $x_1, x_2, \ldots, x_n$ form a linear array of stimuli, then for* $i < j < k$, $d(x_i, x_k) = d(x_i, x_j) + d(x_j, x_k)$.

PROOF. $X_i - X_k = (B_i - B_k)$ and $X_k - X_i = (C_k - C_i)$ by Def. 5, and so

$$d(x_i, x_k) = m(B_i - B_k) + m(C_k - C_i).$$

Because $B_i \supseteq B_j \supseteq B_k$ and $C_i \subseteq C_j \subseteq C_k$,

$$d(x_i, x_k) = m(B_i - B_j) + m(B_j - B_k) + m(C_k - C_j) + m(C_j - C_i)$$
$$= d(x_i, x_j) + d(x_j, x_k).$$

It is evident that a linear array of sets is a monotone sequence of sets if $B_1 = \emptyset$ and that any monotone sequence is a linear array.

The structure of a linear array of sets involves the substitution of some aspects for others to get from one stimulus to another, which seems to correspond to the characterization given by Stevens and Galanter (1957) of a metathetic continuum. Examples are pitch, hue, etc. One problem may exist in making these identifications between the empirically defined scales and those of the aspect model. If the model is correct, the class of metathetic continua includes the prothetic as a special case, or, put another way, the dividing line between the two classes of continua need not be sharp, although in nature it may be. Certain borderline arrays of sets simply may not have counterparts among the psychological continua.

In summary, then, Restle has shown that there is a way to assign distances to pairs of stimuli provided that one assumes that a measure over aspect sets exists and that Eq. 16 defines the distance. Because we have no experimental identification either of aspects or aspect measures, it is anyone's guess whether this notion of distance has any relation to those that have arisen in the response models.

5.2 The Embedding Problem

Assuming that we have stimulus parameters that satisfy the properties of a distance measure (Def. 1), the next question is whether they can be interpreted as distances in some familiar space. If so, that space may then be taken as a multidimensional representation of the stimuli, and, presumably, one would then attempt to discover the relations between coordinates of the space and physical attributes of the stimuli. Little has been done on this last problem.

Although several authors (Attneave, 1950; Galanter, 1956) have suggested that non-Euclidean spaces may be appropriate, little research has been reported on anything other than Euclidean embeddings. There are dangers in limiting ourselves to this familiar space. Because of sampling errors, it is never possible to demand that the estimated distances rigidly meet the mathematical criteria for a particular embedding; and because the statistical features have not been fully worked out, a good deal of judgment is involved in deciding whether a particular embedding is appropriate. But because our judgments are likely to be influenced by our presystematic intuitions about the nature of the space and the arrangement of the stimuli in it, there is some fear that we are simply perpetuating the errors of naïve Euclidean intuition.

The main theorems describing the conditions under which error-free distances can be embedded in an r-dimensional Euclidean vector space were first stated and proved by Young and Householder (1938).[5] Consider a set of n points a_i lying in an Euclidean vector space, the origin of which coincides with say, the nth point. Let α_i be the vector from the nth to the ith point and let α_{ij} be the component of α_i along the jth coordinate. The matrix $A = [\alpha_{ij}]$ has rank r equal to the dimensionality of the space spanned by the given points, which is also the rank of $B = AA'$. It is easy to see that the elements of B, b_{ij}, are the dot product of α_i with α_j, and so by elementary properties of vectors

$$b_{ij} = \tfrac{1}{2}[d^2(i, n) + d^2(j, n) - d^2(i, j)] = d(i, n)\, d(j, n) \cos \theta_{ijn}, \quad (25)$$

[5] To follow their arguments, it is necessary that the reader be familiar with certain basic ideas and results from matrix theory.

where the d's are distances between points. Thus we have proved the following theorem:

Theorem 10. *The dimensionality of a set of n points in an Euclidean vector space with distances $d(i, j)$ is equal to the rank of the $n - 1$ square matrix B whose elements are defined by Eq. 25.*

By Eq. 25, it is clear that B is symmetric, which with $B = AA'$ implies B is positive semidefinite. Conversely, suppose B is positive semi-definite; then we know that it has only nonnegative latent roots. Hence, by a well-known theorem, there exists an orthogonal matrix Q such that

$$B = QL^2Q' = (QL)(QL)',$$

where L is a diagonal matrix of the latent roots of B. If we set $A = QL$, then we have the coordinates of the vectors of the embedding, which proves the following theorem.

Theorem 11. *A necessary and sufficient condition that a set of points with distances $d(i, j) = d(j, i)$ be embeddable in an Euclidean vector space is that the matrix B whose elements are defined by Eq. 25 be positive semidefinite; the embedding is unique up to translations and rotations.*

The condition of positive semidefiniteness implies that the determinant of each of the 2×2 principal minors must be positive, which in turn is equivalent to the triangle inequality (Part 3 of Def. 1). The remaining requirements are, in essence, generalizations of this property.

For error-free data, it does not matter which stimulus is selected as the origin. To be sure, the matrix B depends upon this choice, but the ranks of all the B matrices are equal and the embedding is the same except for translations and rotations. With real data, however, matters are not so simple. Each choice yields a slightly different embedding. Torgerson (1952, 1958) suggested a procedure of locating the origin at the centroid of the several points and finding a single "average" B^* matrix, which can then be factored by the methods of factor analysis to find the matrix of components A^*. A discussion and description of some empirical uses of these methods with distances obtained by the similarity model of Sec. 1.2 is given by Torgerson (1958).

6. CONCLUSIONS

Whereas we tend to be theory-rich and data-poor in discrimination research, the reverse seems to be true in scaling. To be sure, when a close formal analogy exists between a scaling method and an identification experiment (e.g., between similarity scaling and discrimination), scaling theories are often easily constructed simply by reinterpreting the theory for the corresponding identification experiment; but when the analogies are not close, either the theories are not satisfactory, as in category scaling, or they are not well developed, as in magnitude estimation.

To some extent, the directness by which the scaling procedures yield scales has led some psychologists to the view that little in the way of theory is really needed; the methods seem to get at what one wants without any fancy theoretical indirection. In our view, however, these methods presuppose certain theoretical results that need to be explicitly stated and studied. Specifically, until adequate models are evolved, the following three classes of questions, which seem basic in all of psychophysics, are not likely to receive anything like final answers.

1. If we confine our attention to a single physical variable, such as sound energy, and to a single relevant judgment, such as loudness, just how many distinct sensory mechanisms are needed to account for the experimentally observed behavior? The models that we have studied suggest that at least two are needed. For example, in the choice model of Sec. 4.4 the two mechanisms are represented mathematically by the psychophysical scale and by the generalization function. The question is whether these two are sufficient to explain the results from, for example, recognition, discrimination, similarity, category, bisection, and magnitude estimation experiments or whether more mechanisms are needed. We shall probably not answer this question soon because of the complex way in which these functions combine with the ubiquitous, but poorly understood, biasing function to predict the subject's responses. In fact, we suspect that the answer will come only with the rather complete confirmation of an elaborate response theory. If so, then the problem of sensory measurement will have proved to be more analogous to, say, electrical measurement, which was perfected only as electrical theory itself became well understood, rather than to the measurement of length and weight, which was relatively well developed long before any adequate physical theories involving these quantities were stated.

2. In all of the theories in which stimulus functions (or parameters) are defined over pairs of stimuli—in the choice models for recognition, similarity, and magnitude estimation experiments and in the Thurstonian model for similarity experiments—what mathematical structure do they exhibit? Uniformly, we have assumed that they or a simple transformation of them behave like distances in an Euclidean space, but these assumptions have not been carefully tested. They need to be because psychological similarity simply may not be a distance notion.

3. In all psychophysical data there is considerable evidence that subjects bias their responses and that these biases can be affected by presentation

probabilities, payoffs, and other experimentally manipulable factors. In the theories that we have discussed in this and the two preceding chapters these biases are represented as a function defined over responses. The nature of this function—its dependence on things that we can manipulate experimentally—is not known. For some purposes this does not seem to matter critically, although it has some inherent interest to many people, but for other purposes, such as ascertaining the relation between the magnitude estimation scale and the underlying psychophysical function, knowledge of at least the general mathematical form of the biasing function seems to be essential if we are to avoid being misled about sensory scales.

References

Aczél, J. On mean values. *Bulletin of the American Mathematical Society*, 1948, **54**, 392–400.

Adams, E. W., & Messick, S. An axiomatic formulation and generalization of successive intervals scaling. *Psychometrika*, 1958, **23**, 355–368.

Attneave, F. Dimensions of similarity. *Amer. J. Psychol.*, 1950, **63**, 516–556.

Fernberger, S. W. On absolute and relative judgments in lifted weight experiments. *Amer. J. Psychol.*, 1931, **43**, 560–578.

Galanter, E. An axiomatic and experimental study of sensory order and measure. *Psychol. Rev.*, 1956, **63**, 16–28.

Galanter, E., & Messick, S. The relation between category and magnitude scales of loudness. *Psychol. Rev.*, 1961, **68**, 363–372.

Garner, W. R. Advantages of the discriminability criteria for a loudness scale. *J. acoust. Soc. Amer.*, 1958, **30**, 1005–1012.

Helm, C., Messick, S., & Tucker, L. *Psychophysical law and scaling models.* Princeton, N.J.: Educational Testing Service Research Bulletin, 59–1, 1959.

Herrnstein, R. J., & van Sommers, P. Method for sensory scaling with animals. *Science*, 1962, **135**, 40–41.

Luce, R. D. On the possible psychophysical laws. *Psychol. Rev.*, 1959, **66**, 81–95.

Luce, R. D. A choice theory analysis of similarity judgments. *Psychometrika*, 1961, **26**, 151–163.

McGill, W. J. The slope of the loudness function: A puzzle. In H. Gulliksen & S. Messick (Eds.), *Psychological scaling: theory and application.* New York: Wiley, 1960. Pp. 67–81.

Messick, S., & Abelson, R. P. The additive constant problem in multidimensional scaling. *Psychometrika*, 1956, **21**, 1–17.

Michels, W. C., & Doser, Beatrice T. Rating scale method for comparative loudness measurements. *J. acoust. Soc. Amer.*, 1955, **27**, 1173–1180.

Parducci, A. Incidental learning of stimulus frequencies in the establishment of judgment scales. *J. exp. Psychol.*, 1956, **52**, 112–118.

Pfanzagl, J. *Die axiomatischen Grundlagen einer allgemeinen Theorie des Messens.* Schrift. d. Stat. Inst. d. Univ. Wien, Neue Folge Nr. 1, 1959.(a)

Pfanzagl, J. A general theory of measurement: applications to utility. *Naval Research Logistics Quarterly*, 1959, **6**, 283–294.(b)

Plateau, M. H. Sur la mesure des sensations physique, et sur la loi qui lie l'intensité de ces sensations a l'intensité de la cause excitante. *Bull. acad. roy. Belg.*, 1872, **33**, 376–388.

Restle, F. A metric and an ordering on sets. *Psychometrika*, 1959, **24**, 207–220.

Rosner, B. S. Psychophysics and neurophysiology. In S. Koch (Ed.), *Psychology: A study of a science*. Vol. 4. New York: McGraw-Hill, 1961. Pp. 280–333.

Saffir, M. A comparative study of scales constructed by three psychophysical methods. *Psychometrika*, 1937, **2**, 179–198.

Steinberg, J. C., & Gardner, M. B. The dependence of hearing impairment on sound intensity. *J. acoust. Soc. Amer.*, 1937, **9**, 11–23.

Stevens, J. C. Stimulus spacing and the judgment of loudness. *J. exp. Psychol.*, 1958, **56**, 246–250.

Stevens, S. S. *Handbook of Experimental Psychology*. New York: Wiley, 1951.

Stevens, S. S. On the psychophysical law. *Psychol. Rev.*, 1957, **64**, 153–181.

Stevens. S. S. Problems and methods of psychophysics. *Psychol. Bull.*, 1958, **54**, 177–196.(a)

Stevens, S. S. Some similarities between hearing and seeing. *Laryngoscope*, 1958, **68**, 508–527.(b)

Stevens, S. S. Cross-modality validation of subjective scales for loudness, vibration, and electric shock. *J. exp. Psychol.*, 1959, **57**, 201–209.

Stevens, S. S. The psychophysics of sensory function. *Amer. Sc.*, 1960, **48**, 226–253.

Stevens, S. S. To honor Fechner and repeal his law. *Science*, 1961, **133**, 80–86.(a)

Stevens, S. S. The psychophysics of sensory function. In W. A. Rosenblith (Ed.), *Sensory Communication*. New York: Wiley, 1961. Pp. 1–33.(b)

Stevens, S. S., & Galanter, E. Ratio scales and category scales for a dozen perceptual continua. *J. exp. Psychol.*, 1957, **54**, 377–411.

Titchener, E. H. *Experimental Psychology*. Vol. II, Part II (Instructor's Manual). New York: Macmillan, 1905.

Torgerson, W. S. Multidimensional scaling: I. Theory and method. *Psychometrika*, 1952, **17**, 401–409.

Torgerson, W. S. A law of categorical judgment. In L. H. Clark (Ed.), *Consumer Behavior*. Washington Square: New York Univ. Press, 1954. Pp. 92–93.

Torgerson, W. S. *Theory and methods of scaling*. New York: Wiley, 1958.

Torgerson, W. S. *Distances and ratios in psychophysical scaling*. Massachusetts Institute of Technology, Lincoln Laboratory Report, 48G–0014, 1960.(a)

Torgerson, W. S. Quantitative judgment scales. In H. Gulliksen and S. Messick (Eds.), *Psychological scaling*. New York: Wiley, 1960.(b)

Wever, E. G., & Zener, K. E. The method of absolute judgment in psychophysics. *Psychol. Rev.*, 1928, **35**, 466–493.

Young, G., & Householder, A. S. Discussion of a set of points in terms of their mutual distances. *Psychometrika*, 1938, **3**, 331–333.

6

Stochastic Latency Mechanisms[1]

William J. McGill

Columbia University

1. *This research was supported in part by the United States Air Force under Contract No. AF 33 (616)-6100 with Aero-Medical Laboratory, Directorate of Research, Wright Air Development Center, Wright-Patterson Air Force Base, Ohio.*

Contents

Stochastic Latency Mechanisms

No student of behavior needs to be reminded that the route leading from stimulus to response is usually uncertain and occasionally downright mysterious. This air of mystery is no less true of the time intervals between stimulus and response.

Stimuli vanish into a network of sensory apparatus and central processing mechanisms, and responses subsequently emerge from effector systems, often without a clear indication of how the message got through. Something of the complexity of this network is indicated by the fact that it takes time for messages to pass through it and most especially by the fact that the passage times display unpredictable variability. Simple reflexes have rather stable passage times, whereas reaction times (for example) vary over a wide range, suggesting the activity of a very intricate and "noisy" system.

Random fluctuations in latency are certainly not going to be understood merely by assuming that they are normally distributed. We must first clarify what we mean by random fluctuations *in time*, and, in order to do that, we must construct statistical mechanisms that are built specifically to operate in time. In this chapter we shall review a number of such mechanisms. They may be thought of as generating a wealth of important data encountered in the psychological literature. The data include latency effects found in the responses of single nerve fibers, reaction times, decision times, and even the response effects produced by reinforcement schedules. Generally speaking, this material consists of a series of time intervals in which nothing observable happens. The intervals are called latent periods and are so named because only their beginnings and endings are identifiable. The terminal event is usually a response, whereas the initiating event is either a stimulus or a prior response. These boundaries are said to straddle a statistical mechanism that grinds away during the silent interval. With repeated activity, the mechanism builds up its characteristic probability distribution, and, ideally, we hope that the shape of the distribution will be a kind of signature that will help us to identify the underlying process. As we shall see, there are real difficulties with such detective work, but the simple objective furnishes a good place to begin.

A probability mechanism representing a latency process in continuous time will be designated as $F(t)$. Specifically, the function F evaluated at time t gives the probability that a latency is equal to or less than t. For most purposes the derivative of $F(t)$ affords all the information we desire to have, that is, the instantaneous behavior of the mechanism. The derivative form is called the probability density function (sometimes just the "density function" or the "frequency function") and is indicated by $f(t)$. There is no reason for suspecting the continuity of $f(t)$ in any of the distributions we shall consider. Consequently our latency mechanisms are discussed interchangeably in the cumulative form $F(t)$ and in the probability density form $f(t)$. The term "distribution" is used simply to denote the variable behavior of the mechanism. It is applied indiscriminately to any of the ways in which the mechanism can be represented.

The probability that a latency lies between any two points in time, t_0 and t_1, is given either by $F(t_1) - F(t_0)$ or by the integral of $f(t)$ between these limits. An observed relative frequency is assumed to estimate this probability. We shall try to link relative frequencies in our data to stochastic mechanisms that generate particular forms for $f(t)$.

1. RANDOM DELAYS

1.1 Stochastic Latencies

The simplest probability mechanism governing response latencies is one that sets up the response with constant probability at any instant. This restriction leads to an "exponential" distribution of latencies (or inter-response times), a distribution that has been studied extensively because of its importance in physics and engineering. For example, the exponential distribution gives an excellent account of the varying time intervals between successive electrons arriving at the plate of an electron tube (Rice, 1944). This is only one of many related phenomena. A number of interesting physical examples are reviewed in detail in Feller (1957), and in Bharucha-Reid (1960).

1.2 Geometric Distribution

To see how such an elementary probability mechanism might work, imagine a device that makes two responses, A and $\bar{A}$, and that one or the other occurs in sequence. The interval between A responses may then be expressed as a sequence consisting of a run of $\bar{A}$ responses. It is evident that if every response has the same probability p of being an A response, each response in the run will have probability $1 - p = q$. Identify the length of the run as k and call its probability $p(k)$. Assuming independence, we find

$$p(0) = p,$$
$$p(1) = qp,$$
$$p(2) = q^2p,$$

$$\vdots$$

$$p(k) = q^k p. \tag{1}$$

It is easily shown that these probabilities sum to 1 over all possible run lengths:

$$\sum_{k=0}^{\infty} p(k) = p \sum_{k=0}^{\infty} q^k$$

$$= \frac{p}{1-q}$$

$$= 1.$$

The shape of the distribution can be deduced by studying the behavior of the ratio $p(k+1)/p(k)$. This ratio always has the value q and is independent of k. Consequently each successive ordinate $p(k+1)$ is a fraction of the one immediately before it, and the ordinates drop away regularly from a value of p at a run length of zero to a value of zero in the limit as the run of $\bar{A}$ responses approaches infinity. The distribution is called geometric because of this ratio property. It is the simplest type of latency mechanism exhibiting a constant probability of response during the latent period.

There is no contradiction in saying that the response probability remains constant over all values of k, even though the ordinates of the probability distribution show a regular decay as k increases. The decay simply reflects the difficulty of getting long runs of $\bar{A}$ responses. Our basic assumption is that the probability of response A at any point is equal to p, and this fact can be extracted from Eq. 1 by asking for the conditional probability of response A after an arbitrary delay. In other words, we want to find $p(A \mid j)$, the probability of response A, given that a delay consisting of j successive $\bar{A}$ responses has already occurred. The conditional probability is defined as follows:

$$p(A \mid j) = \frac{p(j)}{\sum_{k=j}^{\infty} p(k)}. \tag{2}$$

The numerator was given in Eq. 1 and the denominator is easily shown to be equal to q^j. Consequently we find that

$$p(A \mid j) = p.$$

The conditional probability is fixed and independent of j.

Our development thus far is closely patterned after Estes (1950), who converted the geometric distribution into a latency mechanism by assuming that all $\bar{A}$ responses have the same duration.

1.3 Moment Generating Functions

Let us consider an analogous latency mechanism that operates over continuous time instead of over discrete trials. For this purpose we introduce a transformation that is often used in probability theory. The transformation is called a moment generating function and its chief advantage is that it enables us to simplify proofs that are otherwise complicated. Excellent discussions of the use of such functions can be found in Mood (1950) and Hoel (1954).

The moment generating function of a probability distribution is defined as

$$M_k(\theta) = \sum_{k=0}^{\infty} e^{\theta k} \, p(k), \tag{3}$$

when the distribution is discrete, and

$$M_t(\theta) = \int_0^{\infty} e^{\theta t} f(t) \, dt, \tag{3a}$$

when the distribution is continuous.

$M_t(\theta)$ is called the moment generating function or m.g.f. of $f(t)$. Evaluating the integral (or the sum) leads to an expression that now gives us a new way to identify a latency mechanism. The variable θ is simply a dummy introduced for the purpose of generating moments. Equation 3a obviously works, for when $e^{\theta t}$ is expanded in series the coefficient of $\theta^r/r!$ is the rth raw moment of the distribution,[2] but the real importance of Eq. 3a does not come from the fact that it can be used to calculate moments. The important thing is that $M_t(\theta)$ describes the distribution fully as well as $f(t)$ or $F(t)$. The following three theorems about moment generating functions suggest how they are used. The first is adapted from Cramér (1946, p. 176). The other two are proved in Hoel (1954).

---

[2] The rth raw moment of $f(t)$ is generally symbolized by μ_r' and is defined as

$$\mu_r' = \int_0^{\infty} t^r f(t) \, dt.$$

If the distribution has one or more infinite moments, it will not have a moment generating function. Instances of this sort are not common among latency distributions, but they do occur; see, for instance, Eq. 58.

Theorem I. *If a continuous latency distribution $f(t)$ has a m.g.f. $M_t(\theta)$, and a second continuous latency distribution $g(t)$ has the same m.g.f., then $g(t) \equiv f(t)$.*

Theorem 2. *If $f(x)$ and $f(y)$ are two probability density functions with moment generating functions, $M_x(\theta)$ and $M_y(\theta)$, respectively, the m.g.f. of $x + y$ is $M_x(\theta) \cdot M_y(\theta)$, provided that x and y are independent.*

Theorem 3. *If a probability density function $f(x)$ has a m.g.f. $M_x(\theta)$, a linear function of x, $ax + b$, has a m.g.f. given by $M_{ax+b}(\theta) = e^{\theta b} \cdot M_x(a\theta)$.*

The first theorem states that under broad conditions a latency distribution is uniquely determined by its m.g.f. when there is one. The theorem is stated more generally by Wilks (1943). It is based on the properties of the Laplace transform which the moment generating function resembles closely. The essential point about the theorem is that we can make a table of moment generating functions corresponding to important frequency functions. Then if we operate on a particular m.g.f., the effect of the operation can be studied immediately by looking up the new frequency function corresponding to the changed moment generating function.

Theorem 2 furnishes an example of the practical usefulness of this procedure. Suppose that t_1 and t_2 are two components of the total latency and we want to find the distribution of their sum t. The direct approach requires us to evaluate a "convolution" integral

$$f(t) = \int_0^t f(t_1) f(t - t_1) \, dt_1.$$

Often this is not easy to do. On the other hand, generating functions enable us to short circuit the whole process. We simply write

$$M_t(\theta) = M_{t_1}(\theta) \, M_{t_2}(\theta).$$

When the m.g.f.'s for t_1 and t_2 are substituted, their product forms a new m.g.f. The corresponding $f(t)$ may then be obtained from our table of function pairs and the distribution of the sum has been found. In practice, the efficiency of the whole procedure depends on the existence of a good table, but there are many excellent tables of the Laplace transform that will serve our need with only minor modifications. See, for example, the table of the Laplace transform in Churchill (1944).

1.4 Exponential Limit of the Geometric Distribution

Now let us use the m.g.f. of the geometric distribution to derive a latency mechanism in continuous time. Suppose that each response or event in the latent period takes a brief interval of time Δt. Evidently the probability p will be a function of Δt, since, as the latter decreases, the number of Δt intervals in a given latent period must increase, and the net effect is equivalent to decreasing the probability of the response that terminates the latent period. This kind of exchange is embodied in the restriction

$$\frac{p}{\Delta t} \to \lambda, \tag{4}$$

where λ is a constant (the *time* constant) and the limit holds as Δt approaches zero.

We begin by computing the m.g.f. of the geometric distribution. Substituting Eq. 1 for $p(k)$ and summing the series on the right of Eq. 3 yields

$$M_k(\theta) = \frac{p}{1 - qe^\theta}, \tag{3b}$$

which is the desired m.g.f.

Change now to a new variable $t = k \, \Delta t$. Theorem 3 tells us that the new m.g.f. will be

$$M_t(\theta) = \frac{p}{1 - qe^{\theta \Delta t}}.$$

Now substitute the limiting value in Eq. 4 for p and note that as Δt approaches zero we can write $1 + \theta \, \Delta t$ for $e^{\theta \Delta t}$. We are led to the following simple expression for $M_t(\theta)$:

$$\lim_{\Delta t \to 0} M_t(\theta) = \frac{\lambda \, \Delta t}{1 - (1 - \lambda \, \Delta t + \theta \, \Delta t)}$$

in which the term involving Δt^2 is neglected. We have, finally,

$$\lim_{\Delta t \to 0} M_t(\theta) = \frac{\lambda}{\lambda - \theta}, \tag{5}$$

and this is a well-known moment generating function. It is in fact the m.g.f. of the exponential distribution

$$f(t) = \lambda e^{-\lambda t}, \tag{6}$$

as we can easily demonstrate by evaluating

$$M_t(\theta) = \int_0^\infty e^{\theta t} f(t) \, dt$$

$$= \lambda \int_0^\infty e^{-(\lambda - \theta)t} \, dt$$

$$= \frac{\lambda}{\lambda - \theta}.$$

In view of Theorem 1, we have shown that the geometric distribution has a continuous approximation that is given by the exponential distribution in Eq. 6. A direct proof of this approximation can be found in Feller (1950, pp. 218–221) and also in Bush and Mosteller (1955, pp. 315–316).

1.5 Typical Data

Examples that appear to reflect the constant (conditional) probability mechanism can be found at several places in the behavioral literature, although there are not nearly so many as might be expected. It is known, for instance, that Eq. 6 describes interresponse times obtained early in operant conditioning with certain types of reinforcement schedules. Supporting data have been reported by Mueller (1950), Anger (1956), and Hearst (1956). Figure 1, taken from Mueller's paper, presents a distribution of intervals based on 238 responses made by a rat during a 20-minute session in a Skinner box with reinforcement at three-minute intervals. The response was an operant bar-press, and latency was measured from the end of one bar-press to the beginning of the next. The ordinate of the smooth curve in Fig. 1 is not in the form of Eq. 6. It is the

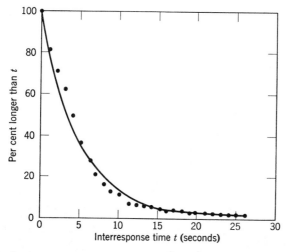

Fig. 1. Distribution of interresponse times obtained when a rat is conditioned to press a bar for reinforcements delivered at three-minute intervals. This distribution was generated during a single 20-minute session early in conditioning and is based on a total of 238 responses. The exponential curve drawn through the data is the expected behavior of a latency mechanism with constant response probability in time. Adapted from Mueller (1950).

area in the tail of the distribution beyond an arbitrary point t_0 and is easily derived from Eq. 6:

$$1 - F(t_0) = \lambda \int_{t_0}^{\infty} e^{-\lambda t}\, dt$$

$$= e^{-\lambda t_0}. \tag{7}$$

It should be emphasized that the exponential distribution is not commonly found for interresponse times during the latter stages of conditioning (see Anger, 1956). We shall return to this problem later.

Records of spontaneously active single nerve fibers sometimes show the exponential distribution. Figure 2 illustrates data from an experiment by Hunt and Kuno (1959) on background spontaneous activity of a single spinal interneurone in the cat. The smooth curve in Fig. 2 is the exponential density function (Eq. 6).

The examples cited here suggest that some kind of constant probability

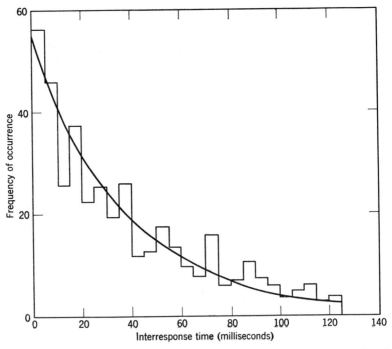

Fig. 2. Frequency distribution of interresponse times in the spontaneous activity of a single spinal interneurone. The distribution consists of 391 intervals recorded by a micropipette inserted in the spinal cord of a cat. Mean interresponse time is 35.6 milliseconds and the exponential density function (heavy line) is fitted to this parameter. Adapted from Hunt & Kuno (1959, p. 366).

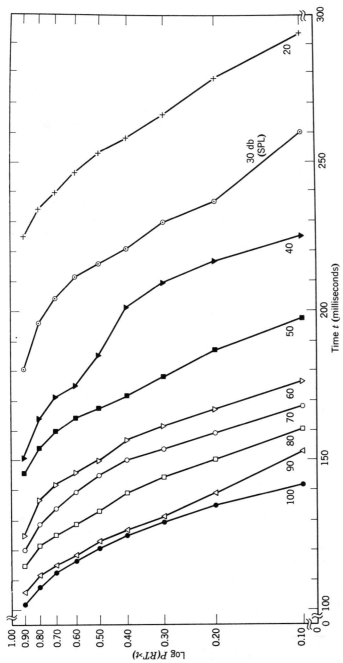

Fig. 3. Distributions of reaction times in response to the onset of a 1000-cps tone. There are 60 *RT*'s in each distribution, and the set of curves is produced by increasing intensity in 10-db steps from 20-db sound pressure level to 100 db. All *RT*'s were obtained from one listener during three experimental sessions (one hour long), following several hours of preliminary training. Points shown are interpolated at the decile points of each distribution. Adapted from McGill (1961).

mechanism is operating in control of the latencies. But the bulk of the behavioral data on latency and interresponse times exhibit systematic departures from constant probability. Figure 3, for instance, is taken from work on reaction time done by McGill (1961). Reaction times were obtained by varying the intensity of a 1000-cps tone in 10-db steps from 20-db sound pressure level to 100 db. After an initial practice period, these intensities were presented repeatedly in random permutations until a frequency distribution consisting of 60 responses was built up at each intensity. The data are displayed as the logarithm of Eq. 7. In this form the latency mechanism based on constant probability is linear with a negative slope equal to the time constant λ. The reaction times show systematic departures from linearity in the early stages of each distribution.

Such deviations are typical of many empirical latency distributions; see, for example, Felsinger, Gladstone, Yamaguchi, & Hull (1947). Early curvature in a latency distribution suggests among other things the possibility of a mechanism in which a series of latencies is strung together, with only the beginning and end of the series under observation.

2. SERIES LATENCY MECHANISMS

2.1 Fixed Time Constants: The Gamma Distribution

The first series latency mechanism we consider is a sequence of exponential random delays all with the same time constant. Specifically, it is assumed that the response latency t can be broken down into, let us say, n steps, where

$$t = \sum_{k=1}^{n} t_k,$$

and each t_k is an independent random variable. The timing of the latency begins with the beginning of the first random delay and ends with the end of the nth delay. In general, the intervening steps are not observable. The quantity n is thus undefined by experimental operations and is treated as a parameter.

If the distribution of t_k follows Eq. 6,

$$f(t_k) = \lambda e^{-\lambda t_k},$$

the distribution of t will be the sum of n such random quantities. Following Theorem 2, we can at once write down its m.g.f.:

$$M_t(\theta) = \left(1 - \frac{\theta}{\lambda}\right)^{-n}. \tag{8}$$

This also happens to be a well-known m.g.f. It comes from the gamma distribution

$$f(t) = \frac{\lambda^n}{(n-1)!}\, t^{n-1}\, e^{-\lambda t}, \tag{9}$$

in which λ and n are both parameters. This is proved by writing down the m.g.f. of Eq. 9:

$$M_t(\theta) = \int_0^\infty \frac{\lambda^n}{(n-1)!}\, t^{n-1}\, e^{-(\lambda-\theta)t}\, dt.$$

We see immediately that

$$M_t(\theta) = \frac{\lambda^n}{(\lambda-\theta)^n} \int_0^\infty \frac{1}{(n-1)!}\, u^{n-1}\, e^{-u}\, du.$$

The integral on the right-hand side of the equation is equal to 1. Consequently

$$M_t(\theta) = \left(1 - \frac{\theta}{\lambda}\right)^{-n}$$

as claimed, and the frequency function of the n-step series latency mechanism is the gamma distribution given by Eq. 9. The same gamma distribution describes the time up to the nth response in a chain of observable interresponse times. Moreover, since the last of the n responses terminates the sequence, the last response may be said to occur in a short interval dt at the end of the total latency. This means that the other $n-1$ responses are distributed at random *anywhere* in an interval that is $t - dt$ in length. Hence the distribution of the time up to the nth response, that is, Eq. 9, may be rewritten in probability form as follows:

$$f(t)\, dt = \left[\frac{(\lambda t)^{n-1}\, e^{-\lambda t}}{(n-1)!}\right] (\lambda\, dt). \tag{9a}$$

The term $\lambda\, dt$ is the probability that the last response is in the interval dt at the very end of the latency. This fact follows from the limit in Eq. 4. Accordingly (see Feller, 1950, p. 221), the probability of $n-1$ responses in a fixed time interval of length t, given a random sequence of interresponse times, must be

$$p(n-1;\lambda t) = \frac{(\lambda t)^{n-1}\, e^{-\lambda t}}{(n-1)!}. \tag{10}$$

Equation 10 is distributed over n. This, of course, is the Poisson distribution. It follows that Eqs. 6, 9, and 10 furnish three different perspectives on the same random process, that is, one consisting of a sequence of pulselike responses separated by latent periods of varying length in which each response has constant probability in time.

Returning now to series mechanisms in which intervening responses (called here subresponses) are not observable, let us consider a case suggested by our treatment of the geometric distribution Eq. 1. We showed that the latter can be converted into a latency mechanism by giving each response a constant duration, but there are other possibilities. Suppose, for instance, each element in the sequence of $\bar{A}$ responses terminated by a single A response is itself a random time variable distributed according to Eq. 6.

If this is difficult to visualize, imagine an urn containing balls labeled A and $\bar{A}$. Suppose the urn is placed in a dimly lighted corner, and let the labels be very small so that they are difficult to find and read. Now assume that this reading time is exponentially distributed for any given ball. We draw balls one by one (with replacement) and check each one until we find the first one labeled A. Evidently the number of balls drawn will have a geometric distribution. We want to find the distribution of the time required to identify the correct ball. The total latency, timed from the beginning of the first subresponse to the end of the A response, is given by

$$t_k = \sum_{j=0}^{k} t_j,$$

where k is the number of $\bar{A}$ responses in the run and has a geometric distribution. The duration of each subresponse and the number of subresponses are *both* random variables. To find the m.g.f. of t, we first note that for any given number k of $\bar{A}$ responses the moment generating function of t_k is obtained from the gamma distribution

$$M_{t_k}(\theta) = \left(\frac{1}{1 - \theta/\lambda}\right)^{k+1}. \tag{8a}$$

This m.g.f. is conditional on the occurrence of a particular value of k, that is, a particular sequence of $\bar{A}$ responses, which has a geometric distribution. Accordingly the m.g.f. of t is obtained by taking each of these generating functions, weighting it by the probability of the sequence determining it, and computing the expectation. We find

$$M_t(\theta) = \sum_{k=0}^{\infty} pq^k \left(\frac{1}{1 - \theta/\lambda}\right)^{k+1}$$

$$= \frac{p}{1 - \theta/\lambda} \sum_{k=0}^{\infty} \left(\frac{q}{1 - \theta/\lambda}\right)^k.$$

For an appropriate choice of θ, the series on the right converges. Hence

$$M_t(\theta) = \left(\frac{p}{1 - \theta/\lambda}\right)\left(\frac{1}{1 - \dfrac{q}{1 - \theta/\lambda}}\right)$$

$$= \frac{1}{1 - \theta/\lambda p} \,. \tag{11}$$

The distribution of t is still exponential, and apparently it is insensitive to the random durations of its subresponse components. This follows because the shape of the distribution is the same as the one obtained when the durations of subresponses were assumed constant. Only the time constant is affected. This is a very important point because it implies an uncertainty principle governing attempts to work backward from the shape of a distribution of latencies to a latency mechanism. Two latency mechanisms differing considerably in complexity may in fact lead to the same frequency function. Only the parameters will differ. We must have a rough idea of the underlying steps and must be prepared to deduce parameters if we wish to specify a latency mechanism uniquely.

Bush and Mosteller (1955) used the mechanism just described (random subresponse durations and a geometric distribution of subresponses) in order to analyze a group of latency distributions obtained by Weinstock (1954) in a learning experiment. The data were taken from observations of the times used by a rat in running a straight alley from the starting box to a fixed point along the alley. In these circumstances Bush and Mosteller assumed that n responses of type A, that is, goal-directed responses, had to occur in order to terminate the latent period. Building from Eq. 11, we see that the m.g.f. of the measured latency must be

$$M_t(\theta) = \left(1 - \frac{\theta}{\lambda p}\right)^{-n}, \tag{12}$$

and the latencies must have a gamma distribution. The terms n, λ, and p are parameters. However, n is fixed by the position of the criterion point along the alley at which the latency is determined, and once determined for any rat it must be the same for all rats. Moreover, the parameter p is the probability of an A response. Consequently, it can be computed from an appropriate model of the learning process. (Bush and Mosteller used their linear model.) Lastly, λ is a personal parameter, determined separately for each rat. It estimates the speed of the rat's reactions and is the only free parameter in Eq. 12. Evidently Bush and Mosteller *do* attempt to provide the information necessary to specify the latency mechanism. This outline does not do full justice to the detail of their

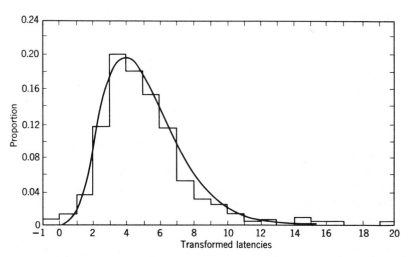

Fig. 4. Pooled latencies obtained on the last 40 trials of acquisition as white rats learned to run down an alley; data from 23 rats. The individual distributions were equated by estimating a fixed delay and a time constant separately for each rat. Latencies were then converted to a common distribution with a delay of zero and a time constant of unity. (Negative latencies apparently are due to sampling errors.) The theoretical curve is a gamma distribution with $n = 5$. Total number of learning trials was 108 and the probability of a goal directed response on these last 40 trials was estimated to be p = 1. Adapted from Bush & Mosteller (1955, p. 323).

analysis, but the essential points are preserved; and Fig. 4 demonstrates that the gamma distribution gives an excellent account of the data. This particular mechanism is especially interesting because Bush and Mosteller made the effort to deduce each parameter and to give it experimental meaning. As a result, they were able to work backward from the data to a unique latency mechanism.

2.2 Variable Time Constants

Now consider a series latency mechanism in which the number of subresponses is fixed but the time constants are not identical. In particular, assume that the response latency has two components,

$$t = t_1 + t_2,$$

where t_1 and t_2 are random delays associated with the two components and

$$f(t_1) = \beta e^{-\beta t_1},$$
$$f(t_2) = \alpha e^{-\alpha t_2}.$$

It will be assumed that $E(t_2) > E(t_1)$ and consequently $\beta > \alpha$. We are considering latencies in which the process can be broken down into something like a reaction time (short latency), followed by a decision time (long latency), although which comes first is unimportant. We can write

$$M_t(\theta) = \frac{\alpha\beta}{(\alpha - \theta)(\beta - \theta)}. \tag{13}$$

The m.g.f. in Eq. 13 can then be manipulated into the following form:

$$M_t(\theta) = \frac{\alpha\beta}{\beta - \alpha} \left(\frac{1}{\alpha - \theta} - \frac{1}{\beta - \theta} \right),$$

$$= \frac{\alpha\beta}{\beta - \alpha} \int_0^\infty [e^{-(\alpha-\theta)t} - e^{-(\beta-\theta)t}] \, dt.$$

Now separate out $e^{\theta t}$ in the integral:

$$M_t(\theta) = \int_0^\infty e^{\theta t} \left[\frac{\alpha\beta}{\beta - \alpha} (e^{-\alpha t} - e^{-\beta t}) \right] dt.$$

The expression in brackets must then be $f(t)$, and we have shown that in the case of the two-step series mechanism with variable time constants

$$f(t) = \frac{\alpha\beta}{\beta - \alpha} (e^{-\alpha t} - e^{-\beta t}). \tag{14}$$

The derivation of Eq. 14 shows that a frequency function can occasionally be plucked directly from its moment generating function. More typically, the form of the frequency function is found either by searching for one that leads to the correct m.g.f. or by looking up the m.g.f. (in this case Eq. 13) in a table of the Laplace transform. There are no special rules concerning which of these procedures is best to follow. Deriving the m.g.f. and demonstrating that a given frequency function produces it is intellectually more satisfying. Looking the result up in a table is easier. The problem is something like trying to decide whether to attempt to integrate an expression or to look up the integral.

The cumulative form of Eq. 14 for any latency t is easily shown to be

$$1 - F(t) = \left(\frac{1}{\beta - \alpha} \right) (\beta e^{-\alpha t} - \alpha e^{-\beta t}). \tag{15}$$

Figure 5 illustrates four different distributions of search times (McGill, 1960) in which the smooth curves are plots of Eq. 15. In this instance

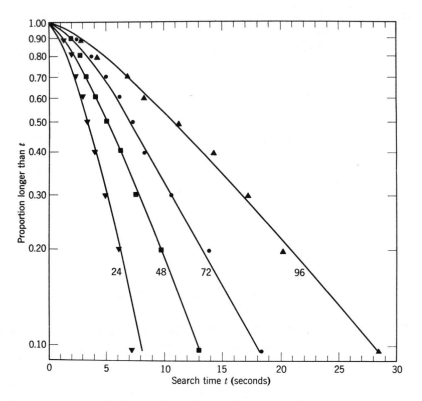

Fig. 5. Search time distributions for small three-digit numbers located randomly among 24, 48, 72, or 96 alternatives on an 18-in. white square. Target numbers were selected with equal probability from the alternatives on each square. Data are based on four searches per stimulus card by each of 25 subjects (total of 100 search times per distribution). The decile points of each distribution are compared with a curve obtained from a two-step series latency mechanism (Eq. 15 in the text). Adapted from McGill (1960).

human subjects searched through sets of three-digit numbers randomly arranged on an 18-in. white square in order to locate a particular target number. The four distributions illustrate search times when 24, 48, 72, and 96 alternatives were on the square.

These distributions exhibit the early curvature described in Sec. 1.5. It is attributed by McGill to an initial reaction time that precedes active searching. Both the curvature and the general appearance of Eq. 15 can be analyzed as follows:

$$\log [1 - F(t)] = -\log \left(1 - \frac{\alpha}{\beta}\right) - \alpha t + \log \left[1 - \frac{\alpha}{\beta e^{(\beta - \alpha)t}}\right].$$

The ratio α/β is small in view of our assumptions. Consequently, we can expand the logs in series and substitute the first term as an approximation for each logarithm. We find

$$\log\left[1 - F(t)\right] \simeq \frac{\alpha}{\beta} - \alpha t - \frac{\alpha}{\beta e^{(\beta-\alpha)t}}. \tag{15a}$$

As t increases, the exponential quantity goes out rapidly and produces a second approximation for large t:

$$\log\left[1 - F(t)\right] \simeq -\alpha\left(t - \frac{1}{\beta}\right). \tag{15b}$$

Equation 15b is plausible if we think of the subresponse t_1 as an initial brief delay, the variability of which is negligible in the relatively long time spent in the second stage of the process. The approximation is merely an exponential distribution displaced from the origin by a constant. The slope of the linear part of the distributions in Fig. 5 is $-\alpha$ and the displacement constant is the mean latency of t_1, namely $1/\beta$. The parameters of the four distributions were estimated in this way.

2.3 Reaction Time

The development in Sec. 2.1 leading to the gamma distribution offers an interesting way to conceptualize reaction times. The idea is expounded in detail by Restle (1961) and is alluded to here as the neural series hypothesis.

Simple reaction times are obtained by instructing a subject to respond (generally by lifting his finger from a response key) as soon as he detects a stimulus; a brief light flash or a brief pure tone, for example. The time between the onset of the stimulus and the point at which the subject breaks the circuit is recorded by driving a fast timer (such as an electronic digital counter) during the latent period. Typical distributions are illustrated in Fig. 3.

The basic point of the neural series hypothesis is that the stimulus is viewed as setting off an extended sequence of neural events, each of which is taken to be a random delay with the same time constant. Reaction times should then have a gamma distribution (Eq. 9) in which the parameter n is the length of the series.

This hypothesis is not considered seriously here. In the first place it assigns all the delays to the route through the nervous system, when in fact much of the latent period appears to be consumed in making the response, that is, in moving the finger. The movement sequence might be viewed as part of the series except for the fact that the muscle contractions form a slow-acting system in comparison with neural firing. These differences would then make any computation of the number of steps in the series somewhat artificial. For example, Restle has attempted to calculate n by inserting Chocholle's (1940) data on auditory reaction times into the expected relation between mean and standard deviation in a gamma distribution. The reader is invited to repeat this interesting little exercise by consulting Restle (1961, pp. 164–172); it will not be reproduced here. In any event, the calculation based on Chocholle's data leads to a figure of $n = 100$ for the number of steps in the neural series. The number is evidently suspect, for if the series were anywhere near this length the central limit theorem would force a gamma distribution to approximate normality, and the observed distributions are obviously nonnormal. Furthermore, since the number of steps in the neural sequence is assumed to be fixed, only the time constant of the gamma distribution is left free to change with stimulus intensity. Reaction time distributions ought then to fan out from a common origin, as illustrated in Fig. 5, whereas in fact the distributions seem to march away from their origin in an entirely different manner. This point is made obvious by comparing Fig. 3 with Fig. 5.

Alternatives to the neural series hypothesis have been proposed by Christie and Luce (1956), Audley (1960), and Mervyn Stone (1960). Each of these papers is addressed to the question of the time required to decide between two or more alternatives, that is, to choice reaction times, but there is an implied application to simple reaction times that we shall now make explicit.

Stone assumes that a reaction time has three components: a neural passage time or input time, a movement time, and a decision time. The character of the decision time obviously depends on the properties of the stimulus. Christie and Luce propose very nearly the same model, whereas Audley considers a specific form of the decision process. The essential similarity of the three papers is their reliance on a decision mechanism for detecting the stimulus.

Referring now to Fig. 3, we observe that there is a fixed dead time roughly 100 ms in duration that cannot be overcome by increasing stimulus intensity. This is the so-called "irreducible minimum" of reaction times (see Woodworth & Schlosberg, 1954, pp. 20–21), and we shall identify it with the neural passage time. We assume that the latter is fixed or shows relatively little variability in comparison with the other two components of the reaction time. (The estimated duration of the neural passage time is very uncertain. In order to avoid click transients, the tone used by McGill to produce the reaction times shown in Fig. 3 was turned on slowly by an electronic switch with a rise time of 120 ms. Timing began 37 ms after stimulus onset, but the point at which neural activity started is completely uncertain. For our purposes, precise measurement of the neural passage time is unnecessary and will not be attempted. The figure of 100 ms is taken therefore as an upper bound.)

The linear portion of the distributions in Fig. 3 is assumed to be the distribution of the time required to make the response movement. We shall treat it as a simple exponential delay whose time constant is independent of stimulus intensity. Stone's model does not carry this restriction.

The remaining part of the reaction time, again following Stone's model, is the decision time. Sensory nerve tracts are "noisy" because of spontaneous firing, and some form of integration mechanism is assumed necessary in order to detect the onset of the stimulus. Imagine a neural "counter" that accumulates an impulse count over time. This counter will register only noise when the stimulus is turned off. When a weak stimulus is introduced, the counting rate increases. Consequently, if there are two counters, and one is accumulating only noise, a stimulus can be detected by observing the systematic divergence of the readings. We assume that the decision mechanism accumulates the difference until it reaches an arbitrary criterion value, at which point the decision to respond is made.

The time to accumulate any fixed difference can be treated as a random walk along a semi-infinite line starting at zero and stopping with the first passage through the criterion. The latter is an absorbing barrier, and the distribution is a familiar problem in the theory of Brownian motion (Feller, 1957; pp. 318–327). The total reaction time is then the sum of this first passage time through the criterion and a movement time that is exponentially distributed. This sum is displaced from the origin by a constant corresponding to the neural input time. The model is not easy to handle analytically, but it affords us a good opportunity to examine a number of experimental consequences of the type of detection assumed.

Our model says that weak stimuli take longer to detect, since the time required to accumulate a fixed difference depends on the rate at which the counters diverge. In addition, the variability of the detection times would be comparatively large for weak stimuli. These expectations taken together lead to reaction time distributions just about like those shown in Fig. 3. Moreover, the effect of instructions or rewards for fast responding would be expected to change the criterion count necessary for a decision and would lead to results similar to those observed when motivational variables are manipulated.

The principal difference between the detection model of reaction times just outlined and the model proposed by Stone is that we have introduced restrictive assumptions at each of the three stages and we have given up

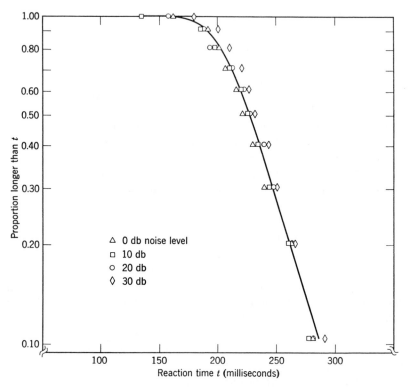

Fig. 6. Four distributions of 100 reaction times to the onset of a brief 1000-cps tone masked by a continuous white noise. Signal-to-noise ratio was fixed at 15 db above the masked threshold and the spectrum level of the noise was varied over an intensity range of 30 db in 10-db steps from an arbitrary reference level. Distributions are based on responses of one listener. Adapted from Greenbaum (1963).

some of Stone's generality. The assumptions were introduced where the data of Fig. 3 seemed to suggest them and were intended to make Stone's model more explicit. The restrictive assumptions on the neural passage time and the distribution of response movements are of the simplest kind and are probably quite wrong. However, one of the main advantages of such restrictions is that they also lead to definite predictions that can be proved wrong. For example, a direct consequence of our extension of Stone's model is that reaction-time distributions should be invariant for signals that are equally detectable. Figure 6 presents four such distributions, each based on 100 reaction times. They were obtained from a single listener in response to the onset of a 1000-cps tone masked by an acoustic white noise. The distributions were gathered by Greenbaum (1963). Signal intensity was pitted against four different noise levels, keeping signal-to-noise ratio constant, and the data were very nearly superimposed by fixing detectability in this way. There are systematic small differences, however, whose origin is unclear.

Another consequence of our detection model is that it predicts an inverse relation between loudness and reaction time, at least for brief tones. Mean reaction time is essentially the time required to obtain a fixed number of auditory impulses, and loudness is assumed to depend on the number of impulses per unit time. They should be inversely related.

The relation has been studied systematically by McGill (1961), and the prediction seems to be verified. The form of the relation between reaction time and estimated loudness as seen in a typical listener is presented in Fig. 7. It is a particularly interesting result because it occurs naturally when reaction times reflect the operation of a neural integration mechanism but not otherwise.

As we have noted, decision devices such as the one just described are easily extended to choices among several alternatives. In fact, simple reactions can be considered as choice reactions when the choice is made between signal and noise as alternatives.

Mean reaction time seems to increase roughly in proportion to the logarithm of the number of stimulus alternatives, or, more generally, in

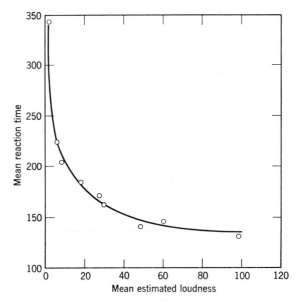

Fig. 7. Relation between mean estimated loudness (arbitrary units) and mean reaction time, obtained with a 1000-cps tone at various intensities. Curve determined on one listener. Adapted from McGill (1961).

proportion to the amount of information in the stimulus alternatives, if an independent response is required for each alternative (Hick, 1952; Hyman, 1953). This fact is not surprising, since a decision mechanism would, in effect, have to wait until a clear difference emerged between the "counter" associated with the stimulus and the largest count coming from the other alternatives, all of which, presumably, are registering noise. With more alternatives, the distribution of the largest noise reading will move toward increasingly higher counts, which is equivalent to inflating the noise level. This, in turn, delays the detection time.

Choice reaction time is a very difficult and complicated area. There are, to say the least, many unanswered questions regarding the mode or modes of operation of assumed decision mechanisms, and the topic is not pursued here. The reader is referred to Christie & Luce (1956), Luce (1960), and Restle (1961) for further discussion.

3. RATE FLUCTUATIONS

Figure 8 illustrates responses recorded from a single nerve fiber of the eye of *limulus* (horseshoe crab) when it is stimulated by a steady white light. The response system is ticking away almost like a watch, and under no stretch of the imagination are the interresponse times to be considered as a random sequence. Similar data are observed when a rat presses the bar in a Skinner box under certain reinforcement conditions that differentially reinforce low rates (Hill, personal communication, 1959).

Figure 9 presents a distribution of interresponse times obtained by Mueller from the *limulus* eye when the eye was responding as shown in Fig. 8. The data were observed after dissecting out a single fiber of the optic nerve and picking off a barrage of nerve impulses as the eye was subjected to steady illumination. The nerve impulses were recorded on magnetic tape and then analyzed by McGill (1962). The tape was played into a flip-flop circuit controlling the gate of a high-speed digital counter, and the time intervals between alternate pairs of responses were thus determined.

The smooth curve fitted to the distribution of latencies in Fig. 9 is the Laplace distribution,

$$f(t - \tau) = \frac{\lambda}{2} e^{-\lambda|t-\tau|}, \qquad -\infty \leqslant t - \tau \leqslant \infty, \qquad (16)$$

in which τ is a parameter reflecting a periodic component of the interresponse times.

Fig. 8. Train of responses recorded from a single nerve fiber of the optic nerve of the horseshoe crab *limulus*. Unpublished data courtesy of C. G. Mueller.

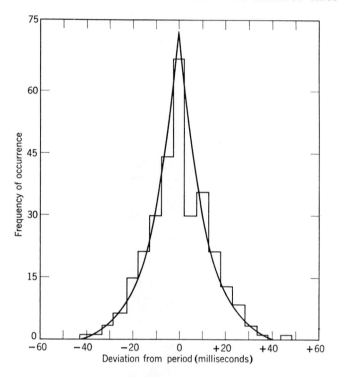

Fig. 9. Frequency distribution of 303 interresponse times recorded from a single optic nerve fiber of *limulus* when the eye was illuminated by a steady light. The nerve fiber adapted continuously and its period increased slowly from about 261 to 291 milliseconds while these data were recorded. The change was isolated by averaging the data in blocks of 25 intervals and fitting a straight line to the trend of the averages. Measured intervals were then converted into deviations from this line, producing the frequency distribution shown above. The theoretical curve is a Laplace distribution. Adapted from McGill (1962, p. 13).

The choice of the Laplace distribution in this instance is not accidental. It reflects the operation of the periodic latency mechanism illustrated in Fig. 10.

In Fig. 10, E and R denote excitation and response, respectively, and it is assumed that each excitation produces a response that follows it after a random delay, s. The excitations are spaced τ seconds apart, where τ is a fixed (but unknown) constant. The interresponse time t is a random variable, and our problem is to deduce the form of its distribution if we are given the distribution of s. We assume that $f(s)$ follows Eq. 6, that is,

$$f(s) = \lambda e^{-\lambda s}.$$

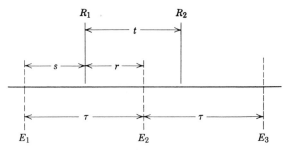

Fig. 10. Diagram of a periodic latency mechanism. Excitations (E) (not observable) come at regular intervals (τ) but are subject to random delays (s) before producing responses (R). Heavy line is the time axis. The variable under observation is t, the time interval between successive responses. Operation of the mechanism is described in the text. Adapted from McGill (1962, p. 4).

Since two excitations are necessary to define τ, there are two independent occurrences of s, which we now call s_1 and s_2. The relations sketched in Fig. 10 permit us to write

$$t = r + s_2,$$

$$\tau = r + s_1,$$

$$t - \tau = s_2 - s_1. \tag{17}$$

Equation 17 states that $t - \tau$ is distributed as the difference between two exponential density functions. Following Theorems 2 and 3 of Sec. 1, we can write

$$M_{s_1 - s_2}(\theta) = \left(\frac{1}{1 - \theta/\lambda}\right)\left(\frac{1}{1 + \theta/\lambda}\right)$$

$$M_{t-\tau}(\theta) = \frac{1}{1 - (\theta/\lambda)^2}. \tag{18}$$

Equation 18 is the moment generating function of the Laplace distribution, and it follows that the distribution of $t - \tau$ has the Laplace density function given by Eq. 16.

The distribution is essentially two exponential distributions turned back to back, resulting in a density function that is more sharply peaked than a normal variable. Figure 11 presents a distribution of interresponse times in operant conditioning reported by Hill (personal communication, 1959), when reinforcement is withheld unless a rat delays his responses by 21 seconds or longer (d.r.l. 21″ schedule). The dotted histogram in Fig. 11 is the best fitting normal curve with mean and variance matched to the empirical data. The leptokurtic character of the distribution of inter-response times is evident.

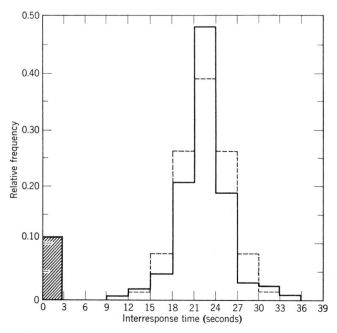

Fig. 11. Distribution of interresponse times generated by a white rat when reinforcement was contingent on delaying at least 21 seconds from the last previous response. Data were obtained during the ninety-third session (184 previous hours of conditioning). Dotted distribution is the best fitting normal approximation and demonstrates the peaking of the empirical distribution. Data in the 0–3 second class interval were not used in fitting the normal curve because such bursts of responses are believed to be unrelated to the main effect. Personal communication from R. T. Hill (1959).

Careful examination of Fig. 10 shows that the Laplace distribution is in fact only an approximation of the exact distribution associated with the periodic latency mechanism. The approximation is based on the assumption that the delay between excitation and response is small compared with the period between excitations, hence no excitation will be received before a response is emitted to the previous excitation.

In a more complete treatment of the problem based on the method used in deriving Eq. 11, McGill (1962) shows that the m.g.f. of the exact distribution is

$$M_t(\theta) = \left(\frac{1}{1 - (\theta/\lambda)^2} \right) \left(\frac{e^{\theta \tau} - \nu}{1 - \nu} \right), \tag{19}$$

where $\nu = e^{-\lambda \tau}$ is a constant.

The average latency between excitation and response is $1/\lambda$. Thus $\lambda \tau$ is large when the delay between excitation and response is small compared with the period between excitations. Clearly ν approaches zero under these conditions. When ν is set equal to zero and the variable is changed from t to $t - \tau$, $M_t(\theta)$ in Eq. 19 yields the m.g.f. of the Laplace distribution (Eq. 18).

The m.g.f. specified by Eq. 19 is obtained from the following probability distribution for t:

$$f(t) = \begin{cases} \dfrac{\lambda \nu}{1 - \nu} \sinh \lambda t, & t \leqslant \tau \\[2ex] \dfrac{1 + \nu}{2\nu} \lambda e^{-\lambda t}, & \tau \leqslant t. \end{cases} \qquad (20)$$

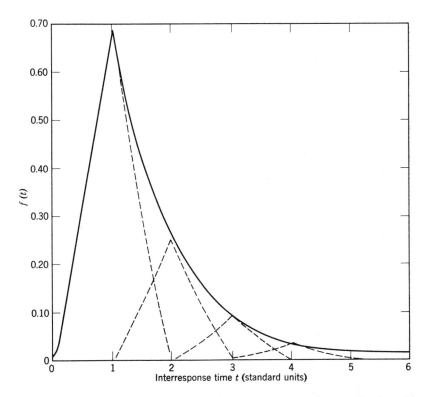

Fig. 12. Theoretical density function produced by a periodic latency mechanism with a very short excitation period. The curve is a plot of Eq. 20 in the text with λ and τ equal to unity. Dashed lines show how the density function is built out of images or reflections of a symmetrical distribution. These images are generated whenever new excitations arrive before the response to a prior excitation has occurred. The density function shown above changes into the Laplace distribution as the period increases. Adapted from McGill (1962, p. 12).

This fact may be verified by computing the m.g.f. of Eq. 20. Consequently, the exact distribution of the periodic latency mechanism of Fig. 10 is given by Eq. 20. The shape of this probability distribution is shown in Fig. 12. It is sharply peaked like the Laplace distribution but asymmetrical, achieving more and more symmetry as $\lambda\tau$ increases.

Figure 13 illustrates empirical distributions of interresponse times based on recordings from four different nerve fibers reported by Hunt and Kuno (1959). These distributions appear to reflect a periodic latency mechanism similar to Eq. 20. The exponentially distributed data in the upper left-hand corner of Fig. 13 were presented earlier in Fig. 2. It is interesting to note that the exponential distribution can be derived from the periodic

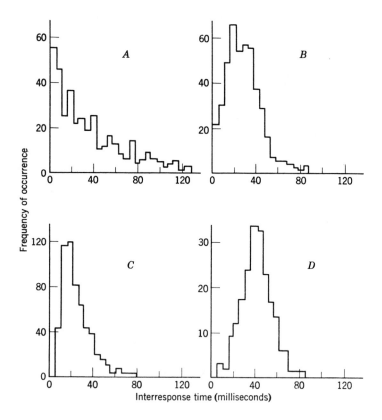

Fig. 13. Examples of frequency distributions believed to reflect a periodic latency mechanism. Data were obtained by recording spontaneous activity in the spinal cord of a cat. The four distributions show interresponse times in four different nerve fibers. The distribution A is illustrated in Fig. 2. Adapted from Hunt & Kuno (1959, p. 366).

latency mechanism when $\tau \to 0$. To do this, it must first be shown that

$$\lim_{\tau \to 0} \left(\frac{e^{\theta \tau} - \nu}{1 - \nu} \right) = 1 + \frac{\theta}{\lambda},$$

and this is easily done by expanding the numerator and denominator on the left-hand side in series. As $\tau \to 0$ the m.g.f. in Eq. 19 becomes

$$\lim_{\tau \to 0} M_t(\theta) = \left[\frac{1}{1 - (\theta/\lambda)^2} \right] \left[1 + \frac{\theta}{\lambda} \right]$$

$$= \frac{1}{1 - \theta/\lambda}, \tag{21}$$

and this is the m.g.f. of the exponential distribution. It is evident that, if excitations are continuously available, the intervals between responses depend only on the random delays, and the latter are assumed to be exponential.

4. RESPONSE CHAINS

In this section we extend our treatment of latency mechanisms with variable time constants. In particular, we want to consider the effects of simple relations among the time constants of successive responses. Sequences of observable responses with constraints that change regularly from response to response are called response chains.

4.1 Three Random Components

Before considering a typical chain, let us find the distribution of time intervals that consist of three components with time constants γ, β, and α, respectively, where

$$t = t_0 + t_1 + t_2.$$

and $\gamma > \beta > \alpha$. Each component is assumed to have an exponential distribution,

$$f(t_0) = \gamma e^{-\gamma t_0},$$
$$f(t_1) = \beta e^{-\beta t_1},$$
$$f(t_2) = \alpha e^{-\alpha t_2}.$$

The moment generating function of t is

$$M_t(\theta) = \frac{\alpha \beta \gamma}{(\alpha - \theta)(\beta - \theta)(\gamma - \theta)}, \tag{22}$$

and its density function $f(t)$ can be found via a table of the Laplace transform:

$$f(t) = \frac{\alpha\beta\gamma}{(\gamma - \beta)(\beta - \alpha)(\gamma - \alpha)} [(\gamma - \beta)e^{-\alpha t} + (\beta - \alpha)e^{-\gamma t} - (\gamma - \alpha)e^{-\beta t}].$$

(23)

Equation 23 is very unwieldy, but it simplifies just as soon as we introduce a few restrictions. For instance, suppose the time constants of successive responses increase systematically in the following manner: $\alpha = \lambda$, $\beta = 2\lambda$, $\gamma = 3\lambda$. Equation 23 then reduces to

$$f_3(t) = 3\lambda(e^{-\lambda t})(1 - e^{-\lambda t})^2,$$

(24)

where $f_3(t)$ is the density function of the time up to the third response in the chain. If there are only two components, α and β, the analogous result from Eq. 14 is

$$f_2(t) = 2\lambda(e^{-\lambda t})(1 - e^{-\lambda t}).$$

(25)

4.2 Yule-Furry Process

These results suggest a simple conjecture for a chain of $k + 1$ responses in which the time constants are integral multiples of λ.

$$f_{k+1}(t) = (k + 1)\lambda(e^{-\lambda t})(1 - e^{-\lambda t})^k.$$

(26)

If successive responses have time constants that increase systematically, the expected latency between successive responses will decrease as we proceed into the chain. Equation 26 will then yield the distribution of the time up to the $(k + 1)$st response. To prove the conjecture, it is sufficient to show that

$$\int_0^\infty e^{\theta t} f_{k+1}(t) \, dt = \prod_{j=1}^{k+1} \frac{1}{1 - \theta/j\lambda},$$

(27)

where $f_{k+1}(t)$ is defined by Eq. 26. The left-hand side of Eq. 27 is $M_t(\theta)$, and some amount of manipulation on Eq. 26 shows that

$$M_t(\theta) = \frac{\Gamma(1 - \theta/\lambda)\Gamma(k + 2)}{\Gamma(k + 2 - \theta/\lambda)}.$$

(28)

The quantities on the right of Eq. 28 are gamma functions that obey the rule

$$\Gamma(x + 1) = x \, \Gamma(x),$$

for $x > 0$. Decomposing $\Gamma(k + 2 - \theta/\lambda)$ according to this rule and noting that $\Gamma(k + 2) = (k + 1)!$, it is a simple matter to show that the ratio of gamma functions on the right of Eq. 28 is equal to the product of generating functions on the right of Eq. 27, and so the conjecture is proved.

Equation 26 is the distribution of the time interval up to the $(k + 1)$st response in a chain where the time constants of successive responses increase in the sequence λ, 2λ, 3λ, etc. It is a surprisingly simple result. Moreover, since the last response is fixed at the end of the sequence and has a probability equal to $(k + 1)\lambda \cdot dt$, it follows that this same mechanism generates a probability distribution for the occurrence of k responses in a fixed interval t. This distribution can be found in the way that we extracted the Poisson distribution from the gamma distribution, that is, by separating the factor $(k + 1)\lambda$ out of Eq. 26. We have at once

$$p(k; \lambda t) = (e^{-\lambda t})(1 - e^{-\lambda t})^k. \tag{29}$$

The latency mechanism described by Eqs. 26 and 29 is a familiar stochastic process known as the Yule-Furry process (Yule, 1924; and Furry, 1937; see also Bharucha-Reid, 1960, pp. 77–78). In view of Eq. 7, the quantity $e^{-\lambda t}$ behaves like a probability. Consequently, Eq. 29 is a geometric distribution. Simon (1957) seems to have used this particular process to describe Zipf's law, the well-known relation between rank and frequency in linguistic data.

Regularly increasing time constants and the cumulative response curves they generate are also reminiscent of response phenomena seen in fixed-interval reinforcement schedules. Clear-cut tests of the Yule-Furry model are lacking, however. To the writer's knowledge, no attempts have been made to study a scalloping response system by observing the probability distribution of the time up to the $(k + 1)$st response (Eq. 26) or the analogous distribution of the number of responses in a fixed time interval following the start of the chain (Eq. 29).

However, Sherman (1959) has done something that is closely related. He used a programmed timer that shunted responses into time slots in the fixed interval between reinforcements. Each slot was one tenth of the length of the interval between reinforcements, and responses in each slot were counted separately. Hence Sherman obtained empirical frequency distributions of responses in the interval between reinforcements. A distribution generated by a rat on the fiftieth day of conditioning is shown in Fig. 14. The exponentially rising curve is typical of the Yule-Furry process as we can show in the following argument.

Consider the mean of the geometric distribution in Eq. 29. It can be computed by expanding the m.g.f. in Eq. 3b in series or by operating directly on Eq. 29. In either case we find that the mean number of

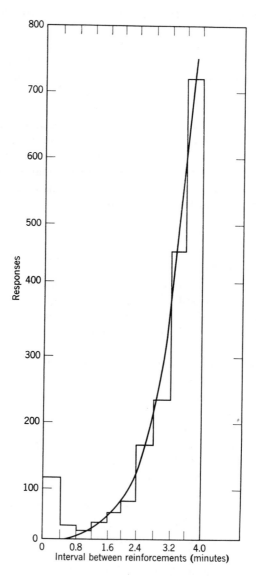

Fig. 14. Distribution of responses during regular four-minute intervals between reinforcements, produced by a rat on the fiftieth day of conditioning with a fixed interval schedule
of reinforcement. The solid line is an exponential curve computed from the Yule-Furry
distribution. Unpublished data courtesy of J. G. Sherman.

responses in time t, which we label $E(k; t)$, is given by

$$E(k; t) = \frac{1 - e^{-\lambda t}}{e^{-\lambda t}} \tag{30}$$

$$= e^{\lambda t} - 1. \tag{30a}$$

$E(k; t)$ is the expected number of responses in the whole interval from time zero up to time t. We want the expected number in the time slot between t and $t + \Delta t$. The latter is

$$E(k; t + \Delta t) - E(k; t) = e^{\lambda(t+\Delta t)} - e^{\lambda t}. \tag{31}$$

With values of Δt sufficiently small, the expression on the right of Eq. 31 is $\lambda e^{\lambda t} \Delta t$, which is an exponentially rising curve with increasing t.

It is apparent that the latency processes underlying interval reinforcement are complex. They seem to evolve from a constant probability mechanism (see Sec. 1) into something approximating the Yule-Furry process and beyond that into other mechanisms. The range of applicability of the Yule-Furry process cannot be determined with any precision by attempts to deduce data such as Sherman's, because many different latency processes might yield similar mean curves in the interval between reinforcements. The cross checks afforded by tests of Eqs. 26 and 29 are really necessary.

4.3 Extinction Processes

The Yule-Furry process is sometimes called a *pure birth process*, which is a latency process that speeds up as the chain unfolds. Now imagine a pure death process or extinction chain in which the time constants of the latency mechanism decrease response by response and the mechanism seems to be slowing down. In particular, suppose that the time constants for successive responses are $n\lambda$, $(n - 1)\lambda$, $(n - 2)\lambda$, etc., so that the mechanism will cease to respond after n responses. In this case Eqs. 14 and 23 become, respectively,

$$f_2(t) = (n - 1)\lambda \binom{n}{1} (e^{-\lambda t})^{n-1}(1 - e^{-\lambda t}), \tag{32}$$

$$f_3(t) = (n - 2)\lambda \binom{n}{2} (e^{-\lambda t})^{n-2}(1 - e^{-\lambda t})^2. \tag{33}$$

The obvious conjecture for the frequency function of the time up to response $k + 1$ is

$$f_{k+1}(t) = (n - k)\lambda \binom{n}{k} (e^{-\lambda t})^{n-k}(1 - e^{-\lambda t})^k, \tag{34}$$

where $k \leqslant n$.

To prove the conjecture, it is enough to show that

$$\int_0^\infty e^{\theta t} f_{k+1}(t)\, dt = \prod_{j=0}^{k} \left[\frac{1}{1 - \theta/\lambda(n - j)} \right]. \tag{35}$$

The expression on the left-hand side of Eq. 35 is $M_t(\theta)$, and when Eq. 34 is substituted for $f_{k+1}(t)$ the integration yields

$$M_t(\theta) = \frac{n!\, \Gamma(n - k - \theta/\lambda)}{(n - k - 1)!\, \Gamma(n + 1 - \theta/\lambda)}. \tag{36}$$

Successive reductions of the gamma functions in Eq. 36 lead directly to the product of exponential m.g.f.'s on the right-hand side of Eq. 35, and this proves the conjecture. Consequently, Eq. 34 is the distribution of the time up to the $(k + 1)$st response in an extinction chain in which the time constants drop from $n\lambda$ in steps of size λ with each successive response.

The distribution of the number of responses in a fixed time interval t is found as before by removing the probability of the $(k + 1)$st response from Eq. 34. This probability is $(n - k)\lambda \cdot dt$. Accordingly, we divide $(n - k)\lambda$ out of Eq. 34 and obtain $p(k; \lambda t)$, the probability of k responses in an interval t measured from the beginning of the chain:

$$p(k; \lambda t) = \binom{n}{k} (e^{-\lambda t})^{n-k} (1 - e^{-\lambda t})^k. \tag{37}$$

Equation 37 is a binomial distribution and it characterizes the extinction chain in the same way that the Poisson distribution characterizes a completely random sequence.

4.4 Verbal Associations

A good example of what seems to be this type of extinction process is found in an experiment on verbal associations by Bousfield and Sedgwick (1944). Subjects were instructed, for instance, to name as many cities in the United States as they could remember. The associations were tabulated, but Bousfield and Sedgwick were chiefly interested in the time intervals between successive responses. They noted that associations came easily and rapidly at first, then more and more slowly and with evident effort as time went on. Figure 15 presents a typical recording of the cumulative number of associations plotted against time. It was obtained from a single subject instructed to name as many cities in the United States as he could think of.

Many different associative restrictions were studied: pleasant activities, quadruped mammals, five-letter words, fellow students, a memorized list of objects, etc. All of them led to essentially the same type of result. Cumulative responses plotted against time yielded a functional relation like the one in Fig. 15, and Bousfield and Sedgwick fitted it with an equation of the form

$$y(t) = c(1 - e^{-at}), \tag{38}$$

where $y(t)$ is the total number of associations given in time t, c is a constant (the asymptote of y), and a is another constant.

This result is just the one predicted by the n-step extinction chain. As we established in Eq. 37, the distribution of the number of responses in time t is binomial. The mean number of responses is thus given by the mean of the binomial

$$E(k; t) = n(1 - e^{-\lambda t}), \tag{39}$$

which is Bousfield and Sedgwick's equation. Of course Fig. 15 is a single sequence, whereas Eq. 39 is the mean of a probability distribution, but this does not seem to create serious problems, since the distribution stabilizes rapidly.

The extinction process offers an interesting interpretation of association times. The step-by-step drop in the time constants implies that the time constant for any response is proportional to the number of unused alternatives at that point. We can imagine a mechanism that searches

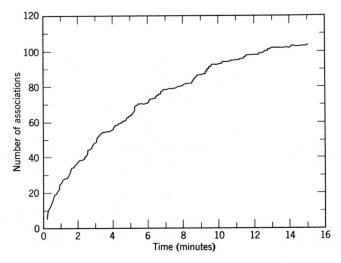

Fig. 15. Cumulative record of associations produced by a single subject under instructions to name cities in the United States. This extinction chain of responses is typical of a type of *pure-death* process described in the text. Adapted from Bousfield & Sedgwick (1944, p. 160).

randomly through a storage consisting of a constant number of alternatives. The examination time for each alternative is an exponential random time function, and the process runs on until an unused alternative is discovered. In this circumstance, as we showed in Eq. 11, the time constant of response $k + 1$ is

$$\frac{n - k}{n} \rho,$$

where ρ is the time constant of the examination process. If we set $\lambda = \rho/n$, the extinction chain characterized by Eqs. 34 and 37 follows directly.

Several weaknesses in the extinction chain model of Bousfield and Sedgwick's data should be recorded. For example, the associations come out in clusters triggered by naming a member of an obvious subclass (e.g. geographic clusters). This sort of clustering produces roughness in the data with which a simple extinction model cannot cope. In addition, systematic deviations from the exponential curve form (Eq. 39) at early stages are often noted. These discrepancies do not appear to be large, and the rough grain in the data due to clustering does not seem to affect the curve shape seriously, but both effects are observed and they are simply ignored by the model.

4.5 Mueller's Theory of the Photoreceptor

An extinction chain that is very similar to the Bousfield and Sedgwick mechanism is found in Mueller's (1954) theory of the production of nerve impulses in a single photoreceptor. The theory assumes that a molecule of photosensitive substance in the receptor undergoes a change of state when it is activated by absorbing a quantum of light. This change eventually leads to a nerve impulse via a constant probability decay mechanism. According to the theory, when a brief flash of light (of the order of 1 to 10 msec) stimulates the photoreceptor, a number of molecules are immediately changed to the activated state. The number is assumed to be fixed by the intensity of flash.[3] Suppose in fact that n quanta are absorbed. Each simultaneously activates a molecule and starts the process leading to a nerve impulse. Call the time constant of the process λ. We have in effect n parallel channels each leading to a response, and the latency of the first

---

[3] This is a deliberate simplification. In practice, the number of quanta in a flash has a Poisson distribution. Many are lost in the eye but the loss is assumed to be random. Consequently the quanta that reach the photoreceptor and are absorbed by it also have a Poisson distribution. It is the mean value of the latter that is fixed by the flash intensity.

nerve impulse will be the shortest of the n latencies. The distribution of the shortest of n latencies all with the same properties is given by

$$f_1(t) = \binom{n}{1} f(t)[1 - F(t)]^{n-1}. \tag{40}$$

Since we have assumed that $f(t)$ in Eq. 40 is exponential and that its time constant is λ, we find at once that

$$f_1(t) = n\lambda e^{-n\lambda t}. \tag{41}$$

The latency of response $k + 1$ is obtained by the same reasoning and is based on the latency of the first $k + 1$ events in a set of n, which are triggered off simultaneously. The density function is found to be

$$f_{k+1}(t) = \frac{n!}{1! \, k! \, (n - k - 1)!} \, \lambda e^{-\lambda t}(1 - e^{-\lambda t})^k (e^{-\lambda t})^{n-k-1}$$

$$= (n - k)\lambda \binom{n}{k} (e^{-\lambda t})^{n-k}(1 - e^{-\lambda t})^k.$$

This distribution is identical to Eq. 34, and it follows that the latencies of the n nerve impulses triggered by a brief light flash form an extinction chain of responses. Moreover, the extinction chain generated by a process that searches randomly looking for an unused alternative (Bousfield and Sedgwick mechanism) is now shown to be indistinguishable from one that conducts n simultaneous searches, each for a separate alternative.

In working out this connection between Mueller's photoreceptor theory and the extinction chain, we have oversimplified the theory considerably. Mueller requires a refractory period of fixed duration τ following each response and allows no storage of the decay effects during the refractory period. Accordingly, any response that would ordinarily occur in the interval τ after a previous response is lost. This leads to a somewhat more complicated extinction chain in which the number of responses observed in extinction is a random variable. It will not be pursued here.

4.6 The Generalized Gamma Distribution

We have touched on only two of a variety of response chains that can be constructed by structuring the changes in time constants in different ways. One would think that the probability distributions of these arbitrary response chains would prove to be forbidding and intractable, but this is not the case at all. The solution for what is in fact the general form of the gamma distribution (in which the time constants are arbitrary and all different) turns out to surprisingly easy, as we shall now demonstrate.

In a paper on a model for free-recall verbal learning Miller and McGill (1952) considered a probability mechanism that we may paraphrase as follows: let the probability of occurrence of an event after k previous occurrences be symbolized by p_k. The corresponding probability of failure is $1 - p_k$. When the event has occurred exactly k times on preceding trials, we may say the event is in state A_k. Miller and McGill show that $p(A_k, n)$, the probability that the event is in state A_k on the nth trial, is given by

$$p(A_k, n) = p_0 p_1 \cdots p_{k-1} \sum_{i=0}^{k} \frac{(1 - p_i)^n}{\prod_{\substack{j=0 \\ j \neq i}}^{k} (p_j - p_i)} \ .$$

If we suppose that the event occurs again on trial $n + 1$, we then have a sequence of $n + 1$ trials terminating in the $(k + 1)$st success. It is, in effect, a string of $k + 1$ samples from geometric distributions (Eq. 1), in which the probability of success changes from one sample to the next. With this single additional success the Miller-McGill formula becomes

$$p_k \cdot p(A_k, n) = \sum_{i=0}^{k} \frac{p_i(1 - p_i)^n}{\prod_{\substack{j=0 \\ j \neq i}}^{k} [1 - (p_i/p_j)]} \ . \tag{42a}$$

We may now plug in the restriction that each trial is Δt long, and as Δt approaches zero

$$\frac{p_i}{\Delta t} \to \lambda_i,$$

which, of course, is merely a more general way of writing Eq. 4. At this point the expression in Eq. 42a is in the form of a sum of weighted geometric distributions. Consequently we can write for $f_{k+1}(t)$, the time up to the $(k + 1)$st event in the chain:

$$f_{k+1}(t) = \sum_{i=0}^{k} \frac{\lambda_i e^{-\lambda_i t}}{\prod_{\substack{j=0 \\ j \neq i}}^{k} [1 - (\lambda_i/\lambda_j)]} \ , \tag{42b}$$

where λ_i is the time constant of the ith event in the chain and the time constants are all different.[4] This is the generalized form of the gamma

---

[4] This distribution is encountered in queuing theory and in the study of radioactive transmutations (see Feller, 1949, p. 406; Bartlett, 1955, p. 55; Bharucha-Reid, 1960, p. 186 and also p. 297). The application here was suggested by J. Gibbon.

distribution. Equations 14 and 23 are special cases. Moreover, several other interesting response chains can be obtained from Eq. 42*b* by inserting the assumptions concerning λ_i and simplifying the resulting expression.

Summaries of well-known birth and death processes, as well as combination chains consisting of birth and death components, can be found in Bartlett (1955), Feller (1957), Bharucha-Reid (1960).

5. TIME CONSTANTS AND TIME FUNCTIONS

The stability of a simple latency mechanism is reflected in its time constant, which remains fixed from response to response as well as during the time interval between responses.

In our treatment of series mechanisms and response chains, one of these restrictions was relaxed. The time constant was allowed to change with successive responses. Now we want to relax the second restriction by replacing the time constant λ with a time function $\lambda(t)$. Let us imagine a mechanism with a time function that passes through the same set of values whenever it is set into motion and is reset to $\lambda(O)$ by the response that terminates the latent period. In other words $\lambda(t)$ will change in the interval between responses but will not be affected by the response history of the mechanism.

The density element $\lambda(t) \cdot dt$ is the "instantaneous" probability that the latent period terminates in the brief interval dt following time t, given that it has not terminated earlier. Clearly, we are now prepared to assume that this probability fluctuates in time. Hence $f(t)$ will not necessarily be exponential, and our first problem is to deduce $f(t)$ given that $\lambda(t)$ is known. This turns out to be easy to do. In fact, each quantity determines the other, so that we can also find $\lambda(t)$ if $f(t)$ is known. Our derivation of $f(t)$ is based on the one given by Christie et al. (1952). Similar arguments are presented by Anderson (1959), Bartlett (1955), Rashevsky (1960), and many other sources.

5.1 Latency Mechanisms with Variable Time Functions

The density element $f(t) \cdot dt$ is the probability that the latent period will terminate in the brief interval dt following time t. Since $\lambda(t) \cdot dt$ is the analogous conditional probability when it is known that the latent period has not terminated earlier and $1 - F(t)$ is the probability that it has not in fact terminated, we can write.

$$f(t) \cdot dt = [1 - F(t)] \, \lambda(t) \, dt. \tag{43}$$

The left-hand side can be written as $dF(t)$. Equation 43 then becomes a differential equation

$$\frac{dF(t)}{1 - F(t)} = \lambda(t)\, dt, \tag{44}$$

and integration between $t = O$ and $t = t_0$ yields

$$\log_e [1 - F(t_0)] = -\int_0^{t_0} \lambda(t)\, dt,$$

$$1 - F(t_0) = \exp\left[-\int_0^{t_0} \lambda(t)\, dt\right]. \tag{45}$$

Equation 45 is the area in the tail of the probability distribution beyond the point t_0 on the t-axis. Hence this result can now be substituted back into Eq. 43 to produce the desired expression for $f(t)$, which is

$$f(t) = \lambda(t) \exp\left[-\int_0^t \lambda(x)\, dx\right], \tag{46}$$

and we have found the frequency function of a latency mechanism that is controlled by a time function $\lambda(t)$ instead of a time constant λ. The exponential distribution is a special case of Eq. 46. This is easily demonstrated if we let $\lambda(t) = \lambda$. The integral is then cleared from the exponent of Eq. 46 by noting that x signifies all points in time earlier than t. Accordingly, the exponent is λt and Eq. 46 turns into the exponential distribution.

It is apparent that $\lambda(t)$ determines $f(t)$ completely. On the other hand, if we refer back to Eq. 44, we find that

$$\lambda(t) = \frac{f(t)}{1 - F(t)}, \tag{47}$$

and it is equally apparent that $f(t)$ determines $\lambda(t)$. In view of Eq. 47, we can call $\lambda(t)$ the conditional density function of the latency mechanism, since $\lambda(t)$ is analogous to the conditional probability in Eq. 2. In fact, Eq. 47 is the continuous analogue of Eq. 2 and leads to a result with the exponential distribution that is essentially the same as Eq. 2 in the case of the geometric distribution. In order to demonstrate this point, substitute Eqs. 6 and 7 into the numerator and denominator of Eq. 47 and observe that

$$\lambda(t) = \frac{\lambda e^{-\lambda t}}{e^{-\lambda t}} = \lambda. \tag{48}$$

Consequently, the conditional density function is constant in the exponential distribution, a conclusion that now comes as no surprise.

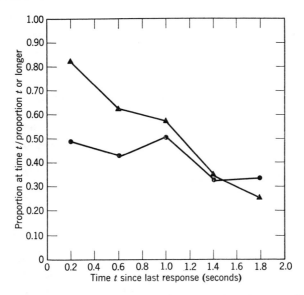

Fig. 16. Decreasing response probability in time as seen in a pigeon conditioned to peck at a small illuminated target. The black-circle function was obtained with a 30-second fixed interval reinforcement schedule. The black-triangle function depicts the case in which reinforcement was restricted to responses made in the first 0.6 second of successive 30-second cycles. Adapted from Hearst (1956).

One important requirement governing the choice of $\lambda(t)$ is the fact that the integral of the conditional density function over the whole range of t must diverge, that is,

$$\int_0^\infty \lambda(t) \, dt = \infty. \tag{49}$$

This point is evident from Eq. 45, which shows that when Eq. 49 is true $F(\infty) = 1$. The alternative, if Eq. 49 is not true, is the existence of a non-trivial probability of an infinite latency. Generally speaking, the forms of $\lambda(t)$ that increase in time offer no difficulty, since such increasing functions force short latencies. On the other hand, time functions that drop sharply may cause the latency mechanism to "sputter" erratically, and if the drop is rapid enough to keep the integral of $\lambda(t)$ small there will be a strong likelihood that the mechanism will stop altogether. This problem is especially interesting because there is more than a mere possibility that it will occur in certain types of animal learning data (see Hearst, 1956, and Fig. 16). Several recent experiments on the effects of reinforcement schedules (Anger, 1956; Kelleher et al., 1959) have made an effort to study estimates of $\lambda(t)$ directly from empirical distributions of interresponse times by means of Eq. 47.[5] This has led to a number of convincing demonstrations that such interresponse times are not simple random sequences, but it does not follow that the mechanism in such cases is best described as if it were governed by a fluctuating time function. Series latency mechanisms, response chains, and periodic mechanisms, for example, show time functions produced by Eq. 47 that increase with time and then level off. In fact, the conditional density function remains constant in each case, and apparent changes in $\lambda(t)$ are due either to fixed delays or hidden subresponses. Accordingly, a certain amount of care should be exercised in interpreting estimates of $\lambda(t)$ when there is no clear picture of the mechanism in operation.

5.2 Mueller's Theory of the Photoreceptor

In Sec. 4.5 we showed that Mueller's theory of visual excitation in the single photoreceptor (Mueller, 1954) leads to an extinction chain of responses (pure death process) when the photoreceptor is stimulated by a brief flash of light. The theory assumes that a molecule of photosensitive substance in the receptor undergoes a change of state when it is activated by absorbing a quantum of light and this change eventually leads to a nerve impulse via a constant probability mechanism. The time constant of the latency of the first response is determined by the number of activated molecules.

A very interesting aspect of Mueller's theory is that it leads to different latency distributions for short exposures as compared with long exposures. If the intensity is chosen so that a single quantum is absorbed following a brief flash, the latency of the first (and only) response has an exponential distribution and is illustrated by Eq. 6. Now suppose that the flash is kept at the same intensity and is lengthened into a steady light. In that case the number of active molecules in the photoreceptor increases linearly with time, since quanta are being absorbed at a steady rate. Evidently the time function of the response increases steadily where, approximately,

$$\lambda(t) = \lambda t, \tag{50}$$

[5] These are the so-called IRT/OPS functions. The label was introduced by Anger (1956) and is interpreted as follows:

$$IRT/OPS = \frac{\text{frequency of a given interresponse time}}{\text{opportunities for that interresponse time to occur}}.$$

Anger indicated that IRT/OPS estimates a conditional probability. The term "conditional density function" seems to have been introduced by D. J. Davis (*J. Amer. Stat. Assn*, 1952, **47**, 113–150). It is sometimes also called a "hazard function."

when t is measured in units of the flash duration. If we substitute this relation into the frequency function of the latency mechanism given by Eq. 46, we obtain immediately

$$f(t) = \lambda t\, e^{-\lambda t^2/2}. \tag{51}$$

Equation 51 is the density function of the latency to the first response of the photoreceptor when the stimulus is a steady light. The expected latency may be found from the "tail" formula:[6]

$$\mu_1' = \int_0^\infty [1 - F(t)]\, dt$$

$$= \int_0^\infty e^{-\lambda t^2/2}\, dt$$

$$= \left(\frac{\pi}{2\lambda}\right)^{\frac{1}{2}}.$$

The analogous expectation of the exponential distribution is

$$\mu_1' = \int_0^\infty e^{-\lambda t}\, dt$$

$$= \frac{1}{\lambda}.$$

Since λ in each instance is the time constant associated with a flash long enough for one quantum to be absorbed and the absorption rate is proportional to the intensity of the stimulus, it follows that this relation holds between expectations at every stimulus intensity. Consequently, the line relating log mean latency of the first response and log intensity should have a slope of -1 for short flashes and a slope of $-\frac{1}{2}$ for long exposures. As Mueller points out, this is precisely what happens when latencies for short and long exposures are compared in single fibers of the optic nerve of *limulus*.

---

[6] The "tail" formula for the moments of $f(t)$ is

$$\mu_{r+1}' = (r + 1) \int_0^\infty t^r [1 - F(t)]\, dt,$$

where μ_{r+1}' is the $(r + 1)$st raw moment of $f(t)$. It is derived from the moment formula in terms of $f(t)$ (see Footnote 2) after integrating by parts. The same result is obtained by integrating the moment generating function by parts. These facts were first demonstrated to the writer by J. Gibbon.

5.3 Urn Schemes

The latency mechanisms we are now considering can be viewed as simple devices that search among various alternatives looking for a particular response under changing conditions. For example, the time function $\lambda(t) = \lambda t$ is not limited to energy addition as displayed in Mueller's theory. The same function characterizes a random search in polar coordinates. In that case Eq. 51 yields the time required to find the nearest neighbor among a set of objects distributed randomly on a plane surface as the search spreads out in ever-widening circles from an arbitrary center (Skellam, 1952). With this interpretation, Eq. 51 describes a latency mechanism in two dimensions, similar to the exponential distribution in one dimension.

Now consider a very simple urn scheme in which the contents of the urn are examined systematically as we search for a particular ball. If the search is performed at constant rate and each ball is removed as it is examined, the search times will be uniformly distributed over a range that is jointly determined by the rate of searching and the size of the storage. We can easily deduce $\lambda(t)$ in this mechanism from the fact that the number of alternatives decreases by unity as each alternative is examined. It follows that after k balls have been removed, the increment in the probability of success on the next selection, that is, $p_{k+1} - p_k = \Delta p_k$, is given by

$$\frac{1}{n - k - 1} - \frac{1}{n - k} \cong p_k{}^2.$$

If we now let $p_k = \lambda(t) \cdot \Delta t$ and assume that a time interval Δt is consumed in examining the $(k + 1)$st object, we can set up a differential equation to approximate $\Delta p_k/\Delta t$:

$$\lambda'(t) = [\lambda(t)]^2. \tag{52}$$

The approximation is satisfactory provided that n is not too small. The solution of Eq. 52 is easily found to be

$$\lambda(t) = \frac{1}{\omega - t}, \tag{53}$$

where $\omega = 1/\lambda(o)$ is a parameter determined by the initial size of the storage, and $0 < t < \omega$. As expected, Eq. 53 is the conditional density function of a uniform distribution of search times. This is demonstrated by substituting Eq. 53 into Eq. 46

$$f(t) = \frac{1}{\omega - t} \exp\left[-\log\left(\frac{\omega}{\omega - t}\right)\right]$$

$$= \left(\frac{1}{\omega - t}\right)\left(\frac{\omega - t}{\omega}\right)$$

$$= \frac{1}{\omega}. \tag{54}$$

Evidently the time function in Eq. 53 then produces a uniform distribution in the time interval from $t = 0$ to $t = \omega$. Since the cumulative distribution of this uniform variable is

$$F(t) = t/\omega,$$

we can redetermine $\lambda(t)$ by means of Eq. 47:

$$\lambda(t) = \frac{f(t)}{1 - F(t)} = \frac{1}{\omega} \cdot \frac{1}{1 - t/\omega},$$

$$= \frac{1}{\omega - t},$$

and our findings are seen to be internally consistent. Mueller (unpublished data, Fig. 17) has reported such uniform distributions of latencies in nerve responses obtained from the *limulus* under certain conditions. They suggest a momentary time function having the form of Eq. 53 or a random latency mechanism with fixed storage and perfect memory.

As a final example, consider an urn scheme in which the contents of the urn increase as we continue to search for a particular ball. Each unwanted ball is returned after examination, and with it another unwanted ball is added to the urn. The ball we are looking for becomes progressively harder to find as the search goes on. The differential equation for the change in λ is analogous to Eq. 52:

$$\lambda'(t) = -[\lambda(t)]^2. \tag{55}$$

This equation has as its solution

$$\lambda(t) = \frac{1}{\omega + t}, \tag{56}$$

where ω is a parameter depending on the original size of the storage and where $t \geqslant 0$.

Equation 56 is a conditional density function that decreases in time. In view of our previous remarks it should be examined with a certain

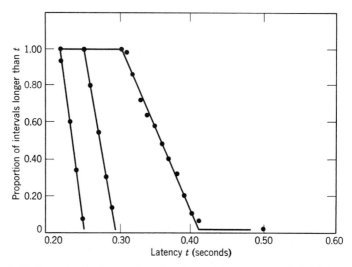

Fig. 17. Uniform distributions of latencies observed in response to brief flashes of light and recorded from a single fiber in the optic nerve of limulus. Three different latency distributions are shown corresponding to three different flash intensities. Unpublished data courtesy of C. G. Mueller.

amount of suspicion. The issue can be settled by finding the probability distribution by means of Eq. 45:

$$1 - F(t) = \exp\left[-\log\left(\frac{\omega + t}{\omega}\right)\right]$$

$$= \frac{\omega}{\omega + t}. \tag{57}$$

It is now apparent that $F(\infty) = 1$. Consequently, the decreasing time function offers no special problems.

The differential equation in Eq. 55 describes a very interesting latency mechanism that is partly self blocking because it builds up a secondary process associated with continued failure to respond. Searching for an object that is very difficult to find is sometimes made more difficult by an increasing sense of frustration. Escape responses are often impeded by an accompanying fear reaction. This emotional activity is viewed here as supplying irrelevant alternatives that progressively burden the response mechanism by making it more and more difficult to locate the appropriate response.

There is an obvious similarity between this type of rationale and the basic ideas in stimulus sampling theory (Estes, 1959). The similarity perhaps rests only on the fact that both are reducible to urn schemes. It is difficult, however, to outline an urn scheme describing the buildup of an inhibitory emotional reaction without feeling that we are dealing with a transient response process in substantially the same terms that stimulus element theory applies to the steady state.

The density function corresponding to Eqs. 56 and 57 is

$$f(t) = \left(\frac{1}{\omega + t}\right)\left(\frac{\omega}{\omega + t}\right)$$

$$= \frac{\omega}{(\omega + t)^2}. \tag{58}$$

It is interesting to observe that Eq. 58 looks something like the exponential distribution when both are plotted. The similarity is a very crude one, however, because the frequency function in Eq. 58 comes down more slowly than the exponential distribution. Consequently, even though the median of $f(t)$ in Eq. 58 is located at $t = \omega$, the mean value is infinite.

Equation 58 is the simplest version of a family of related distributions that can be produced by varying the rate at which irrelevant alternatives are added to the original set. Specifically, if we let

$$\lambda'(t) = -m[\lambda(t)]^2, \tag{59}$$

where $m > 0$, we obtain

$$\lambda(t) = \frac{1}{\omega + mt} \tag{60}$$

and

$$1 - F(t) = \left(\frac{\omega}{\omega + mt}\right)^{1/m}. \tag{61}$$

These equations simplify into Eqs. 55, 56, and 57 respectively when $m = 1$. In fact this value of m seems to mark a critical point in the behavior of Eq. 61. If $m < 1$, the mean value of t exists and is given by

$$\mu_1' = \frac{\omega}{1 - m}.$$

On the other hand if $m \geqslant 1$, the mean is infinite.

The distribution in Eq. 61 is particularly interesting because it is found in the literature with a rationale entirely different from the one offered by the differential equation set up in Eq. 59. Maguire, Pearson, and Wynn (1952) applied this second derivation to the distribution of time intervals between industrial accidents. Later on, Anscombe (1961) used the same arguments to describe the distribution of time up to the first purchase when a new product is put on the market.

The alternative derivation assumes that the basic latency distribution is a simple exponential, as in Eq. 6. However, the time constant λ is assumed to fluctuate at random on successive trials, and its distribution is taken to be a gamma distribution. The parameter n of the latter is set equal to $1/m$. When the exponential distribution of the latent period is combined with the gamma distribution of the time constant, the result is Eq. 61. We obtained the same outcome by varying the "time constant" systematically within a trial but not between trials. This is a surprising convergence of two different logical pathways toward the same distribution. A slightly different version of this conundrum was given by Feller (1949). It might be possible for us to rationalize a random process that operates on the time constant of a simple latency mechanism and changes it at random from trial to trial, but we shall not attempt to do so. Equation 61 will be assumed to illustrate what might be expected from parametric changes in the strength of an inhibitory blocking reaction that occurs during the latent period of the response.

Other examples of variable time functions can be found in Christie et al. (1952), who examined several assumptions concerning $\lambda(t)$ in models for problem solving by small groups.

References

Anderson, N. H. Temporal properties of response evocation. In R. R. Bush, & W. K. Estes (Eds.), *Studies in mathematical learning theory.* Stanford: Stanford Univer. Press, 1959. Pp. 125–134.

Anger, D. A. The dependence of interresponse times upon the relative reinforcement of different interresponse times. *J. exp. Psychol.,* 1956, **52,** 145–161.

Anscombe, F. S. Estimating a mixed-exponential response law. *J. Amer. Stat. Assoc.,* 1961, **56,** 493–502.

Audley, R. J. A stochastic model for individual choice behavior. *Psychol. Rev.,* 1960, **67,** 1–15.

Bartlett, M. S. *An introduction to stochastic processes.* Cambridge: Cambridge Univ. Press, 1955.

Bharucha-Reid, A. T. *Elements of the theory of Markov processes and their applications.* New York: McGraw-Hill, 1960.

Bousfield, W. A., & Sedgewick, C. An analysis of sequences of restrictive associative responses. *J. gen. Psychol.,* 1944, **30,** 149–165.

Bush, R. R., & Mosteller, F. *Stochastic models for learning.* New York: Wiley, 1955.

Chocholle, R. Variations des temps de réaction auditifs en fonction de l'intensité à diverses fréquences. *Année Psychol.,* 1940, **41,** 5–124.

Christie, L. S., Luce, R. D., & Macy, J., Jr. *Communication and learning in task-oriented groups.* Tech. Report 231, Research Lab. Electronics, Mass. Inst. Tech., 1952.

Christie, L. S., & Luce, R. D. Decision structure and time relations in simple choice behavior. *Bull. Math. Biophysics,* 1956, **18,** 89–112.

Churchill, R. V. *Modern operational mathematics in engineering*. New York: McGraw-Hill, 1944.

Cramér, H. *Mathematical methods of statistics*. Princeton: Princeton Univer. Press, 1946.

Estes, W. K. Toward a statistical theory of learning. *Psychol. Rev.*, 1950, **57**, 94–107.

Estes, W. K. The statistical approach to learning theory. In S. Koch (Ed.), *Psychology: A study of a science*, Vol. 2. New York: McGraw-Hill, 1959. Pp. 380–491.

Feller, W. On the theory of stochastic processes with particular reference to applications. In J. Neyman (Ed.), *Proceedings of the Berkeley Symposium on mathematical statistics and Probability*, Vol. 1. Berkeley and Los Angeles: Univer. of California Press, 1949. Pp. 403–432.

Feller, W. *An introduction to probability theory and its applications*. New York: Wiley, 1950, 1st edition; 1957, 2nd edition.

Felsinger, J. M., Gladstone, A., Yamaguchi, H., & Hull, C. L. Reaction latency as a function of the number of reinforcements. *J. exp. Psychol.*, 1947, **37**, 214–228.

Furry, W. On fluctuation of phenomena in the passage of high-energy electrons through lead. *Phys. Rev.*, 1937, **52**, 569–581.

Greenbaum, Hilda B., *Auditory reaction time: a case in signal detection*. Ph.D. dissertation. Columbia Univer., 1963.

Hearst, E. S. *The behavioral effects of some temporally defined schedules of reinforcement*. Ph.D. dissertation, Columbia Univer., 1956.

Hearst, E. S. The behavioral effects of some temporally defined schedules of reinforcement. *J. exp. anal. Behav.*, 1958, **1**, 45–55.

Hick, W. E. On the rate of gain of information. *Quart. J. exp. Psychol.*, 1952, **4**, 11–26.

Hoel, P. G. *Introduction to mathematical statistics*. New York: Wiley, 1954, 2nd ed.

Hunt, C. C., & Kuno, M. Background discharge and evoked response of spinal interneurones. *J. Physiol.*, 1959, **147**, 364–384.

Hyman, R. Stimulus information as a determinant of reaction time. *J. exp. Psychol.*, 1953, **45**, 188–196.

Kelleher, T. R., Fry, W., & Cook, L. Inter-response time distributions as a function of differential reinforcement of temporally spaced responses. *J. exp. anal. Behav.*, 1959, **2**, 91–106.

Luce, R. D. Response latencies and probabilities. In K. J. Arrow, S. Karlin, & P. Suppes (Eds.), *Mathematical methods in the social sciences, 1959*. Stanford: Stanford Univer. Press, 1960. Pp. 298–311.

McGill, W. J. Search distributions in magnified time. In *Visual Search Techniques*. Washington, D.C.: Nat. Acad. Sci.-Nat. Res. Counc. Publication No. 712, 1960, 50–58.

McGill, W. J. *Loudness and reaction time*. Acta Psychol., 1961, **19**, 193–199.

McGill, W. J. Random fluctuations of response rate. *Psychometrika*, 1962, **27**, 3–17.

Maguire, B. A., Pearson, E. S., & Wynn, A. H. A. The time intervals between industrial accidents. *Biometrika*, 1952, **39**, 169–180.

Miller, G. A., & McGill, W. J. A statistical description of verbal learning. *Psychometrika*, 1952, **17**, 369–396.

Mood, A. M. *Introduction to the theory of statistics*. New York: McGraw-Hill, 1950.

Mueller, C. G. Theoretical relationships among some measures of conditioning. *Proc. Nat. Acad. Sci.*, 1950, **36**, 123–130.

Mueller, C. G. A quantitative theory of visual excitation for the single photoreceptor. *Proc. Nat. Acad. Sci.*, 1954, **40**, 853–863.

Rashevsky, N. *Mathematical biophysics.* New York: Dover, 1960, Vol. 1, 3rd ed. revised.

Restle, F. *Psychology of judgment and choice.* New York: Wiley, 1961.

Rice, S. O. Mathematical analysis of random noise. *Bell Syst. tech. J.*, 1944, **23**, 282–332.

Sherman, J. G. *The temporal distribution of responses on fixed interval schedules.* Unpublished Ph.D. dissertation, Columbia Univer., 1959.

Simon, H. A. *Models of man.* New York: Wiley, 1957.

Skellam, J. G. Studies in statistical ecology. (1) Spatial pattern. *Biometrika*, 1952, **39**, 346–362.

Stone, M. Models for choice reaction time. *Psychometrika*, 1960, **25**, 251–260.

Weinstock, S. Resistance to extinction of running response following partial reinforcement under widely spaced trials. *J. comp. physiol. Psychol.*, 1954, **47**, 318–322.

Wilks, S. S. *Mathematical statistics.* Princeton: Princeton Univer. Press, 1943.

Woodworth, R. S., & Schlosberg, H. *Experimental psychology*, New York: Holt, 1954.

Yule, G. U. A mathematical theory of evolution based on the conclusions of Dr. J. C. Willis, F.R.S. *Phil. Trans. Royal Soc.*, 1924, **213**, 21–87.

7

Computers in Psychology

Allen Newell
and Herbert A. Simon

Carnegie Institute of Technology

Contents

Computers in Psychology

The inclusion of a chapter about computers in a handbook of mathematical psychology is a historical accident. Contrary to popular belief, there is no particularly close connection between what computers do and the analytic procedures that have classically been called mathematics. As we shall see in the course of this chapter, there is not even a necessary connection between computers and numerical symbols, although there is certainly a strong historical connection. The largest part of the chapter, in fact, is devoted to the use of computers as nonnumerical symbol manipulating devices capable of simulating, in ways we shall discuss, certain human psychological processes.

1. USES OF COMPUTERS IN PSYCHOLOGY

Historically, the computer was introduced into the service of psychology by the same persons who had used the tools of mathematics; it was introduced to perform chores in the service of mathematical analysis previously done by desk calculators and punched-card equipment. In terms of hours of computer use, these applications of the modern computer probably still account for the bulk of its employment in psychology. But as computers have become more powerful and their versatility more appreciated, their applications have broadened to affect almost every aspect of psychology.

1.1 Statistical Analysis

Almost as soon as modern electronic computers became available, their utility in carrying out large-scale *statistical analysis* was understood, and the programming techniques necessary for using them conveniently and efficiently to this end were soon developed. At present, they are regarded as almost indispensable tools in large factor analyses and other data-reduction tasks. The computer in this application is simply a rapid adder, subtractor, multiplier, and divider. Nothing will be said about statistical uses of computers in this chapter. Such a discussion belongs to the topic of statistics itself.

1.2 Numerical Analysis

A second type of application of computers in psychology is in the *numerical analysis of mathematical models, or theories*.[1] In this application, too, the computer is simply a rapid adder, subtractor, multiplier, and divider. But the difference between a desk calculator that can perform an addition in a second or two and a large computer that can perform the addition in a few millionths of a second may be all the difference in the world. The vast increase in speed has a profound influence on the kinds of theories that are constructed and the kinds of inferences that can be drawn from them and tested empirically. Similar effects exist in statistics, of course, but we shall explore only the consequences for psychological theory.

Other chapters have made it clear that mathematics is a tool for describing complex systems of interrelations and a tool for making inferences about such systems that would be difficult or impossible without its aid. The degree of complexity that a mathematical psychologist introduces into his model depends on the power of his mathematical tools to manipulate the models, once constructed. If his tools are classical mathematics, carried out with pencil and paper, he will generally restrict himself to those systems of equations that he can solve with pencil and paper (or from which he can draw significant inferences, even if he cannot fully solve them). Bush and Mosteller (1955, p. 46) provide us with a typical expression of this strategy:

> The form of these operators is dictated chiefly by mathematical considerations—linear operators are chosen in order to make the theory more manageable. It is seen in later chapters that, even with this simplification, the theory becomes rather complicated.

When an applied mathematician reduces his theory of a complex phenomenon to two equations, or uses linear relations to describe situations that we know are strongly nonlinear, we must not be too quick to accuse him of naïveté. His mathematical models, if they are to be of any use, must reflect the limits of his analytic tools quite as much as they reflect the reality he is trying to model.

The modern computer, employed as a device for numerical analysis, gives the mathematical psychologist license to frame theories of a richness and complexity that would otherwise be superfluous and futile. At the

---

[1] In this chapter we shall use the terms "model" and "theory" substantially as synonyms. The term "model" tends to be applied to those theories that are relatively detailed and that permit prediction of the behavior of the system through time, but the line between theories that are called "models" and other theories is too vague to be of much use.

same time, the ways in which he manipulates and tests his theories with the help of the computer may become quite different from the ways customary with classical mathematical equation-solving and theorem-proving techniques.[2] In general, the computer does not provide new powers of drawing general inferences from models but, instead, allows the behavior of the models to be studied in great detail in particular instances.

1.3 Information-Processing Theories

Although the availability of computers may influence the kinds of models the mathematical psychologist is willing and able to construct and explore, these uses of the computer still lie within the traditional methodology of applied mathematics in the sciences. They call for the same basic steps:

1. Constructing a quantitative mathematical theory of the phenomenon of interest.

2. Deriving empirical consequences (predictions) from the theory for the parameter values, time paths, equilibria, or other characteristics of the phenomena.

3. Testing these consequences by comparing them with numbers derived from the empirical data.

Computers, we have said, enter into the process in the second stage (numerical analysis) and in the third (statistical analysis).

An entirely different use of computers in psychology which dispenses with the first stage (quantitative theory) has emerged; that is, it begins not by building a numerical or algebraic model of the phenomena under study but by building a model directly in the form of a computer program. This possibility stems from the fact that a computer is a device for manipulating symbols of any kind, not just numerical symbols. Thus a computer program becomes a way of specifying arbitrary symbolic processes. Theories of this type, which can be called information processing theories, are essentially nonquantitative (they may involve no numbers at all), although neither less precise nor less rigorous than classical mathematical theories. It is a major task of this chapter to describe the nature of information processing theories.

---

[2] For examples of "classical" approaches, see Simon (1957) Chapters 6 to 8, and Rashevsky (1951), as well as numerous chapters of this book. Comparison of Bush, Mosteller & Thompson (1954) with Flood (1954) provides a particularly instructive example of the differences in approach, goal, and result between classical analysis and numerical analysis, respectively, applied to a common area of theory.

1.4 Stimulus Generation and Experimental Control

The ability of the computer to process all kinds of information according to well-defined rules leads to its use in the creation and control of experimental situations—activities at the opposite pole from theory construction. For example, computers have been used to provide complex perceptual stimuli, such as two-dimensional figures obscured by random noise or two-dimensional projections of rotating three-dimensional figures (Green, 1961b). In these applications the computer displayed the desired figures on a cathode-ray tube for photographing. At the opposite extreme from individual experimentation, computers have been used to generate the environmental inputs to large laboratory-created organizations (Chapman et al., 1959). Here the experimental task environment was a realistic pattern of air traffic as sampled by several geographically separated radars. The computer generated the (simulated) air situation and then determined what each radar would see of the situation. In both examples the computer was used at leisure to produce a fixed set of stimuli for later experimentation. The use of these techniques is just beginning, and we are moving toward using the computer in "real time"—that is, to generate the stimulus when needed as a function of the prior responses of the subject. This possibility necessarily implies the computer's ability to do concurrent data reduction and to monitor the maintenance of experimental conditions.

Any device for producing controlled situations can form part of a training or educational system. For a long time analogue computers have been applied by the military for flight training. The beginning uses of digital computers in the aforementioned ways imply corresponding uses in applied psychology. Thus computers are already being introduced experimentally as teaching machines (Silberman, 1961) and the systems research mentioned above led rather directly to extensive training of field organizations by similar techniques (Goodwin, 1957).

We shall not deal further with any of these applications, since their proper consideration departs too far from the predominately theoretical concerns of this book. Our purpose in mentioning them is to help broaden the picture of the computer as a general information-processing device and to avoid giving the impression that the only need for computers is on the conceptual side of psychological science.

This, then, is the range of applications of computers in psychology: statistical analysis, numerical analysis, information-processing theories, and stimulus generation and control. As we have already indicated, we shall devote the rest of the chapter to clarifying and illustrating the ways computers are used to explore both numerical and information-processing theories. All of these activities (and a great many more as well) go under the name of simulation.

2. SIMULATION

Simulation is the process of studying a system by (1) constructing a model, numerical or not, (2) examining time paths generated by the model, and (3) comparing these time paths with time paths of the phenomena under study. Thus simulation is one of the techniques for analyzing a numerical or nonnumerical theory to which we have already referred. It is the one most suited to the computer.

2.1 Random Elements in Simulation

The model used in a simulation can be deterministic, or it can contain random elements, and models incorporating such elements have become increasingly common. What are the reasons for inclusion of a "random element" in a simulation?

First, the random element may be an integral part of the theory itself. For example, in stochastic learning theories the *state of the organism at the moment of a response may be characterized by the probability of making each of the possible responses.* In such a theory a definite prediction is not made of the particular response of a particular subject on a particular trial. Only the statistical distribution of responses averaged over a number of trials or a number of subjects is predicted.

Stochastic theories (theories incorporating random elements) can be interpreted in either of two ways: the random element can be regarded as being at the heart of things—a genuine and integral characteristic of the subject's constitution—or it can be regarded as an artifact for summing up the unpredictable resultant of a host of minor (and additive) factors that influence behavior.[3] There appears to be, at present, no satisfactory way to choose empirically between these two interpretations of the random element. At present, one can find a wide diversity of viewpoint among the active researchers in stochastic learning theory on the interpretation of randomness. Bush and Mosteller, for example, say

We do not take a position of strict determinism with respect to behavior and its prediction. We tend to believe that behavior is intrinsically probabilistic,

---

[3] The first interpretation has become popular with the rise of an analogous interpretation of the probabilistic element in the physicist's equations of quantum theory. Before the invention of quantum mechanics the second interpretation was by far the more prevalent.

although such an assumption is not a necessary part of our model. Whether behavior is statistical by its very nature or whether it appears to be so because of uncontrolled or uncontrollable conditions does not really matter to us. In either case we would hold that a probability model is appropriate for describing a variety of experimental results presently available (1955, p. 3).

Suppes and Atkinson have a slightly different interpretation of the situation:

The models considered in this book are thoroughly probabilistic. This is a property they share with most of the mathematical models now being investigated in the behavioral sciences. As our understanding of neurophysiology increases, it is possible that more deterministic models will be constructed, but probabilistic models seem likely to play a major role for a long time to come (1960, p. 284).

A second way in which a random element may enter into a mathematical theory is as a means *for characterizing individual differences among members of the population* from which subjects are drawn. If the theory incorporates, for example, a parameter that measures the learning rate of the subject, allowance must be made for the fact that this parameter will have different values for different subjects. Then, if the theory is tested by pooled data obtained from a number of subjects, it may be assumed that the parameter values from these subjects are a sample drawn from a population of such parameter values. This assumption permits statistical sampling theory to be applied to the analysis of the data.

A third way in which a random element may enter the situation is *to account for differences in the task environment* with which the subject is confronted in successive tasks or for different subjects. Here the random element enters into the initial and boundary conditions that specify the model and again allows statistical theory to be used in analyzing the data.

Sometimes this random element in the task environment is not an artifact but is introduced deliberately by the experimenter. For example, in studying rote memorization of nonsense syllables by the paired associate method, it is standard practice to reorder randomly the sequence in which the syllable pairs are presented to the subject on successive trials. Again, in partial reinforcement experiments, one point of interest is the choice behavior of subjects under conditions of uncertainty; hence the sequence of stimuli to which the subject is to respond may be deliberately constructed by a random process.

We may, therefore, distinguish the following possible roles of randomness in a theory:

1. Stochastic parameters.
   a. Assumptions that the subject's behavior is determined only probabilistically by his internal state.

b. Assumption that the behavior is not solely determined by the parameter values but is subject also to influence by myriad unknown causes.
2. Randomly distributed parameters, the sample of subjects having been drawn randomly from a larger population.
3. Random variation in initial and boundary conditions.
   a. Because of factors not controlled by the experimenter.
   b. Introduced deliberately by the experimenter.

As we shall see, the appropriateness of a particular method for simulating behavior with a computer may well depend on the kinds of randomness postulated in the theory.

2.2 Numerical Simulation

The advantages and limitations of studying mathematical systems by numerical simulation should already be apparent from our discussion of numerical analysis, of which simulation is a subspecies. They can be stated simply:

1. The main advantage of numerical simulation is that it places only weak restrictions on the complexity of the systems that can be studied.
2. The main limitation of numerical simulation is that it discloses only how a particular system will behave in particular circumstances—not how a general class of systems will behave over some range of circumstances. If the theory incorporated in the simulation is stochastic, the limitation on generality is even more severe: a single run gives only one of the possible paths that the system could generate through its random components. Hence a whole series of runs must usually be made to learn anything about the probability distributions.[4]

These points were impressed on most of us early in our training in high-school algebra. With arithmetic, we can explore special cases; with algebra, we can derive general relations. But if we cannot solve the algebraic equations we set up, we must perforce fall back on numerical examples. By judicious choice of our examples, we may arrive inductively at some approximate statements about the general behavior of the system, although there is little science to guide our "judiciousness." Sometimes,

---

[4] This statement is not strictly accurate, for in an ergodic system phase averages may be estimated by time averages. For a brief discussion and references, see Bush & Mosteller (1955), pp. 98–99.

analysis may provide partial assistance by giving us estimates of the goodness of our approximations, even when it cannot give us the exact answers.

MONTE CARLO SIMULATIONS. Because such a large proportion of the mathematical theories investigated in psychology in recent years have contained random elements, numerical simulations have frequently used *Monte Carlo* methods (Flood, 1954; Bush & Mosteller, 1955). A Monte Carlo simulation is simply a numerical simulation in which some of the numbers that enter into the model's behavior are random, or pseudo-random.

Let us take as a concrete example a simple stochastic learning theory in which the state of the organism at each trial, t, is specified by a parameter $p(t)$. This parameter is interpreted as the probability that the organism will make a particular response, say R, on that trial. The experimenter will either reinforce the response (call it correct) or not. We assume (learning postulate) that if the subject makes response R, and it is reinforced, the parameter that describes him is increased:

$$p(t + 1) = a\,p(t) + (1 - a), \quad 1 > a > 0, \tag{1}$$

whereas, if he makes the response R and it is not reinforced, the parameter is decreased:

$$p(t + 1) = a\,p(t), \tag{2}$$

and if he makes a response other than R, p remains unchanged.

The Monte Carlo simulation of this model would be computed as follows:

1. Take an initial value of p—say, $p(1) = \frac{1}{2}$.
2. Compute a random number, F, in the interval $1 > F \geqslant 0$ with all three-place decimals in that interval equally likely. If $F \leqslant p$, call the subject's response R; otherwise, call it non-R.
3. If the response is R, compute whether it will be reinforced. (We will specify later the nature of this computation, which is part of the environment, not the subject.)
4. Compute the value of p for the next time interval:
$p(t + 1) = p(t)$ for non-R response,
$p(t + 1) = a\,p(t)$ for nonreinforced R response,
$p(t + 1) = a\,p(t) + (1 - a)$ for reinforced R response.
Repeat Steps 2, 3, and 4 for as many time periods as desired.

Since Step 2 involves the computation of a random number, if we repeat the simulation a second time, we expect to obtain a different sequence of values for $p(t)$, and a different sequence of responses. (But see the qualification, below, concerning the reproducibility of pseudorandom numbers.)

GENERATING RANDOM NUMBERS.   We must ask next how we shall use a computer, presumably a completely deterministic mechanism, to obtain random numbers. There is a simple way to do this that has the added advantage of avoiding philosophic discussion regarding what random numbers "really" are. For all practical purposes, a sequence of numbers may be considered random if it passes some set of standard statistical tests for randomness and if we cannot detect any obvious regularities in it that make it predictable.

Now, if we take an arbitrary number, multiply it by a suitably irregular large number, take the low-order digits of the product as our next number, and repeat this step, we shall obtain a sequence that, by the foregoing test, can be regarded as a random number drawn from a rectangular distribution.[5] If we wish to indicate that we know it has actually been generated by a regular process and that, by repeating the process, we can obtain exactly the same sequence of numbers, we can call the sequence "pseudo-random." It does not matter whether Nature is really random or merely inscrutable if we wish to obtain a sequence of random numbers for a Monte Carlo process.

Because of the widespread use of Monte Carlo methods in the social and natural sciences, subroutines exist for generating sequences of random numbers in many computer programming languages—FORTRAN, and IPL-V among others—so that a psychologist wishing to use these methods has ready-made random number generators available to him and does not have to construct one of his own.

Let us return now to Step 3 in our Monte Carlo calculation. On each trial on which the simulated organism gives response R, this step calls for a determination whether the response will be reinforced or not. In many applications—for example, partial reinforcement experiments—this step also involves computing a random number. For example, reinforcement may be provided randomly with probability π, constant for all trials. Then the same mechanism can be used as in Step 2 for generating the random number, but using the inequality $F \leqslant \pi$ instead of $F \leqslant p$ to determine which trials will be reinforced.

From the standpoint of the mechanics of computation, there is complete symmetry between these two uses of random numbers. In considering replications of the Monte Carlo runs, however, we might well wish to handle them differently. The random numbers computed in Step 3 are entirely within the control of the experimenter, whereas those computed

---

[5] There is a theory behind this; see Tausky & Todd (1956).

in Step 2 are internal to the organism. Hence we would, in general, wish to study the probability distribution of the organism's responses to a *fixed* pattern of the experimenter's reinforcements. From one run to the next, we would normally use the same sequence of random numbers in Step 3 but a varying sequence in Step 2. Using a varying sequence in Step 3 would introduce an additional, and avoidable, source of variance into the situation. On the other hand, sometimes this cost has to be paid in order to make possible a mathematical analysis of the results, for the mathematical derivations for particular sequences may be much harder to handle than the derivations for distributions of random sequences.

2.3 Information-Processing Theories

We now come to an explanation, promised in Sec. 1, of how computers can be used to formulate and test psychological theories without the mediation of classical mathematical models. Let us consider the case of a subject in a simple partial reinforcement experiment, similar to the one we have already used as an example. The subject is asked to predict whether the next of a series of stimuli that is being presented to him will be a "check" or a "plus." His behavior, the empirical data from the experiment, will consist of a series of utterances of the symbols "check" and "plus."

First, let us consider how we would construct a mathematical theory of the usual kind for this situation. We construct some concepts that can serve as variables in the model and as the basis for quantitative measurements of the subject's behavior. We can count, for example, the *number* of pluses and the number of checks in a sequence of responses and define the *probability* that his next response would be a plus or a check. The model permits inferences from the probabilities (which are not directly observable) to the sampling distribution of the responses. In this way, we take a series of symbol-emitting behaviors and construct a quantitative theory to account for certain statistical properties of this series.

However, the subject's behavior in this experiment, and in most other situations with which psychology concerns itself, is much richer and involves symbols with a much wider meaning than is captured by these counts. Thus our subject might comment during the experiment (if we would let him) "This is a run of checks," or "You gave me that plus last time just to throw me off," or even (it has happened) "Say, each block of ten trials has seven checks and three pluses." What are we to do with this sort of symbolic behavior? All might agree that some violence has been done to the behavior by translating it into numerical form; yet there is no apparent way to quantify these utterances. Is there any alternative?

Suppose we construct a sentence of the following form:

If H, the previously held hypothesis about the sequence, was verified, then use H to predict the next symbol and emit H as the reason for the prediction; but if H was not verified, then select as a new hypothesis the one from the set S that best fits the past sequence,

where the set of hypotheses and the criteria of fit are as complicated as we please. For example, we might have the following:

Let S consist of the two hypotheses: *run of checks* and *run of plusses.* Let the criterion of fit be the majority in the last three trials.

If we add these specifications to the original statement, then that statement becomes a perfectly definite theory of the subject's behavior. It makes specific predictions of his responses on each trial (after the first few)—as specific as could be made by any quantitative theory. Further, the predictions it makes correspond directly to the verbal responses of the subject.

Let us put aside the question whether the particular theory given above (the completed statement) is a *correct* theory of any subject's behavior—or whether it pleases our esthetic sensibilities. Let us focus solely on its definiteness and on the kinds of inferences that can be made from it.

One virtue of mathematical statement is the guarantee it offers that an unambiguous theory has been stated. With the simple statement above, we might argue that its ambiguity is equally low, but what if our specification of the hypotheses and criteria filled several pages? If we could transform the statement, and its more elaborate cousins, into a program for a digital computer, then we would have achieved equal guarantees of unambiguity. If the program emitted a prediction (and reason for it) at each point in the sequence no matter what the stimulus, we would know that we had a completely definite theory no matter how involved the hypotheses or criteria.[6]

To understand how such programming is possible, we must appreciate the fact that a digital computer is not (except in terms of its history and the motivation for its development) peculiarly a device for manipulating *numerical* symbols. It is a general-purpose device capable of all kinds of manipulation of all kinds of symbols. Inside the computer a symbol is simply represented by a pattern of electromagnetism of some sort. The meaning of the symbol (i.e., what it denotes) is determined by the programs

[6] The guarantees of unambiguity are usually overrated both for mathematics and for programs. The successive waves of rigorization that have swept through the mathematical world testify that what is unambiguous in one generation is not in the next. Similarly, the fact that most complex programs never are fully debugged indicates a similar failing in programs.

that recognize it, that compare it with other symbols, or that process it in other ways.

A relatively small set of elementary processes, together with appropriate combinations of them, will provide a quite general capacity for symbol manipulation. To have such a capacity, a symbol-manipulating system needs means for *reading symbols* (taking patterns in some external form and transforming them into an internal representation), *writing symbols* (transforming internal patterns into external symbols), *comparing symbols* (determining whether two patterns are identical or different) and *behaving conditionally* on the outcome of the comparison (proceeding one way if the symbols are equal, another way if they are unequal), *copying symbols* (creating patterns isomorphic to given patterns), and *associating symbols* (storing with a symbol information that identifies another symbol). The general-purpose, symbol-manipulating systems that we call electronic digital computers have all these means.

Consequently, we can store in computers symbols that represent English letters, words, and sentences as readily as we can store numerals. In particular, we can store in a computer a *program* (a structure of symbols) of such form that the computer will behave according to the foregoing statements, printing out either "plus" or "check" and a statement of the hypothesis used.

Unambiguity, although important, is only one advantage of putting theories in mathematical form. The power of mathematics is its ability to draw inferences from the model, using all the available techniques of mathematical reasoning, numerical analysis, and statistics. How much of this power is available for an information-processing theory expressed as a program?

Here we are less well off. Having reached the point of a running program, we can use the computer to simulate a subject's behavior in exactly the same way that we use the computer as a tool of numerical analysis to simulate the behavior of a mathematical model. Thus we can study the model empirically, exploring its behavior under variations of parameters and so on. But to date there is no body of theorems and general means of inference that allow us to derive general properties of the program given in symbolic form. Almost no interesting theorems, in the accepted mathematical sense of the word, have ever been proved about particular programs.

The reasons for this deficiency are not hard to find. They lie in the complexity of the programs, which derives inherently from the complexity of the theory; that is, such models postulate an actual replica of the content and organization of the subject's memory. The processes postulated are replicas of the actual inferences and transformations carried out by the subject on the information in his memory. In obtaining the freedom to characterize the complexities of human cognitive processes directly, we have given up the power of generalized inference. And, as we saw earlier, it is this same shift toward greater complexity that forces the mathematician to go to numerical simulation to explore a mathematical theory that has outgrown his powers of analysis.

Being able to deal with the content of the subject's responses entails a deficiency in assessing the fit of the model to data similar to the deficiency in making general inferences. The relative simplicity of our example may obscure this, so let us illustrate the situation with a model, the General Problem Solver, which is discussed later in the chapter. The model asserts, at a certain point in a problem-solving task, that the subject will request the experimenter to "Apply Rule 6 to the right-hand side of expression $L1$." The subject actually said "So I'd apply Rule 6 to the second part of what we have up there." We see that the program success-fully reflects the content of the subject's remark but not the form. An inference is required to assert that "the right-hand side of expression $L1$" designates the same object as "the second part of what we have up there." This inference is easy enough for a qualified human being to make but not easily objectified. Matters are not usually so clean-cut as this. For example, assume that the application of Rule 6 would in fact lead up a blind alley. Then the subject might have said "Apply rule—aw no, that won't work . . ." Have we enough evidence still to conclude that the program agrees with the subject? Thus, in gaining a form of prediction that seems hard to achieve by classical numerical models, we lose most of our standard statistical techniques for treating data and raise many difficult problems about assessing the goodness of our theories.

2.4 Analogue Simulation

In all of our references thus far to computers we have been concerned with *digital* computers. As we have seen, a digital computer is a device in which symbols are represented (stored or held in memory) and processed (manipulated), the symbols being discrete and distinguishable patterns. The digital computer operates at a microscopic level on an all-or-none basis. One symbol is not gradually and continuously modified into another. The changes are "discontinuous," like the jumps from one frame to the next of a motion picture.

This does not mean that we cannot handle systems of continuous variables with a digital computer. We can approximate the continuous system by making the jumps in the discontinuous model imperceptibly small, relative to the degree of accuracy significant for our theory. Digital computers are often used for numerical analysis of systems of differential equations.

An *analogue* computer is a device in which the values of variables are represented by physical quantities that vary continuously. Thus we might compute the behavior of a system of differential equations by building an electrical network in which voltages are used to measure the variables of interest and in which the capacitances, inductances, and resistances of the physical elements of the network are calibrated to be proportional to the corresponding parameters of the mathematical system.

At present, digital computers are much more widely used in mathematical psychology than analogue devices, and there is no reason to suppose that this situation will change rapidly. Analogue computers are tied very closely to systems of differential and integral equations, and these systems have not found a large place in psychology. The digital computer, on the other hand, can be used to simulate almost any system that is not too large (a not unimportant restriction). Attempts to build special analogue circuits for tasks such as factor analysis, although successful, have not proved competitive with digital computers programmed for the same tasks (where the single application does not have to bear the full cost of the computer). The analogue computer is also limited in its accuracy to two to three decimal places, compared to the digital computer whose accuracy is essentially unlimited. Low accuracy is often entirely acceptable, but many investigators find themselves forced to switch to digital methods as their work becomes more refined. An important factor favoring analogue computers has been the accessibility of the machines. Analogue computers are small and relatively inexpensive and often belong to the research laboratories that use them. Digital computers have only recently begun to be widely available.

One area of research in which analogue systems seem to offer some real advantages over general-purpose digital computers is in simulating systems consisting of large numbers of relatively simple elements operating in parallel. All digital devices designed up to the present time—or foreseeable in the near future—are basically serial in their operation: they do one thing, then another, then a third. They do things, of course, in extremely rapid sequence, sometimes only a few microseconds (millionths of a second) per step, so that it is usually not hard to simulate parallel systems with such a fast serial device.

Nevertheless, to simulate a system of a thousand parallel elements with a digital computer requires a cycle time several thousand times as long as that required to compute each successive approximation of the change in each element. If the process performed by each element is simple—the interest in the system residing in the indirect consequences of the inter-actions of its parts—then cheap analogue components can generally be devised and hooked up to operate in parallel with a shorter cycle time. It is for this reason that many researchers interested in the problems of simulating neural networks have gone to analogue devices for their computations.

Existing analogue devices do not lend themselves to direct simulation of complex information processes. Hence computer research on such prob-lems as human problem solving makes use almost exclusively of digital computers.

3. GENERAL DESCRIPTION OF A DIGITAL COMPUTER

The specific details of anatomy and program construction in digital computers will not be relevant to the discussion in this chapter. These details vary widely, of course, from one machine to another. Nevertheless, most readers will find it helpful to have some concrete notion of the basic principles on which a general-purpose digital computer operates—not the physical principles, or "hardware," but the fundamental logical organiza-tion of the system and its processes. In this section we shall describe a hypothetical computer. Most existing general-purpose computers would fit the description in its essentials.

3.1 Computer Anatomy

Anatomically speaking, a computer is a relatively simple system, comprised of a few specialized parts (Fig. 1).

1. The *memory*, or store. The memory is a device capable of holding symbols by some physical means that permits the symbol in any particular location to be changed (written) or to be read (i.e., copied in another location). In large computers there are usually several kinds of inter-connected memory, differentiated by *size*, by the *rapidity* with which read and write operations can be executed, and by their *addressability* (a term we shall explain). Since it is cheaper to construct slow than fast memories, most computers are equipped with a relatively small, high-speed, addressable memory (this is the one that is meant in any reference to "the" memory), backed up by larger, slower auxiliary memories. At the present time, the high-speed memory is generally a magnetic core (a magnetic drum on

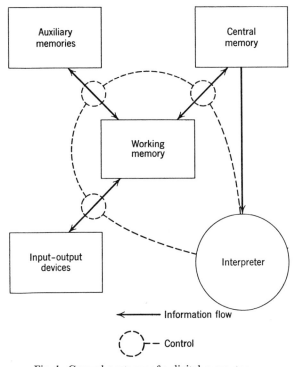

Fig. 1. General anatomy of a digital computer.

many of the smaller machines), and the principal auxiliary memory is magnetic tape or magnetic disk. The memory is universally divided into uniform small units, called *words*. A word is typically large enough to hold a single large integer (say, 12 decimal places), or six alphabetic symbols. The high-speed memory, and sometimes the auxiliary memory as well, is addressable: each word is designated by a number (its *address*), and access can be gained to the symbol in a word by referring to its address; that is, instructions can be given in the form: "Add the integer at address *A* to the integer at address *B*, and place the sum at address *C*."

2. The *working memory*, or arithmetic unit. The working memory is a device capable of holding several words (generally only two) associated with devices for performing operations on these words. In most current computers the only operations that can be performed on locations in the general memory are transporting symbols to these locations from the working memory ("store" operations) and transporting symbols from these locations to the working memory ("find" or "add" operations). All other symbol manipulating is done in the working memory. Thus, to perform arithmetic operations on numbers stored in memory, these numbers are

brought into the working memory, and the arithmetic or other processing is done there. It is for this reason that the working memory is generally called the arithmetic unit.

3. The *interpreter*, or control unit. The interpreter, whose operation is explained in detail below, is the device for following the program of instructions that has been put into the computer. It normally has two registers: the *current instruction register*, which holds the instruction to be obeyed at a given instant, and the *sequence register*, which holds the place in the program where the next instruction is to come from.

4. *Input and output units.* These are devices capable of reading symbols presented in some external form (e.g., punched cards or magnetic tapes) and transforming them into symbols in memory, and devices capable of transforming symbols in memory into symbols in some external form (e.g., symbols printed on paper). They are the channels that permit communication between the computer and its environment.

3.2 Interpretation Cycle

To understand the operation of the computer, let us follow through the basic *interpretation cycle* carried out by the interpreter (Fig. 2). The interpretation cycle comprises a sequence of processes that is determined by the contents of the registers in the interpreter. These processes change the contents of one or more locations in the memory, the working memory, and the interpreter itself. The interpretation cycle has two major phases:

EXECUTE PHASE A. One portion of the word in the current instruction register is interpreted as an instruction, and this instruction is executed. For example, if the instruction part of the word in the instruction register is interpreted as "Store in location x the symbol in the working memory," then during this phase of the cycle the word at address x of the main memory will be changed to be identical with the word that was in the working memory at the beginning of the cycle.

EXECUTE PHASE B. The other portion of the word in the instruction register, used to link to the next instruction, is placed in the sequence register.

FETCH PHASE. The sequence register is examined, and the contents of that register are interpreted as the address of a memory location. The word in that memory location is copied into the instruction register, where it is interpreted in the Execute Phase of the next cycle.

Hence in the Execute Phase the computer is under control of the word in the instruction register. It executes the instruction named in the

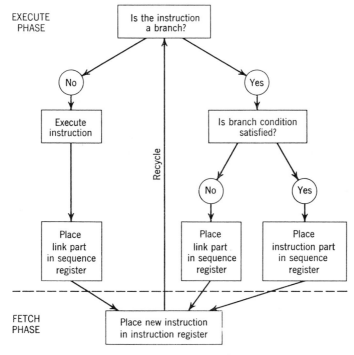

Fig. 2. Interpretive cycle.

instruction part of that word and puts in the sequence register the address of the next instruction, named in the link part of the word. In the Fetch Phase the computer comes under control of the address in the sequence register. It brings the word addressed there into the instruction register as the next instruction. The computer operates simply by repeating this Fetch-Execute cycle again and again—a quarter million times per second in the case of a very fast machine.

There is only one essential variation in the cycle we have just described, but it is of fundamental importance. An important subclass of instructions called *branch* or *transfer* instructions has a slightly different cycle. A typical branch instruction is shown in Fig. 3; it would be read as:

"If the working memory is zero, branch to X, otherwise go to Y." When a branch instruction enters the current instruction register, the basic cycle goes as follows:

EXECUTE PHASE A. The instruction part of the current instruction is interpreted. This causes the content of the working memory to be examined to determine if it is zero.

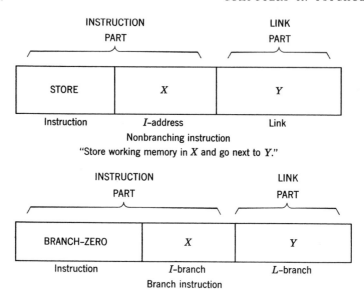

Fig. 3. Structure of computer instruction word.

EXECUTE PHASE B. If the working memory is zero then the address (*X*) of the instruction part is placed in the sequence register; if the working memory is not zero, then the link part (*Y*) of the instruction is placed in the sequence register.

FETCH PHASE. The instruction register is reloaded under control of the sequence register exactly as in the normal cycle.[7]

3.3 Programs

To solve a problem on the computer, the input channels are used to store in the computer's memory a *program* and some *information* (usually called *data*). Any word in the memory may be selected to store a piece of information or a single instruction (the latter in the form just described). A program is simply a set of such instructions, arranged as a branching list; that is to say, each instruction word (except those holding branch instructions) contains in its link part the address of the *next* instruction to be executed. A branch instruction, as already explained, contains the

[7] The particular scheme we have been describing represents a computer with a so-called one-plus-one address instruction word—the IBM 650 is an example of such a computer. However, with minor alterations, the description would fit any other computer that is commercially available today.

addresses of *two* "next" instructions, the one or the other of them to be executed, depending whether or not the condition stated in the branch instruction is satisfied. Since the instructions are stored in memory (computers having this characteristic are said to have "internally stored programs"), processes can be executed on the instructions themselves. This potentiality for modifying instructions is employed in most, but not all, programming schemes, although we shall have no occasion to discuss it here.

PROGRAM LOOPS. A typical computer program contains many *loops*. A loop is a sequence of instructions, the last member of which has as its "next" the first instruction of the loop. After A_n, the final instruction of the loop, has been executed, the initial instruction of the loop, A_1, is again returned to the instruction register and re-executed, followed again by A_2, A_3, and so on. Each loop in a program must contain at least one conditional branch; if it did not, the loop could never be left once it had been entered. It would be repeated indefinitely, like the looping of a desk calculator when the operator inadvertently tries to divide by zero. The meaning of the sequence of instructions in a loop is as follows:

"Repeat this sequence of instructions until *a*, then go to *B*."

"If *a* go to *B*, otherwise continue" is the branch instruction in the loop.

By using loops, a small number of program instructions can be made to govern the processes of the computer over a considerable period of time. Thus, the "program"

1 Step with left foot, then 2.
2 Step with right foot, then 3.
3 If end of block, do 4; if not, do 1.
4 Terminate.

could govern the processes of a man walking the length of a city block. If the block were 500 ft long, the loop would be executed about a hundred times.

HIERARCHIES OF SUBROUTINES. When our pedestrian has reached the end of the block, a different program also incorporating a loop could get him across the street intersection. Then a repetition of the original program, described above, would continue him down the next block. Let us designate the first program: "*A*. Walk the length of a block;" and the second program: "*B*. Cross an intersection." We can now instruct him to walk to the 1400 block by defining the program: "*C*. Walk to the 1400 block."

1 Do *A*, then 2.
2 Do *B*, then 3.
3 If "1400" reached, do 4; if not, do 1.
4 Terminate.

The programs *A* and *B* are used as *subprograms* or *subroutines* in the loop of the executive program *C*. This is a prototype of a typical computer-program structure that contains loops and, by the use of named sub-routines, whole complex hierarchies of such loops. The reader may find it instructive to take some example of everyday behavior—getting up in the morning, grading a set of examination papers, or what not—and write a program that describes the hierarchy of episodes that organizes this behavior.

3.4 Summary

Anatomically, a digital computer is a device comprised of a general memory, a working memory, an interpreter, and input and output units. Its operation follows a definite two-phase interpretation cycle, involving executing one instruction and fetching the next instruction. The (branching) sequence of instructions that governs the repetition of this cycle is called a program. Complex programs generally consist of hierarchically organized routines whose components are loops of instructions and of subroutines.

4. TELEOLOGICAL MECHANISMS

In Secs. 4 through 9 of this chapter we shall examine a number of the models that have been developed for simulating phenomena of interest to psychology. We shall not survey or review the rather sizable collection of models that has been reported in the literature—most of them in the last five years—but shall instead select a set of examples that will illustrate the main techniques used, the kinds of results obtained, and the methodological lessons learned from this activity. We have excluded models, however interesting as theories, that have not actually been realized and at least partly tested as analogue devices or programs for digital computers. Thus we shall not discuss psychological theories that have been motivated by information processing considerations without using computer tech-nology for their realization and testing. This choice reflects our view that the future significance of the computer in psychology lies not so much in providing a useful analogy or metaphor as in providing a powerful formal tool for constructing and testing theories.

In Sec. 4 we describe some relatively abstract simulations whose main significance has been to demonstrate the realizability of adaptive, goal-seeking learning mechanisms. In Sec. 5 we examine an example of adaptive behavior based on heuristic devices (a concept that will prove central to the subsequent analysis); in Sec. 6 we describe some programs for self-organizing neural nets and for pattern-recognizing systems; in Secs. 7, 8, and 9 we consider some completely nonnumerical simulations of human cognitive processes; and in Sec. 10 we note briefly some references to simulation in social psychology.

4.1 Robotology: the Imitation of Life

The earliest uses of simulation in psychology antedate by many years the introduction of the digital computer. They involved analogue devices —mechanical, electrical, and electronic—and were mainly devised to combat vitalism by demonstrating, in the metal, that mechanisms could behave as though they had goals and drives, could adapt and could learn.[8]

The "tortoises" of Grey Walter (1953) are among the most elaborate and impressive of these pioneering analogical simulations. The tortoises are battery-driven mechanisms, capable of locomoting over smooth surfaces. One type, *Machina speculatrix*, explores the surface in somewhat random fashion and approaches lights of moderate intensity when it senses them. A light is placed at the site of its battery charger, so that the tortoise tends to return to that location when the battery needs recharging.

Thus *Machina speculatrix* exhibits drive and behavior oriented toward drive reduction; and it incorporates both a high-priority "hunger" drive and a low-priority "curiosity" drive. Even this relatively simple system exhibited behaviors that were not predicted by the designer and that had not been predicted from the numerous similar verbal drive-reduction theories which have long been in the literature (see Walter, 1953, Chapter 5). It is possible also (Simon, 1957, Chapter 15) to construct mathematical theories of systems like the tortoises. The existence of verbal and mathematical theories alongside the simulation provides instructive material for an exercise in comparative methodology.

Walter has designed a similarly simple piece of circuitry that may be regarded as a simulation of Pavlovian conditioning (Walter, 1953, Appendix C). When this is attached to *Machina speculatrix*, a new species, *Machina docens*, which has the capacity to learn from its interaction with the environment, is produced.

Although the tortoises aroused considerable interest and have been further developed by other investigators, they appear no longer to be in the main line of evolution of psychological simulations. The interesting

---

[8] Boring (1946) surveys some of these early devices in a most instructive and entertaining manner. See also Walter (1953), Chapter 6.

properties they exhibited could be rather easily simulated by digital computers, and the digital simulation lent itself to greater elaboration than did the analogue devices.

4.2 The Homeostat

W. Ross Ashby (1952) has constructed an analogue device, the homeostat, that simulates adaptive behavior and learning of a more abstract character than that exhibited by the tortoises. Consider a dynamic system represented by the variables $x_1, \ldots, x_n$ and governed by the system of differential equations:

$$\frac{dx_i}{dt} = f_i(x_1, \ldots, x_n), \qquad i = 1, \ldots, n. \tag{3}$$

This system, starting from any initial point, will trace a path through the n-dimensional space of the x's. We suppose that in this space there exists a subspace representing a range of values of the variables, within which the system can survive; that is, if the system remains inside the cube, $X_i' \leqslant x_i \leqslant X_i''$, it survives; if it goes outside the boundaries of this cube, it is destroyed. We can think of the boundaries of the cube as representing critical values of certain physiologically significant variables—for example, temperature and amount of oxygen.

Ashby supposed a second cube, inside the first, that defines a self-preserving mechanism. For example, in the temperature dimension, if the outer cube defines "freezing" and "burning up," the inner cube defines "painfully cold" and "painfully hot." Whenever the system, starting from a point within the inner cube, hits the boundary of that cube, a random change (a "mutation") takes place in one or more of the functions, f_i, so that we now have the new dynamic system:

$$\frac{dx_i}{dt} = f_i'(x_1, \ldots, x_n). \tag{4}$$

The new system will have a different set of paths in phase space from the old one. Its trajectory may again bring it into contact with the inner cube, in which case a new mutation will occur. On the other hand, the mutated dynamic system may possess a position of stable equilibrium within the inner cube. In this case its trajectory will carry it toward this point, and it may remain within the cube without striking its boundary. In this case the system has "adapted" to the conditions for survival.

If the system is at rest at a position of stable equilibrium and is then disturbed slightly, it will tend to return to the equilibrium, exhibiting

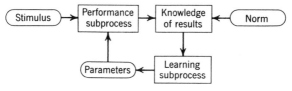

Fig. 4. Schema for a learning simulation.

homeostasis. However, if some of the parameters of the system that represent its environment are altered, it may no longer have a stable equilibrium within the region of survival. It will then undergo a new course of mutations until it again acquires such an equilibrium, thus exhibiting learning. If it is subjected to a fluctuating environment, it will tend to mutate to a condition that possesses a stable equilibrium within the cube for both of these environments.

Because of its abstract character, it is possible to carry out a certain amount of mathematical analysis of the homeostat. For example, if we limit the analysis to linear dynamic systems with constant coefficients, the probability can be calculated that a matrix of coefficients selected at random will represent a system with a stable equilibrium within the critical cube. From this probability and the speed of mutation the mean time required for the homeostat to adapt successfully can be calculated.

The homeostat exhibits in clear-cut form the central feature of all simulations of learning. A system that learns consists of at least two subsystems: a *performance* subsystem and a subsystem by which the actual *learning* is accomplished (Fig. 4). The behavior of the performance subsystem (in Ashby's analogue device, the homeostat, it was the magnet deflections) is compared with some norm of behavior (in the homeostat, a zero deflection). An excessively large discrepancy between them activates the learning system, which, in turn produces a parametric or structural change in the performance system. This cycle of events repeats until the discrepancy between behavior and norm is sufficiently reduced. From a psychological standpoint, the comparison between behavior and norm represents *knowledge of results*. In the simplest schemes, like this one, there is no explicit representation of reward—the discrepancy between behavior and norm constituting the drive that activates the learning subsystem.

5. IDENTIFYING SYMBOLS

Among the psychological processes that have been the object of simulation attempts are the perceptual processes by which a human can recognize that a certain visual pattern represents a particular written or printed letter of the English alphabet or that an aural pattern represents an English phoneme. Machine simulation of such processes is often referred to as "pattern recognition," but to distinguish it from some other simulations to be discussed later we call it *symbol identification*.

It would be of great practical importance to empower a machine to accept spoken or written language as input, and it would be of great value to psychology to know how humans do this. Each of these goals has provided part of the motivation for research on symbol identification.

5.1 Speech Recognition

Extensive study of human identification of oral language shows fairly definitely (1) that the phoneme is the basic unit of identification, (2) that spoken English involves, for practical purposes, an alphabet of about forty phonemes, and (3) that phonemes are identified by humans by testing for the presence or absence of a number of binary characteristics (Fatehchand, 1960, especially p. 218). From the standpoint of the speaker, phonemes can be classified in terms of the positions of lips and tongue, the voicing, and so on. Thus, for example, "*f*" is an unvoiced fricative formed by the continuous passage of breath through the lips. From the standpoint of the auditor, phonemes can be classified in terms of the principal frequencies present in the sound (formants) and the constancy and duration of the sound. Duration would be a significant characteristic for distinguishing an "*f*" from a "*p*."

These principles of speech production and recognition have been demonstrated by standard experimental techniques in the psychological laboratory, still without producing a *detailed* knowledge of the cues involved, and the ways in which they are detected and used, and without leading to satisfactory machine simulation of the process. Within the last two years, however, several programs on digital computers (Fatehchand, 1960; Forgie & Forgie, 1959) with limited abilities to identify phonemes have been devised and tested.

Since the programs for speech recognition are rather involved, we shall not describe them in detail but shall look, instead, at a rather successful program for the recognition of hand-transmitted Morse code. The simulation of recognition of hand-sent telegraphic messages is undoubtedly an order of magnitude less difficult than the simulation of speech recognition, but the program for solving it illustrates the same fundamental points about simulation methods.

5.2 Recognition of Hand-Sent Morse Code

At first blush it might appear that machine recognition of hand-sent Morse code would be a trivial problem. A message in Morse code is a well-defined sequence of marks and spaces, in which each mark has a duration of one (dot) or three (dash) units and each space has a duration of one (symbol-space), three (character-space), or seven (word-space) units. At least these are the norms used to define the alphabet of symbols, and mechanical devices (the teletypewriter) have long been available that are capable of encoding, transmitting, receiving, and decoding messages of signals that obey these norms. The simulation problem arises because human senders do not, in fact, obey the norms—the dots, dashes, and various spaces in hand-sent Morse code are not sufficiently uniform to permit decoding by machine in a simple and straightforward manner. For this reason recognition of hand-sent code presents the same problems, albeit less severely, as recognition of speech or handwriting.

A partially successful code-recognition scheme MAUDE (Morse Automatic Decoder) has been devised by Gold (1959), using the following general strategy:

1. Search for rules of thumb that *usually* hold for hand-sent code even if sometimes there are exceptions to the rules.

2. In searching for such rules use whatever information and hints are available regarding the cues that humans use in performing the same identification task.

3. Build the rules into a mutually correcting system, so that errors resulting from the failure of one rule will be detected and corrected by the operation of others. (In information theory terms this means building redundancy into the rules or, properly speaking, making use in the rule system of the redundancies in the messages to which it is applied.)

4. Test the rules against a growing sample of messages and add new rules as they prove essential. Examine not only the number of errors made by the system but the nature of these errors in order to obtain diagnostic information about the inadequacies of the system.

The initial system used five encoding and language rules:

1. The longest of six successive spaces is almost always a long space (character or word space).

2. The shortest of six successive spaces is almost always a symbol space.

3. The shortest of three successive long spaces is usually a character space.

4. The longest of three, four, or five successive spaces is almost always a long space if the succession of marks they separate does not constitute a character of the Morse alphabet.

5. The shortest of six successive marks is usually a dot.

These rules identify a subset of the total sequence of marks and spaces in a message. The subset, in turn, estimates the average durations for the five types of signals. From these average durations, criterion times are calculated for distinguishing the three kinds of spaces and two kinds of marks. Further improvement is made in certain parameters entering into the criteria by basing these parameters on running averages computed from the message being decoded. This adjustment is important in altering the calibration of the system to fit the idiosyncratic features of the styles of different senders.

The author evaluates the program in these terms:

MAUDE has successfully decoded between 90 per cent and 95 per cent of 184 messages. A successful decoding is one which results in a text which can be easily read by a man who knows the language.

It is felt that MAUDE can be a practical piece of equipment for a site with heavy traffic. Its performance will be inferior to that of a man until more sophisticated language rules, using at least a word vocabulary, are included (1959, p. 17).

Let us turn from the applied goals of this work to questions of mathematical psychology. First, the incorporation of "rules of thumb" in this program is highly typical of programs that have been devised for symbol identification, pattern recognition, learning, and problem-solving tasks. We call processes of this kind, which generally contribute to a result but whose effects are not "guaranteed," *heuristic processes*. These programs, then, are constructed largely from heuristic processes. There appear to be two not entirely independent reasons for this. First, there are no known ways of accomplishing tasks of the kinds under discussion that do not employ heuristic processes; second, we know that humans make very great use of heuristic processes.

We can put the matter in a different way. There are many tasks that have been mechanized in such a way that the machine processes are quite different from the human processes they replace. For example, it is easily demonstrated that a computer, as ordinarily programmed, does not use the same processes for multiplying two numbers that humans use. In such cases the machine process does not constitute a simulation of the human process and generally has relatively little value for psychological research. On the other hand, there are many tasks (like the one under discussion) in which mechanization has been accomplished only by simulating, in greater or less detail, the processes used by humans. In these cases the goals of automation and of understanding the human process go hand in hand. Progress toward either goal can hardly fail to contribute to the other and may, in fact, be the best means for progressing toward the other.

An information-processing theory of human recognition of hand-sent code would be a description of the cues people detect and use for decoding messages, plus a description of the processes that accomplish the decoding. Suppose we had a theory of this kind: how could we test it? We could determine some of the consequences of the theory—for example, we could predict the errors or kinds of errors it would make in decoding particular messages—and compare them with actual human behavior.

But, if the theory were at all complicated—say, as complicated as MAUDE—probably the only feasible way to determine its consequences would be to simulate it with a machine and compare its output with the outputs of human decoders. The Morse decoder was not devised primarily as a human simulation. Even so, it casts considerable light on the human decoding process. In its present form it gives a reasonable measure of the limits of accuracy of decoding that does not make any use of word meanings, hence some measure of the dependence of humans upon word meanings in their decoding. In the words of the author:

> The conclusion is inescapable, therefore, that for the automatic reception of a language encoded by even a simple process like Morse code, a machine must have some knowledge of the language if it is to approximate the performance of a man. In particular, MAUDE must, to some extent, know English if it is to decode English sent by Morse code. . . . If allowed to generalize somewhat from the experience with MAUDE, it would be concluded that efforts to decode by machine "noisily" encoded language symbol by symbol, e.g., speech recognizers using only the waveform of the speech, are bound to be severely limited. It must be recognized that better decoding machines depend not only on ingenious decoding schemes, but also on more use of the structure of the language and greater understanding of human decoding processes (1959, p. 23).

5.3 Conclusion

Our examination of programs for identifying symbols can be summarized as follows.

1. People appear to make extensive use of heuristic processes in symbol-identification tasks.

2. Computer programs for such tasks, whether their purpose is simulation or automation, appear also to require the use of heuristics.

3. The adequacy of specific computer programs as simulations of the

human processes can be tested by comparing the behavior through time of the computer with the behavior of human subjects when both are confronted with the same tasks.

6. SELF-ORGANIZING NETS AND PATTERN RECOGNITION

Simulation of complex systems can be carried out at various levels of concreteness and to various degrees of detail. The simulations described in the section on teleological mechanisms were highly abstract. Grey Walter's tortoises and Ashby's homeostat simulate general mechanisms and processes such as "drive," "adaptiveness," and "learning." The simulations described in the section on symbol identification are somewhat more detailed and certainly more concrete. Nonetheless, although they simulate some of the information processes that people use in performing recognition tasks, they do not simulate—nor do they pretend to—the neural processes that underlie the information processes.

This distinction of levels in theory building is familiar enough in the natural sciences. Chemistry had explanations for many reactions at the level of molecular interactions long before these same reactions were provided with physical explanations in terms of interactions of elementary subatomic particles. As a matter of fact, although our present knowledge of physical chemistry allows us to carry out "in principle" a reduction of an explanation of the former kind to an explanation of the latter kind, this reduction cannot be carried out "in fact" and in detail except in the simplest cases.

The same distinction applies to explanations of human behavior at the information processing level and at the neurological level. Although we may anticipate the development of the same kind of "in principle" reduction, theories will be needed at both levels.

In this section we consider approaches to simulation at the level of neurological organization. We shall leave out of account the detailed theory of the individual neuron and consider only the problem of organization of sets of neurons in the central nervous system to produce adaptive behavior of the organism. A large proportion of the applications of computers to psychology fall in this area. The simulations that have been produced can generally be characterized as follows (some of these general statements will be qualified when we take up particular examples):

1. The principal phenomenon to be explained is *pattern recognition*: how the nervous system, given its known gross characteristics, can learn

to classify, say, patterns of light that fall on the retina in an appropriate way. (In discussing symbol identification, we were concerned with rules of classification but not with acquisition of these rules by the nervous system.)

2. The nervous system is represented as a *network of individual elements*—neurons—that are initially connected in a more or less *random* fashion, subsequent appropriate organization being a function of *learning*. (Hence the simulations incorporate stochastic parameters that are intrinsic to the theory of the structure of the nervous system.)

3. Only *gross properties* of neurons are represented, not their detailed biological structure. In general, each neuron is represented by a few *numerical parameters*, and the connections between neurons also by numerical parameters. Hence explicit mathematical models can readily be written for most of these simulations. It is only their complexity that requires the use of simulation techniques rather than classical mathematical analysis for analyzing them.

6.1 Pattern Recognition

Any system that makes different responses to different stimuli can be viewed as a pattern recognizer. Hence all the systems we have described in Secs. 4 through 6 are pattern recognizers. However, the term pattern recognition tends at the present time to be used in a somewhat more limited sense. That narrower meaning is best characterized by an example:

We consider a learning system and its environment, which is controlled by an experimenter. The learning system is capable of distinguishing among a large number of different stimuli coming from the environment. The experimenter has (without informing the learning system) partitioned the different stimuli into a number of classes, such that any two stimuli in the same class are to be regarded as the "same" stimulus and to elicit the same response. The task of the learning system is to learn enough about the partitioning in order to produce distinct responses for distinct stimuli and identical responses for identical stimuli.

The possible stimuli may be, for example, all possible combinations of 1's and 0's in a large two-dimensional grid of 1's and 0's:

$$1001011000$$
$$1010110100$$
$$1011101011$$
$$0101011101$$
$$1101101011$$

The experimenter may equate particular subsets with letters of the alphabet. Thus the following stimuli might be "M's":

11100111	10100101
11011011	10011001
11000011	10000001
11000011	10000001

The task of the learning system, then, is to learn to distinguish the various letters of the alphabet, which may appear in different positions on the grid, different sizes, different orientations, and different styles.

All the systems we have considered have at least a limited capacity to discriminate among stimuli. The tortoise, for example, responds to moderate light with "approach" and to an obstacle with "withdraw." The code-recognition program responds to different signal patterns as English letters. These systems, however, fall very short of the capacities of humans, or even lower organisms, to discriminate among stimuli on the basis of "appropriate" criteria of similarity and to learn such discriminations. They are deficient in learning, they are deficient in the variety of stimuli that can be presented to them, and they are deficient in the complexity and arbitrariness of the criteria of similarity they can apply. Several research efforts have been directed at removing one or more of these limitations.

Most of the work in this area is in a direct line of descent from the pre-computer mathematical work of McCulloch and Pitts and the verbal theories of Hebb. McCulloch and Pitts (1943) showed how neuron "circuits" could represent all the fundamental functions of symbolic logic and later (Pitts & McCulloch, 1947) showed in general terms how a neural net not unlike the central nervous system could abstract invariants ("universals" or "concepts") from patterns presented to input organs in various orientations, sizes, and so on. Hebb (1949), starting from somewhat different hypotheses, developed a theory to account for the gradual organization of the central system to accomplish pattern recognition and the other processes of which it is capable.

We describe first a program by Farley and Clark (1954) (also Clark & Farley, 1955), which illustrates the general technique that has been used in pattern-recognition work for simulating neuron nets and the processes of reinforcement. Next, we examine the attempts by Rochester, Holland, Haibt, and Duda (1956) to formulate and test in an unambiguous model some of Hebb's theories. This program will give us further insight into the relations between verbal theories and computer simulations and into techniques for testing theories by simulation. A third section characterizes briefly the class of pattern recognition schemes called perceptrons, which have been studied extensively by Rosenblatt and his associates at the Cornell Aeronautical Laboratories. In the final part we describe the pattern recognition scheme of Selfridge and Dinneen, which is different in a number of respects from the others considered in this section and which will provide something of a bridge to the cognitive simulations that are the topic of Secs. 7 and 8.

6.2 Self-Organizing Networks

Clark and Farley (1955, p. 86) describe their system thus:

Briefly, the self-organizing system was composed of two parts. The first part received input patterns and transformed them into outputs and the second part acted upon parameters of the first so as to modify the input-output transformation according to certain fixed criteria. These parts were termed the transformation and the modifier, respectively.

We see that this simulation fits the same paradigm of a learning system that we used to characterize the homeostat. The Farley-Clark "transformation" corresponds to the performance subsystem, and their "modifier," to the learning subsystem (see Fig. 4). In the Farley-Clark scheme the performance subsystem consisted of a randomly interconnected network of elements. At each instant an element was in either an excited or an unexcited state. The interconnections transmitted excitations unidirectionally between pairs of elements, the strength of an excitation being proportional to a weight associated with the connection. An excitation was transmitted only when the element at the origin of the connection was in the excited state. The total excitation transmitted to a given element was the simple sum of the weighted excitations of the various elements with which it was connected. Each element was characterized by a threshold; if the excitation impinging on it exceeded this threshold, it was transformed into the excited state. The net was stimulated by imposing upon certain elements (an *input group*) an excitation in addition to that impinging on them from the other elements of the system. Two subsets of elements in the net were designated positive and negative *output groups*, respectively. The *output* of the net was defined as the difference between the total excitations of the positive and negative output groups.

To exercise the performance system, two distinct input groups were excited on different trials to represent different stimuli. A positive response to the one input group and a negative response to the other input group were defined as "correct" responses. The learning process was simple: whenever a correct response was made, the weights of all connections that had just previously participated in firing an element were increased; whenever an incorrect response was made, the weights of all connections that had just previously participated in firing an element were decreased. The network succeeded in learning to discriminate, substantially without error, between a pair of distinct stimuli. Moreover, in later experiments Clark and Farley (1955) showed that the system generalizes from this simple discrimination to discriminations between stimuli that "resemble" more or less the stimuli on which it has learned.

6.3 Simulation of Cell Assemblies

One theory of how the brain works, which has attracted much attention, is Hebb's (1949) theory of cell assemblies. Hebb's theory is neurological in a broad sense, that is, it is based on some gross characteristics of neural structure and cortical organization, but it does not make strong postulates about the details of neural processes, anatomy, or chemical and physical mechanisms involved. Its principal goal is to explain long-term memory—how new stimuli that resemble stimuli experienced in the past can cause the latter to be recalled.

A cell assembly is a set of nerve cells having the property that, when a subset is excited, these tend to arouse the others. Thus the total set aroused tends to be independent of the exact stimulus. Hebb sets forth some hypotheses about how cell assemblies might come into existence and the functions they might perform in perceptual organization, memory, and the government of attention. Hebb's verbal description of the theory has established it as plausible in the minds of many psychologists, but its complexity and generality are such that it is not at all apparent how to test it. It is impossible to establish by verbal reasoning reliable conclusions about how a system of the kind specified by Hebb would actually operate—what it would do. It is even far from clear just how fully the system is specified, whether the set of mechanisms postulated by Hebb is either necessary or sufficient to produce the observed phenomena.

Mathematical analysis appears scarcely more promising than verbal reasoning as a means for testing Hebb's theory. The model lacks the simplicities needed to make it amenable to classical analysis, and there is reason to believe that simplifying it to make such analysis possible would destroy some of the properties of the system on which its hypothesized performance depends.

In the face of these difficulties simulation has been proposed as a method of studying Hebb's theory, and such a simulation has been undertaken by Rochester, Holland, Haibt, and Duda (1956). Their initial simulation, carried out on the IBM 704 computer, resembles in many respects the Farley-Clark scheme, even though the tasks imposed on the two systems were somewhat different.

The main portion of the computer memory was organized in 69 parts, each representing a single neuron. With each neuron was stored such information as its state of fatigue, the numbers of the neurons to which it was connected, and the "weight" of each connection. During any given run, each neuron was connected, at random, to 10 others. The firing of neurons by excitation from other neurons was governed much as in the Farley-Clark scheme. To represent permanent memory, the program simulated Hebb's postulate:

When an axon of cell *A* is near enough to excite a cell *B* and repeatedly or persistently takes part in firing it, some growth process or metabolic change takes place in one or both cells such that *A*'s efficiency, as one of the cells firing *B*, is increased (1949, p. 62).

Thus the weights of the connections among neurons were increased as a consequence of firing, as in the Farley-Clark scheme, but the changes did not in this case depend on the result of the excitation being "correct."

The simulation produced two kinds of useful information. First, it showed that the theory had been incompletely specified and that additional assumptions had to be added to produce a working mechanism. Second, it showed that the theory, in its original form, would not produce the predicted phenomena. A modified theory, developed by Rochester et al., in collaboration with Hebb and Milnor, proved substantially more satisfactory:

The second set of experiments were designed to test P. M. Milnor's revision of Hebb's theory . . . . Cell assemblies formed and exhibited the "fractionation" and "recruiting" required by the theory. The cell assemblies, however, were not able to arouse one another, so this model was too heavily dominated by environment (1956, p. 88).

The authors themselves state very clearly the way in which this kind of simulation can be used fruitfully as a part of a program of theoretical and experimental work:

This kind of investigation cannot prove how the brain works. It can, however, show that some models are unworkable and provide clues as to how to revise the models to make them work. Brain theory has progressed to the point where it is not an elementary problem to determine whether a model is workable. Then, when a workable model has been achieved, it may be that a definitive experiment can be devised to test whether or not the workable model corresponds to a detail of the brain (1956, p. 88).

6.4 Perceptrons

Perceptron is the name of a class of pattern-recognizing devices developed by Frank Rosenblatt and his associates. The behavior of perceptrons has been simulated on both digital and analogue devices (Rosenblatt, 1958, 1961). The basic elements in a perceptron are simulated neurons, not unlike those described in the two preceding parts of this section. One set of the neurons originates in the *sensory system* or retina and receives all inputs to the system. A second set of the neurons constitutes the *association system*, and a third, usually small set, the *response system*. There are interconnections from sensory to association system, from association to response system, and among neurons within the association system. The net is organized so that each neuron in the association is connected with a number of neurons in the sensory system, the latter being selected essentially at random. Learning is achieved in this system, as in the other neural net models we have discussed, by changing weights of the elements as a function of their participation in successful performance.

Simple perceptrons have been studied extensively both theoretically and experimentally and their properties are well understood. They classify stimuli essentially by determining sets of shared sensory inputs among exemplars of the task. They can perform impressively on discrimination learning and can fail dismally on generalization learning (in the extreme case of no sensory overlap between the test figure and the prior exemplars there is zero generalization). Much more goes on in human perception than the detection of "identical elements." What these systems reveal is the kind of psychological properties to be expected from certain simple types of organization. They also form the basis for developing more complicated systems with more adequate characteristics (see Rosenblatt, 1961, for the variety of directions that has opened up).

6.5 The Selfridge-Dinneen Pattern Recognition Scheme

The approach of Selfridge (1955) and Dinneen (1955) to learning pattern recognition differs in several respects from those considered in the previous parts of this section. It contains no explicit neural model—its elements are processes rather than neural structures. Moreover, it is basically nonnumerical in spirit, although if one examines its detail, one will discover underlying arithmetic processes. Like the models already considered, it takes a condition of randomness as its starting point. In its emphasis on processes and its generally nonnumerical character it has important points in common with the simulations to be considered in subsequent sections.

The task of the Selfridge-Dinneen program was the recognition of simple visual patterns presented as dots on a square array. The performance program is shown in Fig. 5. The program computes a set of characteristics for a particular input stimulus. Each characteristic is formed by a sequence of transformations of the input array. Thus the first characteristic would be computed by performing A on the input, then B on the resulting array, then B again, and finally C. The general effect of these transformations is to reduce the number of dots in the array so that the final numerical value of the characteristic is obtained by counting the number of dots still left—for example, if a sequence reduced a triangular array of dots to one dot for each corner, the count would be 3. Each pattern that the program is prepared to recognize is represented by a normative set of characteristic values with which the computed values for an input stimulus are compared. If the correspondence is sufficiently good, then the program classifies the input as an example of the particular pattern in question.

The elementary operations used to build up the sequences were modeled, at least in gross terms, on operations known to be performed at the human retina. An *averaging* operation filtered out small local irregularities in the

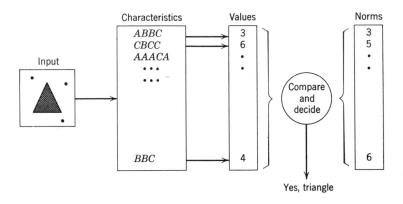

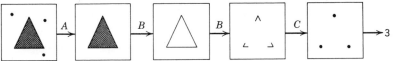

Fig. 5. Schematic diagram of the Selfridge-Dinneen pattern recognizer.

visual field; an *edging* operation emphasized local discontinuities, thus replacing solid shapes by their boundaries. As Dinneen (1955, p. 100) observes:

> We tried to pick operations which were simple in structure and unrelated to particular patterns. In other words, we avoided special operations which might work very well for *A*'s and *O*'s, but not very well for other shapes. There is evidence in neuro-physiology, moreover, that both averaging and edging of visual images are performed by the nervous system of many animals.

The features of this program that make it of interest are the ways in which it builds up its repertoire of characteristics. This occurs at two levels. For any particular characteristic the program gradually builds up information about its performance on exemplars of a pattern (i.e., the experimenter trains the system by repeatedly showing it examples of the pattern he wishes the program to learn). It finds out whether the characteristic carries information about the pattern. If it does, then it tends to have almost the same characteristic value for many exemplars. This characteristic value becomes the "norm" that is used to identify the pattern. If no such norm emerges—if the characteristic yields a fairly flat distribution over many values—then the characteristic is discarded as irrelevant to recognizing the pattern.

Since it discards characteristics, the program has the opportunity to generate new ones. Thus it gradually enriches the set of characteristics that it uses. The important notion here is that characteristics are expressed symbolically (as sequences of their names), so that processes can easily be defined to generate new expressions representing new characteristics. In the Selfridge-Dinneen program this was done by gathering statistics on the good characteristics that had already been found and generating sequences that were statistically similar to these good ones. Selfridge (1955, p. 93) says:

> We do not claim that this method is necessarily a very good way of choosing sequences—only that it should do better than not using at all the knowledge of what kind of sequence has worked. It has seemed to us that this is the crucial point of learning.

6.6 Summary

We have described in this section a class of simulations that attends strongly to neurophysiological considerations about the components that make up the brain. With only a few exceptions, these simulations seek to find interesting gross behavioral properties of networks of artificial neurons patterned closely upon the model put forward by McCulloch and

Pitts in 1943. The tasks have been almost universally the learning of patterns from exemplars.

Although still hampered by the size of simulation possible, large enough nets have been simulated or constructed to show that marvelous forms of adaptation will not arise just by hooking many elements together at random. On the other hand enough work has been done to clarify the nature of the simpler organizational schemes, to establish that they have some power, and to lay the groundwork for continuing elaboration. (See Hawkins, 1961, for a more detailed review.)

The Selfridge-Dinneen program does not fit easily into this categorization, since it is not based on neural nets and indeed depends on symbolic representations for the ingenuity of its learning. In fact, it has generated a somewhat separate stream of work (Selfridge 1959, Doyle 1960). It also has a strong historical connection with the work in symbolic processing to be discussed in the next section.

7. SIMULATING COGNITIVE PROCESSES: PROBLEM SOLVING

The programs we have described thus far tend to fall into two broad classes: (1) programs to demonstrate that mechanisms are capable of certain kinds of behavior usually thought to be characteristic of organisms, such as goal seeking and learning; (2) programs that simulate the neural organizations underlying some of the major perceptual and memory processes.[9] In the first class the exact details of the realization are relatively unimportant. In a sense, they constitute existence proofs, demonstrating that there are mechanisms capable of performing the required functions.

The second class of programs lends itself to more detailed and quantitative comparison with both neurological and behavioral evidence. It is tested in the same way a mathematical theory is tested.

The programs to be discussed in this section do not model neurological detail but purport to explain behavior in terms of elementary information processes. Nevertheless, at their level, these theories are specific and can be tested by detailed comparison with behavioral data. We have already explained how it is possible to construct and test theories that explain phenomena in terms of middle-level constructs even though the theories that would reduce these constructs to more elementary ones have not yet been developed or fully tested.

---

[9] The programs discussed in Sec. 5 do not really belong to either of these classes but are more closely allied to the programs we shall take up in the present section.

7.1 Problem-Solving Programs

Computer programs have been written that enable computers to discover proofs for theorems in logic (Newell & Simon, 1956; Newell,
Shaw, & Simon, 1957) and geometry (Gelernter, 1959), to play chess (see
Newell, Shaw, & Simon, 1958, for references), to design motors (Goodwin,
1958), to set up production lines (Tonge, 1961), to improve their skills at
some of these tasks (Samuel, 1959), to compose music (Hiller & Isaacson,
1959; Reitman, 1961), and even to solve double-crostics (Spiegelthal,
1960). Some of these programs are aimed at detailed simulation of human
processes—hence at understanding higher mental processes; others are
aimed at finding ways, humanoid or not, of doing the tasks well. From
almost all of them, whether intended as simulations or not, we have learned
something about human problem solving, thinking, and learning. We
have already illustrated this point in discussing the hand-sent code
recognition program, which was not primarily designed as a human
simulation. For an excellent general discussion of these programs and an
analysis of their capabilities, see Minsky (1961).

The first thing we have learned—and the evidence is by now quite
substantial—is that we can explain many of the processes of human
thinking without postulating mechanisms at subconscious levels which
are different from those that are partly conscious and partly verbalized.
The processes of problem solving, it is turning out, are the familiar
processes of noticing, searching, modifying the search direction on the
basis of clues, and so on. The same symbol-manipulating processes that
participate in these functions are also sufficient for such problem-solving
techniques as abstracting and using imagery. It looks more and more as if
problem solving is accomplished through complex structures of familiar
simple elements. The growing proof is that we can simulate problem solving in a number of situations using no more than these simple elements
as the building blocks of our programs.

7.2 The General Problem Solver

A human problem solver brings to the task both specific knowledge and
skills relevant to the particular subject-matter area in which the problem
lies and that collection of broadly applicable general knowledge and
broadly transferable problem-solving techniques we call intelligence.
Most of the computer simulations of problem solving have been special-
purpose programs—they simulate processes that go on (or might go on)

in problem solving in one particular task environment and do not segregate out generally applicable techniques from the techniques special to that kind of task. The existing chess- and checker-playing programs, music-composing program, motor-design programs play chess or checkers, compose music, or design motors, respectively. Each one is entirely helpless and inoperative in the face of any task that does not belong to the environment the program was designed to handle. In this respect, if in no other, they are strikingly unhuman.

This is not to say that humans can solve problems in areas about which they are totally ignorant. They cannot solve algebra problems without knowing the rules of algebra. To do so would be *inventing* algebra, not solving algebra problems, two very different tasks indeed. But humans bring to a new task environment a whole kit of tools, which, when combined with knowledge of the specific area, enables them to solve problems in it. A theory that purports to be an explanation of human problem solving has to have this same property—it has to contain some general problem-solving means, some way of acquiring knowledge of specific task environments and of improving both its general and specific techniques (learning capabilities).

One computer simulation of human problem solving that exists at the present time meets these specifications, at least to a limited extent (Newell, Shaw, & Simon, 1959; Newell & Simon, 1961a,b). It is labeled the General Problem Solver (GPS), not because it can solve any kind of problem—it cannot—but because the program itself makes no specific reference to the subject matter of the problem. GPS is a program that can reason in terms of means and ends about any problem that is stated in a certain general form.

Much human problem solving proceeds by erecting *goals*, detecting *differences* between present situation and goal, finding in memory or by search *tools* or *processes* that are relevant to reducing differences of these particular kinds, and applying these tools or processes.[10] Each problem generates subproblems until a subproblem is reached that can be solved—for which a program is already stored in memory. The problem solver proceeds, by successive solution of such subproblems, until he eventually achieves his over-all goal—or gives up.

The general problem solver simulates this process as follows. Its programs enable it to formulate and attack three kinds of goals:

1. *Transform* goals: Change object or situation *a* into object or situation *b*.

---

[10] See Duncker (1945), Chapters 1 and 2, and Bartlett (1958), Chapters 2–4, for typical characterizations of human problem solving in these terms.

2. *Reduce difference* goals: Eliminate or reduce the difference between *a* and *b*.

3. *Apply operator* goals: Apply the program (or operator or method) *q* to the situation *a*.

With each of these types of goal is associated one or more methods for accomplishing it. When the goal is formulated by GPS, these methods are evoked in memory and tried. One method for *transforming a* into *b* is to find a difference, *d*, between them and to formulate the *reduce difference* goal of eliminating this difference. A method for *reducing a difference* between *a* and *b* is to find an operator that is relevant for removing differences of the kind in question and to *apply that operator*. A method for *applying an operator* is to compare the actual situation with the situation that would allow application of the operator and to formulate the transform goal of changing the actual situation into the required situation.

Goal type No. 1: Transform object *a* into object *b*

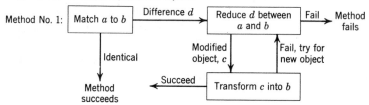

Goal type No. 2: Reduce the difference, *d*, between object *a* and object *b*

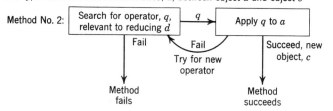

Goal type No. 3: Apply operator *q* to object *a*

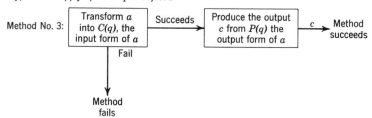

Fig. 6. Principal methods employed by the General Problem Solver.

A general flow diagram of GPS, incorporating these goals and these methods, is shown in Fig. 6. In addition to those already described, the program includes numerous other mechanisms. Thus, in selecting relevant operators to try, GPS can perform inexpensive tests to determine if there is some obvious reason why the operator would not work. If GPS does create a new object, it determines if this object has already been created elsewhere in the problem-solving sequence in order to avoid going around in circles. Similarly, GPS determines whether goals have been previously created and can use this information to determine what to do next. GPS has a method, called planning, which works as follows: if the goal is to transform a into b, abstract a and b, eliminating most of their detail and creating the new objects (abstractions or images) a' and b'. Now formulate the goal of transforming a' into b'. This new problem will generally be far easier to solve than the original one. Once it has been solved, it is used to guide the solution of the original unabstracted problem. GPS also has means for selecting goals for a second and third try, after its direct attempts at a solution have failed. The reason for enumerating a series of mechanisms we cannot describe in any detail is to point out the complexity of the program and to avoid the impression that we have given a complete description of the relevant parts of GPS.

7.3 Realizing the General Problem Solver

GPS has been realized by programming it in a computer interpretive language (to be explained briefly in a later section) called IPL-V (information processing language V). Some experience has been gained with GPS in runs on the IBM 704 and 7090 computers, and it has also been hand simulated rather extensively—although it is sufficiently complex that really exact hand simulation is virtually impossible.

We will indicate briefly how a computer can carry out the processes called for by the GPS program. The *objects* that the program transforms are structures whose elements are symbols.[11] Suppose, for example, that GPS is instructed to solve the familiar puzzle of the missionaries and the cannibals: three missionaries and three cannibals are to cross a river in a boat that will hold only two men at a time; no mixed group of missionaries and cannibals in which the missionaries are outnumbered can be permitted, even for a brief moment, or the missionaries would be eaten. How

---

[11] Thus GPS may be visualized as a program for a central nervous system that receives communications from its sensors in the form of symbol structures and sends communications to its effectors in the form of symbol structures. The encoding of these structures by the sensors and the decoding by the effectors is outside the program.

can the whole party get to the other side of the river? The problem would be stated to GPS as change a into b, where a is the object,

$$MMMCCCB/—$$

(the object consisting of three missionaries, three cannibals, and the boat on the left bank, nothing on the right bank), and b is the object

$$—/MMMCCCB.$$

In this representation *differences* between objects are simply differences in the numbers and kinds of symbols that comprise their several parts— they correspond to statements like: "The missionaries are on the left bank and we want them on the right bank" or "the boat is on the wrong side for the next trip." *Operators* are processes that delete one or two of the symbols M and C, together with B, from the part of the object to which B belongs, and add these same symbols to the other part (i.e., these operators correspond to taking a boatload across). For example, applying the operator $MCB/$ to a produces the object $MMCC/CMB$. The condition for the application of an operator is that after it has been applied there should not be M's outnumbered by C's in either half of the resulting object.

These statements about the nature of differences and operators and the conditions that have to be met to apply operators define the task environment for the problem of missionaries and cannibals and for all problems that may be stated in the same general terms. This information would be provided to GPS in the form of (1) subroutines for matching pairs of objects to find what differences exist between them, (2) subroutines for applying the admissible operators, and (3) subroutines for testing whether the conditions for application of an operator are met. These subroutines, together with the subroutines that constitute the program of GPS itself would enable GPS to tackle the problem and—if its problem-solving power was adequate—to solve it. In fact, GPS has proved itself capable of solving the problem of missionaries and cannibals.

7.4 Testing GPS as a Theory of Problem Solving

The general problem solver can be tested for its adequacy as a theory of human problem solving in a number of ways (Newell & Simon, 1961a,b). First, it can be instructed about a particular task environment (in the same way that it was instructed about missionaries and cannibals) and then given a series of problems from that environment. The same problems can be given to a sample of human subjects, and the successes, failures, and relative solution times of GPS can be compared with the successes, failures, and relative solution times of the human subjects. GPS will be an adequate simulation, from this standpoint, to the extent that measures of problem difficulty obtained from its behavior correlate with measures of problem difficulty obtained from the human behavior.

The test just described is a relatively weak one—although it is based on the kinds of data that are customarily obtained in laboratory experiments on human problem solving. However, a more severe test can be devised. A sample of human subjects is given a series of problems and asked to solve them while thinking aloud. Their protocols are tape recorded. The same series of problems is presented to GPS, and a *trace* is obtained from the computer, printing out the principal steps that were taken during its problem-solving attempts. The trace is then compared, statement by statement, with one or more of the human protocols.

Comparison with thinking-aloud protocols has been the principal technique used to test and improve the theory embodied in GPS. Unfortunately, almost no relevant statistical theory exists for deriving precise statements of goodness of fit. Instead, one must compare in detail samples of computer runs (traces) with the protocols to arrive at a qualitative picture of the agreements and disagreements between the two. The human simulation with GPS has been done in a symbolic logic task which requires too much description and discussion to present detailed comparisons in this chapter. Examples can be found in Newell & Simon (1961a) and especially in Newell & Simon (1961b). We will be able to show the nature of these comparisons when we discuss the binary choice model in Sec. 8.

Apart from the question of measuring goodness of fit objectively, the technique of comparing traces with protocols has proved a powerful means for finding the particular ways in which the program's behavior deviates from the human behavior, hence for suggesting the directions in which the theory needs to be modified in order to improve its fit. This feedback from test of theory to theory improvement is exactly the sort of thing we observed in our discussion of the "cell assembly" simulations and constitutes an important value of simulation as a tool of research.

8. SIMULATING COGNITIVE PROCESSES: "ELEMENTARY" TASKS

In the last two or three years a number of programs have been written which simulate the behavior of human subjects in handling some of the standard tasks used in the experimental psychology laboratory: in rote memory experiments, partial reinforcement experiments, experiments on stimulus differentiation and generalization, and concept attainment experiments. The most extensive of these simulations thus far are the binary choice program of Feldman (1959), which simulates decision making in partial-reinforcement situations, and the EPAM (elementary perceiver and memorizer) program of Feigenbaum and Simon (Feigenbaum, 1959), which simulates learning in rote-memory tasks. Hunt and Hovland (1961) and Laughery (1961) have simulated certain concept-attainment processes.

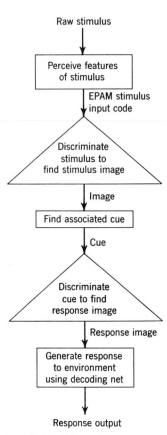

Fig. 7. EPAM performance system adapted from Feigenbaum and Simon (1961, p. 5).

8.1 The EPAM Program

EPAM is a program that incorporates two major learning processes and one performance process (Feigenbaum, 1959), which enable it to simulate human behavior in standard rote learning situations (e.g., learning nonsense syllables by the paired-associate or serial anticipation methods); to simulate the learning of discriminations; and to simulate some aspects of the acquisition of spoken and written language. With a trivial extension, it will simulate behavior in the verbal maze situation. EPAM successfully simulates the phenomena of recall or forgetting only over brief time intervals.

Figure 7 shows the performance system that enables EPAM to do these things. When a stimulus (a symbol structure) is presented, EPAM seeks to "recognize" it by sorting it through a *discrimination net*. At each node of the net, one or more tests are performed on the stimulus (comparable to the difference tests in GPS), and the appropriate branch is taken to the next node. With each terminal node of the net is associated an *image* that can be compared with a stimulus that is sorted to that node. If the two are similar, the stimulus has been successfully recognized.

Also associated with the terminal node for a stimulus is a (partial or complete) image of any response that has been associated with it. For example, if there is a node for the aural syllable "dawg," there could be associated with this node the image of that syllable, as well as the image of the written syllable "dog," an image (aural or visual) of the spelling of the syllable ("dee" "oh" "jee"), a visual image of the object named by the syllable (a dog), and other symbolic information related to the syllable. In this way recognizing the syllable, by sorting it, gives access to information that can be interpreted as its *meaning*. Thus after a stimulus has been recognized, if an appropriate response has been associated with it, that response can be produced.

Of the two principal learning programs that EPAM possesses, one enables it to grow the discrimination net to the extent necessary to discriminate among the various stimuli that exist in the task environments to which it is exposed. The other learning program builds and stores at terminal nodes the images that constitute responses associated with the stimuli. Thus, in a paired-associate nonsense-syllable situation, the discrimination net is elaborated until the program can discriminate among all the stimulus and response syllables. At each terminal a partial image of the syllable sorted to that terminal is stored, and at the terminal for each stimulus syllable a partial image of the paired response syllable is stored. The learning process depends on knowledge of results: comparison of a stimulus with its image governs the elaboration of the sorting net; comparison of a response with the correct response shown in the (simulated) memory drum window governs the association processes.

Interestingly enough, EPAM, although designed for rote memory situations, learns to read in the following sense (Feigenbaum & Simon, 1961). By the paired associate method, responses representing pointing at visual objects (a dog) are associated with stimuli representing the spoken names of the objects (dawg). Next, responses representing the spoken names of the objects (dawg) are associated with stimuli representing the printed names of the objects (dog). Now, without further learning trials, if EPAM is presented with the printed name of an object as stimulus, it can respond by pointing to the visual representation of the object.

On the other hand, EPAM (analogously with the program for cell-assembly simulation) reveals some fundamental ambiguities and inadequacies in standard associationist theories of rote learning—of which it may be regarded as a translation. For example, it readily learns the serial list, CEF-DAX-GAH-MEQ-SIJ-TOV-NUB-YIL-ZOK-WUK; but it cannot learn the list E-X-5-3-3-2-1 because of the presence of two occurrences of the symbol "3" in the list. Analysis of the reasons for the failure indicates that any of the existing theories of rote learning, reasonably interpreted, would suffer the same fate. The difficulty arises from the failure of the program to distinguish between an association of one *symbol* to another and an association of one *token* (symbol occurrence) to another. Hence the program has no way of representing (in the second list) that a 3 is associated with the *first occurrence of a 3* in the list but a 2 is associated with the *second occurrence of a 3*. (At the same time it has to recognize that both are occurrences of 3.) The necessity for such a distinction between symbols and their tokens has long been known to symbolic logicians, but the simulation of rote memory with the EPAM program has finally focused on the significance of this distinction for psychological processes.

8.2 The Binary Choice Program

The binary choice program was designed to simulate the behavior of subjects in partial reinforcement experiments (Feldman, 1959). We have already used this situation in Sec. 2.3 in trying to make clear the nature of information-processing theories. We recall that the task is one of having the subject predict the next item in a binary sequence ("plus" or "check"), giving him immediate knowledge of results, so that he gradually can accumulate knowledge of the past history of the sequence. Psychological experiments with such tasks usually determine the sequence randomly with fixed statistical structure: Feldman used independent trials with a probability of 0.7 for check and 0.3 for plus. Feldman attempted to produce detailed simulations of human subjects, so that each subject is simulated by a separate program. All the programs are highly similar, but each has a number of features that fit it to the particular data.

The flow chart for one subject (DH) is shown in Fig. 8. The central assumptions (common to all programs) are that the subjects developed hypotheses about the nature of the sequence; that they used these hypotheses to predict the next item; that the information about the actual sequence was used to evaluate the hypotheses and to generate and select new ones; and that they would use pattern hypotheses—for example, "runs of checks," "runs of plusses," and "single alternations." It was also assumed that the subject would adopt some mechanism to account for failures in prediction (the random character of the sequence making it impossible for any pattern hypothesis to succeed for very long) while still maintaining his hypothesis intact. For DH this mechanism was an additional hypothesis that the experimenter had rigged the sequence to deceive him—to throw him off. Thus the hypothesis held by the subject could be a compound one—for example, "the pattern is a run of checks but the experimenter will try to throw me off." The prediction from this compound hypothesis, of course, would be that the next item would be a plus.

As with all programs, this one cannot be described adequately in a few sentences. Yet from Fig. 8 the tree of questions that the subject asks about each situation (at the point when he has just found out what the correct item was at trial $t - 1$ and now has to generate the prediction for trial t), that leads to an evaluation of the current hypothesis in terms of an a posteriori explanation, and that leads in turn to the retention of the old hypothesis or the selection of a new one, can be seen. The details can be found in Feldman (1959, Chapter 2).

Even with this brief description, however, we are in a position to appreciate the manner in which programs can be compared with behavior and some of the problems involved in making such comparisons. Figure 9 gives a page from Feldman (1959, p. 69).[12] In it we have the model of Fig. 8 in the first column matched against the subject's behavior in the second. The page shows trials 11 through 22 of the total sequence of 200. From the model, by observing the processing done in Fig. 8 at each trial, we can obtain both the prediction of the new item, the explanation of the old situation, and the hypothesis currently accepted. This information can be put into stylized form, and a close reading of the model column will reveal the stereotopy of statement. The comparison makes evident that the model is matching the subject over most of the range of his task-relevant behavior—that it is providing close to the full content of the behavior rather than just a few quantitative measurements of it. Of course, the model also agrees with the behavior when the usual measures of fit are applied, as it must to agree qualitatively so well. Thus DH chooses check and plus in almost the same proportion as they appear in the stimulus sequence (event matching); so does the model.

We can see here how it is possible to compare computer traces and protocols and be fairly sure of the kind of fit obtained, even though no statistical theory of goodness of fit exists. Thus trial 13 clearly shows complete agreement and trial 16 clearly shows complete disagreement. On the latter we can verify that the program did not evoke the throw-me-off hypothesis either as explanation or future expectation and we can score a clean miss. Trial 20 is an example in which there can be some argument on how much of the information in the behavior has been captured in the model.

Since this situation is one in which both mathematical models of the stochastic type and information processing models have been constructed, a comparison of the two should be possible. Feldman has attempted this

---

[12] This is a hand simulation. Machine simulations have since been carried out (Feldman, 1961).

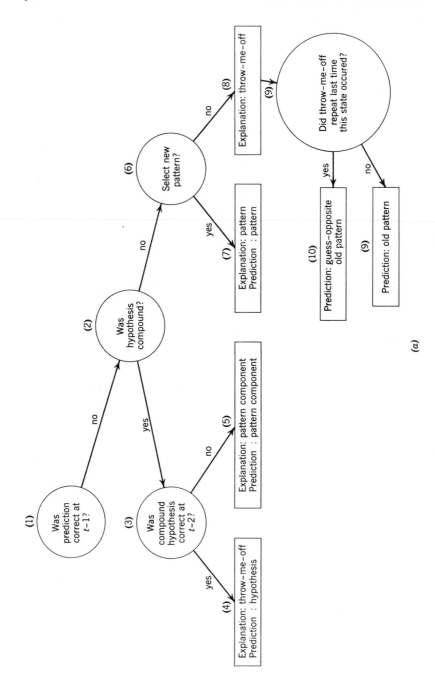

(a)

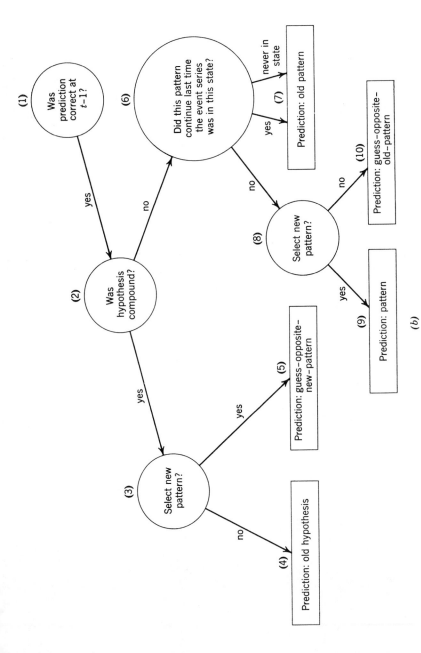

Fig. 8. Binary choice model for DH—behavior after correct predictions. Adapted from Feldman (1959, p. 62).

(b)

Trial	Model		Subject			Remarks
	Comment	Pre-diction	Comment	Pre-diction	Event	
11	The 11th one will be a C. You'll continue the progression of C's.	C	The 11th one will be a C. You're continuing the progression.	C	C	
12	The 12th one will be a C. You'll continue the progression of C's.	C	The 12th one will be a C because you're continuing the progression.	C	P	
13	The 13th one will be a C. You gave me the p to throw me off. The progression of C's will continue.	C	The 13th one will be a C. The 12th one was a P. You were trying to throw me off. The progression will continue.	C	P	
14	The 14th one will be a P. You've begun a progression of P's.	P	The 14th one will be a P. You're beginning a new progression with P's.	P	P	
15	The 15th one will be a P. You'll continue the progression of P's.	P	The 15th one will be a P. You're still continuing the progression.	P	P	
16	The 16th one will be a P. You'll continue the progression of P's.	P	The 16th one will be a C. …to throw me off now.	C	C	Mistake: Model fails to predict negative recency when subject does.

17	The 17th one will be a C. You're going to try to throw me off this progression of P's again.	C	The 17th one will be a C. You're going to see if I'll revert to the progression of P's.	C	C
18	The 18th one will be a P. You're going to break this progression of C's.	P	The 18th one will be a P. You're going to break this progression of C's.	P	C
19	The 19th one will be a P. You're going to break this progression of C's.	P	The 19th one will be a P. You're going to get off this progression of C's.	P	P
20	The 20th one will be a P. You're going to try to throw me off this progression of C's again.	P	The 20th one will be a P. You're going to try to throw me off trying to make me think that all —think you're going to going back to the other progression which I'm confused about now. I don't remember what the last one was —C, I believe.	P	P
21	The 21st one will be a C. You're going to break this progression of P's.	C	The 21st one will be a C. You won't continue with the progression of P's.	C	P
22	The 22d one will be a C. You're going to break this progression of P's.	C	The 22d one is a C. You're doing this so that I might think the P progression will continue.	C	C

Fig. 9. Sample of simulation of DH. Adapted from Feldman, (1959, p. 69).

in some detail (1959, pp. 138–142), but there are several difficulties. The program predicts a much broader range of behavior. The program is deterministic, whereas the stochastic models are probabilistic. Thus the stochastic models do not attempt to predict individual responses. On the other hand, the stochastic models try to use one parameter to fit a whole population, whereas the program is fitted to each individual separately with no way yet of determining how many "degrees of freedom" are absorbed in doing so. However, as an over-all evaluation, there is little doubt that the information-processing model comes much closer to describing the processes that are going on inside the human subject than the stochastic models.

8.3 A Concept Attainment Program

A typical laboratory experiment on concept attainment confronts the subject with a sequence of figures that can vary along a number of dimensions—a large black circle, for example, is characterized by size, color and shape. The subject is told that certain of the figures are instances of a concept the experimenter has selected and that others are not. When a figure is presented the subject is to guess whether it is an instance of the concept; he is told whether his answer is correct before the next figure is presented to him. Thus, if the concept is "black," a large black circle is an instance, whereas a large white square is not.

A digital-computer program to simulate the strategies used by subjects to find the correct concept has been written and tested by Hunt and Hovland (1961). The program generates hypotheses—for example, "the concept is large white figures," starting with simple conjunctive hypotheses and proceeding to more complicated ones. A hypothesis is tested against the instances that are presented until it fails, then is rejected for the next one produced by the generator. Hovland and Hunt comment on the simulation technique:

The adequacy of a machine simulation must be judged in terms of how well it will perform on new tasks and how well it will predict the outcome of empirical experimental research. We derive some assurance that the order in which conjunctive, relational, and disjunctive problems are solved by the computer in the foregoing example corresponds to that obtained with college-student subjects in the experiment by Hovland and Hunt (1961). But to some extent this research was also the source of ideas for the computer program. Will it work on old experiments done under different conditions and how well will it be able to predict the outcome of experiments not yet done? This will be the "proof of the pudding" and constitutes the whole rationale of this type of procedure, since discrepancies between simulation and actual performance by subjects represent flaws somewhere in the conceptual theoretical apparatus which can be detected and often then corrected (1960, pp. 6–7).

8.4 Conclusion

In Secs. 7 and 8 we have described four information-processing programs for simulating various classes of cognitive processes. The general theoretical approach underlying all of these programs is similar, and all of them make use of particular computer programming techniques that are described in Sec. 11.

The tasks handled by the simulations described in this section are closer to the main stream of experimental work in American psychological laboratories than the problem-solving programs of Sec. 7. Hence, these programs afford a number of opportunities for confronting the information-processing theories with data and for comparing these theories with mathematical and verbal theories that seek to explain the same phenomena. The predictions of Feldman's model, for example, can be compared directly with the predictions of stochastic learning theories; the behavior of EPAM and the concept former can be compared with a large body of data from experiments on rote learning and concept attainment, respectively.

9. LANGUAGE BEHAVIOR

In information-processing theories great emphasis is placed on the simulation of the full content of the task and on trying to explain the full range of the symbolic behavior exhibited by subjects. Hence it would be natural to expect programs such as GPS and the binary choice to produce idiomatic English output. This they do not do, and the language emitted by the subject must still be dealt with simply as evidence of internal symbolic processes. The reason is not far to seek: the level of sophistication of information-processing theories is tied to the general level of knowledge of how to accomplish symbolic processes on machines. Detailed simulation of human behavior in symbolic logic (by GPS) followed upon several successful theorem-proving programs having much more the flavor of artificial than natural intelligence. Comparable development of language-using programs has not yet occurred, although for the last decade the more basic capabilities of language-data processing have been developing in attempts to translate languages by machine.

Programs are now appearing that directly attack the use of language. A program, called Baseball, developed by Green, Wolf, Chomsky, and Laughery (1961), is prepared to answer questions about baseball put to it in English. Examples are "Where did the Red Sox play on July 7?" and "Did every team play at least once in each park in each month?" The point of the program is not that it answers questions *like* these, but that if the linguistic expressions above are key-punched exactly as written and fed into the machine it will be able to provide the answer. In the initial version there are still several restrictions—for example, constructions involving relations such as *most* are prohibited—but even so the program accepts an extremely wide range of linguistic expressions.

A second program, by Lindsay (1961), is more directly focused on psychological issues (although it should be noted that in the group that did Baseball, Green and Laughery are psychologists). Lindsay's program is a mechanization of the hypothesis that the process of understanding involves building up an internal model of the external world. As language expressions are taken into the organism, information about the world is extracted to fill out and extend the model. His program works with a restricted subject matter—family relations—but it accepts sentences in Basic English as inputs. From these sentences it extracts whatever information may exist about family relations to build an internal representation of the way people are related. Questions asked of it are answered by consulting the model directly rather than the corpus of sentences that was input to it. For example, if it has been told previously that "Mary is the mother of Bill" and that "Jane, Bill's sister, went to see Barbara," then it would answer affirmatively to the question whether Jane was Mary's daughter. Thus the internal model organizes the information so that many simple, direct inferences can be made.

Both of these programs focus on receiving and analyzing natural language expressions rather than on responding in good language. It is a short step to the latter, once the input side—where the program does not control the form of the information it must process—is successfully handled.

10. SIMULATING SOCIAL BEHAVIOR

When mathematical methods are used to study social behavior, the stage is usually reached, even sooner than in individual psychology, when the complexities of the model put them beyond the resources of classical mathematical analysis. Hence we would expect that simulation with the aid of digital computers will have an even more central role in mathematical social psychology than in individual psychology. Since the methodology required is the same, no more specific examples are presented here. The work ranges from numerical simulations, such as those in macroeconomics (Orcutt, Greenberger, Korbel, & Rivlin, 1961) and voting behavior (Abelson & Pool, 1961; McPhee, 1961), through mixed numerical and symbolic simulations, such as work in microeconomics (Cyert, Feigenbaum, & March, 1959) and small groups (Hare, 1961), to information processing models (Clarkson, 1961). A more detailed review may be found in Clarkson & Simon (1960).

11. PROGRAMMING FOR NONNUMERICAL SIMULATION

None of the simulations discussed in Sec. 7 through 10 of this chapter make use of special analogue equipment or special digital equipment. All have been carried out with the use of standard commercial electronic digital computers. Nevertheless, the construction of the simulations would have been difficult if they had not been facilitated by advances in methods for programming computers, developments that were specifically designed to make nonnumerical simulation easier and more practicable.

11.1 Compilers and Interpreters

Associated with each computer is an *instruction code*—in *machine language*—that is, a list of the instructions, which, when stored in the instruction register at the appropriate time, can be executed by the computer. We said in Sec. 3 that sequences of instructions (subroutines) can be given names, so that when the name is encountered during execution of a program the entire subroutine can be executed. This device can be used to define a set of *pseudoinstructions*, each one corresponding to a subroutine of machine-language instructions. Any set of pseudoinstructions rich enough to permit a wide range of information processes to be carried out can also be viewed as defining a language. If a program is written in this language and provided to a computer in which the routines that define the pseudoinstructions (i.e., the subroutines named by the pseudoinstructions) have been stored, the computer can execute that program. In fact, the computer will literally imitate another (real or hypothetical) computer whose machine-language instruction code corresponds to the language of the pseudoinstructions. If a computer is to execute a program written in a code, there must be stored in its memory not only the definitions of the pseudocode subroutines but also a program that actually carries out the translation into machine language and the subsequent execution.

Pseudoinstruction languages of this general sort are of two main kinds, called interpretive languages and compiler languages, respectively. The difference between an interpreter and a compiler is simple (although it is possible to construct hybrid types): the interpreter takes each pseudoinstruction in turn, translates it into machine language, and executes it immediately. The compiler takes each pseudoinstruction and translates it into machine language without executing it. When it has finished with all the pseudoinstructions, it has created a program in machine language that corresponds to the total pseudoprogram, which can then be executed in the ordinary way. The interpreter translates during the time of execution of the program, the compiler translates before execution time. Interpreters and compilers each have their peculiar characteristics and their peculiar advantages and disadvantages, which we need not discuss here.

Most complex simulation programs, particularly information-processing programs, have been written in pseudocode rather than machine language. An appropriate pseudocode enables one instruction to do the work of many and relieves the programmer, who needs all his wits about him to handle the substantive content of the program, of a large part of the "housekeeping" responsibility—assigning specific memory locations to specific uses, keeping track of such assignments, and so on.

Several information-processing languages, some compilers, others interpreters, have been constructed specifically for handling tasks of the sort under discussion here (see Green, 1961b for a general discussion). The most widely used up to the present time is IPL-V, the fifth of a series of interpretive languages, which has been coded for a number of the computers in common use (Newell, 1961). If a program is written in IPL-V, it can then be run on any computer for which an IPL-V code is available—subject only to speed and memory-size limitations of the particular computer in relation to the particular program. At present, IPL-V codes exist for the IBM 650, 704, 709, and 7090 and are in preparation for Univac 1105, Bendix G20, and other machines. The program for EPAM, for example, was partly debugged in its early stages on the IBM 650 and was later successfully run on the 704 and the 7090. A published programming manual has been prepared for IPL-V, and program decks or tapes are available to permit its use with any of the computers named above.

11.2 Example of an Interpreter: IPL-V

We cannot give even a sketchy description of an interpretive language here, but we shall comment on some central features of IPL-V (most of which are shared by other information-processing languages) that have significance for simulation in psychology. It will be helpful to think of IPL-V simply as the instruction code of a hypothetical computer and to compare it with the instruction code of a conventional computer.

The gross anatomy of an IPL computer is like that of a conventional computer: it has a memory, working memory, interpreter, and input and output devices. Hence our earlier description of a computer fits the IPL computer without significant change.

In a conventional computer the important symbolic unit, for most purposes, is the simple addressable *word*. In an IPL computer individual words (called "symbols") can be manipulated, as in the conventional computer, but there are instructions specially designed to manipulate *lists* of symbols and arbitrary lists of lists (*list structures*). In the instruction code of an IPL computer one finds instructions such as the following:

Copy the list named in the working-memory location W. Store the name of the copy in working-memory location W.

Find the symbol that occurs next after symbol S on list L.

Find the value of attribute A on the description list of list L.

Generate the symbols of list L and perform process P on each of them.

Thus, to program the missionary and cannibal problem for an IPL computer, an object can be represented as a list having two items, each item also a list. The first list belonging to the object is that of things on the left bank, the second list, the list of things on the right bank. Then a process like "determine if the boat is on the left bank" is given in information-processing terms:

Test if there is a symbol of type B in the first sublist of list L.

The test, in turn, can be carried out in some such way as this:

Generate the symbols of the first sublist of list L.

Test whether each symbol is a B.

If result of test is negative, generate the next symbol. If positive, report positive.

If no more symbols on sublist, report negative.

From this brief example it can be seen that processes we would call "noticing" and "discriminating" in the human subject can be represented in a quite direct and natural way (although, in this instance, quite macroscopically) as IPL routines. In our description of the discrimination nets in the EPAM program we saw how complex discriminations could be constructed (for purposes of more microscopic simulation) from more elementary ones like those just described.

The IPL computer provides direct means for representing the notion of *association* and means for making the distinction, whose importance to learning theory we have already remarked, between token associations and symbol associations. The relation between a particular occurrence of a symbol on a particular list and the next token on that list is a token association. Thus we could represent the sequence E-X-5-3-3-2-1 as a list of symbol tokens. Then, a *token* of 3 is *next to* (associated with) the first occurrence of a 3 in this list, whereas a token of 2 is next to the second occurrence of a 3.

On the other hand, if we wish to represent the association expressed by *dog is pronounced dawg*, we can define an attribute that we shall interpret as "pronunciation" and assign "dawg" as the value of the attribute pronunciation on the description list of the symbol "dog." Then, the symbol "dawg" will have been associated with the symbol "dog."

11.3 Psychological Implications of IPL

It has been said that Aristotle sometimes mistook the rules of Greek grammar for immutable verities of logic. We can raise an analogous issue about computer simulation. To what extent do we make implicit assumptions of psychological theory when we decide to write a simulation program in an information-processing language?

A literal, but misleading, answer to this question is that we make no psychological commitments when we use such a language to write a program. It can be shown rigorously that not only can any general-purpose computer be programmed to imitate an IPL computer but an IPL computer can be programmed to simulate any general-purpose computer. Neither is more general than the other.[13]

The answer is misleading because it does not distinguish what can be computed in principle from what can easily be computed in fact. A program for a particular process written in conventional machine language is arranged in a different way than when it is written in a list-processing

---

[13] Every general-purpose computer and every IPL computer is, except for the limits on memory size, what in modern logic is called a universal Turing machine; and, roughly speaking, anything that can be computed can be computed by any universal Turing machine.

language. This is one of the main sources of convenience of the interpreter —it permits the program to be put down more "naturally." Under these circumstances, the mode of expression almost surely influences the thought (the Whorfian hypothesis applied to computer programming). Hence it is probable that psychological postulates enter the simulation by way of the structure of the programming language.

Figure 10 illustrates the methodological situation. It is hypothesized that the behaviors of a human which the psychologist studies are to be explained in terms of *programs of elementary information processes* (EIP's). The elementary information processes are to be explained, in turn, in terms of neural processes. Turning to the computer, we try to devise an interpretive language whose instruction code will resemble, at least grossly, the kinds of elementary information processes that we postulate for a human. The elementary information processes of the interpretive language are to be defined in terms of machine-language codes.

We conclude that a list-processing language like IPL-V is a (weak) psychological theory. It is an assertion that the elementary information processes that will be discovered to underlie human behavior are easily constructable from the instructions of the list-processing language. This is a testable hypothesis.

One aspect of the list-processing languages that amounts to a psychological postulate is the capacity of the IPL interpreter to execute programs that are organized as hierarchies of subroutines. To do this, he must keep

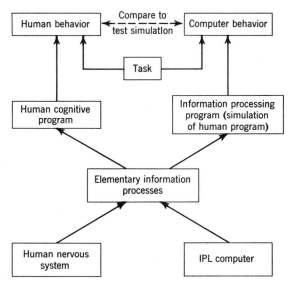

Fig. 10. Relation of computer processes to cognitive processes in nonnumerical simulation.

track, in some manner, not only of the next instruction in the subroutine currently being executed but also of the next instruction in the routine of which that subroutine is a part, and so on. He must hold in a "sequence register" or some equivalent mechanism not simply a single instruction but a whole list of instructions. Thus, in the example of the man walking down the street (Sec. 3.3), if he is at a given moment executing instruction 2 of subroutine A, he must also hold in memory that when he completes subroutine A he next executes instruction 2 (subroutine B) of routine C. It is interesting that the same device (associative lists) that is used to organize memory also serves, in the interpreter, to handle the hierarchical organization of programs.

The use of extensive hierarchical programs—and the implied mechanics for executing them—is a pervasive feature of many of the particular programs we have presented in this chapter. It is also a central theme of the treatment of information processing theories by Miller, Galanter, and Pribram (1960). These authors use the term "plan" to refer to what are here called "programs."

Perhaps the fundamental psychological assumption implicit in the IPL's is that the central nervous system does, in fact, both store and transmit symbols of some kind. The capacity for symbol transmission implies the distinction between symbol type and token to which we have several times referred. It is not at all easy to see how theories of the central system that do not provide for the explicit representation of transmittable symbols can make this distinction. It is not obvious how systems of elementary symbolic processes like those of IPL can be reduced to cell assemblies or random neural networks. Hence the simulations discussed in the last several sections follow more nearly in the tradition of Craik (1943) than in any of the more widely current psychological theories of the operation of the central nervous system.

12. CONCLUSION

In less than a decade computers have become a major tool for psychological research. Originally used as a mechanical aid in large-scale statistical calculations, they have found more and more employment in numerical analysis of mathematical theories and, most recently, in the construction and testing of information-processing theories.

Simulation was initially undertaken to demonstrate that mechanisms could exhibit adaptive behavior and could learn. The simulations often took the form of special-purpose analogue devices. Primarily by reason of their flexibility, electronic digital computers have become the most used instruments of simulation. Attention has advanced from general demonstrations of "humanoid" behavior to detailed models of cognitive processes. There are at least two major lines of investigation currently being pursued. The first of these employs models that simulate properties of neurons and organizations of neurons into nets. The recognition of patterns in a complex stimulus field is the task most often posed by investigators in this area.

The second main line of investigation uses models that simulate the information processes involved in problem solving and in certain perceptual, memorizing, "guessing," and concept-attaining tasks. These generally use an information-processing language that allows direct representation of nonnumerical symbol manipulation.

Computer languages (interpretive languages and compilers) are now available to facilitate the construction of programs for nonnumerical simulation. These languages themselves have properties that amount to implicit psychological assumptions: that the central nervous system is a symbol-processing system, that its memory is organized in terms of lists and list structures of associated symbols, and that it is capable of executing sequences of behaviors organized as hierarchical list structures.

The testing of theories that take the form of computer programs is still in a rudimentary stage, depending on comparison of computer traces with tape-recorded protocols of human behavior. Nothing is available at present in the way of statistical tests of significance applicable to these kinds of data.

The exploitation of computer simulation, especially in the form of information processing theories, has been limited so far by the general unavailability of large computers and by the need for psychologists to absorb yet another technology. (Psychologists are only now getting used to the fact that some mathematical sophistication is a prerequisite for their science.) However, it appears that both limitations will vanish within the next five years and that these simulation techniques can become part of the standard armatorium of the theoretical psychologist.

References

Abelson, R. P., & Pool, I. de S. The simulmatics project. *Public Opinion Quart.*, 1961, 167–183.

Ashby, W. R. *Design for a brain.* (2nd ed.) New York: Wiley, 1960.

Bartlett, F. *Thinking.* New York: Basic Books, 1958.

Boring, E. G. Mind and mechanism. *J. Psychol.*, 1946, **59**, 173–192.

Bush, R. R., & Mosteller, F. *Stochastic models for learning.* New York: Wiley, 1955.

Bush, R. R., Mosteller, F., & Thompson, G. L. A formal structure for multiple choice situations. In R. M. Thrall, C. H. Coombs, & R. L. Davis (Eds.), *Decision processes.* New York: Wiley, 1954. Pp. 99–126.

Chapman, R. L., Kennedy, J. L., Newell, A., & Biel, W. C. The System Research Laboratory's air defense experiments. *Management Science*, 1959, **5**, 250–269.

Clark, W. A., & Farley, B. G. Generalizations of pattern recognition in a self-organizing system. *Proc. 1955 western joint computer conference*, New York: IRE, 1955, 86–91.

Clarkson, G., & Simon, H. A. Simulation of individual and group behavior. *Amer. Econom. Rev.*, 1960, **50**, 920–932.

Clarkson, G. *Portfolio selection: a simulation of trust investment.* Englewood Cliffs, N.J.: Prentice-Hall, 1962.

Craik, K. J. W. *The nature of explanation.* New York: Cambridge Univer. Press, 1943.

Cyert, R., Feigenbaum, E., & March, J. Models in a behavioral theory of the firm. *Behavioral Science*, 1959, **4**, 81–95.

Dinneen, G. P. Programming pattern recognition. *Proc. 1955 Western Joint Computer Conference*, New York: IRE, 1955, 94–100.

Doyle, W. Recognition of sloppy hand-printed characters. *Proc. 1960 Western Joint Computer Conference*, New York: IRE, 1960, 133–142.

Duncker, K. On problem-solving. *Psychol. Monographs*, 1945, **58**, 270.

Farley, B. G., & Clark, W. A. Simulation of self-organizing systems by a digital computer. *IRE Trans. on Inform. Theory*, 1954, **IT-4**, 76–84.

Fatehchand, R. Machine recognition of spoken words. In F. Alt (Ed.), *Advances in computers*, Vol. 1. New York: Academic Press, 1960. Pp. 193–229.

Feigenbaum, E. *An information processing theory of verbal learning*, P-1817, The RAND Corporation, October 1959.

Feigenbaum, E., & Simon, H. A. *Performance of a reading task by EPAM*, P-2358, The RAND Corporation, July 1961.

Feldman, J. *Analysis of predictive behavior in a two-choice situation.* Unpublished doctoral dissertation, Carnegie Institute of Technology, 1959.

Feldman, J. Simulation of behavior in the binary choice experiment. *Proc. 1961 Western Joint Computer Conference*, New York: IRE, 1961, 133–144.

Flood, M. M. Game-learning theory and some decision-making experiments. In R. M. Thrall, C. H. Coombs, & R. L. Davis (Eds.), *Decision Processes*, New York: Wiley, 1954. Pp. 139–158.

Forgie, J. W., & Forgie, C. D. Results obtained from an auditory-recognition computer program. *J. acoust. Soc. Amer.*, 1959, **31**, 1480–1484.

Gelernter, H. Realization of a geometry theory-proving machine. *Proc. of the international conference on information processing*, UNESCO, 1959, 273–282.

Gold, B. Machine recognition of hand-sent Morse code. *IRE Trans. on Inform. Theory*, 1959, **IT-5**, 17–24.

Goodwin, G. L. Digital computers tap out designs for large motors ... fast. *Power*, April 1958, 12–15.

Goodwin, W. R. The System Development Corporation and system training. *Amer. Psychol.*, 1957, **12**, 524–528.

Green, B. F. Computer languages for symbol manipulation. *IRE Trans. on Human Factors in Electronics*, HFE-2, March 1961, 2–3. (a)

Green, B. F. Using computers to study human perception. *Education and Psychological Measurement*, 1961, **21**, 227–233. (b)

Green, B. F., Wolf, A., Chomsky, C., & Laughery, K. Baseball: an automatic question-answerer. *Proc. 1961 Western Joint Computer Conference*, New York: IRE, 1961, 219–224.

Hare, A. P. Computer simulation of interaction in small groups. *Behavioral Science,* 1961, **6**, 261–265.

Hawkins, J. K. Self-organizing systems—a review and commentary. *Proc. IRE,* 1961, **49**, 31–48.

Hebb, D. O. *Organization of behavior.* New York: Wiley, 1949.

Hiller, L. A., & Isaacson, L. M. *Experimental music: composition with an electronic computer.* New York: McGraw-Hill, 1959.

Hovland, C. I., & Hunt, E. B. Computer simulation of concept attainment. Talk presented at meeting of American Association for the Advancement of Science. Mimeo, December 29, 1960.

Hunt, E. B., & Hovland, C. I. Programming a model of human concept formulation. *Proc. 1961 Western Joint Computer Conference,* New York: IRE, 1961, 145–156.

Laughery, K. *An information processing analysis of human problem solving behavior.* Unpublished doctoral dissertation, Carnegie Institute of Technology, 1961.

Lindsay, R. *The reading machine problem.* Unpublished doctoral dissertation, Carnegie Institute of Techology, 1961.

McCulloch, W. S., & Pitts, W. A logical calculus of the ideas imminent in nervous activity. *Bull. Math. Biophys.,* 1943, **5**, 115–137.

McPhee, W. Empirical inputs in a voting model. *Public Opinion Quart.,* 1961, 184–193.

Miller, G. A., Galanter, E., & Pribram, K. *Plans and the structure of behavior.* New York: Holt, 1960.

Minsky, M. Steps toward artificial intelligence. *Proc. IRE,* 1961, **49**, 8–30.

Newell, A. (Ed.). *Information processing language-V manual.* Englewood Cliffs, N.J.: Prentice Hall, 1961.

Newell, A., Shaw, J. C., & Simon, H. A. Empirical explorations of the logic theory machine. *Proc. of the Western Joint Computer Conference,* New York: IRE, 1957, 218–230.

Newell, A., Shaw, J. C., & Simon, H. A. Chess playing programs and the problem of complexity. *IBM Journal of Research and Development,* 1958, **2**, 320–335.

Newell, A., Shaw, J. C., & Simon, H. A. A report on a general problem-solving program. *Proc. of the International Conference on Information Processing,* UNESCO, 1959, 256–265.

Newell, A., & Simon, H. A. The logic theory machine. *IRE Trans. on Inform. Theory,* 1956, **IT-2**, 61–79.

Newell, A., & Simon, H. A. The simulation of human thought. In *Current trends in psychological theory.* Pittsburgh: Univer. of Pittsburgh, 1961. Pp. 152–179. (a)

Newell, A., & Simon, H. A. GPS, a program that simulates human thought. In H. Billing (Ed.), *Proceedings of a conference on learning automata,* Karlsruhe, Germany, April 1961, 109–124. (b)

Orcutt, G., Greenberger, M., Korbel, J., & Rivlin, A. *Microanalysis of socio-economic systems: a simulation study.* New York: Harper, 1961.

Pitts, W., & McCulloch, W. S. How we know universals, the perception of auditory and visual form. *Bull. Math. Biophys.,* 1947, **9**, 127–147.

Rashevsky, N. *Mathematical biology of social behavior.* Chicago: Univer. of Chicago Press, 1951.

Reitman, W. Programming intelligent problem solvers. *IRE Trans. on Human Factors in Electronics,* 1961, **HFE-2**, 26–33.

Rochester, N., Holland, J., Haibt, L., & Duda, W. Test on a cell assembly theory of the action of the brain, using a large digital computer. *IRE Trans. on Inform. Theory,* 1956, **IT-2**, 80–93.

Rosenblatt, F. The Perceptron: a probabilistic model for information storage and organization in the brain. *Psych. Rev.*, 1958, **65**, 386–407.

Rosenblatt, F. *Principles of neurodynamics.* Cornell Aeronautical Laboratory, March 1961.

Samuel, A. Some studies in machine learning using the game of checkers. *IBM J. Research and Development*, 1959, **3**, 210–229.

Selfridge, O. G. Pattern recognition and modern computers. *Proc. 1955 Western Joint Computer Conference*, New York: IRE, 1955, 91–93.

Selfridge, O. G. Pandamonium. *Proc. symposium on the Mechanization of Thought Processes*, Teddington, England, 1959, 511–529.

Silberman, H. F. A computer-controlled teaching machine. *Behavioral Science*, 1961, **6**, 259–261.

Simon, H. A. *Models of man.* New York: Wiley, 1957.

Spiegelthal, E. S. Redundancy exploitation in the computer solution of double-crostics. *Proc. 1960 Western Joint Computer Conference*, New York: IRE, 1960.

Suppes, P., & Atkinson, R. C. *Markov learning models for multiperson interactions.* Stanford: Stanford Univer. Press, 1960.

Taussky, O., & Todd, J. Generation and testing of pseudo-random numbers. In H. A. Meyer (Ed.), *Symposium on Monte Carlo Methods*, New York: Wiley, 1956. Pp. 15–28.

Tonge, F. M. A heuristic program for assembly line balancing. Englewood Cliffs, N.J.: Prentice-Hall, 1961.

Walter, G. *The living brain.* New York: Van Nostrand, 1953.

8

Estimation and Evaluation[1]

Robert R. Bush
University of Pennsylvania

1.   *This work was supported in part by grant NSF G-14839 from the National Science Foundation to the University of Pennsylvania.*

Contents

Estimation and Evaluation

In the last two decades the field of statistics has become a well-established discipline, both in the academic world and in industrial-government settings. Indeed, many of the most conservative universities have established departments of statistics separate from mathematics and the various fields that consume statistics. Furthermore, applied statistics has become a standard part of the training of every psychologist in most, if not all, countries of the world. It has become increasingly evident, however, that the prevalent "cook-book" course in psychological statistics is not adequate for research in many branches of psychology. Even the experimentalist with only a casual interest in mathematical models feels the need for a deeper understanding of theoretical statistics. For the student of mathematical psychology a thorough grounding in mathematical statistics is absolutely essential. Familiarity with statistical techniques is useful, but even more important is the statistical sophistication that can emerge from a relatively thorough study of the subject.

This chapter is in no way a substitute for an intensive course in mathematical statistics. On the contrary, the author assumes that the reader has already had such a course. If the student is thoroughly familiar with Feller's (1957) book on probability theory and Cramér's (1946) advanced text on statistics (or the equivalent), he will be well prepared for digesting the material that follows. The attempt in this chapter is to provide the student with a summary of those parts of statistics most relevant to mathematical model testing, to argue for a "common-sense" approach to the use of statistical methods, and to present a few specific techniques that have been developed and found useful in mathematical psychology.

The subject of statistical inference (as distinct from probability theory) consists of two parts: hypothesis testing and parameter estimation. The average psychologist is far more familiar with the first part. Of course, he knows that a sample mean is a fair estimate of a population mean and he may even know that a sample standard deviation is a biased estimate of the population standard deviation. But estimation techniques such as maximum likelihood and minimum chi-square are seldom in his kit of tools. A superficial reason for this strong bias is clear: textbooks and courses in psychological statistics seldom include material on estimation. In a more profound sense, the reason for the bias is not so evident. Why do the courses and books not cover estimation? If there is a rational answer to this question, it must be closely related to the present state of psychological theory. Except for the theories described in the various chapters of this *Handbook*, psychological theories have been stated only in verbal terms, and their "theorems" seldom involved more than "greater than" relations. Although most research psychologists know the difference between "statistical significance" and "theoretical significance," they continue searching for the statistical. Furthermore, they exhibit great reluctance to discuss the power of a statistical test (Mosteller & Bush, 1955). The fact that a significant difference can always be found if the sample sizes are large enough does not seem to bother them. The burning question is whether a difference exists. Even more primitive researches are still commonplace. Many studies explore numerous variables to see if any have an effect, and so complicated analysis of variance and covariance designs are used. Exploratory research is useful and often necessary, but a science must progress beyond this stage if it is to be a mature science. Herein lies the great hope of mathematical model building, of course. We attempt to state our theories in precise and testable terms. Those theories involve parameters whose values must be determined experimentally, and so statistical estimation becomes a necessity.[2] This line of argument suggests that the maturation of psychological theory must be accompanied by a shift in emphasis from hypothesis testing to parameter estimation. It is with this assumption that this chapter was written.

Having estimated the parameters of a model or theory, an investigator still wants to know how well his theory and data agree. He wants to measure "goodness-of-fit." This is sometimes viewed as a problem in hypothesis testing, but in my opinion this is a serious error. Model evaluation is not the "acceptance-rejection" problem with which hypothesis testing deals. Factory products and men's hunches may be accepted or rejected, but formal theories are evaluated, modified, and extended. Thus we should not "test" goodness-of-fit, we should "measure" it. And the measures used are most valuable when two or more theories are being compared. A few techniques for this purpose are presented in Sec. 7.

---

[2] It is difficult to give a precise definition of the term parameter, but some examples may help: If a model involves the assumption of a linear relation between two variables, the slope of the line and its intercept are parameters. If a normal distribution of a random variable is assumed, its mean and variance may be considered parameters. In general, experimental variables that are directly measured, such as brightness and shock intensity, are not called parameters. Individual response probabilities or latencies are usually considered dependent variables rather than parameters, but constants that arise when one assumes how those response measures change are called parameters. In Clark Hull's behavior theory, habit strength, H, is assumed to be a negative exponential function, e^{-at}, of the time, t, between the response and the reinforcement; in this system t is the independent variable, H, the dependent variable, and the quantity a is a parameter.

1. GRAPHICAL AIDS

Formal methods of estimation and evaluation are useful tools but should not be used as substitutes for thinking. To be sure, scientific thought must be disciplined, but this can be accomplished in more than one way. Probably the most important aid to careful thinking about data in comparison to a theory is a graph. A simple plot of one's data often reveals regularities or anomalies that seem to defy numerical analysis. To an engineer or physicist, this point is so obvious that no further comment is necessary, but few psychologists have been brought up in a tradition of graphical analysis. Thus an elementary example is in order.

Suppose that a model predicts a linear relation between the expectation of a random variable y and some experimentally controlled variable x. Suppose the sample means for y are plotted against x and Fig. 1 results. One could use the method of least squares, for example, to estimate the parameters of the linear function and then use some numerical index to measure goodness-of-fit. The result would probably be discouraging. But as any freshman can see by looking at the graph, the fit is really very good except for one point. Probably that one point was an experimental or computational error, but possibly it may lead to an important discovery. Ignoring data points that do not fit a model cannot be recommended, of course. On the contrary, they should be carefully noticed and examined.

A somewhat more complicated example arises from Bush and Mosteller's (1955, Chapter 14) analysis of Weinstock's data on latency and running times of rats in a runway. The model predicted a gamma distribution of

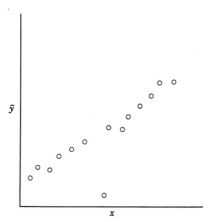

Fig. 1. Plot of fictitious data having one anomalous observation.

those times, but the initial parameter estimates led to theoretical distributions that were not close to the observed ones. A graphical study revealed that the data contained a few abnormally large observations—but many more than would be predicted by any sensible gamma distribution. Therefore, an estimation procedure, insensitive to the outer tail of the distribution, was developed. These estimates led to close agreement between the model and the bulk of the data. The anomalous large observations were not explained, but suggestions for further theoretical and empirical research emerged.

When a model predicts a linear relation between two variables, the appropriate graphical plot is obvious. When the prediction is a nonlinear one, it is less obvious what to do. Often it is possible and convenient to transform the variables in order to obtain a linear relation; this can be done numerically or graphically.

For example, Stevens' power law asserts that the number assigned, y, by human subjects to a stimulus of intensity x obeys the law $y = x^a$; by taking logarithms, we get the linear relation, $\log y = a \log x$, and so log-log graph paper is useful in plotting data. The reason for converting to a linear function is simple: one can detect systematic deviations from straight lines most easily when looking at graphs. Lines can readily be fitted to data by eye, and these often lead to parameter estimates that are fairly close to "best" estimates obtained by formal methods. (It is a rare man who can draw a good exponential through data points.)

Recent technological advances in psychology have made possible the automatic mechanical plotting of data. When data are cheap, this is a great time saver. Such techniques are most prevalent in operant conditioning studies in which the cumulative curve of number of responses versus time is the record of behavior. There is a serious danger in this practice. The basic information from an operant experiment is a time record of responses—the exact moment at which each response occurs. When one cumulates these data, he reduces the apparent effect of irregularities. The curves are smooth (compared to rate curves) but information is lost. (A few years ago a well-known experimentalist seriously proposed cumulating his cumulative curves, but his audience discouraged him from doing so.) There can be no doubt that cumulative curves are often convenient and useful, but they should be used with caution and as an aid, not as an end product.

Modern psychology has apparently bred extremists. On the one hand we have the cumulative-curve school which avoids numbers, and on the other hand we have the analysis-of-variance school which ignores graphs. The best advice to the student, of course, is to become familiar with all research tools and select the ones most appropriate for each problem.

2. PROPERTIES OF ESTIMATORS

Formally, an estimator (of a parameter) is defined as any function of random variables (from data); it is a statistic of data. Clearly, then, an estimator has utility only when it possesses certain desirable properties. Generally speaking, its possible values should be tightly clustered around the true value of the parameter being estimated. Ideally, we would know the complete sampling distribution of every possible estimator and then select the one we liked most. In the best of all possible worlds we would find one estimator whose mean value equaled the true parameter value and whose higher moments about the mean were smaller than the corresponding higher moments of all other estimators. But such utopian estimators rarely exist, and so we accept the conventional definition of the *best* estimator: the one whose mean squared deviation from the true parameter value is smallest. Let θ be a parameter, and let $\hat{\theta}$ be some estimator. Then the best estimator of θ is the one whose sum (or corresponding integral)

$$\sum(\hat{\theta} - \theta)^2$$

is minimum. Such an estimator may not always exist.

An estimator $\hat{\theta}$ is said to be *unbiased* if and only if

$$E(\hat{\theta}) = \theta.$$

If $\hat{\theta}$ is unbiased and if it is a best estimator of θ, then its variance is smaller than all other unbiased estimates of θ, for by definition

$$\text{Var}(\hat{\theta}) = E[\hat{\theta} - E(\hat{\theta})]^2.$$

In general, however, the minimum variance estimator is not the best estimator, and vice versa.

In practical estimation problems we would usually be quite happy if we could compute the bias and variance of each estimator. (Other important properties of estimators, such as sufficiency and efficiency, are primarily of theoretical interest.) Generally speaking, we are in a most happy situation if we can find the maximum likelihood estimators of our parameters. Among the reasons why this is true are the following: (1) If a best estimator exists, the method of maximum likelihood will find it; (2) if a sufficient estimator exists, maximum likelihood will find it; and (3) the theory of maximum likelihood estimation provides a method for estimating the variance of the estimators (see Fisher, 1922, 1925). Even though maximum likelihood estimators are usually biased, they are to be preferred because of the reasons just listed.

3. METHODS OF ESTIMATION

When estimating parameters of psychological models, formal methods of estimation often lead to equations that are not readily solved. Nevertheless, those formal methods can serve as guides to less formal procedures, approximations, and numerical schemes. Thus the basic ideas of the major formal methods are reviewed here.

3.1 Modified Method of Moments

One of the earliest estimation techniques was Pearson's method of moments. A population has a theoretical distribution function with k parameters. One derives formulas for the first k moments of the distribution and equates them to the corresponding observed sample moments. The equations are then solved for the parameters, and the values obtained are the desired estimates. A modification of this procedure can be and has been used to estimate parameters of psychological models that predict more than a single distribution function. One equates expected and observed values of k statistics (not necessarily moments of a single distribution) in order to estimate k parameters. For example, with a linear learning model, the mean total number of errors and the mean number of trials before the first success were used to estimate the two learning rate parameters. This procedure depends on the availability of explicit formulas for expected values of several statistics; this is one of the reasons why the derivation of such formulas from detailed analysis of models is so important.

From the point of view of estimation the total number of errors is probably the most important statistic of learning models. Its expected value often converges as the number of trials gets large and its variance is usually smaller than that of other statistics. It represents the "area" under the curve of errors versus trials and so is a reasonable quantity to use in matching a theoretical learning curve to an observed one. If two parameters are to be estimated, another statistic is needed, but its selection is less obvious. A sensible approach is to find a statistic that is related to the shape of the learning curve, because two curves could cover the same area but have very different shapes. One possibility is the expected number of errors on the first N trials, where N is selected so that learning is about half complete.

As an example, consider the simplest linear learning model for which the probability of an error on trial n is

$$p_n = \alpha^{n-1} p_1, \qquad (0 < \alpha < 1).$$

The expected number of errors on the first N trials is

$$\sum_{n=1}^{N} p_n = \frac{1 - \alpha^N}{1 - \alpha} p_1.$$

By selecting N appropriately, one obtains a formula which along with the asymptotic result will yield estimates of the two parameters, α and p_1.

Most learning models are not so simple. Most of them imply a branching process, and few of them permit a direct computation of the mean probability of an error on trial n. In spite of this, it sometimes turns out that one can get an asymptotic result for total errors. Functional equations have been extensively used for this purpose. But with those same models, no one has been able to compute the expected number of errors up to some finite trial N. Thus we must search for some other statistic that depends on the shape of the learning curve. The number of trials before the first success has been used; it depends upon the shape of the early part of the learning curve. Its disadvantage is that it usually has a large variance, but it has been used because one has been able to compute its expectation. Let p_n be the probability of an error on trial n and consider the class of two-operator models defined by

$$p_{n+1} = \begin{cases} Q_1 p_n & \text{if an error on trial } n, \\ Q_2 p_n & \text{if a success on trial } n. \end{cases}$$

The probability that the first success occurs on trial v is

$$(p_1)(Q_1 p_1)(Q_1^2 p_1) \cdots (Q_1^{v-2} p_1)(1 - Q_1^{v-1} p_1),$$

and the expected number of trials before the first success is readily shown to be

$$p_1 + p_1(Q_1 p_1) + p_1(Q_1 p_1)(Q_1^2 p_1) + p_1(Q_1 p_1)(Q_1^2 p_1)(Q_1^3 p_1) + \cdots$$

This is often easy to evaluate. For example, if

$$Q_1 p_n = \alpha p_n, \qquad (0 \leqslant \alpha < 1),$$

the expected number of trials before the first success is

$$\sum_{i=1}^{\infty} \alpha^{i(i-1)/2} p_1^{\,i}.$$

This sum can be approximated by an integral or it can be tabulated. Both have been done in the literature. For any two-operator models of the kind being considered here, the distribution of the number of trials before the first success depends only on one of the two operators, Q_1. This is a very desirable property from the point of view of computation and application.

A statistic that is sensitive to the tail of the learning curve is the trial of the last error. Its expectation often exists, but it is usually extremely hard to compute.

A statistic that is sensitive to the steepness of the learning curve is the total number of runs of errors. If the curve is a step-function that drops from 1 to 0 on a single trial, there will be only one run of errors, whereas a curve that decreases gradually will lead to fairly large number of error runs. The expectation of this statistic can be computed in closed form quite often (Bush, 1959; Kanal, 1962), and so it has been one of the more useful statistics.

The method of moments as modified here has several disadvantages, the chief one being that we seldom know anything about the properties of the resulting estimators. They are probably biased because data from a finite number of trials are used in asymptotic formulas for expected values. If it is possible to compute the variances of the statistics being used for estimation, one obtains some information about the variance of the estimators, but not complete information. Finally, one must worry a bit about the covariance of two or more estimators. It is nearly impossible to find two or more independent statistics, but one should be careful not to select statistics that are too highly correlated. The number of trials before the second success and the number before the third success, for example, are two statistics that would surely have a high positive correlation. Thus they are not likely to yield very good estimators of two parameters.

3.2 The Monte Carlo Method

Any well-defined probability model can be used to generate "data" from a table of random numbers. If we have a set $\{p_i\}$ of probabilities that can be assigned numerical values, we can generate a binary sequence $\{X_i\}$ in which $p_i = \Pr(X_i = 1)$ and $1 - p_i = \Pr(X_i = 0)$ by the following rule: if $RN < p_i$, then $X_i = 1$, and if $RN \geqslant p_i$, then $X_i = 0$, where RN is the selected random number with a decimal point properly placed. This procedure of computing is known as the Monte Carlo method, and its application to learning models is described elsewhere (Bush & Mosteller, 1955, Chapter 6). The computations can be carried out only with numerical values of the model parameters, of course; the pseudodata from a particular group of "stat-rats" are an example of how real data would look if the model fitted perfectly and if the parameters had the values in fact used in the Monte Carlo computations. Thus the parameters can be estimated by exploring the parameter space with Monte Carlo runs and stopping at that point in the space where the real data and the pseudodata best agree.

As with all estimation schemes, we need clear-cut criteria for what constitutes "best." With the Monte Carlo method, we have complete freedom in choosing a criterion—we can select any statistics we like for matching. But with this method we are likely to acquire little information about the properties of the estimators. Thus it appears desirable to use matching statistics that arise naturally in formal estimation schemes such as maximum likelihood. This point is illustrated in Sec. 4.5, where estimation of parameters in Luce's beta model is discussed.

Even with precisely defined and easily applied criteria, Monte Carlo estimation is not child's play. In spite of the increased availability of high-speed computers, the method is costly. Millions of random digits may be needed and many hours of computer time may be required to explore adequately a three-dimensional parameter space. Therefore, at the present time the Monte Carlo method of estimation is not generally feasible unless supplementary techniques are used to restrict the region in the parameter space to be explored. Otherwise the estimation procedure may be too costly in time and labor. This points up, once again, the great need for detailed mathematical analyses of models. Even approximate formulas, upper and lower bounds, and, yes, good intuition are useful adjuncts to Monte Carlo explorations.

3.3 Method of Least Squares

Suppose we have a set of random variables X_i and predicted expectations $E(X_i)$ which are functions of a parameter θ. The method of least squares involves minimizing the sum

$$S^2 = \sum_i [X_i - E(X_i)]^2,$$

with respect to θ. We get

$$\sum_i [X_i - E(X_i)] \frac{\partial E(X_i)}{\partial \theta} = 0.$$

If it should happen that $\partial E(X_i)/\partial \theta$ is independent of i, then we have

$$\sum_i E(X_i) = \sum_i X_i,$$

and the computation of the estimate is especially simple. For learning models in which X_i is a binary random variable for the ith trial and in which $p_i = E(X_i)$ is a function of i and the parameters, the simplification does not obtain.

3.4 Minimum Chi-Square

With the same notation as in the preceding paragraph, a statistic chi-square is defined by

$$\chi^2 = \sum_i \frac{[X_i - E(X_i)]^2}{E(X_i)}.$$

For a binary random variable X_n with expectation p_n, this becomes

$$\chi^2 = \sum_n \left\{ \frac{[X_n - p_n]^2}{p_n} + \frac{[(1 - X_n) - (1 - p_n)]^2}{1 - p_n} \right\}$$

$$= \sum_n \frac{(X_n - p_n)^2}{p_n(1 - p_n)},$$

so we see that χ^2 is similar to the sum of squares s^2 of the preceding paragraph, except that each square is weighted by the reciprocal of the binomial variance $p_n(1 - p_n)$. Analytic minimization of χ^2 seldom leads to simple estimation equations because the denominator contains a function of the parameter being estimated. Thus the minimum chi-square method of estimation is usually employed only when numerical methods of minimization are used.

3.5 Maximum Likelihood

The most elegant and satisfactory method of estimation is Fisher's maximum likelihood procedure. One merely writes down an expression for the likelihood, L, of obtaining the data actually observed. For discrete random variables, L will be a function of parameters to be estimated and of the random variables. Maximization is usually accomplished by setting

$$\frac{\partial \log L}{\partial \theta} = 0,$$

where θ is the parameter being estimated.

Consider a set of independent binomial processes. Each has a parameter $p_j (j = 1, 2, \ldots, J)$ which will be interpreted as a probability of a "correct" response. The associated binary random variables are X_{ij}. For simplicity, let the same number I of observations be made on each process ($i = 1, 2, \ldots, I$). Finally, let each of the p_j be a function of some single parameter, θ. From one application to another, this functional dependence of the p_j on θ will vary, and so it will not be specified in general. We need only require that it be twice differentiable.

The likelihood function is

$$L = \prod_{j=1}^{J} \prod_{i=1}^{I} p_j^{X_{ij}} (1 - p_j)^{1-X_{ij}}.$$

Equating to zero the logarithmic derivative with respect to θ gives the basic estimation equation

$$\sum_{j=1}^{J} \frac{\bar{X}_j - p_j}{p_j(1 - p_j)} \frac{\partial p_j}{\partial \theta} = 0,$$

where

$$\bar{X}_j = \frac{1}{I} \sum_{i=1}^{I} X_{ij}.$$

The solution of the estimation equation yields the maximum likelihood estimate $\hat{\theta}$ of the parameter θ.

A famous theorem of Fisher's asserts that the sampling distribution of any maximum likelihood estimator approaches, as the sample size increases, the normal distribution with variance

$$\text{AVar}\,(\hat{\theta}) = \frac{1}{-E(\partial^2 \log L/\partial \theta^2)}.$$

(The operator symbol AVar is used to indicate the asymptotic variance.) For the class of models being explored here, this theorem leads to the equation

$$\text{AVar}\,(\hat{\theta}) = \frac{1}{I \sum_{j=1}^{J} [1/p_j(1 - p_j)](\partial p_j/\partial \theta)^2}.$$

4. MAXIMUM LIKELIHOOD ESTIMATES IN LEARNING

The maximum likelihood method outlined in the preceding section will now be applied to several models for simple learning. The index j is interpreted as trial number, and so we replace it by the symbol n. The index i could refer to the subject number, but for simplicity we suppress it; the theory will be developed for a single organism but it will be obvious how to generalize the results to a group of identical subjects.

The estimation equation then becomes

$$\sum_{n=1}^{N} \frac{X_n - p_n}{p_n(1 - p_n)} \frac{\partial p_n}{\partial \theta} = 0$$

and the asymptotic variance formula is

$$\text{AVar}(\hat{\theta}) = \frac{1}{\sum_{n=1}^{N} [1/p_n(1 - p_n)](\partial p_n/\partial \theta)^2} .$$

4.1 The Single-Operator Linear Model

The simplest model for learning that has been studied (Bush & Sternberg, 1959) is defined by the transition law

$$p_{n+1} = \alpha p_n,$$

which leads at once to the explicit formula

$$p_n = \alpha^{n-1} p_1.$$

The partial derivatives with respect to the two parameters are

$$\frac{\partial p_n}{\partial p_1} = \frac{p_n}{p_1}, \qquad \frac{\partial p_n}{\partial \alpha} = \frac{n-1}{\alpha} p_n,$$

and these lead to the estimation equations

$$\sum_{n=1}^{N} \frac{X_n - p_n}{1 - p_n} = 0,$$

$$\sum_{n=1}^{N} (n-1) \frac{X_n - p_n}{1 - p_n} = 0.$$

It is not possible to write these equations in such a way that the random variables X_n are separated from the model parameters. Therefore, only numerical methods can be used to solve the equations for particular data. The asymptotic variances of the estimators are

$$\text{AVar}(\hat{p}_1) = \frac{p_1^2}{\sum_{n=1}^{N} p_n/(1 - p_n)} ,$$

$$\text{AVar}(\hat{\alpha}) = \frac{\alpha^2}{\sum_{n=1}^{N} (n-1)^2 p_n/(1 - p_n)} .$$

Once the estimates $\hat{p}_1$ and $\hat{\alpha}$ are obtained, their variances can be estimated from these formulas.

4.2 Commuting-Operator Linear Model

The most completely investigated model having two operators is the commuting-operator linear model (Tatsuoka & Mosteller, 1959) defined by

$$p_{n+1} = \begin{cases} \alpha_1 p_n & \text{if } X_n = 1, \\ \alpha_2 p_n & \text{if } X_n = 0. \end{cases}$$

This rule may be written more compactly as

$$p_{n+1} = \alpha_1^{X_n} \alpha_2^{1-X_n} p_n.$$

The solution to this recursive formula is

$$p_n = \alpha_1^{S_n} \alpha_2^{(n-1)-S_n} p_1,$$

where

$$S_n = \sum_{v=1}^{n-1} X_v.$$

The three partial derivatives are readily obtained, and the estimation equations are

$$\sum_{n=1}^{N} \frac{X_n - p_n}{1 - p_n} = 0,$$

$$\sum_{n=1}^{N} S_n \frac{X_n - p_n}{1 - p_n} = 0,$$

$$\sum_{n=1}^{N} (n - 1 - S_n) \frac{X_n - p_n}{1 - p_n} = 0.$$

The second and third equations can be added together and the sum used to replace the third equation. Hence the estimation equations can be written

$$\sum_{n=1}^{N} \frac{X_n - p_n}{1 - p_n} = 0,$$

$$\sum_{n=1}^{N} (n - 1) \frac{X_n - p_n}{1 - p_n} = 0,$$

$$\sum_{n=1}^{N} S_n \frac{X_n - p_n}{1 - p_n} = 0.$$

Note that the first two equations in this set are identical to the estimation equations obtained for the single-operator linear model in the preceding section.

4.3 Two-Absorbing-Barrier Linear Model

To illustrate how untidy the estimation equations can become, we shall consider briefly a model with "two absorbing barriers" and a single rate parameter. It is defined by

$$p_{n+1} = \begin{cases} \alpha p_n + (1 - \alpha) & \text{if } X_n = 1, \\ \alpha p_n & \text{if } X_n = 0. \end{cases}$$

More compactly,

$$p_{n+1} = \alpha p_n + X_n(1 - \alpha).$$

The explicit solution is

$$p_n = \alpha^{n-1} p_1 + (1 - \alpha) \sum_{\nu=1}^{n-1} X_\nu \alpha^{n-1-\nu},$$

and the source of the untidiness is already clear; the random variables do not appear in a simple sum separate from the parameters. The partial derivatives are

$$\frac{\partial p_n}{\partial p_1} = \alpha^{n-1},$$

$$\frac{\partial p_n}{\partial \alpha} = (n - 1) \frac{\alpha^{n-1} p_1}{\alpha} - \sum_{\nu=1}^{n-1} X_\nu \alpha^{n-1-\nu} + \frac{1 - \alpha}{\alpha} \sum_{\nu=1}^{n-1} (n - 1 - \nu) X_\nu \alpha^{n-1-\nu}.$$

When these derivatives are inserted into the estimation equations, the resulting sums are unpleasant, to say the least. It is evident that other estimation techniques are to be preferred for such a model.

4.4 The Single-Operator Beta Model

It is somewhat surprising that Luce's nonlinear beta model (Luce, 1959, and Bush, Galanter, & Luce, 1959) leads to maximum likelihood estimators that are simpler than those for the linear models just considered. The simplest form of the beta model has one operator:

$$p_{n+1} = \frac{p_n}{p_n + \beta(1 - p_n)}.$$

The explicit formula is

$$p_n = \frac{p_1}{p_1 + \beta^{n-1}(1 - p_1)}.$$

The partial derivatives are

$$\frac{\partial p_n}{\partial p_1} = \frac{p_n(1 - p_n)}{p_1(1 - p_1)},$$

$$\frac{\partial p_n}{\partial \beta} = \frac{n - 1}{\beta} p_n(1 - p_n).$$

The appearance of the terms $p_n(1 - p_n)$ in these derivatives is most pleasing because the estimation equations become simple. They are

$$\sum_{n=1}^{N} X_n = \sum_{n=1}^{N} p_n,$$

$$\sum_{n=1}^{N} (n - 1)X_n = \sum_{n=1}^{N} (n - 1)p_n.$$

The sums on the left are determined completely by data, and the sums on the right are functions of the parameters only. If N is sufficiently large, one needs only a table of the two infinite sums as functions of p_1 and β. Thus the estimation problem for this model is completely solved. Note that the right-hand side of each equation is the expected value of the statistic on the left-hand side. We thus see a close correspondence between maximum likelihood and the "modified method of moments."

For the single-operator beta model the asymptotic variances of the estimators also have simple formulas:

$$\text{AVar}(\hat{p}_1) = \frac{[p_1(1 - p_1)]^2}{\sum\limits_{n=1}^{N} p_n(1 - p_n)},$$

$$\text{AVar}(\hat{\beta}) = \frac{\beta^2}{\sum\limits_{n=1}^{N} (n - 1)^2 p_n(1 - p_n)}.$$

4.5 More General Beta Models

Much of the beauty of the maximum likelihood method carries over to the beta models with two or four operators. Their explicit formulas for the response probabilities can be written in the form

$$p_n = \frac{p_1}{p_1 + \beta_1^{f_1}\beta_2^{f_2}(1 - p_1)},$$

where f_1 and f_2 are functions of random variables. For example, the two operator model,

$$p_{n+1} = \begin{cases} \dfrac{p_n}{p_n + \beta_1(1 - p_n)} & \text{if } X_n = 1, \\[2ex] \dfrac{p_n}{p_n + \beta_2(1 - p_n)} & \text{if } X_n = 0, \end{cases}$$

leads to the functions

$$f_1 = S_n, \qquad f_2 = (n - 1) - S_n,$$

where

$$S_n = \sum_{\nu=1}^{n-1} X_\nu.$$

The symmetric four-operator model

$$p_{n+1} = \begin{cases} \dfrac{p_n}{p_n + \beta_1(1 - p_n)} & \text{if } X_n = 1, \quad Y_n = 1, \\[2ex] \dfrac{\beta_2 p_n}{\beta_2 p_n + (1 - p_n)} & \text{if } X_n = 1, \quad Y_n = 0, \\[2ex] \dfrac{\beta_1 p_n}{\beta_1 p_n + (1 - p_n)} & \text{if } X_n = 0, \quad Z_n = 1, \\[2ex] \dfrac{p_n}{p_n + \beta_2(1 - p_n)} & \text{if } X_n = 0, \quad Z_n = 0, \end{cases}$$

leads to the functions

$$f_1 = \sum_{\nu=1}^{n-1} [X_\nu(Y_\nu + Z_\nu) - Z_\nu],$$

$$f_2 = \sum_{\nu=1}^{n-1} [1 - Z_\nu - X_\nu(2 - Y_\nu - Z_\nu)].$$

If $Y_n + Z_n = 1$ (reward on one side only), these functions simplify to

$$f_1 = S_n - T_n,$$

$$f_2 = (n - 1) - S_n - T_n,$$

where

$$S_n = \sum_{\nu=1}^{n-1} X_\nu, \qquad T_n = \sum_{\nu=1}^{n-1} Z_\nu.$$

Thus we can dispose of all such beta models at once. The partial derivatives are

$$\frac{\partial p_n}{\partial p_1} = \frac{p_n(1 - p_n)}{p_1(1 - p_1)},$$

$$\frac{\partial p_n}{\partial \beta_1} = \frac{f_1}{\beta_1} p_n(1 - p_n), \quad (n > 1),$$

$$\frac{\partial p_n}{\partial \beta_2} = \frac{f_2}{\beta_2} p_n(1 - p_n), \quad (n > 1).$$

The estimation equations are then

$$\sum_{n=1}^{N} X_n = \sum_{n=1}^{N} p_n,$$

$$\sum_{n=1}^{N} f_1 X_n = \sum_{n=1}^{N} f_1 p_n,$$

$$\sum_{n=1}^{N} f_2 X_n = \sum_{n=1}^{N} f_2 p_n.$$

The strikingly simple form of these three equations may be a bit misleading. Although the left-hand sides are statistics of data not involving model parameters, the right-hand sides are functions of parameters and data. Indeed, p_n itself is a function of data because it depends on f_1 and f_2. Nevertheless, the equations are manageable if numerical methods are used. Furthermore, they suggest the following procedure which should lead to somewhat modified maximum likelihood estimates: replace the right-hand sides of the equations with expected values. Wherever analytical methods of obtaining those expected values fail, Monte Carlo computations can be made. At the very least, we now have a criterion to be applied when Monte Carlo explorations are being made: we find those parameters that equate the values of the three statistics

$$\sum X_n, \quad \sum f_1 X_n, \quad \sum f_2 X_n,$$

of data with the corresponding "statistics" of the Monte Carlo runs.

5. MAXIMUM LIKELIHOOD ESTIMATES IN PSYCHOPHYSICS

5.1 A Psychometric Function

One of the fundamental problems in psychophysics is the problem of human discrimination. A person is presented with two stimuli and is asked to report whether the second stimulus is louder, higher in pitch, sweeter, brighter, etc., depending on the stimulus modality or dimension being studied. (It is interesting that Fisher introduced his exposition of experimental design principles with a psychophysical example much like this.) When the two stimuli presented to a person are very similar, the discrimination is imperfect, and so one speaks of the probability of a correct response. The curve that gives this probability as a function of the difference between the two stimuli, as measured on some physical continuum, is monotone increasing and is called the psychometric function.

The cumulative normal has often been used to offer a theoretical representation of the psychometric function, but a mathematically simpler function, and a very similar one, is the logistic. Recently, Luce (1959) gave an axiomatic justification for using the logistic instead of the cumulative normal. Denote by u_j the physical stimulus difference for the jth stimulus presentation and, by p_j, the corresponding probability of a correct response. Then the logistic function is

$$p_j = \frac{1}{1 + e^{-(u_j - c)/a}},$$

where c and a are two parameters which have simple interpretations. The parameter c is simply a scale factor and is called the "constant error." It is the stimulus difference value at which the probability of correct responding is $\frac{1}{2}$. The parameter a is a measure of spread. The jnd (just noticeable difference) is defined as half the difference between the π percentage point and the $1 - \pi$ percentage point. Most commonly, π is chosen to be 0.75. It is easy to show that for the logistic given above

$$\text{jnd} = a \log \frac{\pi}{1 - \pi}.$$

Thus the parameter a is proportional to the jnd.

The logistic, as well as the cumulative normal, has been used extensively in bio-assay research. The physical variable is dosage and the "correct response" is death. The parameter c is called the "LD.50," to indicate the 50 per cent point of lethal dosage. This is the parameter of major importance; there is only secondary interest in the spread of the function. Several authors, but notably Berkson (1944, 1953), have studied various methods of estimating the logistic parameters, including the method of maximum likelihood. Thus the material presented in this section is not new.

Two separate but parallel problems are considered together: estimation of the constant error c and estimation of the jnd parameter a. The needed partial derivatives are

$$\frac{\partial p_j}{\partial c} = \frac{1}{a}\, p_j(1 - p_j),$$

$$\frac{\partial p_j}{\partial a} = -\,\frac{u_j - c}{a^2}\, p_j(1 - p_j).$$

Thus, from the basic estimation equation of Sec. 3.5, we get the two estimation equations

$$\sum_{j=1}^{J}(\overline{X}_j - p_j) = 0,$$

$$\sum_{j=1}^{J}(u_j - c)(\overline{X}_j - p_j) = 0.$$

By adding c times the first equation to the second equation, we get

$$\sum_{j=1}^{J} u_j(\overline{X}_j - p_j) = 0.$$

The equations to be solved are then more conveniently written

$$\sum_{j=1}^{J} \overline{X}_j = \sum_{j=1}^{J} p_j,$$

$$\sum_{j=1}^{J} u_j \overline{X}_j = \sum_{j=1}^{J} u_j p_j.$$

The experimental observations appear only on the left-hand sides of these equations and the u_j are known experimental numbers. Thus in an actual application the left sides become simple numbers. The right-hand sides, however, are functions of the u_j and the two parameters, c and a, being estimated. Tables of p_j are thus very useful (see Table 2).

If all one cares to do is estimate the two parameters, it is necessary to obtain data at only two stimulus points, u_1 and u_2. In this case the estimation equations can be solved to yield the explicit formulas

$$\hat{c} = \frac{u_2\hat{\lambda}_1 - u_1\hat{\lambda}_2}{\hat{\lambda}_2 - \hat{\lambda}_1},$$

$$\hat{a} = \frac{u_2 - u_1}{\hat{\lambda}_2 - \hat{\lambda}_1},$$

where

$$\hat{\lambda}_j = \log\frac{\overline{X}_j}{1 - \overline{X}_j} \qquad (j = 1, 2).$$

It is interesting to note that these estimation equations for $J = 2$ are identical to the equations obtained when the method of least squares is applied to the variable

$$\lambda_j = \log \frac{p_j}{1 - p_j} \, .$$

Minimizing the sum

$$S^2 = \sum_{j=1}^{J} (\lambda_j - \hat{\lambda}_j)^2$$

with respect to c and a leads, for $J = 2$, to the foregoing equations. In the bio-assay literature the function

$$\lambda = \log \frac{p}{1 - p}$$

is given the name "logit p" and the inverse function

$$p = \frac{1}{1 + e^{-\lambda}}$$

is called "antilogit λ." Berkson (1953) has provided tables of these functions which are reproduced in Tables 1 and 2.

A numerical example illustrates this use of Table 1. Suppose at stimulus value $u_1 = -5$ we obtain a proportion $\bar{X}_1 = 0.19$ and at stimulus value $u_2 = +4$ we observe $\bar{X}_2 = 0.76$. From Table 1 we find that $\hat{\lambda}_1 = -1.450$ and $\hat{\lambda}_2 = 1.153$. We then get $\hat{c} = +0.013$ and $\hat{a} = 3.46$.

The logistic curve and the cumulative normal are easily compared by using the logit transformation. For the logistic,

$$\text{logit } p = \frac{u - c}{a} \, ,$$

and so when we plot logit p versus $(u - c)$ we obtain a straight line through the origin with slope $1/a$. If ϕ is the cumulative standard normal (zero mean and unit variance), which can be found in any statistics textbook, we can easily compute logit ϕ by using Table 1. Figure 2 is the result. The two functions can be matched at any desired point; two examples of logit p are shown in Fig. 2—one matched to logit ϕ at one standard deviation and the other at two standard deviations. As can be seen, the logistic and normal differ mainly in the tails. This is because the derivative of the logistic is going to zero as $e^{-u/a}$, whereas the derivative of the cumulative normal is going to zero as $e^{-u^2/2}$.

Table 1 Logits

TABLE 1
LOGITS

For p less than .50 on left, logit is negative. For p greater than .50 on right, logit is positive.

p	0	1	2	3	4	5	6	7	8	9	p
				Thousandths, for p in left column							
.00	—	6.90675	6.21261	5.80614	5.51745	5.29330	5.10998	4.95482	4.82028	4.70149	4.59512	.99
.01	4.59512	4.49880	4.41078	4.32972	4.25460	4.18459	4.11904	4.05740	3.99922	3.94413	3.89182	.98
.02	3.89182	3.84201	3.79447	3.74899	3.70541	3.66356	3.62331	3.58455	3.54715	3.51103	3.47610	.97
.03	3.47610	3.44228	3.40950	3.37769	3.34680	3.31678	3.28757	3.25914	3.23143	3.20441	3.17805	.96
.04	3.17805	3.15232	3.12718	3.10260	3.07857	3.05505	3.03202	3.00947	2.98736	2.96569	2.94444	.95
.05	2.94444	2.92358	2.90311	2.88301	2.86326	2.84385	2.82477	2.80601	2.78756	2.76941	2.75154	.94
.06	2.75154	2.73394	2.71662	2.69955	2.68273	2.66616	2.64982	2.63371	2.61783	2.60215	2.58669	.93
.07	2.58669	2.57143	2.55637	2.54149	2.52681	2.51231	2.49798	2.48382	2.46984	2.45601	2.44235	.92
.08	2.44235	2.42884	2.41548	2.40227	2.38920	2.37627	2.36348	2.35083	2.33830	2.32591	2.31363	.91
.09	2.31363	2.30149	2.28946	2.27754	2.26574	2.25406	2.24248	2.23101	2.21965	2.20839	2.19722	.90
.10	2.19722	2.18616	2.17520	2.16433	2.15355	2.14286	2.13227	2.12176	2.11133	2.10100	2.09074	.89
.11	2.09074	2.08057	2.07047	2.06046	2.05052	2.04066	2.03087	2.02115	2.01151	2.00193	1.99243	.88
.12	1.99243	1.98299	1.97363	1.96432	1.95508	1.94591	1.93680	1.92775	1.91876	1.90983	1.90096	.87
.13	1.90096	1.89215	1.88339	1.87469	1.86605	1.85745	1.84892	1.84043	1.83200	1.82362	1.81529	.86
.14	1.81529	1.80701	1.79878	1.79059	1.78246	1.77437	1.76632	1.75833	1.75037	1.74247	1.73460	.85
.15	1.73460	1.72678	1.71900	1.71126	1.70357	1.69591	1.68830	1.68072	1.67318	1.66569	1.65823	.84
.16	1.65823	1.65081	1.64342	1.63607	1.62876	1.62149	1.61425	1.60704	1.59987	1.59273	1.58563	.83
.17	1.58563	1.57856	1.57152	1.56451	1.55754	1.55060	1.54369	1.53681	1.52996	1.52314	1.51635	.82
.18	1.51635	1.50959	1.50286	1.49615	1.48948	1.48283	1.47621	1.46962	1.46306	1.45652	1.45001	.81
.19	1.45001	1.44353	1.43707	1.43063	1.42423	1.41784	1.41148	1.40515	1.39884	1.39256	1.38629	.80
.20	1.38629	1.38006	1.37384	1.36765	1.36148	1.35533	1.34921	1.34310	1.33702	1.33096	1.32493	.79
.21	1.32493	1.31891	1.31291	1.30694	1.30098	1.29505	1.28913	1.28324	1.27736	1.27150	1.26567	.78
.22	1.26567	1.25985	1.25405	1.24827	1.24251	1.23676	1.23104	1.22533	1.21964	1.21397	1.20831	.77
.23	1.20831	1.20267	1.19705	1.19145	1.18586	1.18029	1.17474	1.16920	1.16368	1.15817	1.15268	.76
.24	1.15268	1.14720	1.14175	1.13630	1.13087	1.12546	1.12006	1.11468	1.10931	1.10395	1.09861	.75

This table is reproduced from Berkson (1953) with the permission of the American Statistical Association.

Table 1 Logits (continued)

Thousandths, for *p* in left column

p	0	1	2	3	4	5	6	7	8	9	p
.25	1.09861	1.09329	1.08797	1.08268	1.07739	1.07212	1.06686	1.06162	1.05639	1.05117	.74
.26	1.04597	1.04078	1.03560	1.03043	1.02528	1.02014	1.01501	1.00990	1.00479	0.99970	.73
.27	0.99462	0.98955	0.98450	0.97945	0.97442	0.96940	0.96439	0.95939	0.95440	0.94943	.72
.28	0.94446	0.93951	0.93456	0.92963	0.92471	0.91979	0.91489	0.91000	0.90512	0.90025	.71
.29	0.89538	0.89053	0.88569	0.88086	0.87604	0.87122	0.86642	0.86162	0.85684	0.85206	.70
.30	0.84730	0.84254	0.83779	0.83305	0.82832	0.82360	0.81889	0.81418	0.80949	0.80480	.69
.31	0.80012	0.79545	0.79079	0.78613	0.78148	0.77685	0.77222	0.76759	0.76298	0.75837	.68
.32	0.75377	0.74918	0.74460	0.74002	0.73545	0.73089	0.72633	0.72179	0.71724	0.71271	.67
.33	0.70819	0.70367	0.69915	0.69465	0.69015	0.68566	0.68117	0.67669	0.67222	0.66775	.66
.34	0.66329	0.65884	0.65439	0.64995	0.64552	0.64109	0.63667	0.63225	0.62784	0.62344	.65
.35	0.61904	0.61465	0.61026	0.60588	0.60150	0.59713	0.59277	0.58841	0.58406	0.57971	.64
.36	0.57536	0.57103	0.56669	0.56237	0.55804	0.55373	0.54942	0.54511	0.54081	0.53651	.63
.37	0.53222	0.52793	0.52365	0.51937	0.51509	0.51083	0.50656	0.50230	0.49805	0.49379	.62
.38	0.48955	0.48531	0.48107	0.47683	0.47260	0.46838	0.46416	0.45994	0.45573	0.45152	.61
.39	0.44731	0.44311	0.43891	0.43472	0.43053	0.42634	0.42216	0.41798	0.41381	0.40963	.60
.40	0.40547	0.40130	0.39714	0.39298	0.38883	0.38467	0.38053	0.37638	0.37224	0.36810	.59
.41	0.36397	0.35983	0.35570	0.35158	0.34745	0.34333	0.33922	0.33510	0.33099	0.32688	.58
.42	0.32277	0.31867	0.31457	0.31047	0.30637	0.30228	0.29819	0.29410	0.29002	0.28593	.57
.43	0.28185	0.27777	0.27370	0.26962	0.26555	0.26148	0.25741	0.25335	0.24928	0.24522	.56
.44	0.24116	0.23710	0.23305	0.22900	0.22494	0.22089	0.21685	0.21280	0.20875	0.20471	.55
.45	0.20067	0.19663	0.19259	0.18856	0.18452	0.18049	0.17646	0.17243	0.16840	0.16437	.54
.46	0.16034	0.15632	0.15229	0.14827	0.14425	0.14023	0.13621	0.13219	0.12818	0.12416	.53
.47	0.12014	0.11613	0.11212	0.10811	0.10409	0.10008	0.09607	0.09206	0.08806	0.08405	.52
.48	0.08004	0.07604	0.07203	0.06803	0.06402	0.06002	0.05601	0.05201	0.04801	0.04401	.51
.49	0.04001	0.03600	0.03200	0.02800	0.02400	0.02000	0.01600	0.01200	0.00800	0.00400	.50
p	9	8	7	6	5	4	3	2	1	0	

Thousandths, for *p* in right column

Reproduced from Berkson (1953) with the permission of the American Statistical Association.

Table 2 Antilogits

TABLE 2
ANTILOGITS

Entries give value of p for specified positive value of logit l;
if l is negative, p is 1 minus the tabled value.

l	0	1	2	3	4	5	6	7	8	9
0.0	.50000	.50250	.50500	.50750	.51000	.51250	.51500	.51749	.51999	.52248
0.1	.52498	.52747	.52996	.53245	.53494	.53743	.53991	.54240	.54488	.54736
0.2	.54983	.55231	.55478	.55725	.55971	.56218	.56464	.56709	.56955	.57200
0.3	.57444	.57689	.57932	.58176	.58419	.58662	.58904	.59146	.59387	.59628
0.4	.59869	.60109	.60348	.60587	.60826	.61064	.61301	.61538	.61775	.62011
0.5	.62246	.62481	.62715	.62948	.63181	.63414	.63645	.63876	.64107	.64337
0.6	.64566	.64794	.65022	.65249	.65475	.65701	.65926	.66150	.66374	.66597
0.7	.66819	.67040	.67261	.67481	.67700	.67918	.68135	.68352	.68568	.68783
0.8	.68997	.69211	.69424	.69635	.69847	.70057	.70266	.70475	.70682	.70889
0.9	.71095	.71300	.71504	.71708	.71910	.72112	.72312	.72512	.72711	.72909
1.0	.73106	.73302	.73497	.73692	.73885	.74077	.74269	.74460	.74649	.74838
1.1	.75026	.75213	.75399	.75584	.75768	.75951	.76133	.76315	.76495	.76674
1.2	.76852	.77030	.77206	.77382	.77556	.77730	.77903	.78074	.78245	.78415
1.3	.78583	.78751	.78918	.79084	.79249	.79413	.79576	.79738	.79899	.80059
1.4	.80218	.80377	.80534	.80690	.80845	.81000	.81153	.81306	.81457	.81608
1.5	.81757	.81906	.82054	.82201	.82346	.82491	.82635	.82778	.82920	.83062
1.6	.83202	.83341	.83480	.83617	.83753	.83889	.84024	.84158	.84290	.84422
1.7	.84553	.84684	.84813	.84941	.85069	.85195	.85321	.85446	.85570	.85693
1.8	.85815	.85936	.86057	.86176	.86295	.86413	.86530	.86646	.86761	.86876
1.9	.86989	.87102	.87214	.87325	.87435	.87545	.87653	.87761	.87868	.87974
2.0	.88080	.88184	.88288	.88391	.88493	.88595	.88695	.88795	.88894	.88993
2.1	.89090	.89187	.89283	.89379	.89473	.89567	.89660	.89752	.89844	.89935
2.2	.90025	.90114	.90203	.90291	.90378	.90465	.90551	.90636	.90721	.90805
2.3	.90888	.90970	.91052	.91133	.91214	.91293	.91373	.91451	.91529	.91606
2.4	.91683	.91759	.91834	.91909	.91983	.92056	.92129	.92201	.92273	.92344
2.5	.92414	.92484	.92553	.92622	.92690	.92757	.92824	.92891	.92956	.93022
2.6	.93086	.93150	.93214	.93277	.93339	.93401	.93462	.93523	.93584	.93643
2.7	.93703	.93761	.93820	.93877	.93935	.93991	.94048	.94103	.94159	.94213
2.8	.94268	.94321	.94375	.94428	.94480	.94532	.94583	.94634	.94685	.94735
2.9	.94785	.94834	.94883	.94931	.94979	.95026	.95073	.95120	.95166	.95212
3.0	.95257	.95302	.95347	.95391	.95435	.95478	.95521	.95564	.95606	.95648
3.1	.95689	.95730	.95771	.95811	.95851	.95891	.95930	.95969	.96007	.96046
3.2	.96083	.96121	.96158	.96195	.96231	.96267	.96303	.96339	.96374	.96408
3.3	.96443	.96477	.96511	.96544	.96578	.96610	.96643	.96675	.96707	.96739
3.4	.96770	.96802	.96832	.96863	.96893	.96923	.96953	.96982	.97011	.97040
3.5	.97069	.97097	.97125	.97153	.97180	.97208	.97235	.97262	.97288	.97314
3.6	.97340	.97366	.97392	.97417	.97442	.97467	.97491	.97516	.97540	.97564
3.7	.97587	.97611	.97634	.97657	.97680	.97702	.97725	.97747	.97769	.97790
3.8	.97812	.97833	.97854	.97875	.97896	.97916	.97937	.97957	.97977	.97996
3.9	.98016	.98035	.98054	.98073	.98092	.98111	.98129	.98148	.98166	.98184
4.0	.98201	.98219	.98236	.98254	.98271	.98288	.98304	.98321	.98337	.98354
4.1	.98370	.98386	.98402	.98417	.98433	.98448	.98463	.98478	.98493	.98508
4.2	.98523	.98537	.98551	.98566	.98580	.98594	.98607	.98621	.98635	.98648
4.3	.98661	.98674	.98687	.98700	.98713	.98726	.98738	.98751	.98763	.98775
4.4	.98787	.98799	.98811	.98823	.98834	.98846	.98857	.98868	.98879	.98890
4.5	.98901	.98912	.98923	.98933	.98944	.98954	.98965	.98975	.98985	.98995
4.6	.99005	.99015	.99024	.99034	.99043	.99053	.99062	.99071	.99081	.99090
4.7	.99099	.99108	.99116	.99125	.99134	.99142	.99151	.99159	.99167	.99176
4.8	.99184	.99192	.99200	.99208	.99215	.99223	.99231	.99239	.99246	.99253
4.9	.99261	.99268	.99275	.99283	.99290	.99297	.99304	.99310	.99317	.99324
l	0	1	2	3	4	5	6	7	8	9

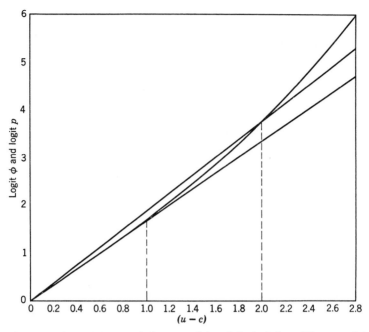

Fig. 2. Comparison of the cumulative normal ϕ and the logistic p. The curve is logit ϕ and the straight lines are examples of logit p matched to the normal at two different points.

5.2 A Signal Detection Model

Another type of psychophysical experiment involves a subject reporting whether he detects a weak signal in the presence of noise. Again, various sensory modalities can be used, but the principle is the same. In a typical experiment, noise alone is presented on a random half of the trials and signal plus noise are presented on the other trials. On each trial the subject responds "yes" or "no." This class of experiments and models for describing the data have been explored most extensively by Swets and Tanner. More recently, Luce (1959) has developed a simpler model (though a less elaborate one) based upon his axiomatic treatment of choice behavior. (See also Chapter 3 of this *Handbook*.)

Let p represent the (conditional) probability of the response "yes" when signal and noise are present and let q represent the probability of "yes" when noise alone is presented. For a particular set of experimental conditions, one obtains estimates of these two probabilities. Two important experimental variables that affect the values of these probabilities are signal strength and the payoff conditions. Obviously, if the signal is quite strong, p will be near 1.0 and q will be near 0, whereas if the signal is very weak both probabilities may be in the region of 0.5. For weak signals the probability values will depend largely on the relative costs of the two kinds of possible errors: saying "yes" when the signal is absent and saying "no" when it is present. Luce's model asserts that

$$p = \frac{1}{1 + \eta b},$$

$$q = \frac{\eta}{\eta + b},$$

where η is a perceptual parameter (depends on signal strength) and b is a motivational parameter (depends on the payoffs and other variables).

If we hold the signal strength constant and vary the payoff conditions, then the parameter b becomes a variable, but hopefully the parameter η is constant. When the variable b is eliminated from the last two equations, we get

$$p = \frac{q}{q + \eta^2(1 - q)}.$$

Such functions have been called ROC curves (receiver operating characteristics) by Swets and Tanner and are called isosensitivity curves by Luce.

Consider an equal signal strength experiment with K different payoff conditions, each with its own motivational parameter b_k ($k = 1, 2, \ldots, K$). The $2K = J$ probabilities of the general model are then

$$p_k = \frac{1}{1 + \eta b_k},$$

$$q_k = \frac{\eta}{\eta + b_k}.$$

The necessary partial derivatives are

$$\frac{\partial p_k}{\partial \eta} = -\frac{1}{\eta} p_k(1 - p_k),$$

$$\frac{\partial q_k}{\partial \eta} = \frac{1}{\eta} q_k(1 - q_k),$$

$$\frac{\partial p_k}{\partial b_k} = -\frac{1}{b_k} p_k(1 - p_k),$$

$$\frac{\partial q_k}{\partial b_k} = -\frac{1}{b_k} q_k(1 - q_k).$$

For $i \neq k$,

$$\frac{\partial p_k}{\partial b_i} = \frac{\partial q_k}{\partial b_i} = 0.$$

Denote the mean observed random variable corresponding to p_k by $\bar{X}_k$ and the one corresponding to q_k by $\bar{Y}_k$. The basic estimation equation of Sec. 3.5 then gives

$$\sum_{k=1}^{K} [(\bar{X}_k - p_k) - (\bar{Y}_k - q_k)] = 0,$$
$$(\bar{X}_k - p_k) + (\bar{Y}_k - q_k) = 0, \qquad (k = 1, 2, \ldots, K).$$

These $K + 1$ equations can be solved for the $K + 1$ estimates, $\hat{\eta}$, $\hat{b}_1$, $\hat{b}_2$, $\ldots$, $\hat{b}_k$. Ordinarily, we are interested only in $\hat{\eta}$, the estimator of the single parameter of the isosensitivity curve. The last set of equations can be written in the following somewhat more convenient form:

$$\sum_{k=1}^{K} \bar{X}_k = \sum_{k=1}^{K} p_k,$$
$$\sum_{k=1}^{K} \bar{Y}_k = \sum_{k=1}^{K} q_k,$$
$$\bar{X}_k + \bar{Y}_k = p_k + q_k, \qquad (k = 1, 2, \ldots, K).$$

One of these equations is redundant.

If the sole purpose of the experiment is to estimate η, one can take $K = 1$; that is, he can use a single set of payoffs (and a single value of signal strength, of course). In this case the estimation equations simplify to

$$\bar{X} = p = \frac{1}{1 + \eta b},$$
$$\bar{Y} = q = \frac{\eta}{\eta + b}.$$

When solved for η, these give

$$\hat{\eta} = \sqrt{[(1 - \bar{X})/\bar{X}][\bar{Y}/(1 - \bar{Y})]}.$$

We incidentally also get the estimate of b which is

$$\hat{b} = \sqrt{[(1 - \bar{X})/\bar{X}][(1 - \bar{Y})/\bar{Y}]}.$$

6. DESIGN OF EXPERIMENTS FOR PARAMETER ESTIMATION

The term "design of experiments" has acquired a rather technical meaning in statistics since the publication of Sir Ronald Fisher's book by that name in 1935. Among many consumers of statistical methods, in particular, among psychologists, the term is intimately associated with a special set of statistical techniques: analysis of variance and related methods. This highly restricted use of the term by the psychologist is curious because he knows that he faces many nonstatistical design problems in planning a good experiment. All too often he will use the analysis of variance, whether or not it is sensible, in dealing with his data. Sir Ronald warned against such abuses when he said,

Any brilliant achievement, on which attention is temporarily focused, may give a prestige to the method employed, or to some part of it, even in applications to which it has no special appropriateness. (Fisher, 1953, p. 184).

It is clear from Fisher's book that he has a much broader conception of the principles of designing experiments than have many of his followers.

6.1 The General Principle

When quantitative theories and models become important in a science, there is a shift in emphasis from testing hypotheses to estimating parameters. Instead of testing a null hypothesis, which asserts that an experimental variable has no effect (a "know-nothing hypothesis," as S. S. Stevens calls it), we wish to obtain information about the value of some parameter of the system being studied. In designing an experiment for this purpose, one should select experimental conditions to provide the most information about the value of that parameter. Fisher made this point very clearly in Chapter XI of his book. He defined the precision of an estimator (or the "amount of information" obtained) as the reciprocal of the variance of the estimator. He argued that one should design the experiment so that the precision is maximized for a fixed "cost" of the experiment. This is an example of Fisher's fundamental principle of experimental design: efficiency. Fisher was much concerned about the waste of scientific effort.

In most modern treatments of estimation theory the "best" estimator, $\hat{\theta}$, of a parameter, θ, is the one that has the smallest expected squared deviation from the true value. Thus a reasonable design principle would be to select experimental conditions such that this quantity is minimized; instead of just minimizing the variance, we would minimize the mean squared deviation. To do this, we must be able to compute both the variance and the bias, and this is not always easy. Of course, if the estimator is unbiased (or asymptotically unbiased), the problem is simplified.

An elementary example of design for estimation is the following: consider a variable X whose values $X_1, X_2, \ldots, X_j, \ldots, X_J$ are under complete experimental control, that is, whose values can be selected and maintained by an experimenter with complete precision. Assume that for theoretical or practical reasons there exists a smallest value $X_{\min}$ and a largest value $X_{\max}$. At each value X_j, let there be a random variable Y_j whose observed values are Y_{ij} where $i = 1, 2, \ldots, I$ for all j. The restriction that the same number of observations be made at all values of X is not necessary, but it simplifies the argument.

The model to be explored is a familiar one; we assume

$$E(Y_j) = a + bX_j,$$

and

$$\mathrm{Var}\,(Y_j) = \sigma^2, \quad \text{for all } j.$$

It is well known and easy to show that the least squares estimate of the slope parameter b is

$$\hat{b} = \sum_{i=1}^{I} \sum_{j=1}^{J} Y_{ij} \frac{X_j - \bar{X}}{IJ\,\mathrm{Var}\,(X)},$$

where

$$\bar{X} = \frac{1}{J} \sum_{j=1}^{J} X_j,$$

$$\mathrm{Var}\,(X) = \frac{1}{J} \sum_{j=1}^{J} (X_j - \bar{X})^2.$$

A simple computation shows that b is unbiased, that is, that

$$E(\hat{b}) = b.$$

Because the Y_j are independent random variables, it follows that

$$\mathrm{Var}\,(\hat{b}) = \frac{\sigma^2}{IJ} \frac{1}{\mathrm{Var}\,(X)}.$$

It follows at once that if σ^2 is a fixed parameter and if the total number, IJ, of observations is fixed, then the variance of the estimator $\hat{b}$ is minimized if $\mathrm{Var}\,(X)$ is maximized. Furthermore, $\mathrm{Var}\,(X)$ is maximized if half of the IJ observations are taken at $X_{\min}$ and half at $X_{\max}$.

The design problem posed by Fisher is thus solved for the simple model presented. For a fixed number of observations, the greatest "information" about the true parameter value is obtained if the observations are equally divided between the two extreme values of the experimental variable. Many may feel that the conclusion is obvious; the purpose of presenting the proof here is simply to illustrate the principle. The truth of the theorem depends, in particular, upon the assumption of equal variances. If the variance of Y_j is appreciably larger at the extreme values of X than it is at intermediate values, it is obvious that Var $(\hat{b})$ would be minimized by selecting some intermediate values of X. The fact that b is unbiased circumvents the question of whether one should minimize Var $(\hat{b})$ or $E[(\hat{b} - b)^2]$; the two quantities are equal in this case.

One can also inquire about the precision of estimates of the other two parameters, a and σ^2, but this would be a digression. In the following sections more psychologically interesting models will be explored in greater detail.

6.2 A Psychometric Function

Return now to the problem, discussed in Sec. 5.1, of estimating the parameters of a particular psychometric function, the logistic. First consider the asymptotic variance of $\hat{c}$, the maximum likelihood estimator of the constant error. Assume the jnd parameter, a, is fixed for the moment. The general formula of Sec. 3.5, plus the partial derivative in Sec. 5.1, give

$$A\,\mathrm{Var}\,(\hat{c}) = \frac{1}{(I/a^2)\sum_{j=1}^{J} p_j(1 - p_j)}.$$

If we want to keep fixed the total number of observations IJ and minimize $A\,\mathrm{Var}\,(\hat{c})$, it is clear that we shall want to select data points such that the sum

$$\frac{1}{J}\sum_{j=1}^{J} p_j(1 - p_j)$$

is maximized. This is accomplished by making all the observations at the value of u_j, which makes $p_j = 0.5$. This is not a surprising result; c is by definition the value of u_j which makes $p_j = 0.5$.

Now assume that c is fixed and consider the asymptotic variance of the jnd parameter a. We have in this case,

$$A\,\mathrm{Var}\,(\hat{a}) = \frac{1}{(I/a^4)\sum_{j=1}^{J}(u_j - c)^2 p_j(1 - p_j)}.$$

For fixed IJ, this variance is minimized when the sum

$$\frac{1}{J}\sum_{j=1}^{J}(u_j - c)^2 p_j(1 - p_j)$$

is maximized. Solving the logistic function of Sec. 5.1, we get

$$(u_j - c) = a \log \frac{p_j}{1 - p_j} .$$

Thus we need to maximize

$$\frac{1}{J} \sum_{j=1}^{J} \left[\log \frac{p_j}{1 - p_j} \right]^2 p_j(1 - p_j).$$

The summand has a single maximum value that obtains when p_j is a solution of the transcendental equation

$$\log \frac{p_j}{1 - p_j} = \frac{1}{p_j - \frac{1}{2}} .$$

There are two solutions, obtained numerically:

$$p_j = 0.08, \quad 0.92.$$

If all the data are collected at the values of u_j, which correspond to these two values of p_j, the asymptotic variance of $\hat{a}$ has its minimum value of

$$\min \left[\text{AVar} (\hat{a}) \right] = \frac{2.40a^2}{IJ} .$$

If one wants low variance estimates of both parameters, c and a, simultaneously, it is evident that a compromise is required. If half the observations are placed at $p_j = 0.2$ and half at $p_j = 0.8$, for example, then the asymptotic variance of $\hat{c}$ would be about 1.6 times its minimum value and the asymptotic variance of $\hat{a}$ would be about 1.4 times its minimum value. There would be a covariance term in addition, of course.

6.3 A Signal Detection Model

In Sec. 5.2 we obtained the maximum likelihood estimation equations for Luce's signal detection model. Consider the equal signal strength experiment which leads to an estimated isosensitivity curve. It possesses a single parameter η which we need to estimate. The asymptotic variance of the estimator can be written

$$\text{AVar} (\hat{\eta}) = \frac{1}{(I/\eta^2) \sum_{k=1}^{K} [p_k(1 - p_k) + q_k(1 - q_k)]} .$$

The total number of observations is $2IK$ and this is to be fixed. Thus we want to maximize the sum

$$\frac{1}{K} \sum_{k=1}^{K} [p_k(1 - p_k) + q_k(1 - q_k)].$$

We need to find the point or points on the isosensitivity curve that maximize the summand. Let

$$t = p(1 - p) + q(1 - q).$$

The derivative with respect to q is

$$\frac{dt}{dq} = (1 - 2p)\frac{dp}{dq} + (1 - 2q).$$

From the equation for the isosensitivity curve, we can show that

$$\frac{dp}{dq} = \frac{p(1 - p)}{q(1 - q)}.$$

Thus, when we set the foregoing derivative of t equal to zero, we get the equation

$$(1 - 2p) p(1 - p) + (1 - 2q) q(1 - q) = 0.$$

The solution that maximizes t is

$$p = 1 - q.$$

This corresponds to the point where the isosensitivity curve crosses the secondary diagonal. Along that diagonal the motivational parameter b has the value 1. Also we see that when $p = 1 - q$ we have

$$p(1 - p) = q(1 - q) = \frac{\eta}{(1 + \eta)^2}.$$

Thus at this point the asymptotic variance of η has its minimum value

$$\min[\text{AVar}\,(\hat{\eta})] = \frac{\eta(1 + \eta)^2}{2IK}.$$

We infer from the foregoing analysis that the most efficient estimate of the perceptual parameter η is obtained by eliminating any motivational bias. This suggests using a symmetric payoff matrix and presenting the stimulus on half of the experimental trials. The problem of the "bias" parameter may be more complicated than this, however. But, in any case, we can readily tell from experimental data whether we are on or near the secondary diagonal where the variance of η is minimized. The practical design problem is to arrange this in advance.

6.4 The Single-Operator Linear Learning Model

In Sec. 4.1 the maximum likelihood estimation equations were developed for the simplest kind of learning model. Equations for the asymptotic variances of the estimators of the initial probability p_1 and the rate parameter α were obtained. We see at once that the way to minimize AVar $(\hat{p}_1)$ is to make p_n as large as possible, that is, to make it equal to p_1. Thus we minimize the variance of p_1 by running each subject for only one trial, an obviously wasteful procedure unless large groups of subjects can be obtained cheaply.

More than one trial is needed if we wish to minimize the variance of the rate parameter estimate. Indeed, a single trial gives us no information at all. AVar $(\hat{\alpha})$ is minimized for fixed IN (subjects times trials) when

$$\frac{1}{N} \sum_{n=1}^{N} (n - 1)^2 \frac{p_n}{1 - p_n}$$

is maximized. Because learning data are necessarily collected sequentially, we are not free to choose a particular value of n and collect all our data there. Thus we cannot simply maximize the summand as we did in the preceding two sections. For given parameters p_1 and α, we need to find the number of trials N that maximizes

$$\frac{1}{N} \sum_{n=1}^{N} (n - 1)^2 \frac{\alpha^{n-1} p_1}{1 - \alpha^{n-1} p_1} .$$

This requires numerical methods. Table 3 shows a few values of N for ranges of α when $p_1 = 1$.

7. EVALUATION TECHNIQUES

It was argued at the beginning of this chapter that the evaluation of scientific models and theories is not a simple acceptance-rejection problem. We do not "test" for goodness-of-fit and then either throw the model away or send it to the Bureau of Standards. Rather, we assemble evidence of various kinds pertaining to a model and compare its successes and failures with those of other models. This procedure does not fit the pattern of

Table 3   Values* of N which Minimize the Asymptotic Variance of the Estimator $\hat{\alpha}$ for the Single-operator Linear Learning Model with $p_1 = 1$

α	N
$0.00 < \alpha < 0.14$	2
$0.14 < \alpha < 0.33$	3
$0.33 < \alpha < 0.45$	4
$0.45 < \alpha < 0.54$	5
$0.54 < \alpha < 0.60$	6
$0.60 < \alpha < 0.65$	7
$0.65 < \alpha < 0.69$	8
$0.69 < \alpha < 0.73$	9
$0.73 < \alpha < 0.75$	10

* These computations were carried out by Mr. Joseph Goguen.

deductive logic nor does it follow the rules of classical statistical inference. Modern statistical decision theory is closer in principle—it introduces more of the relevant considerations—but it demands far more information than is ever available. Perhaps the most candid and clearest exposition of how science really works today is found in Polya's volume on "plausible inference" (Polya, 1954).

If we accept the unavailability or even undesirability of a formal evaluation procedure, we still need some tools for informal evaluation. We need a list—perhaps an ordering—of model characteristics that can be compared to data. Such a list must depend heavily on the type of model and the class of phenomena being described, but some generalizations may be useful. The following list is purported to be generally applicable to psychological models, but, admittedly, it was formulated from experience with stochastic learning models.

7.1 Gross Features of Data

A psychophysical model must predict accurately the shape of observed psychometric functions. A learning model must predict the shape of the learning curve. These requirements seem to take precedence over all others and they are, indeed, usually met by the estimation criteria; the area under such a curve, for example, is almost always used as a matching statistic in estimating parameters. It is not guaranteed, however, that with the best possible estimates the data and model will agree satisfactorily on these gross features (Galanter & Bush, 1959), but if a model has two or more parameters it is seldom difficult to fit the learning curve or psychometric function. (If it is, the model is rarely published or discussed.) Thus we must look elsewhere for more sensitive evaluation criteria.

7.2 Variances of Statistics

When data are obtained from groups of subjects or from repeated observations on single subjects, one can compute the variances of several statistics. Models should predict the values of these variances. For example, in a learning model the total number of errors made by a subject is a random variable; its expectation is generally used in estimating the parameters, but its variance may be used in evaluating the model. One expects individual differences to occur in real data, and these should be reflected in distributions of model parameters rather than in single values for a group of real subjects. Thus one would expect that the observed variance of a statistic would be greater than predicted by a model analysis that assumes identical subjects. If the observed variance is larger than predicted, we then have no strong evidence against the model; but, if the observed variance is significantly *smaller* than predicted, it is clear that there is something seriously wrong with the model (Bush, Galanter, & Luce, 1959). For this reason, it is always worth comparing the variances.

7.3 Sequential Properties

Some psychological models predict strong sequential dependencies, whereas others do not. Some data exhibit strong sequential dependencies and other data do not. Whichever type of prediction is made, it is useful to see if it is correct. In the study of learning models the most useful sequential statistics are the expected number of runs of various lengths and the autocorrelation of errors (Sternberg, 1959). Such properties are especially useful in comparing several models, all of which fit the gross features of the data (Bush & Mosteller, 1959).

Consider a sequence of binary random variables $(X_1, X_2, \ldots, X_n, \ldots, X_N)$. It is helpful to consider the number of k-tuples

$$U_k = \sum_{n=1}^{N+1-k} X_n X_{n+1} \cdots X_{n+k-1}, \qquad (k = 1, 2, \ldots, N).$$

(For $k > N$, we take $U_k = 0$.) The number of runs of 1's of length j is readily shown to be

$$R_j = (U_j - U_{j+1}) - (U_{j+1} - U_{j+2}),$$

and the number of runs of any length is

$$R = \sum_{j=1}^{N} R_j = U_1 - U_2.$$

The N statistics R_j, are then isomorphic to the N statistics U_k; each set is a linear combination of the other set. In computing expected values of the R_j, it has been found useful to compute the expectations of the U_k first (Bush, 1959). In most problems one is primarily interested in R, R_1, R_2, and perhaps R_3. Longer runs are usually infrequent.

It is also useful to compute the set of correlation statistics

$$C_i = \sum_{n=1}^{N-i} X_n X_{n+1}, \qquad (i = 0, 1, \ldots, N - 1).$$

We see at once that $C_0 = U_1$ and $C_1 = U_2$, but that C_2, C_3, ... give us information not contained in the U_k's. Sternberg (1959) has used these statistics in studying several models.

The sequential statistic that best distinguishes between a model and data or between two models is a matter for inquiry in each problem. None is hard to tabulate from data, but the computation of their expectations is sometimes difficult. Monte Carlo methods can always be used, of course.

7.4 Parameter Invariance

When a model predicts how behavior depends upon some experimental variable, the model parameters should be invariant to changes in that variable. This is a strong demand to place on a model, but it is a necessary one if we want more than local, descriptive models. Stochastic models for simple learning, for example, explicitly contain two experimental variables: trials and reward probabilities. The model parameters presumably depend on other experimental variables such as amount of deprivation, amount of reward, and the intertrial interval. But if those parameters also depended upon the trial number or the reward probabilities, the models would become rather useless. Thus we want to require parameter invariance to those variables made explicit in the models. This question has been studied by Galanter and Bush (1959), by Bush, Galanter, and Luce (1959), and by Fey (1960).

A similar requirement can and should be placed upon psychophysical models. Several such models predict the shape of a psychometric function, for example, and usually contain two parameters related to the jnd and the constant error. They should be invariant to changes in the stimulus intensity variables which explicitly enter the model.

7.5 Tests of General Axioms

In most attempts to evaluate models, predictions (theorems) of the models are compared with data. One seldom has an opportunity to test the axioms directly, but when he has he should certainly do so. If a broad class of axioms can be tested with one experiment, all the better. Three examples follow.

Every stochastic learning model contains an axiom that is a special case of a general conditioning axiom which says that whenever a certain kind of event occurs it will increase the probability of a particular response. For example, in a binary prediction experiment the occurrence of one of the two events (such as a light coming on) will increase the probability that the subject will predict that event. In a T-maze experiment, with partial reinforcement, whenever food is placed in the left goal box (and not in the right-hand goal box), the probability that the rat will choose the left side should increase, regardless of the response just made. In some models the magnitude of the increment depends on the response just made, but the relevant point here is that it is always assumed positive (or at least non-negative). This general axiom can be tested directly with data if they contain a sufficient abundance of runs of the alleged reinforcing event. The test can be made on data from a single subject if there are enough trials, or it can be made on data from a group of subjects which need not be assumed identical. The axiom says that for each run of K reinforcing events $p_1 < p_2 < \ldots < p_K < p_{K+1}$, where p_i is the response probability on the ith trial of the event run. If we sum over the different event runs of length K in one subject's data or across subjects, letting the index j denote a particular event run, we get

$$\sum_j p_{1,j} < \sum_j p_{2,j} < \ldots < \sum_j p_{K,j} < \sum_j p_{K+1,j}.$$

Now $p_{i,j}$ is the expectation of the corresponding random variable $X_{i,j}$, that is,

$$E(X_{i,j}) = p_{i,j},$$

and if we let

$$T_i = \sum_j X_{i,j},$$

then

$$E(T_1) < E(T_2) < \ldots < E(T_K) < E(T_{K+1}).$$

The test is obvious: we plot the sample values T_i versus i and see if we obtain a monotone increasing function. If significance tests are considered necessary, it is useful to note that

$$\text{Var}(T_i) = \sum_j p_{i,j}(1 - p_{i,j}) \leqslant \frac{J}{4},$$

where J is the total number of event runs used in the analysis.

The preceding test pertained to a general conditioning axiom which characterizes a large class of learning models. A second example also pertains to a large class of models which have been applied to problems in learning and multiperson interactions (Suppes & Atkinson, 1960). Suppose we postulate that a process can be described by a stationary m-state Markov chain. The $m(m-1)$ transition probabilities could be considered parameters, but, if $m > 2$, the number of parameters is too large for most purposes in psychological models. Thus additional axioms, such as those derived from stimulus-sampling theory, are needed. Nevertheless, it is useful to test the basic general axiom of stationarity. One could estimate the entries of the transition matrix for each of several blocks of trials and inspect them. If a large trend were apparent, the general axiom would be under serious suspicion. In a less obvious case one could use a chi-square test devised by Anderson and Goodman (1957) and used extensively by Suppes and Atkinson (1960, pp. 56, 87, 119, 132, 176, 190, 199).

The third example is the basic choice axiom introduced by Luce (1959). It is fundamental to a large number of results in psychophysics, utility theory, and learning. It specifies a simple relation between the probability measure defined on a set T of alternatives and the corresponding measure defined on any subset, S, of T. Because of its generality and its importance, it is extremely valuable to test it directly. Luce (1959) presents one empirical test and it supports the axiom. But a dozen such tests, equally successful, would not justify the conclusion that the axiom was universal. The test should be made, if possible, in every application of a model based upon Luce's choice axiom. Presumably, the test will sometimes be favorable to the axiom and sometimes it will be unfavorable. As a result, we will assemble information about the range of phenomena to which the axiom applies. If our interest is in a particular phenomenon, the test will tell us whether it is reasonable to explore models based upon the axiom.

In conclusion, it may be worth reminding the reader that models are more often destroyed by better models than by experiments. A series of empirical studies may diminish the usefulness of a model by restricting its range of application, but a new model, which does everything the old one does and more, will quickly replace its predecessor. The failure of a model to fit particular data is important only if it leads someone to develop a better one.

References

Anderson, T. W., & Goodman, L. A. Statistical inference about Markov chains. *Annals Math. Stat.*, 1957, **28,** 89–110.

Berkson, J. Application of the logistic function to bio-assay. *J. Amer. Statist. Assoc.*, 1944, **39,** 357–365.

Berkson, J. A statistically precise and relatively simple method of estimating the bio-assay with quantal response, based on the logistic function. *J. Amer. Statist. Assoc.*, 1953, **48,** 565–599.

Bush, R. R. Sequential properties of linear models. In R. R. Bush & W. K. Estes (Eds.), *Studies in mathematical learning theory.* Stanford: Stanford Univer. Press, 1959. Pp. 215–227.

Bush, R. R., Galanter, E., & Luce R. D. Tests of the "beta model." In R. R. Bush & W. K. Estes (Eds.), *Studies in mathematical learning theory.* Stanford: Stanford Univer. Press, 1959. Pp. 382–399.

Bush, R. R., & Mosteller, F. *Stochastic models for learning.* New York: Wiley, 1955.

Bush, R. R., & Mosteller, F. A comparison of eight models. In R. R. Bush & W. K. Estes (Eds.), *Studies in mathematical learning theory.* Stanford: Stanford Univer. Press, 1959. Pp. 293–307.

Bush, R. R., & Sternberg, S. H. A single-operator model. In R. R. Bush & W. K. Estes (Eds.), *Studies in mathematical learning theory.* Stanford: Stanford Univer. Press, 1959. Pp. 204–214.

Cramér, H. *Mathematical methods in statistics.* Princeton: Princeton Univer. Press, 1946.

Feller, W. *An introduction to probability theory and its applications,* Vol. 1. New York: Wiley, 1957.

Fey, C. An investigation of some mathematical models for learning. *J. exp. Psychol.,* 1961, **61,** 455–461.

Fisher, R. A. On the mathematical foundations of theoretical statistics. *Phil. Trans. Royal Soc., London,* 1922, **222,** 309–369.

Fisher, R. A. Theory of statistical estimation. *Proc. Camb. Phil. Soc.,* 1925, **22,** 700–725; and in J. Tukey (Ed.), *R. A. Fisher, Contributions to mathematical statistics.* New York: Wiley, 1950. Pp. 265–289.

Fisher, R. A. *The design of experiments.* New York: Hafner, 1935, reprinted 1953; and in J. Tukey (Ed.), *R. A. Fisher, Contributions to mathematical statistics.* New York: Wiley, 1950.

Galanter, E., & Bush, R. R. Some T-maze experiments. In R. R. Bush & W. K. Estes (Eds.), *Studies in mathematical learning theory.* Stanford: Stanford Univer. Press, 1959. Pp. 265–289.

Kanal, L. A functional equation analysis of two learning models. *Psychometrika,* 1962, **27,** 89–104.

Luce, R. D. *Individual choice behavior.* New York: Wiley, 1959.

Mosteller, F., & Bush, R. R. Selected quantitative techniques. In G. Lindzey (Ed.), *Handbook of social psychology*, Vol. I. Cambridge, Mass.: Addison-Wesley, 1955. Pp. 289–334.

Polya, G. *Patterns of plausible inference.* (Vol. 2. of *Mathematics and plausible reasoning.*) Princeton: Princeton Univer. Press, 1954.

Sternberg, S. H. A path-dependent linear model. In R. R. Bush & W. K. Estes (Eds.), *Studies in mathematical learning theory.* Stanford: Stanford Univer. Press, 1959. Pp. 308–339.

Suppes, P. & Atkinson, R. C. *Markov learning models for multiperson interactions.* Stanford: Stanford Univer. Press, 1960.

Tatsuoka, M., & Mosteller, F. A commuting-operator model. In R. R. Bush & W. K. Estes (Eds.), *Studies in mathematical learning theory.* Stanford: Stanford Univer. Press, 1959. Pp. 228–247.

Author Index

Page numbers in **boldface** indicate bibliography references.

471

Subject Index